D0771291

MARINE ALGAE

OF THE MONTEREY PENINSULA
CALIFORNIA

MARINE ALGAE
OF THE MONTEREY PENINSULA
CALIFORNIA

By

Gilbert M. Smith

PROFESSOR OF BIOLOGY
STANFORD UNIVERSITY

STANFORD UNIVERSITY PRESS
Stanford, California

OXFORD UNIVERSITY PRESS
London GEOFFREY CUMBERLEGE

STANFORD UNIVERSITY PRESS
STANFORD, CALIFORNIA

London : Geoffrey Cumberlege
Oxford University Press

———

THE BAKER AND TAYLOR COMPANY
HILLSIDE, NEW JERSEY

HENRY M. SNYDER & COMPANY
440 FOURTH AVENUE, NEW YORK 16

W. S. HALL & COMPANY
457 MADISON AVENUE, NEW YORK 22

———

COPYRIGHT 1944 BY THE BOARD OF TRUSTEES
OF THE LELAND STANFORD JUNIOR UNIVERSITY

PRINTED AND BOUND IN THE UNITED STATES
OF AMERICA BY STANFORD UNIVERSITY PRESS

First printing, May 1944
Second printing, September 1951

PREFACE

Students interested in marine life have long felt the need of a book describing the seaweeds growing along the Pacific Coast of the United States. Realizing fully the need for such a comprehensive treatise I have preferred to restrict my account of Pacific Coast algae to the Monterey Peninsula, California. This Peninsula, which lies at the southern end of Monterey Bay 100 miles south of San Francisco, is a region where I have collected intensively for the past 17 years and one where I have a firsthand knowledge of the living seaweeds. The flora of the Monterey Peninsula is far richer than that of any other portion of the west coast of this country. The area is also noteworthy in that it is the type locality for approximately a quarter of the species found along the west coast. Descriptions of species found in the Monterey area will enable one to identify at least 80 per cent of the species to be found anywhere between Puget Sound and southern California. Thus, although limited to a very small geographical range, this book describes a large majority of the seaweeds along the western coast of the United States.

The descriptions of species are based upon specimens from the Monterey Peninsula and are not a re-phrasing of the original or other descriptions. In many cases the dimensions given in the descriptions vary somewhat from those of specimens from other localities. Wherever possible there is an illustration for each species. These drawings bring out the general aspect of the plant; but when the general appearance is not distinctive, drawings showing details of vegetative or reproductive structures also are included to help in distinguishing between genera and species. For most of the species there is a reference to authentic specimens distributed in uniform sets (exsiccatae). Wherever possible the reference is to the most widely distributed of all American exsiccatae—Collins, Holden, and Setchell's *Phycotheca Boreali-Americana.* The citations preceding each description include the original description and, if this is brief and inadequate, one or more references to recent descriptions. Synonyms (other than primary synonyms) have not been included unless used in published records of algae from the Monterey Peninsula. All citations marked with an asterisk state that the species occurs on the Monterey Peninsula. Data on the local distribution of species are based in large part upon collections by myself and by students at the Hopkins Marine Station. The extensive phycological herbarium at the University of California has been the primary source of data concerning the range of species along the Pacific Coast. The range of many species is incompletely known; undoubtedly it will be extended with further studies on distribution of algae along the western coast of North America, especially in the portion between Puget Sound and northern California and the coast line from San Diego southward.

A key may be defined as an arrangement of contrasting characteristics by which, through selection of proper alternatives, one may determine the name of an "unknown" plant. A key may utilize either fundamental or trivial characteristics. On the pages that follow the keys to orders of a class, to families of an order, and to genera of a family emphasize the distinctive, though often obscure, reproductive and structural differences between members of each category. The primary purpose of these keys is to show the fundamental differences between members of the various groups. The primary purpose of the comprehensive keys on pages 399–412 is to afford a means of determining the correct generic name of an alga unknown to the student. These keys are based almost wholly upon external form and internal vegetative structure. If a genus, as *Gigartina,* has species differing markedly in form, it may appear more than once in the key; and in the cases where the student may have difficulty in deciding between two alternatives, both alternatives lead to the same genus. Four successive revisions of these keys have been used by students in the course on marine algae given at the Hopkins Marine Station, and it is hoped that the form in which they are now presented eliminates the difficulties encountered in previous editions.

My thanks are due to many persons who have rendered assistance. First and foremost is my companion on many collecting trips, Professor G. J. Hollenberg of the University of Redlands. His uncanny ability to find rare algae has brought to my attention species not previously known from the Monterey Peninsula. He has aided also in numerous other ways, including the lending of specimens and notes on the algae of southern California. Members of the Department of Botany at the University of California have afforded every possible facility for studying the extensive phycological herbarium of that institution. The late Professor W. A. Setchell was a constant source of aid, especially through giving me free access to his comprehensive personal library, to his field notes on Monterey algae, and to the field notes of the late Professor N. L. Gardner. Mrs. L. R. Blinks, of Carmel, California, has loaned me her collection' of algae from Friday Harbor, Washington. This collection has been of great service because its determinations were made under the immediate supervision of Professor Kylin. The collections and notes on Oregon algae of Mr. Maxwell Doty, of Stanford University, have been useful because they cover an area little known to phycologists.

Correspondents have been equally helpful in answering numerous questions. Professor Harald Kylin of the University of Lund, Sweden, has answered many questions concerning types in Agardh's herbarium and has confirmed certain determinations by comparing them with the types in his personal herbarium and in that of Agardh. Professor H. H. Dixon of Dublin University, Ireland, has answered inquiries concerning algae in Harvey's herbarium; Dr. D. H. Linder, curator of the Farlow Herbarium of Harvard University, has answered questions concerning Farlow's algae; and a similar service with respect to the collections of Anderson has been rendered by Miss Rosalie Weikert of the New York Botanical Garden. Professor B. M. Davis of the University of Michigan has given information concerning his collections made in the Monterey area in 1892 and 1922; and his colleague, Professor W. R. Taylor, has helped in other ways.

Grateful mention must be made of the assistance of Mrs. Carl F. Janish in the preparation of illustrations. All figures involving magnification of less than ten times are from her pen. Her services were made possible by several grants from the Research Committee and from the Campbell Fund, both of Stanford University.

Thanks are also due to the Director of the Hopkins Marine Station and to the Campbell Fund for appropriations to assist in the costs of publication.

GILBERT M. SMITH

STANFORD UNIVERSITY
November 29, 1943

CONTENTS

MARINE ALGAE

OF THE MONTEREY PENINSULA
CALIFORNIA

INTRODUCTION

The first botanist to collect algae on the Pacific Coast of North America was Dr. Archibald Menzies. He visited the Oregon-Washington area in a fur-trading vessel, the "Prince of Wales," during 1786. In 1792–1794 he was a member of the exploring expedition under the command of Captain George Vancouver. Menzies collected algae and other plants at Monterey from November 26, 1792, to January 14, 1793. Some of the algae taken back to Europe are described by Turner.[1] Menzies' collection of algae and other cryptogams was bequeathed to the Edinburgh Botanical Garden.

Alexander Collie and G. T. Lay, the naturalists of the exploring expedition under command of Captain F. W. Beechey in H.M.S. "Blossom," collected algae at Monterey in November 1827. The algae of Lay and Collie, together with those collected at San Francisco by Dr. Sinclair of the Beechey expedition, were determined by Harvey, and a list of them was published by him in 1833. This short paper on the algae of California is the first paper published on the algae of North America. In this connection it is interesting to note that algae of the then relatively inaccessible and practically uninhabited coast of California were studied before those of the more accessible and better settled Atlantic Coast.

The botanical explorer David Douglas arrived at Monterey on December 22, 1830, and remained there until December 1831. Douglas had been especially requested to collect algae along the Pacific Coast, and in a letter to Hooker[2] he mentions collecting algae at Monterey. The algae collected by Douglas are given in a second paper by Harvey on the marine algae of California.[3] Douglas' algae are in the Harvey Herbarium at the University of Dublin, Ireland.

Thomas Coulter arrived from the south while Douglas was

[1] Turner, 1808, 1809, 1819. For full reference, see the Bibliography, p. 383.
[2] Hooker, 1836.   [3] Harvey, 1841.

3

at Monterey. Coulter botanized at Monterey until some time in 1832, and during that time he collected many algae. They remained undetermined until after his death, when Harvey, his successor at Dublin, found them in the University Herbarium and described them in the first (and only) full systematic account of the marine algae of North America.[4] Sometimes Harvey gives Monterey as the station for Coulter's algae and sometimes he gives "California." In the latter case there is a strong presumption that "California" means Monterey, both because Harvey states that Coulter's algae came from the Bay of Monterey and because Monterey is the only place along the shore of California where Coulter collected plants.[5]

Harvey's herbarium of angiosperms was purchased from his estate by Stanford University. An empty herbarium folder accidentally included in one of the packages confirms the presumption that "California" and "Monterey" were used interchangeably by Harvey. On the front of the folder there is the following in Harvey's handwriting: "Coulter's / Californian Algae / for Herbarium"; on the back is the notation "Monterrey/Algae/11–32."

The first botanist of California to specialize on the marine algae was Dr. C. L. Anderson, who resided at Santa Cruz from 1866 until his death in 1910. Anderson did more or less collecting on the Monterey Peninsula between 1881 and 1900. During this time he also received algae from several collectors residing on the Peninsula, including the Misses Bayles, Miss Mary J. Westfall, and Mrs. B. C. Winston. Most of the new species collected by Anderson were described by Professor W. G. Farlow of Harvard and by Professor J. G. Agardh of Lund, Sweden. Anderson was associated with Farlow and D. C. Eaton in issuing the first exsiccata of American algae, the *Algae Exsiccatae Americae Borealis*. His chief publication is an annotated list of the marine algae of California[6] in which he specifically designates the algae occurring "100 miles North or South of Monterey." Anderson's herbarium is now at the New York Botanical Garden.

In 1892 M. A. Howe spent the summer collecting algae at Monterey. His algae, determined in part by Anderson and by Farlow, are in the Herbarium of the University of California. The annotated list he published the following year[7] is the only published account devoted exclusively to Monterey algae.

[4] Harvey, 1852, 1853, 1858.   [5] Coville, 1895.
[6] Anderson, 1891.   [7] Howe, 1893.

DeAlton Saunders collected intensively on the Monterey Peninsula during the summers of 1896 and 1897, and there are numerous references to local species in his publications on the brown algae.[8] Saunders' herbarium was purchased by Farlow and is now in the Farlow Herbarium of Harvard University.

Since 1895 practically all investigations of Monterey Peninsula and other Pacific Coast marine algae have been done by or under the direction of Professors W. A. Setchell and N. L. Gardner of the University of California. Setchell made numerous collections in the Monterey area during the decade 1895–1905. Gardner began to collect algae on the Monterey Peninsula in 1907 and continued to collect yearly, especially on the Carmel Bay side, until his death in 1937. Numerous specimens collected in the local area by Setchell, by Gardner, and by their students are to be found in the widely distributed exsiccata of Collins, Holden, and Setchell, the *Phycotheca Boreali-Americana*. The individual publications of Setchell and of Gardner and their publications as joint authors contain many references to algae of the Monterey Peninsula. The summation of their long-continued study of Pacific Coast algae is to be found in their *Marine Algae of the Pacific Coast of North America*.[9] The Monterey Peninsula algae collected by Setchell and by Gardner are in the Herbarium of the University of California. So also are collections by most of their students, except those of C. P. Nott, which are at the Hopkins Marine Station.

Occasional mention of algae from Monterey or Pacific Grove is to be found in many papers by European phycologists. In almost all cases the observations are based upon specimens collected by Americans. References to local algae in the publications of Kylin and his students are based in large part upon material that Kylin collected from various localities on the Monterey Peninsula during the summer of 1922.

COLLECTING STATIONS ON THE MONTEREY PENINSULA

Since the algal flora varies so greatly along the shore line of the Monterey Peninsula, it is essential that the distribution of species in the local flora be indicated as precisely as possible. There is also the question of the precise locality where previous workers have collected on the Monterey Peninsula. There are many specimens of algae from the Monterey Peninsula in various

[8] Saunders, 1898, 1899.   [9] Setchell and Gardner, 1919, 1920, 1925.

herbaria throughout the United States. Most of those collected before 1890 are simply labeled "Monterey" or "Pacific Grove." Those collected since 1890 bear a wide variety of names for localities on the Monterey Peninsula. Some of these place names are to be found on the Monterey Quadrangle (California) of the topographic map published by the United States government in 1913, and on the Monterey Bay Sheet (No. 5403) published by the United States Coast and Geodetic Survey in 1935. Other place names are to be found on maps published locally, especially those issued by the Del Monte Properties Company. A third group of place names consists of those unpublished names used by local residents and by scientists working at the Hopkins Marine Station. Several of these local names are no longer in current use. For example, twenty-five years ago practically every resident of Pacific Grove used the name China Point; today one rarely hears that name. The most troublesome of all unpublished names are those used by early investigators at the Hopkins Marine Station. In ferreting out these obsolete local names, Professors Harold Heath and F. M. McFarland of Stanford University, Professor B. M. Davis of the University of Michigan, and Professor C. W. Greene of the University of Missouri have given invaluable aid because they have known the Marine Station ever since it was established in 1892.

In the following list, names designated *official* appear on maps published by the United States government; those designated *unofficial* include both the names from maps published locally and unpublished names.

LOCATION NAMES

Arch Rock, Pacific Grove. Unofficial name for the arch rock near Aumentos Rock.

Arch Rock, Pebble Beach. Unofficial name for Pescadero Rocks.

Asilomar Beach. Unofficial name for Moss Beach.

Asilomar Point. Unofficial name for rocks north of Moss Beach.

Arrowhead Point. Unofficial name for the first point south of Pebble Beach.

Bathhouse Beach, Pacific Grove. Unofficial name for the beach east of Point Aulon.

Bathing Beach, Pacific Grove. Unofficial name for the beach east of Point Aulon.

Berkeley Beach, Pacific Grove. Unofficial name for beach at foot of Third Street, Pacific Grove.

Bird Rock. Unofficial name for the largest of the Seal Rocks.

Cabrillo Point. Unofficial name for Mussel Point.

Carmel Bay. Official.

Carmel Beach. Unofficial name for the beach fronting the city of Carmel-by-the-Sea.

Carmel City Point. Unofficial name for the point at the south end of Carmel Beach.

Carmel Point. As above. Not to be confused with Point Carmel (Point Lobos) south of Carmel Bay.

Chautauqua Beach, Pacific Grove. Unofficial name for the beach east of Point Aulon.

China Point. Unofficial name for Mussel Point.

Chinatown Point. Another unofficial name for Mussel Point.

Chinese Cove, Carmel Bay. See next entry.

Chinese Fishing Huts, Carmel Bay. These huts situated near the east end of Pebble Beach were torn down about 1895.

Cypress Point. Unofficial name for Point Cypress.

Fanshell Beach. Unofficial name for the beach east of Point Cypress.

First Beach, Pacific Grove. Unofficial name for the first sandy beach west of Point Aulon.

Fisherman's Wharf, Monterey. The wharf at the old Mexican Custom House, Monterey.

Joe's Point. Unofficial name for Point Joe.

Laboratory Point, Pacific Grove. Unofficial name for Point Aulon until 1918; since 1918 Mussel Point has been called Laboratory Point.

Lighthouse Point. Unofficial name for Point Pinos.

Lover's Point, Pacific Grove. Unofficial name for Point Aulon.

Middle Reef, Moss Beach. Unofficial name for the rocky point in the middle of Moss Beach.

Midway Point. Unofficial name for the small point midway between Point Douty and Pescadero Point.

Mission Point, Carmel Bay. Unofficial name for the point at the south end of Carmel Beach.

Monterey Cove. Unofficial name for the small cove west of Fisherman's Wharf, Monterey.

Monterey Wharf. The wharf at the old Mexican Custom House, Monterey, built in 1870. Until 1926 it was the only wharf at Monterey, so that all collections made before 1926 and labeled Monterey Wharf refer to this wharf, now called

Fisherman's Wharf. The Municipal Wharf at the foot of Figueroa Street, Monterey, is now called the Monterey Wharf.

Moss Beach. Official.

Municipal Wharf, Monterey. See Monterey Wharf.

Mussel Point. Official.

Pebble Beach. Official.

Pescadero Point. Official.

Pescadero Rocks. Official.

Picnic Ground Point, Pebble Beach. Unofficial name for Pescadero Point.

Point Alones. Official.

Point Aulon. Official.

Point Cypress. Official.

Point Douty. Official.

Point Joe. Official.

Point Loeb. Unofficial name for Point Alones.

Promontory Point. Unofficial name for the first point south of Pebble Beach.

Pyramid Point. Early editions of the Monterey Bay Sheet (5403) published by the United States Coast and Geodetic Survey use this name for Point Joe. The 1935 edition of Sheet 5403 uses the name Point Joe.

Seal Rocks. Official.

Second Beach, Pacific Grove. Unofficial name for the second sandy beach west of Point Aulon.

Spanish Bay. Unofficial name for the western half of Moss Beach.

Station Point, Pacific Grove. See Laboratory Point.

Steamer Wharf, Monterey. See Monterey Wharf.

Stillwater Cove. Unofficial name for the small cove between Pescadero Point and Arrowhead Point.

Third Beach, Pacific Grove. Unofficial name for the third sandy beach west of Point Aulon.

U.C. Beach. See Berkeley Beach.

Whaler's Point, Monterey. Unofficial name for the point on which the Monterey breakwater is built.

DISTRIBUTION OF MARINE ALGAE ON THE MONTEREY PENINSULA

Ecological factors are of primary importance in determining the distribution of marine algae on the Monterey Peninsula. First of all, there must be an adequate substratum for the perma-

nent attachment of algae. Sandy beaches with continually shift-
ing sands, as Moss Beach and Carmel Beach, rarely have permanently attached algae. On the other hand, the rough surface
of rocks and cliffs affords so favorable a surface for the attachment of algae that all rocky surfaces are densely clothed with
algae. The numerous epiphytic algae of the local flora need a
condition of the host suitable for lodgment of a spore and its
development into a plant. This is well exemplified by the epiphytes growing on *Nereocystis Luetkeana*. Throughout the
spring and summer the stipe of this alga is smooth and free from
epiphytes; in the autumn and after the surface of the stipe becomes rough it is densely covered with epiphytes.

Whenever the substratum is suitable there are certain ecological factors affecting the vertical distribution of each species
with respect to the tide levels. Species of the intertidal belt have
rather definite limits above and below which they do not grow. As
a result there is a clearly evident zonation of the intertidal belt,
and several zones, each with its characteristic algae, may be
recognized.

One of the major factors affecting the upper limit at which
an alga will grow in the intertidal belt is its ability to withstand
desiccation when the tide is out. Algae growing high in the intertidal belt are exposed several hours a day every day of the
month; those growing very low in the belt are exposed for only
a short time on three or four successive days once a month. Experiments made at Friday Harbor, Washington, show[10] that
algae from the uppermost part of the intertidal belt (as *Fucus*
and *Porphyra perforata*) may survive 24–48 hours' exposure to
air. The same experiments show that algae from the middle of
the intertidal belt (including *Colpomenia sinuosa, Halosaccion
glandiforme,* and certain species of *Ulva*) are killed by an exposure of more than 4–6 hours.

Light is also an important factor affecting vertical distribution. Measurements of light penetration into sea water at Friday
Harbor show[11] that in calm weather 25 per cent of the light is
cut off at the water's surface and about 20 per cent more at a
depth of a meter. There is also a qualitative screening out of light
entering the water, and an alga growing at a depth of 10 meters
receives only 10 per cent of the violet-blue and 1 per cent of the
red rays of full sunlight. The total amount rather than the quality

[10] Muenscher, 1915.   [11] Shelford and Gail, 1919.

of light is of greater importance to algae growing high in the intertidal belt. In certain of these high-dwelling algae the lower limits at which they will grow seems to be determined by the amount of light. For example, it has been shown[12] for *Fucus* that if the amount of light it receives is reduced by one-half, the plant sickens and dies. For algae growing below the low-tide level the quality of the light seems to be more important than the quantity of light. The ability of sublittoral Rhodophyta to grow at greater depths than do sublittoral Phaeophyta seems to rest upon the fact that they are more efficient photosynthetically where there is only blue light.

In addition to a vertical distribution there is also a horizontal distribution of algae along the shores of the Monterey Peninsula. The horizontal distribution is always interrupted where there are sandy beaches, as at Carmel and at Moss Beach. On the remainder of the Peninsula, wherever the rocky shore affords a firm substratum, certain algae are present irrespective of the degree of exposure to the action of waves. Such algae include those growing high in the intertidal belt (as *Endocladia muricata, Porphyra perforata,* and *Pelvetia fastigiata*), those growing in the mid-littoral (as *Iridophycus flaccidum, Prionitis lanceolata,* and *Ulva lobata*), and those of the lower littoral (as various crustose and jointed Corallinaceae).

However, horizontal distribution of the great majority of algae in the intertidal belt is correlated with the degree of exposure to the action of waves. Certain portions of the Peninsula, as Point Cypress, Mission Point, and Point Joe, are exposed to the full force of waves sweeping in from the open ocean. Many other portions of the shore line appear to be freely exposed, but actually they are more or less sheltered by an offshore reef of rocks or a gradually sloping strand that breaks the full force of waves pounding on the shore. The shore line inward from the Seal Rocks exemplifies one protected by an outlying reef, and the Middle Reef of Moss Beach is representative of one with a gradually sloping strand. The algal flora of such partially protected portions of the shore line differs from that of freely exposed portions. Stillwater Cove is the one portion of the Monterey Peninsula where the shore is so thoroughly protected by projecting headlands and outlying rocks that there is practically no wave action.

12 Gail, 1918.

The algal flora of freely exposed portions of the Peninsula is especially rich in Laminariales. *Postelsia palmaeformis* and *Lessoniopsis littoralis* grow only on rocks exposed to the full pounding of the surf, the former high in the intertidal belt, the latter just above the low-water line. *Laminaria Andersonii* and *Alaria marginata* are somewhat more widely distributed at the low-water line along exposed portions of the Peninsula. Among other algae growing low on surf-swept rocks are *Botryoglossum Farlowianum*, *Erythrophyllum delesserioides* and *Gigartina corymbifera*. The commonest of the algae growing above mid-tide level on exposed rocks are *Pelvetiopsis limitata*, *Heterochordaria abietina*, and *Microcladia borealis*.

The flora of partially protected portions of the shore line is richer than that of freely exposed portions, especially in the lower half of the intertidal belt. Between Point Cypress and Point Pinos the tops of rocks in partially protected areas are covered with *Halosaccion glandiforme*, *Rhodomela larix*, and various species of *Gigartina*.

Stillwater Cove, with its warmer and much calmer water, has an algal flora quite different from that elsewhere on the Peninsula. *Egregia laevigata* and its epiphyte, *Halorhipis Winstonii*, are found only along Pebble Beach, but here they grow in profusion. The same is true of *Leathesia nana*. Several algae occasionally found elsewhere on the Peninsula grow in abundance at Pebble Beach. They include *Laurencia spectabilis*, *L. pacifica*, *Rhodoglossum americanum*, *Cumagloia Andersonii*, *Ilea fascia*, *Petrospongium rugosum*, and *Scytosiphon Lomentarium*.

Several algae grow only in special habitats. Among these are the algae restricted to shaded places. For example, *Rhodochorton Rothii* is found only at the upper tide level and either in caves or beneath overhanging ledges. Many of the rarer Delesseriaceae of the lower littoral are found only in recesses below rocky ledges. *Prasiola meridionalis*, *Gayella constricta*, and the various unicellular Volvocales are restricted to rocks covered with the droppings of sea birds. Readily accessible rocks of this type are to be found at Mussel Point and at Point Pinos. The piling of wharves at Monterey is another habitat with a distinctive algal flora. Here are to be found several filamentous Rhodophyta not known elsewhere on the Monterey Peninsula.

Lastly, there are a number of algae of extremely localized distribution which for unknown reasons do not grow in abundance elsewhere. Except for a few isolated individuals, *Nemalion lubricum* is found only on a couple of rocks at Pebble Beach and along a short stretch of the shore line one hundred yards west of Point Aulon. Isolated individuals of *Stenogramme californica, Gloiosiphonia verticillaris,* and *Haplogloia Andersonii* have been found here and there on the Peninsula, but these algae are found regularly each year only on the Middle Reef of Moss Beach. The same is true for the various species of *Ptilota.* On the open-ocean side of the Peninsula individual tufts of *Codium fragile* may be seen almost anywhere, but the alga is found in profusion only just west of Fanshell Beach.

GEOGRAPHICAL DISTRIBUTION OF PACIFIC COAST MARINE ALGAE

The algal flora of the entire Pacific Coast of North America has been divided[13] into four zones: (*a*) the Boreal Zone, which extends as far south as the Strait of Juan de Fuca; (*b*) the Temperate Zone, extending south from the Strait of Juan de Fuca to Point Conception, Santa Barbara County, California; (*c*) the Subtropical Zone, extending south from Point Conception to Magdalena Bay, Baja California, Mexico; and (*d*) the Tropical Zone, from Magdalena Bay to the Isthmus of Panama. A majority of the species found along the Pacific Coast are restricted to one zone. A minority of the species range through two adjoining zones or more than two zones. For example, omitting species known from but a single station, a tabulation of the larger Pacific Coast brown algae (Laminariales, Dictyotales, Fucales) shows that 37 of the 49 species recognized by Setchell and Gardner[14] are restricted to a single zone, 10 are found in two zones, and two range through three zones.

The general relationship between temperature of the water and nature of the flora has been recognized for nearly a hundred years. A more specific relationship to temperature was first pointed out for the Laminariales when it was shown[15] that the surface water isotheres (mean maxima for the warmest month) of 10°, 15°, 20°, and 25° C. are of deep significance when correlated with geographical distribution of the various species. Later[16] this was extended to a generalization covering all marine algae and one holding that with an increase or decrease of 5° C. in the isotheres there is a marked change in the algal flora.

[13] Setchell and Gardner, 1903.   [14] Setchell and Gardner, 1925.
[15] Setchell, 1893.   [16] Setchell and Gardner, 1903; Setchell, 1920, 1920.*A.*

The Monterey Peninsula lies in the Temperate Algal Zone, which is limited on the north by the 15° isothere and on the south by the 20° isothere. On the Pacific Coast of North America the northern limit of the Temperate Zone shades gradually into the Boreal Zone. At the southern limit there is a much more abrupt change to the flora characteristic of the Subtropical Algal Zone. The more abrupt change at the south is undoubtedly connected with the fact that the cool California Current flowing down the coast of California sweeps out to sea at Point Conception and so produces a sharp change in gradient of water temperatures. Many of the anomalies in distribution of algae within a zone are due to locally higher or lower temperatures of the water. Along the Atlantic Coast of North America there is a rather abrupt change from a northern to a southern type of algal flora at Cape Cod. However, three local areas of warm water have been discovered north of Cape Cod where there may be an abundant growth of algae characteristic of the flora south of the Cape.[17]

Stillwater Cove on the Carmel Bay side of the Monterey Peninsula appears to be another example of a warm-water area within a cold-water region. Several algae not otherwise known north of Point Conception have been collected at Stillwater Cove. Perhaps the most striking of these is *Egregia laevigata*.

COLLECTING MARINE ALGAE

The cardinal rule in gathering marine algae is to collect only living plants and, wherever possible, to collect entire plants with holdfasts. This means that the collector should do the major portion of his collecting in the intertidal belt. Algae are frequently cast ashore in abundance on sandy beaches. The dried and half-decayed seaweeds found above high-tide level are worthless; but living algae often become stranded in the zone exposed by an outgoing tide. Almost all of the specimens thus cast ashore are torn and fragmentary. However, the collector cannot afford to ignore this collecting ground because he may encounter specimens of deep-water algae not to be found growing in the intertidal belt. The best time for gathering algae on a beach is shortly after the tide turns. The collector stands quietly where the water is about a foot deep and picks up suitable specimens as they are washed past him.

[17] Setchell, 1922.

Some collecting from the intertidal belt may be done at any low tide, but really good collecting on the Monterey Peninsula is possible only at the three or four extremely low (spring) tides at the new and the full moon of each month. The exact time of these, as well as of other, tides is given in the tide tables obtainable from most local dealers in fishermen's supplies. The local daily newspaper at Monterey also publishes daily the predicted times of low and high tides for the next day. During the summer all of the spring tides occur at or shortly after sunrise, during the winter at or shortly before sunset. In the summer the best that a collector can do is to be at the desired station and ready to collect at sunrise. In the winter he should reach the prospective collecting station about two hours before the time of extreme low water, so that he may work down the intertidal zone as the tide ebbs and then up it as the tide comes in. This makes the period available for collecting the longest possible.

There are certain precautions one should always take when collecting in the intertidal zone. Rocks covered with algae are exceedingly slippery, and there is always the possibility of the collector slipping and falling. Usually this means only an involuntary wetting or a spilling of the day's collections; but there is a possibility that the fall may be more serious. Collecting on exposed rocky headlands, as Point Cypress or Point Joe, involves certain actual dangers. The tide rises quite rapidly, once it has turned, and there is always the danger of being marooned on an outlying rock. The only safe rule after wading to some outlying rock is to keep the incoming tide constantly in mind. In collecting at the water's edge along the bottom of exposed cliffs or other vertical rock surfaces there is always the danger of being caught by unexpected waves of unusual size. Unless the distance to safety is very, very short, it is dangerous to run when one catches sight of a large wave about to break over him. The thing to do is to keep a cool head, drop everything, flatten one's self against the rock like a starfish, and let the water pour over. The day's collections may be lost, but there remains the consolation that a brief wetting is better than a permanent one.

Collecting in the intertidal zone always involves a certain amount of wading. Hip boots, although cumbersome, are essential in the numbingly cold waters of the Monterey Peninsula. One needs comparatively little field equipment on a collecting trip. A fairly powerful pocket lens (either 12× or 15×) is needed, both for identifying delicate filamentous algae and for distinguishing between sterile and fertile specimens of many of the larger algae. One needs a container for transportation of the material collected. Some collectors prefer a canvas or a rubber bag with a broad strap for the shoulder. Others prefer a two- or three-gallon pail; but pails are somewhat inconvenient if one has to do much scrambling over rocks. Large glass jars are unsuitable as containers, both because they are cumbersome and because of the danger of breakage. Special provision should be made for the smaller algae. The writer has found sheets of paraffin paper excellent for wrapping up small algae that might otherwise become lost among the larger ones in the general collecting receptacle. Other collectors prefer small wide-mouthed bottles with snugly fitting corks. The field equipment should also include a hammer and a stone mason's chisel for removing crustose algae from rocks. Wherever possible one should chip off portions of the underlying rock as well as the crustose alga. The hammer and chisel are also useful in breaking loose the holdfasts of kelps and other firmly attached algae. A very useful, though not essential, piece of equipment is an ordinary teaspoon. It is very useful as a scraper for removing small algae from rocks.

Care should be exercised in the collection of specimens of each species encountered. Mature, fully grown individuals should be selected, and whenever possible those densely covered with diatoms or other epiphytes are to be avoided. Generally more than one individual of a particular species is available, and several specimens should be collected to show the range in size and shape of blades and branches, range in amount of branching, and range in other variable features. Sometimes only one individual of a species will be encountered. Even if it appears to be a poorly developed individual, it is better to collect it than to take the chance of finding better-developed specimens later in the day. Fruiting specimens should be selected in preference to sterile ones. If all of the specimens appear to be sterile, even when examined with a hand lens, the largest and most promising ones should be selected in the hope that examination with a compound microscope will show the reproductive structures.

As the algae are collected they are piled one on top of the other in the general collecting receptacle. The one exception among the larger algae is *Desmarestia*. It should always be placed in a separate pail because it soon discolors any alga in contact with it. One need not cover algae with water to keep them fresh, because the temperatures of the Monterey area are so low that algae are not injured by two or three hours' exposure to air. Slips of tough paper giving collection data written with a soft black pencil should be placed among the specimens. The data should include the approximate height above low water, the substratum, and the place of collection when algae have been gathered from more than one station.

On any field trip it is better to collect intensively over a limited area than superficially over a long stretch of shore line. As one works down through the *Pelvetia* zone and the *Egregia* zone, the collecting is relatively poor so far as the number of species is concerned. Below these zones one may expect to find a large number of species. The tops of rocks in the lower intertidal zone are a fairly good collecting ground. The vertical sides of the same rocks are far better, but here the richness of the algal flora is not always evident because of the curtain of larger algae hanging down from the tops of rocks. A pushing aside of the overhanging algal curtain and a working over of the rock surface foot by foot frequently reveals small Rhodophyta that would otherwise have been overlooked. Small tide pools of the low littoral should never be neglected, for they sometimes contain isolated migrants from the sublittoral region.

Collecting from below the level exposed by the lowest tides can be done only by some type of dredging. If the algae are growing within five or six feet of the surface of the water they may be harvested by means of the long-handled scrapers designed by zoölogists for collecting animals living just below the low-tide level. Such collections from rocks seldom contain algae not found low in the intertidal zone. The same cannot be said for specimens taken from below the low-tide level on the piling of wharves at Monterey. Here one finds a number of delicate filamentous Rhodophyta not found elsewhere on the Monterey Peninsula. Collecting from deeper water requires specially designed dredges dragged along the ocean bottom by a motor-driven boat.

A temporary visitor to the Monterey Peninsula wishing to obtain the greatest possible number of species in a couple of days should spend one day collecting on the Middle Reef of Moss Beach and another on Pebble Beach. For a third day, either Point Cypress, Pescadero Point, or Point Pinos is recommended.

GLOSSARY

Abaxial. On the side away from an axis or branch.

Abscission. The natural separation of a part from the rest of a thallus.

Aculeus. A spine-like outgrowth.

Acuminate. Tapering gradually to a point.

Adaxial. On the side toward an axis or branch.

Adherent. More or less closely attached.

Air bladder. An intercellular air-filled space acting as a float.

Akinete. A spore formed singly within a cell and one with the spore wall fused with the parent cell wall.

Alternate. Not opposite or secund.

Anastomose. To unite by cross connections.

Anisogamy. Gametic union in which both gametes are flagellated but the two gametes are unlike in size.

Annular, Annulate. Ring-shaped or showing rings.

Antheridium. The sex organ producing flagellated male gametes.

Antherozoid. A flagellated male gamete.

Anticlinal. Perpendicular to the surface.

Apical. Situated at or referring to the apex.

Apical cell. A special cell initiating growth at the apex of a thallus or its branches.

Aplanospore. A nonmotile spore formed within a cell or a sporangium and one with the spore wall free from the parent cell wall or the sporangial wall.

Arcuate. Bent or curved like a bow.

Articulate. Jointed.

Articulation. A joint of a more or less jointed thallus.

Asexual. Reproduction which does not involve a union of gametes.

Assimilating filaments. Superficial filaments containing pigmented plastids.

Attenuate. Narrow and gradually tapering.

Auxiliary cell. A cell which receives a nucleus from the zygote and then produces gonimoblasts (found only in Florideae).

Axial filament. A filament running longitudinally through the center of a thallus or its branches.

Axil. The angle between an axis and an organ borne on it.

Axis. The stem-like portion bearing branches of a thallus; or the primary filament of a branched filamentous thallus.

Basipetalous. With progressively younger organs from base to apex.

Biflagellate. Possessing two flagella.

Bipinnate. Twice pinnate.

Bisporangium. A sporangium whose contents divide to form two spores (usage restricted to Florideae).

Bispore. A spore formed within a bisporangium.

Blade. An erect, leaf-like, flattened portion of a thallus.

Branchlet. A small branch.

Bullate. Swollen, blistered.

Bullation. An inflated or blister-like swelling.

17

Caecostoma (pl., *caecostomata*). Cryptostomata without hairs or an ostiole.

Calcified. Stony and impregnated with lime.

Carpogonial filament. A special filament which terminates in a carpogonium (found only in Florideae).

Carpogonium. The female sex organ of the Rhodophyta.

Carposporangium. A sporangium containing carpospores.

Carpospore. A spore formed by Rhodophyta as a result of fertilization.

Carposporophyte. The gonimoblast filaments and the carposporangia borne on them, plus the carpogonium or the auxiliary cell producing the gonimoblast filaments.

Carpostome. The pore of a pericarp around a cystocarp or the pore in the sterile tissue overlying a cystocarp.

Cartilaginous. Hard and tough, and having the texture of cartilage.

Catenate. Placed end to end as in a chain.

Cellulose. A carbohydrate constituting the major portion of walls of many algae.

Chlorophyll. The green coloring matter of plants.

Chloroplast. A plastid containing chlorophyll only.

Chromatophore. A plastid containing chlorophyll only or a plastid containing one or more pigments in addition to chlorophyll.

Circinate. Curled downward from the apex.

Clavate. Club-shaped.

Coenocyte. A multinucleate cell.

Conceptacle. A cavity opening to the thallus surface and containing reproductive organs.

Coralline. Referring to algae of the family Corallinaceae.

Cordate. Heart-shaped, the point upwards or outwards.

Coronate. Crowned, furnished with a crown.

Cortex. The thallus tissue between the epidermis and medulla; if no epidermis is present, the region surrounding the medulla or the axial filament.

Cortical. Occurring in or belonging to the cortex.

Corticated. Having a cortex.

Corymb. A flat-topped cluster.

Crenate. The edge scalloped with rounded teeth.

Cruciate. The contents of a tetrasporangium divided in two planes at right angles to each other.

Crustose. Crust-like; in the case of algae, the term restricted to thin thalli growing flattened against the substratum.

Cryptostoma (pl., *cryptostomata*). A cavity sunken in a thallus and containing hairs only.

Cuneate. Wedge-shaped.

Cystocarp. The "fruit" resulting from fertilization in Rhodophyta. In Bangioideae it consists solely of carpospores; in Florideae it consists of carpospores, gonimoblast filaments, and the cell from which they grow.

Deciduous. Falling away, not persistent.

Decumbent. Prostrate but with the apex bent upward.

Dentate. Toothed.

Dichotomous. Forked.

Dichotomy. A forking into two similar parts.

Dioecious. With male and female organs borne on separate thalli.

Diploid. Having in each cell double the haploid number of chromosomes.

Discoid. Like a disc.

Distichous. Arranged in two vertical rows along opposite sides of an axis or a branch.

Distromatic. Two cells in thickness (with reference to blades).

Dorsal. The upper surface of a dorsiventral thallus.

Dorsiventral. In algae, with reference to prostrate thalli having the upper and lower surfaces unlike.

Egg. A nonflagellated female gamete.

Ellipsoid. Elliptical in section (of solids).

Endogenous. Formed below the surface of a thallus.

Endophyte. A thallus growing endophytically.

Endophytic. Growing within the tissues of another plant.

Endozoic. Growing within an animal.

Entire. Without divisions or lobes.

Epidermis. The outermost cell layer of a thallus.

Epiphyte. A thallus growing epiphytically.

Epiphytic. Growing upon another plant but attached to the surface only.

Epizoic. Growing upon the surface of an animal.

Excrescent. Growing out or forming an outgrowth.

Exogenous. Formed at the surface of a thallus.

Falcate. Sickle-shaped.

Filament. A branched or unbranched row of cells joined end to end.

Fimbriate. Fringed.

Flabellate. Fan-shaped.

Flagellum. A thread-like cytoplasmic outgrowth. The swimming organ by means of which a cell moves through water.

Foliaceous. Leaf-like.

Forcipate. Forked and incurved like a pair of pinchers or crab claws.

Fruiting. Bearing sporangia or gametangia.

Fucoxanthin. A brown pigment in plastids of Phaeophyta.

Gametangium. A sex organ containing a gamete or gametes.

Gamete. A sexual cell capable of uniting with another sexual cell.

Gametophyte. The sexual or gamete-bearing generation of an alga.

Genicula. The portion between two successive segments of erect, jointed, coralline algae.

Geniculate. Bent abruptly, like a knee.

Gland. A secreting organ.

Gland cell. A colorless cell with glassy contents (found in certain Florideae).

Globose. Approximately spherical.

Gonimoblast. A carposporangium-producing filament growing from the carpogonium or from an auxiliary cell of Florideae.

Hair. A filament growing from the surface of a thallus.

Haploid. Having in each cell the number of chromosomes characteristic of the gamete.

Hapteron (pl., *haptera*). A basal organ of attachment; usually cylindrical and much branched.

Heterogamy. Gametic union in which the two gametes are unlike in size.

Heterosporous. Producing spores of two sizes.

Heterothallic. With male and female organs borne on separate thalli.

Homosporous. Producing spores of but one size.

Homothallic. With male and female organs borne on the same thallus.

Hyaline. Colorless, transparent.

Hypothallium. The lower portion of a crustose thallus differentiated into unlike upper and lower portions.

Intercalary. Occurring anywhere throughout a filament; not at apex or at base.

Intergenicula. A segment of an erect, jointed, coralline alga.

Internode. A segment of a jointed thallus.

Intramatrical. Within a matrix.

Involucre. A sterile envelope surrounding one or more reproductive organs.

Isogamous. Characterized by isogamy.

Isogamy. Gametic union in which the two gametes are of the same size.

Lacerate. With margin appearing as if torn.

Laciniate. Slashed; cut into deep narrow lobes.

Lanceolate. Lance-shaped, narrow and tapering.

Ligulate. Strap-like and short.

Linear. Long and narrow, with sides parallel.

Macroscopic. The shape discernible without magnification.

Macrospore. The larger spore when there are spores of two sizes.

Medulla. The central tissue of an internally differentiated thallus.

Medullary. Occurring in or belonging to the medulla.

Meiosis. That type of nuclear division in which the number of chromosomes is halved.

Meristem. A tissue which initiates growth.

Microscopic. Shape discernible only with magnification.

Microspore. The smaller spore when there are spores of two sizes.

Midrib. The thickened longitudinal axis of a flattened thallus.

Monoaxial. With a single axial filament terminating in an apical cell.

Monoecious. With male and female organs borne on the same thallus.

Monopodial. With a distinct axis bearing lateral branches of smaller size than the axis.

Monosporangium. A sporangium containing one spore (usage restricted to Rhodophyta).

Monospore. A spore formed in a monosporangium.

Monostromatic. One cell in thickness (with reference to blades).

Multiaxial. With a medulla of several parallel longitudinal filaments, each terminating in an apical cell.

Multinucleate. Containing more than one nucleus.

Nemathecium. A wart-like elevation containing many reproductive organs (usage restricted to Florideae).

Node. The region between two successive joints of a jointed thallus.

Nurse cell. A cell filled with reserve food and borne near the carpogonium (found only in Florideae).

Nurse tissue. Cells filled with reserve foods and utilized in development of a carposporophyte.

Ob-. Used as a prefix and meaning inversed; as *obcordate*.

Ooblast. A connecting tube through which a zygote nucleus migrates from a carpogonium to an auxiliary cell (found only in Florideae).

Oögamous. Characterized by oögamy.

Oögamy. Gametic union in which an antherozoid unites with an egg.

Oögonium. A single-celled female sex organ containing one or more eggs.

Ostiole. The pore-like open mouth of a conceptacle or of a pericarp.

Ovate. In the form of a longitudinal section of an egg and having the broader end toward the base.

Palisade. Erect cylindrical cells laterally united in a compact tissue.

Papilla. A short, nipple-like, superficial outgrowth.

Papillate. Bearing papillae.

Paraphysis (pl., *paraphyses*). A short sterile filament borne adjacent to a reproductive organ.

Parasite. Borne upon or within another organism and deriving food from it.

Parasitic. Living as a parasite.

Parenchyma. A tissue composed of thin-walled cells which are not markedly elongated.

Parenchymatous. Composed of parenchyma.

Parietal. Adjoining the wall of a cell.

Pectinate. With lateral branches restricted to one side and set close together like the teeth of a comb.

Pedicel. The stalk of a reproductive organ.

Pedicellate. Borne on a pedicel.

Peltate. Having the shape of a circular shield.

Percurrent. Extending through the entire length.

Perfoliate. Passing through a blade.

Pericarp. The sterile envelope around a cystocarp (found only in Florideae).

Pericentral. Surrounding a central filament or layer.

Periclinal. Parallel to the surface.

Peripheral. Belonging or referring to the surface or to the margin.

Phaeophycean hairs. Hairs in which the meristematic region is near the base (found only in Phaeophyta).

Phycocyanin. A blue pigment in chromatophores of certain Rhodophyta and in protoplasts of Myxophyceae.

Phycoerythrin. The red pigment in chromatophores of Rhodophyta.

Pinna. A primary branch of a pinnately divided thallus.

Pinnate. With leaflets or filaments on opposite sides of an axis; feather-like.

Pinnule. A secondary branch of a pinnately divided thallus.

Placenta. A large flattened cell bearing gonimoblasts (found only in Florideae).

Plastid. In algae the specialized portion of the cytoplasm containing the chlorophyll or chlorophyll and other pigments.

Plurilocular. Term applied to many-celled reproductive organs in which each cell produces a single reproductive body. (Usage restricted to Phaeophyta.)

Pluriseriate. More than one cell broad.

Pneumatocysts. Large air-bladders.

Polysiphonous. With transverse tiers of vertically elongated cells whose vertical walls are parallel.

Polysporangium. A sporangium containing more than four spores (usage restricted to the Florideae).

Polyspore. A spore formed in a polysporangium.

Protandrous. With male reproductive organs developing before the female organs.

Pseudoparenchyma. A tissue having the appearance of a parenchyma.

Quadriflagellate. Possessing four flagella.

Ramellus. A ramulus of the ultimate order of branching.

Ramulus. A secondary branch.

Reniform. Kidney-shaped.

Rhizoid. In algae a unicellular or multicellular filament functioning as an organ of attachment.

Rhizoidal. Pertaining to a rhizoid.

Rhizome. The prostrate, stem-like portion of a thallus with an upright leaf-like or branch-like portion.

Rugose. Wrinkled.

Saccate. Sac-like or pouch-like.

Saxicolous. Growing on rock.

Secund. With branches restricted to one side of the structure bearing them.

Segment. A joint or node.

Septate. With transverse partitions.

Serrate. Toothed like a saw and with the teeth pointing toward the apex.

Sessile. Not borne on a stalk.

Seta. A bristle or stiff hair.

Simple. Unbranched (with reference to a filament or to a blade).

Siphonaceous. Tubular and composed of one cell (usage restricted to Chlorophyceae).

Sorus. A group or cluster of reproductive organs.

Spatulate. Oblong and with the basal end narrowed; shaped like a spatula.

Spermatangium. The male sex organ producing the spermatia of Rhodophyta.

Spermatium. The nonflagellated male gamete of Rhodophyta.

Spore. A specialized motile or nonmotile cell which eventually becomes free from the parent plant and is capable of developing into a new plant.

Sporophyll. A blade producing sporangia (usage restricted to Laminariales).

Sporophyte. The diploid spore-producing generation developed from the zygote of an alga.

Stichidium. An inflated, specialized branch bearing tetrasporangia in transverse rows (found in a few Florideae).

Stipe. The upright, stem-like region below an erect blade.

Stipitate. Borne on a stipe.

Sub-. A prefix denoting a less degree of the word in combination with it; as *subacute.*

Substratum. The object upon or within which an alga is growing.

Supporting cell. The cell bearing the carpogonial filament of Florideae.

Sympodial. A method of development wherein a branch continues growth in the direction of the axis and the axis continues growth as a lateral branch.

Synonym. An illegal name for a species.

Terete. Cylindrical, tapering, and circular in cross section.

Tetrahedral. Having contents of a tetrasporangium triangularly divided so that only three of the tetraspores can be seen in one view.

Tetrasporangium. A sporangium whose contents divide to form four spores. (Florideae are the only Monterey Peninsula algae with tetrasporangia.)

Tetraspore. A spore formed within a tetrasporangium.

Tetrasporophyte. A diploid generation producing tetraspores.

Thallus. The plant body of an alga.

Trichoblast. A simple or branched filament growing from the surface of a thallus (usage restricted to Florideae).

Trichogyne. The hair-like, apical prolongation of a carpogonium.

Trichome. Any sterile filamentous outgrowth from the surface of a thallus.

Trichothallic. A method of growth in which thallus development is initiated at the base of one or more filaments (found only in Phaeophyta).

Uncinate. With the free end hook-shaped.

Unilateral. Occurring or developing on one side only.

Uniaxial. With a single longitudinal filament through the center of the thallus (usage restricted to Florideae).

Unilocular. Term applied to one-celled sporangia producing many spores (usage restricted to Phaeophyta).

Uniseriate. With cells joined end to end in a row one cell broad.

Vein. Branches from midrib of a blade or linear thickened regions within a blade.

Ventral. The lower surface of a dorsiventral thallus.

Verrucose. Warty or wart-like.

Verticil. One whorl in a verticillate system of branching.

Verticillate. With successive whorls of branches along an axis.

Zonate. Contents of a tetrasporangium divided by three parallel planes so that the tetraspores lie above one another.

Zoogamete. A gamete with flagella.

Zooid. A flagellated reproductive cell; either gamete or spore.

Zoospore. A sport with flagella.

Zygote. The cell formed by a union of two gametes.

DIVISION CHLOROPHYTA

Cells uninucleate or multinucleate, with the photosynthetic pigments localized in one or more plastids (chloroplasts) containing only chlorophyll and carotenoid pigments. The chloroplasts usually with one or more pyrenoids. The thalli unicellular or multicellular; if multicellular, either filamentous or nonfilamentous, microscopic or macroscopic, and of definite or indefinite shape.

Asexual reproduction by zoospores, aplanospores, or akinetes. Zoospores with two, four, or more flagella of equal length and restricted to anterior end. One or more zoospores either produced within an unmodified vegetative cell or within a special cell (sporangium). The aplanospores produced in same manner as zoospores.

Sexual reproduction isogamous, anisogamous, or oögamous. Motile gametes usually biflagellate. The gametes either produced within unmodified vegetative cells or within gametangia of distinctive shape. The zygote usually secreting a thick wall, entering upon a period of rest, and with the zygote nucleus dividing reductionally before germinating to form one or more zoospores or aplanospores. In a few genera with an alternation of generations and with an immediate germination of the zygote to form the diploid spore-producing generation (sporophyte).

With but one class, the Chlorophyceae, in the local flora.

Class CHLOROPHYCEAE

Thalli unicellular or multicellular; if multicellular never with growth initiated by apical cells.

The sex organs unicellular, borne freely exposed, and only in rare cases becoming surrounded by a sheath of sterile cells after fertilization.

KEY TO THE ORDERS IN THE LOCAL FLORA

1. Vegetative cells flagellate and motile.............*Volvocales* (p. 26)
1. Vegetative cells nonflagellate and immobile...................... 2

25

Order VOLVOCALES

With flagellate motile vegetative cells. Unicellular or colonial; if colonial nonfilamentous, with the cell number a multiple of two, and with no increase in number of cells after the colony is mature. Cells variously shaped, with 2–8 flagella of equal length and the flagella restricted to anterior end of cell. Chloroplasts cup-shaped or stellate, usually one within a cell and with a single pyrenoid. The cells regularly with an eyespot and frequently with contractile vacuoles at the anterior end. At times producing amorphous colonies (Palmella stages) of immobile cells within a common gelatinous matrix.

Asexual reproduction by longitudinal bipartition or by a repeated division of the protoplast to form 2–16 zoospores with the same number of flagella as vegetative cells. The zoospores separating from one another when liberated or remaining united in a colony of definite shape.

Sexual reproduction isogamous, anisogamous, or oögamous. Zoogametes usually biflagellate. The zygote immobile, thick-walled, and entering upon a period of rest before germination.

Key to the Families in the Local Flora

1. Unicellular and without a cell wall.......*Polyblepharidaceae* (p. 27)
1. Unicellular and with a homogeneous cell
    wall ....*Chlamydomonadaceae* (p. 29)

Family POLYBLEPHARIDACEAE

Unicellular. The cells without a wall and at times changing slightly in shape while motile. Cells ellipsoid, ovoid, pyriform, or spindle-shaped; at times somewhat compressed. With two to eight flagella of equal length at the anterior end. Chloroplast single, usually cup-shaped and with one pyrenoid. Cells generally with an eyespot. The cells rarely forming a temporary colony of immobile cells within a common gelatinous matrix. Immobile thick-walled stages (cysts) known for most genera.

Asexual reproduction by longitudinal bipartition while swimming through the water.

Sexual reproduction, so far as known, isogamous and by a union of biflagellate gametes. The zygote thick-walled, germinating to form 2–8 motile cells.

KEY TO THE GENERA IN THE LOCAL FLORA

1. Surface of cell with longitudinal ridges.......*Stephanoptera* (p. 27)
1. Surface of cell without longitudinal ridges........*Dunaliella* (p. 28)

Stephanoptera Dangeard, 1910

Unicellular and biflagellate. The cells obovoid, with four or six longitudinal ridges running from base to apex. The cells stellate in outline when seen in polar view. Chloroplast at posterior end of cell, cup-shaped, and the margin with as many vertical projections as there are ridges on the cell. With an eyespot in upper half of cell. The cells at times losing their flagella, becoming spherical, and secreting a wall.

Asexual reproduction by longitudinal bipartition while swimming through the water. .

Sexual reproduction unknown.

STRUCTURE AND REPRODUCTION. Artari, 1913, pp. 455–456; pl. 6, figs. III¹–III⁴ (as *Asteromonas*). Dangeard, 1912, pp. ii–x; pl. 1.

With one species in the local flora.

Stephanoptera gracilis (Artari) G. M. Smith   Pl. 1, fig. 2

G. M. Smith, 1933, p. 301; fig. 201.
Asteromonas gracilis Artari, 1913, p. 455; pl. 6, figs. III¹–III⁴.

Cells with six longitudinal ridges; the ridges straight or bent. Chloroplast with six projections at the upper end; the pyrenoid large and without starch on the upper side. The cells 10–14 μ broad, 14–20 μ long. Flagella with a length about 1.5 times that of cell.

LOCAL DISTRIBUTION. Near high-tide mark in spray pools on rocks coated with the excrement of sea birds. Point Pinos.

TYPE LOCALITY. Crimean Peninsula, Russia.

PACIFIC COAST DISTRIBUTION. Known only from San Francisco Bay and from the Monterey Peninsula.

Dunaliella Teodoresco, 1905

Unicellular and biflagellate. The cells elliptical to obpyriform, at times slightly compressed. Without a cell wall. Chloroplast cup-shaped, at posterior end of cell, with one pyrenoid. The chlorophyll frequently becoming masked by a reddish-orange pigment (haematochrome). Cells without haematochrome usually with an evident eyespot. At times the cells losing their flagella, becoming spherical, and secreting a wall.

Asexual reproduction by longitudinal bipartition while swimming through the water.

Sexual reproduction isogamous and by biflagellate zoogametes. Homothallic or heterothallic. The zygote thick-walled; eventually germinating to form 2–4–8 biflagellate cells.

STRUCTURE AND REPRODUCTION. Teodoresco, 1906. Lerche, 1937.

With one species in the local flora.

Dunaliella salina (Dunal) Teodoresco   Pl. 1, fig. 1

Teodoresco, 1905, p. 230; figs. 1–5; pls. 8–9 (in part).
Protococcus salinus Dunal, 1838, p. 173.
Dunaliella viridis Teodoresco, 1905, p. 230; pl. 8, figs. 5, 8, 19, 23, 27–29.

Cells ellipsoidal or ovoid. The chloroplast cup-shaped, frequently with the chlorophyll masked by haematochrome. Eyespot small, about one-third the distance from apex to base of cell. Cells 6–13 μ broad, 12–21 μ long. Flagella with a length 1.0–1.25 that of cell.

LOCAL DISTRIBUTION. Near high-tide mark in spray-filled pools. Mussel Point; Point Pinos.

TYPE LOCALITY. Mediterranean coast of France.

PACIFIC COAST DISTRIBUTION. Known only from San Francisco Bay and the Monterey Peninsula.

Red and green forms of this species also differ in shape. The two have long been considered different species, but it has recently been shown that these differences are due to environmental conditions.

Family CHLAMYDOMONACACEAE

Unicellular and biflagellate or quadriflagellate. Cells with a homogeneous wall which is not separable into two halves (valves). Cell shape various. Chloroplasts cup-shaped or stellate, usually one within a cell and with one pyrenoid. Anterior end of cell frequently with two contractile vacuoles. Eyespot variously shaped and located. The cells often forming a temporary colony (Palmella stage) of immobile cells within a common gelatinous matrix; rarely forming thick-walled, immobile resting cells (akinetes).

Asexual reproduction by division of protoplast into 2–32 zoospores. The zoospores liberated either by gelatinization or by rupture of parent-cell wall.

Sexual reproduction isogamous, anisogamous, or oögamous. Zoogametes usually biflagellate, rarely quadriflagellate; formed in same manner as zoospores. Zygote thick-walled, producing 2–8 zoospores upon germination.

With one genus in the local flora.

Platymonas G. S. West, 1916

Unicellular and quadriflagellate. The cells compressed; elliptical to oval in front view; linear-oblong in side view, with one side convex and the other straight. With a distinct, though delicate, cell wall. Chloroplast cup-shaped, with a cup-shaped pyrenoid in which there is no starch on side toward anterior end of cell. Eyespot fairly conspicuous.

Asexual reproduction by division of protoplast into two zoospores. The zoospores so oriented that the anterior ends face in opposite directions.

Sexual reproduction unknown.

STRUCTURE AND REPRODUCTION. Lewis in Lewis and Taylor, 1921, pp. 249–251; pl. 133, figs. 1–19. West, 1916. Zimmerman, 1925, pp. 9–11; pl. 1, figs. 2ª–2'.

With one species in the local flora.

Platymonas subcordiformis (Wille) Hazen

Hazen in Lewis and Taylor, 1921, p. 251. Lewis in Lewis and Taylor, 1921, pp. 249–251; pl. 133, figs. 1–19.
Carteria subcordiformis Wille, 1903, p. 93; pl. 3, figs. 1–3.

Cells oval in front view, at times with posterior end somewhat pointed. As seen in side view with one side convex and the other straight. Anterior end of cell flattened and with the flagella inserted in a small depression. Chloroplast cup-shaped. Eyespot fairly conspicuous and lying at level of the pyrenoid. The cells 13–17 μ long, 7–8 μ broad, and 4–5 μ in thickness.

LOCAL DISTRIBUTION. In high-lying spray pools fouled with excrement from gulls. Mussel Point.

TYPE LOCALITY. Aalesund, Norway.

PACIFIC COAST DISTRIBUTION. Known only from the Monterey Peninsula.

Known locally from a single collection made by I. F. Lewis. The description given above (including dimensions) is based upon I. F. Lewis' description of specimens collected in Massachusetts.

Order TETRASPORALES

Thalli usually multicellular, rarely unicellular. If colonial, usually with the cells lying within a common gelatinous matrix and never with them joined end to end in filaments. The cells dividing vegetatively. Vegetative cells at any time capable of entering upon a flagellate, free-swimming phase. The cells uninucleate, usually with a single cup-shaped chloroplast with one pyrenoid. Immobile vegetative cells at times with contractile vacuoles and an eyespot.

Asexual reproduction by zoospores, aplanospores, and akinetes. The zoospores biflagellate or quadriflagellate, usually formed in multiples of two within a cell.

Sexual reproduction by biflagellate zoogametes formed in the same manner as zoospores. Gametic union usually isogamous.

With but one family, the Chlorangiaceae, in the local flora.

Family CHLORANGIACEAE

Thallus unicellular and terminal on a simple stipe or multicellular and with the cells on a branched stipe. The cells with the anterior pole toward the stipe. The chloroplast cup-shaped to laminate, with one pyrenoid. Vegetative cells frequently with contractile vacuoles and an eyespot.

Asexual reproduction by zoospores or aplanospores. The zoospores biflagellate or quadriflagellate.

Sexual reproduction by a union of biflagellate isogametes.

Collinsiella Setchell and Gardner, 1903

Thallus a multicellular globose gelatinous colony in which the cells are scattered throughout a gelatinous matrix. The cells terminal on branches of a dichotomously branched stalk system in which one arm of each successive dichotomy does not develop further. The stalk system and gelatinous matrix of colony not distinguishable from each other unless treated with appropriate reagents. The cells pyriform, with the anterior poles toward the stalks on which they are borne. The chloroplast cup- or band-shaped, at posterior end of cell; with one pyrenoid.

Reproduction by division of contents of cells into 8–16 rounded protoplasts (zoospores?). Reproduction restricted to cells near surface of colony.

STRUCTURE AND REPRODUCTION. Setchell and Gardner, 1903, pp. 204–205; pl. 17, figs. 1–7. Yendo, 1903 (as *Ecballocystis*).

With one species in the local flora.

Collinsiella tuberculata Setchell and Gardner

Setchell and Gardner, 1903, p. 204; pl. 17, figs. 1–7. Collins, 1909, p. 141. Setchell and Gardner, 1920, p. 144; pl. 10, figs. 4–10. Phyc. Bor.-Amer. No. 909. *Ecballocystis Willeana* Yendo, 1903, p. 199; pl. 8, figs. 1–15.

Thalli 2–4 mm. in diameter, bright green, globose, of a firm gelatinous texture. The cells pyriform, 12–20 µ long, 5–12 µ broad.

LOCAL DISTRIBUTION. Growing between the 2.5- and 1.5-foot tide levels on rocks scoured smooth by sand. Point Aulon.

TYPE LOCALITY. Whidbey Island, Washington.

PACIFIC COAST DISTRIBUTION. British Columbia (Vancouver Island) to central California (Pacific Grove).

Living plants seem to have the cells radially scattered through a homogeneous gelatinous colonial matrix. The dichotomously branched stalk system upon which the cells are borne becomes evident only after treatment with zinc chloriodide.

Prasinocladus Kuckuck, 1894

Thallus multicellular; with the cells terminal on a dichotomously branched, transversely septate stalk system whose branches are of the same diameter as the cells. The cells and branching stalk system not lying within a common homogeneous gelatinous matrix. The cells ellipsoidal, with the anterior end toward the stalk. The chloroplast cup-shaped but lobed at the anterior end. Pyrenoid single and with the surrounding starch sheath incomplete on side toward anterior pole of cell. Cells at all times with a single eyespot. Cell division by a longitudinal bipartition of the protoplast and the two daughter protoplasts quadriflagellate for a short time. The daughter protoplasts usually remaining permanently imprisoned within the gelatinous cell wall but at times escaping and functioning as zoospores. Under certain conditions the cells developing into aplanospores.

Sexual reproduction unknown.

STRUCTURE AND REPRODUCTION. Davis, 1894 (as *Euglenopsis*). Kuckuck, 1894, pp. 261–262; fig. 28. Kylin, 1935*A*, pp. 7–12; fig. 3. Lambert, 1930. Zimmermann, 1925, pp. 11–14; pl. 1, figs. 3*A*–3*K*.

Prasinocladus lubricus Kuckuck   Pl. 1, fig. 3

Kuckuck, 1894, p. 261; fig. 28. G. M. Smith, 1933, p. 366; fig. 246. Taylor, 1937, p. 38.

Stalk system of colony up to 250 μ tall, repeatedly dichotomous; with the segments of the branches barrel-shaped, 6–8 μ broad, and with a length 2–4 times the breadth. The cells 14–20 μ long, 5–7 μ broad.

LOCAL DISTRIBUTION. Growing on rocks in the upper littoral. Point Pinos; Cypress Point.

TYPE LOCALITY. Helgoland, Germany.

PACIFIC COAST DISTRIBUTION. Known only from the Monterey Peninsula.

Order ULOTRICHALES

Thalli filamentous, branched or unbranched; if branched, at times with the branches laterally compacted into a pseudoparenchyma. The chloroplast single, parietal, laminate, entire or perforate, with one to several pyrenoids. Cells uninucleate, at times becoming multinucleate when mature.

Asexual reproduction by zoospores, aplanospores, or akinetes. The spores formed within unmodified vegetative cells or within sporangia of distinctive shape. Zoospores biflagellate or quadriflagellate; usually many formed within a cell or a sporangium.

Sexual reproduction isogamous, anisogamous, or oögamous.

Zoogametes usually biflagellate, rarely quadriflagellate; formed either within unmodified vegetative cells or within gametangia of distinctive shape.

Family ULOTRICHACEAE

Thalli filamentous, unbranched, sessile or free-floating. The filaments with or without a gelatinous envelope. The cells cylindrical to subspherical. Chloroplast single, parietal, usually a complete or incomplete ring; with one to several pyrenoids. Cells uninucleate.

Asexual reproduction by zoospores, aplanospores, or akinetes. The zoospores biflagellate or quadriflagellate, formed within unmodified vegetative cells; several formed within a cell and escaping through a pore in the cell wall.

Sexual reproduction by a union of biflagellate isogametes. The gametes formed and liberated in same manner as zoospores.

With one genus in the local flora.

Ulothrix Kützing, 1833

Thalli filamentous, unbranched. The filaments usually sessile and with the basal cell somewhat modified to form a holdfast. The cells cylindrical. Chloroplast single, parietal, band-like, completely or incompletely encircling cell; with one or several pyrenoids. Cells uninucleate.

Asexual reproduction by zoospores, aplanospores, or akinetes. The zoospores quadriflagellate, formed in multiples of two within a cell and liberated through a single pore in the cell wall.

Sexual reproduction by a union of biflagellate isogametes. The gametes formed and liberated in the same manner as zoospores. The zygote secreting a thick wall, not germinating immediately, producing zoospores or aplanospores upon germination.

STRUCTURE AND REPRODUCTION. Dodel, 1876. Grosse, 1931.

With one species in the local flora.

Ulothrix implexa Kützing   Pl. 1, figs. 4–5

Kützing, 1849, p. 349. Hazen, 1902, p. 153; pl. 21, figs. 1–2. Setchell and Gardner, 1920, p. 283.

Ulothrix subflaccida Osterhout and Gardner [not of Wille]. Osterhout and Gardner in Phyc. Bor.-Amer. No. 1275.

Thalli forming a soft, silky, green coating on the substratum. The filaments, as found on the Monterey Peninsula, 5–15 mm. long. The cells cylindrical, 5–15 μ broad, with a length 0.5–1.0 times the breadth. The chloroplast not extending from end to end of cell, often an incomplete ring; usually with one pyrenoid.

LOCAL DISTRIBUTION. Growing at the water line on fishing boats. Monterey harbor.

TYPE LOCALITY. Germany.

PACIFIC COAST DISTRIBUTION. Alaska (St. Michael) to central California (Monterey).

Family CHAETOPHORACEAE

Thalli filamentous, branched; the branches either not touching one another laterally, or laterally compacted into a pseudoparenchyma. Chloroplasts laminate, parietal, at times more or less dissected; with one or more pyrenoids.

Asexual reproduction by zoospores, aplanospores, or akinetes. The zoospores biflagellate or quadriflagellate, not produced within sporangia of distinctive shape, usually produced in multiples of two within a cell.

Sexual reproduction usually isogamous, rarely anisogamous or oögamous. Zoogametes biflagellate (rarely quadriflagellate) and not produced within gametangia of distinctive shape.

KEY TO THE GENERA IN THE LOCAL FLORA

1. Thalli endophytic 2
1. Thalli epiphytic, epizoic, or saxicolous 4
   2. Within cell walls at surface of host............*Entocladia* (p. 34)
   2. Growing between cells of host 3
3. Not growing below cortex of host.............*Pseudodictyon* (p. 36)
3. Growing below cortex of host..................*Endophyton* (p. 36)
   4. With rhizoids from the lower surface..*Pseudopringsheimia* (p. 37)
   4. Without rhizoids from the lower surface 5
5. Zoospores biflagellate ....*Ulvella* (p. 38)
5. Zoospores quadriflagellate ....*Pseudoulvella* (p. 39)

Entocladia Reinke, 1879

Thalli usually endophytic. The thallus a prostrate irregularly branched filament with the branches radiating from a common center; at times with branches at center of thallus compacted into a pseudoparenchyma. The branches without setae. The cells with a single laminate parietal chloroplast with one or more pyrenoids. Cells uninucleate.

Asexual reproduction by quadriflagellate zoospores and akinetes. Zoospores formed in cells near center of thallus and usually eight or more formed within a cell.

Sexual reproduction by biflagellate isogametes 'formed in same manner as zoospores.

STRUCTURE AND REPRODUCTION. Annand, 1937, pp. 12–16; figs. 1–2 (as *Endoderma*). Borzi, 1895, pp. 291–302; pl. 15 (as *Entoderma*). Huber, 1892, pp. 313–326; pls. 14–15 (as *Endoderma*). Kylin, 1935, pp. 12–19; figs. 5–7.

KEY TO THE SPECIES IN THE LOCAL FLORA

1. Center of older thalli not pseudoparenchymatous............*E. viridis*
1. Center of older thalli pseudoparenchymatous..............*E. codicola*

Entocladia viridis Reinke

Reinke, 1879, p. 476; pl. 6, figs. 6–9. Setchell and Gardner, 1920, p. 289. Taylor, 1937, p. 53; pl. 2, figs. 1–2.
Endoderma viride (Reinke) Lagerheim, 1883, p. 74. Phyc. Bor.-Amer. No. 2236.

Endophytic within outer cell walls of various algae. Freely branched and without the branches at center of older thalli laterally adjoined to form a pseudoparenchyma. Cells at center of thallus irregular in shape; those at periphery of thallus cylindrical and with a length 2–6 times the breadth. The cells 3–8 µ broad.

LOCAL DISTRIBUTION. On *Callithamnion Pikeanum*. Point Joe.
TYPE LOCALITY. Germany.
PACIFIC COAST DISTRIBUTION. Known only from Moss Beach (San Mateo County, California) and from the Monterey Peninsula.

Entocladia codicola Setchell and Gardner   Pl. 1, fig. 7

Setchell and Gardner, 1920*A*, p. 293; pl. 24, fig. 7. Setchell and Gardner, 1920, p. 290; pl. 19, fig. 7.

Endophytic within cell walls of utricles of *Codium*. Radiately branched, and with branches in central portion of thallus laterally compacted into a pseudoparenchyma. Cells at center of thallus polygonal; those toward the periphery cylindrical and with a length 2.5–4 times the breadth. The peripheral cells 3–4 µ broad. The chloroplast with or without one pyrenoid.

LOCAL DISTRIBUTION. Growing within tips of utricles of *Codium fragile*. Fanshell Beach; Pescadero Point.
TYPE LOCALITY. Redondo, California.
PACIFIC COAST DISTRIBUTION. As above.

Endophyton Gardner, 1909

Thalli endophytic within blades of Gigartinaceae; filamentous, abundantly branched, the branches not laterally compacted and penetrating deeply within the host. Branches in cortical tissues of host perpendicular to surface of blade; branches in medulla of host parallel to surface of blade. The cells cylindrical; terminal cells of erect branches ovoid and apiculate at tip. Chloroplast single, laminate, parietal; with one pyrenoid.

Asexual reproduction by biflagellate zoospores formed within the inflated terminal cells of erect branches.

Sexual reproduction unknown.

STRUCTURE AND REPRODUCTION. Gardner, 1909, pp. 371–373; pl. 14, figs. 3–4.

Endophyton ramosum Gardner   Pl. 1, fig. 6

Gardner, 1909, p. 372; pl. 14, figs. 3–4. Setchell and Gardner, 1920, p. 292; pl. 11, figs. 3–4. Phyc. Bor.-Amer. No. 1627.

Thalli producing irregularly shaped, expanded, dark-colored areas in basal portion of blade of host. Portion of thallus in medulla and in inner cortex of host with cylindrical cells 4–6 μ broad and the cells with a length 2–6 times the breadth. The fertile terminal cells of erect branches with a breadth about double that of other cells.

LOCAL DISTRIBUTION. Endophytic within *Rhodoglossum americanum* and various species of *Iridophycus*. Mussel Point; Point Pinos; Middle Reef of Moss Beach; Pebble Beach; north end of Carmel Beach; Mission Point.

TYPE LOCALITY. San Francisco, California.

PACIFIC COAST DISTRIBUTION. As above.

Pseudodictyon Gardner, 1909

Thalli endophytic within Laminariales, not penetrating beneath cortex of host. Thalli filamentous and with long branches which lie parallel to and a short distance beneath surface of host. The long branches branched at right angles in a plane parallel to surface of host; these branches so disposed that they form a reticulum. Cells of long branches cylindrical. Many cells of the long branches bearing short two- or three-celled branches on side toward surface of host. The short, erect branches with ovoid terminal cells. Chloroplast single, parietal; with one pyrenoid.

Reproduction unknown.

STRUCTURE AND REPRODUCTION. Gardner, 1909, pp. 374–375; pl. 14, figs. 5–6.

Pseudodictyon geniculatum Gardner

Gardner, 1909, p. 374; pl. 14, figs. 5–6. Setchell and Gardner, 1920, p. 293; pl. 11, figs. 5–6. *Phyc. Bor.-Amer. No. 1628.

Thalli producing greenish areas on host. Lateral branches of horizontal filaments arising from middle of a cell. Cells of horizontal branches 3–4 μ broad when young and with a length 2–3 times the breadth. Terminal cells of erect branches 8–12 μ broad.

LOCAL DISTRIBUTION. In cortex of *Dictyoneurum californicum*. Pacific Grove.

TYPE LOCALITY. San Francisco, California.

PACIFIC COAST DISTRIBUTION. As above.

Known locally only from specimens distributed as No. 1628*B* of Phyc. Bor.-Amer.

Pseudopringsheimia Wille, 1909

Thalli epiphytic, cushion-shaped. With a pseudoparenchymatous monostromatic basal layer of laterally compacted radiating branches in which growth is terminal. The basal layer producing rhizoidal branches which penetrate the host. All but the peripheral cells of basal layer bearing an erect simple or sparingly branched filament of several cells. The erect filaments laterally adjoined. Cells of erect filaments with one chloroplast; the chloroplast lying at upper end of a cell, containing one pyrenoid.

Asexual reproduction by quadriflagellate (?) zoospores. The zoospores usually formed only in terminal cells of erect filaments; eight or more zoospores formed within a cell.

Sexual reproduction unknown.

STRUCTURE AND REPRODUCTION. Wille, 1909, pp. 88–89; fig. 47.

With one species in the local flora.

Pseudopringsheimia apiculata Setchell and Gardner

Setchell and Gardner, 1920*A*, p. 297; pl. 22, figs. 1–2. Setchell and Gardner, 1920, p. 299; pl. 17, figs. 1–2.

Thalli hemispherical when not crowded. The erect filaments 145–160 μ tall, with 9–12 cylindrical or slightly inflated cells. Cells of erect filaments 8–12 μ broad and with a length 0.5–2.5 times the breadth. Terminal cells of erect filaments conical to apiculate. Rhizoids from lower surface of thallus aggregated in short conical clusters.

LOCAL DISTRIBUTION. On stipe and cysts of *Egregia Menziesii*. Point Pinos.

TYPE LOCALITY. San Francisco, California.

PACIFIC COAST DISTRIBUTION. Known only from San Francisco and from the Monterey Peninsula.

Found on *Egregia Menziesii* at Point Pinos by N. L. Gardner. A minute epiphytic green alga of rather widespread distribution on blades of *Dictyoneurum californicum* is here referred to this species with reservations. It has been found at Mussel Point, the Middle Reef of Moss Beach, Point Joe, Pebble Beach, and Mission Point, and has been dredged from a depth of 15–20 feet at Still-water Cove.

Ulvella Crouan, 1859

Thalli epiphytic or saxicolous. Disc-shaped. At first mono-stromatic but eventually becoming more than one cell in thickness in central portion. Without rhizoids from lower surface. Mono-stromatic portion with cells in laterally adjoined rows radiating from center of thallus. Marginal cells frequently Y-shaped. Por-tion more than one cell in thickness not with cells in vertical rows. The cells with a single laminate chloroplast with or without a single pyrenoid. Cells uninucleate (at times multinucleate ?).

Asexual reproduction by biflagellate zoospores. The zoospores formed in cells inward from the thallus margin and 4–8–16 pro-duced within a cell.

Sexual reproduction unknown.

STRUCTURE AND REPRODUCTION. Dangeard, 1931. Feldmann, 1937, pp. 185–188; figs. 9B–9C.

With one species in the local flora.

Ulvella Setchellii Dangeard

Dangeard, 1931, p. 318; text figs. 1D–1E and pl. 1. Feldmann, 1937, p. 188; fig. 9C.

Ulvella lens Setchell and Gardner [not of Crouan]. *Setchell and Gardner, 1920, p. 295; pl. 33.

Thalli up to 2 mm. in diameter. Cells of the monostromatic portion radiately disposed and those at the periphery 3–5 μ broad and 10–50 μ long. Marginal cells frequently Y-shaped. Central portion of thallus regularly 2–4 cells in thickness; the cells rounded or rectangular, 5–8 μ in diameter. Chloroplast laminate, parietal, regularly with one pyrenoid. Cells uninucleate.

LOCAL DISTRIBUTION. On *Laurencia* sp. Pacific Grove.
TYPE LOCALITY. Not designated.
PACIFIC COAST DISTRIBUTION. Known only from Pacific Grove.

The dimensions given above are those of Dangeard for specimens collected in France.

Pseudoulvella[1] Wille, 1909

Thalli usually epizoic but at times epiphytic. Mature thalli disc-shaped; monostromatic at margin and several cells in thickness at center. Without rhizoids growing down from the under side. Monostromatic portion with or without the cells in radial rows. The portion more than one cell in thickness usually with cells in vertical rows. The chloroplast laminate to cup-shaped, with a single pyrenoid. The cells uninucleate.

Asexual reproduction by quadriflagellate zoospores. The zoospores formed in surface cells of portion more than one cell in thickness.

Sexual reproduction unknown.

STRUCTURE AND REPRODUCTION. Annand, 1937, pp. 16–17; fig. 3.

With one species in the local flora.

Pseudoulvella applanata Setchell and Gardner

* Setchell and Gardner, 1920*A*, p. 295. Setchell and Gardner, 1920, p. 298. Annand, 1937, p. 16; fig. 3.

Thalli epizoic, up to several millimeters in diameter. Central portion with cells in vertical rows 45–55 μ tall. The cells subcubical, 6–7.5 μ in diameter. Chloroplast usually toward upper side of cells, with one pyrenoid.

LOCAL DISTRIBUTION. On shells of periwinkles (*Littorina planaxis* Nutt.) growing in pools above high-tide mark. Carmel Bay.
TYPE LOCALITY. As above.
PACIFIC COAST DISTRIBUTION. As above.

Family TRENTEPOHLIACEAE

Thalli filamentous and branched, at times with the branches laterally compacted into a pseudoparenchyma. The cells cylin-

---

[1] The characters usually used to distinguish between *Ulvella* and *Pseudoulvella* (the presence or absence of pyrenoids and uninucleate or multinucleate cells) have been shown (Dangeard, 1931) to be invalid. The only constant distinction seems to be the number of flagella of zoospores.

drical or angular. Thalli rarely with colorless hairs. Chloroplasts laminate, parietal, entire or perforate, with one to several py-renoids, at times with the chlorophyll masked by a red pigment (haematochrome). Cells uninucleate when young, often becom-ing multinucleate when mature.

Asexual reproduction by zoospores, aplanospores, or akinetes. The spores produced within sporangia of distinctive shape. The sporangia terminal or intercalary; if terminal frequently becom-ing detached when mature. Zoospores biflagellate or quadriflagel-late and many produced within a sporangium.

Sexual reproduction of a union of biflagellate isogametes. The gametes produced within gametangia of distinctive shape. The gametangia usually intercalary; not becoming detached from thal-lus when mature.

With one genus, *Gomontia,* in the local flora.

Gomontia Bornet and Flahault, 1888

Thalli usually endozoic and perforating calcareous shells of mollusks, but at times perforating chalky rock or wood. The thallus an irregularly and profusely branched filament. The cells cylindrical or irregularly inflated. Young cells with an entire or perforate parietal laminate chloroplast with one to several py-renoids. The cells usually uninucleate.

Asexual reproduction by zoospores or aplanospores. Many spores formed within a sporangium[2] several times the diameter of a vegetative cell and apparently developed from either a ter-minal or an intercalary cell. The sporangia pyriform to irregular in shape, with one to several thick-walled rhizoidal processes at one side. The zoospores quadriflagellate.

Sexual reproduction unknown, but biflagellate "zoospores" have been recorded.

STRUCTURE AND REPRODUCTION. Bornet and Flahault, 1889, pp. clii–clx; pls. 6–8. Kylin, 1935, pp. 3–8; figs. 1–2. Setchell and Gardner, 1920A, pp. 298–300; pl. 23, figs. 1–2; pl. 24, figs. 1–3.

With one species in the local flora.

[2] Kylin (1935) is of the opinion that what has been called the sporangium is a unicellular *Codiolum*-like alga. However, there seems to be convincing evidence that the sporangia are developed from cells of the filaments always found in as-sociation with the sporangia.

Gomontia polyrhiza (Lagerheim) Bornet and Flahault

Pl. 1, figs. 8–11; pl. 2, figs. 1–7

Bornet and Flahault, 1888, p. 163. Bornet and Flahault, 1889, p. clviii; pls. 6–8. Setchell and Gardner, 1920, p. 302; pl. 19, fig. 1. Setchell and Gardner, 1920*A*, p. 298; pl. 24, fig. 1. Kylin, 1935, p. 3; figs. 1–2.

Codiolum polyrhizum Lagerheim, 1885, p. 22; pl. 28, figs. 1–16.

Gomontia Bornetii Setchell and Gardner, 1920*A*, p. 298. Setchell and Gardner, 1920, p. 302.

Gomontia habrorhiza Setchell and Gardner, 1920*A*, p. 299; pl. 24, figs. 2–3. Setchell and Gardner, 1920, p. 304; pl. 19, figs. 2–3.

Gomontia caudata Setchell and Gardner, 1920*A*, p. 300; pl. 23, figs. 1–2. Setchell and Gardner, 1920, p. 304; pl. 18, figs. 1–2.

Thalli forming green patches within shells of host. The filaments abundantly and irregularly branched; with cells 4–10 µ broad and a length 2–6 times the breadth. Sporangia variously shaped; with one to several simple or bifurcate rhizoids. The sporangia up to 200 µ broad and 180 µ long.

LOCAL DISTRIBUTION. In empty shells of clams and mussels. Mussel Point.

TYPE LOCALITY. Kristineberg, Sweden.

PACIFIC COAST DISTRIBUTION. Known only from Neah Bay, Washington, and from the Monterey Peninsula.

On the basis of shape of sporangia Setchell and Gardner recognize three species in addition to *G. polyrhiza*. Kylin (1935) finds all of these sporangial forms in material collected from the type locality and thinks that they all belong to a single species. In collections from Mussel Point the sporangia from a single thallus (figs. 9–10, pl. 1; figs. 1–2, pl. 2) show much the same variation in shape of sporangia. The local material indicates that production of sporangia with a single rhizoidal process or with two or more rhizoidal processes depends upon whether a cell developing into a sporangium is terminal or intercalary.

Order ULVALES

Thalli multicellular and nonfilamentous; tubular or membranous, sessile or becoming free-floating. The cells uninucleate and cell division intercalary. Chloroplast single, laminate or cup-shaped, usually with one pyrenoid. The thalli at times multiplying vegetatively by fragmentation.

Certain genera with an alternation of identical sexual and asexual generations; other genera without a multicellular diploid asexual generation.

Asexual reproduction by zoospores and aplanospores. The zoospores usually quadriflagellate; produced in multiples of two within a cell and liberated through a single pore in the cell wall.

Sexual reproduction by biflagellate zoogametes formed and liberated in same manner as zoospores. Gametic union isogamous or anisogamous. Gametes at times parthenogenetic. The zygote either developing immediately into a thallus or secreting a thick wall, not germinating immediately, and producing quadriflagellate zoospores at the time of germination.

Family ULVACEAE

All Ulvales are placed in a single family, the Ulvaceae, whose characters are the same as those of the order.

KEY TO THE GENERA IN THE LOCAL FLORA

1. Adult thallus wholly or in part tubular.........*Enteromorpha* (p. 48)
1. Adult thallus a broadly expanded blade.......................... 2
   2. Blade distromatic ....*Ulva* (p. 43)
   2. Blade monostromatic ....*Monostroma* (p. 42)

Monostroma Thuret, 1854

Thallus at first a sessile, closed, monostromatic sac; sooner or later the sac splitting and becoming an expanded monostromatic blade. Mature blades sessile or free-floating; of definite shape or irregularly broadened. The cells either angular and parenchymatous or rounded and in groups of 2–4 surrounded by a sheath distinct from gelatinous matrix of blade. Chloroplast single, usually laminate and with one pyrenoid. Cells uninucleate. Blades of free-floating species usually multiplying vegetatively by fragmentation.

Certain species with cells of a blade producing quadriflagellate zoospores; other species not producing zoospores in cells of blades. The zoospores either germinating to form new blades or developing into large akinetes each producing many zoospores.

Sexual reproduction by biflagellate zoogametes produced only by cells of a blade. Gametic union isogamous. Gametes at times germinating parthenogenetically. The zygote forming a thick wall, enlarging to several times the original diameter, and forming 32 or more quadriflagellate zoospores. The zygote uninucleate until just before zoospore formation.

STRUCTURE AND REPRODUCTION. Carter, 1926. Moewus, 1938, pp. 364–370; figs. 1–2. Moewus, 1940. Yamada and Kanda, 1941, pp. 217–221; text figs. 1–4; pls. 49–50. Yamada and Saito, 1938, pp. 43–49; text figs. 9–12; pl. 16.

With one species in the local flora.

Monostroma zostericola Tilden

Tilden in *Amer. Alg. Exsicc.,* No. 388. *Setchell and Gardner, 1920, p. 238; pl. 14, figs. 12–13. Yamada and Kanda, 1941, pp. 217–221; text figs. 1–4; pls. 49–50.

Thalli sessile and epiphytic, up to 3.5 cm. tall. The blades funnel-shaped and with irregularly lobed margins immediately after splitting of the closed sac; later becoming hood-shaped or irregularly expanded. Blades 7–10 μ in thickness. The cells, as seen in cross section, rectangular to vertically oblong, 5–8 μ tall.

LOCAL DISTRIBUTION. Epiphytic on leaves of *Zostera.* Monterey. Epiphytic on leaves of *Phyllospadix.* Pacific Grove.

TYPE LOCALITY. San Juan Island, Washington.

PACIFIC COAST DISTRIBUTION. Known only from Vancouver Island, Puget Sound, and the Monterey Peninsula.

In Japan, where this species is epiphytic on *Phyllospadix,* the thalli appear in January and disappear at the end of June. The fact that the two collections known from the Monterey Peninsula were both made in June indicates that the same may be true of local plants.

Ulva Linnaeus, 1753

Thallus with a broadly expanded distromatic blade. The blade usually solid but in certain species at times hollow at margins. Sessile or stipitate; if stipitate the stipe either solid or tubular. Lower cells of thallus producing rhizoids which grow down between the two cell layers and then outward to form the holdfast. Holdfast perennial, the blade annual. Chloroplast single, cup-shaped or laminate, usually on outer face of protoplast; with one pyrenoid. Cells uninucleate. Thalli at times multiplying by fragmentation.

With an alternation of identical sexual and asexual generations.

The asexual generation producing quadriflagellate zoospores. Spore production beginning at margin of blade and each cell producing 4–8–16 zoospores. The zoospores liberated through a beak-like pore in wall on outer face of cell.

The sexual generation heterothallic and producing biflagellate zoogametes. The zoogametes formed and liberated in same manner as zoospores. Gametic union isogamous or anisogamous. Gametes at times germinating parthenogenetically. The zygote germinating immediately and developing directly into a thallus.

STRUCTURE AND REPRODUCTION. Delf, 1912. Föyn, 1934*A*. Moewus, 1938, pp. 370–374. Yamada and Saito, 1938, pp. 36–40; figs. 1–5.

KEY TO THE SPECIES IN THE LOCAL FLORA

1. Base of blade tubular and hollow.........................*U. Linza*
1. Base of blade solid 2
    2. Blades spirally twisted, densely ruffled, margins more or
       less dentate ....*U. taeniata*
    2. Blades, if spirally twisted or densely ruffled, without
       dentate margins 3
3. Cells subrectangular in cross section............................ 4
3. Cells vertically elongated in cross section........................ 5
    4. Length of blade over 8 times the breadth...............*U. angusta*
    4. Length of blade not over 4 times the breadth...........*U. Lactuca*
5. Length of blade over 6 times the breadth..............*U. stenophylla*
5. Length of blade less than 5 times the breadth..................... 6
    6. Blades with a distinct short cylindrical stipe.............*U. rigida*
    6. Blades sessile 7
7. Blades deeply divided or lobed............................*U. lobata*
7. Blades not deeply divided or lobed ....*U. expansa*

Ulva Linza Linnaeus   Pl. 3, figs. 4–5

Linnaeus, 1753, p. 1163. *Anderson, 1891, p. 218. Setchell and Gardner, 1920, p. 262; pl. 12, figs. 1–4.

Enteromorpha Linza (Linnaeus) J. G. Agardh, 1883, p. 134; pl. 4, figs. 110–112. Phyc. Bor.-Amer. No. 967.

Thalli, as found on the Monterey Peninsula, up to 40 cm. tall; grass-green in color. The blade linear to lanceolate, 35–45 μ in thickness; usually with crisped or ruffled margins and at times spirally twisted. Margins of blades frequently hollow because of separation of the two cell layers. Base of blade gradually tapering to a hollow cylindrical stipe. Cells, as seen in cross section, rectangular to vertically elongate. Chloroplast cup-shaped and with walls of the cup relatively thin.

LOCAL DISTRIBUTION. Growing on rocks between the 2.0-foot and mean low-tide levels. At times epiphytic. Asilomar Point; Cypress Point; north end of Carmel Beach; Mission Point.

TYPE LOCALITY. England.

PACIFIC COAST DISTRIBUTION. Alaska (Orca) to Baja California (La Paz).

This distinctive species is easily recognized, but its systematic position is controversial. The structure of the basal portion is typical of *Enteromorpha;* that of the upper portion is typical of *Ulva.*

Ulva angusta Setchell and Gardner — Pl. 4, figs. 1–3

Setchell and Gardner, 1920*A*, p. 283; pl. 27; pl. 31, fig. 1. Setchell and Gardner, 1920, p. 264; pl. 22; pl. 26, fig. 1.

Thalli, as found on the Monterey Peninsula, up to 35 cm. tall; of a pale grass-green color. Blades lanceolate to oblanceolate, up to 5 cm. broad, gradually tapering or abruptly tapering at base; usually with a few spiral twists and with ruffled margins. Blades 35–45 µ in thickness. The cells, as seen in cross section, subquadrate. Chloroplasts laminate, on outer face of protoplast and covering entire outer face.

LOCAL DISTRIBUTION. Epiphytic on *Egregia laevigata.* Pebble Beach.
TYPE LOCALITY. San Francisco, California.
PACIFIC COAST DISTRIBUTION. Northern California (Humboldt County) to central California (Carmel Bay).

Except for their larger blades the local plants agree well with the description of Setchell and Gardner. Living plants show one conspicuous feature they do not mention—a regular spiral twisting of the blades.

Ulva Lactuca Linnaeus — Pl. 3, figs. 6–7

Linnaeus, 1753, p. 1163. *Anderson, 1891, p. 218. Setchell and Gardner, 1920, p. 265.
Ulva Lactuca var. *latissima* Howe [not of (Linnaeus) De Candolle]. *Howe, 1893, p. 67.
Ulva latissima Anderson [not of Linnaeus]. *Anderson, 1891, p. 218.

Thalli, as found on the Monterey Peninsula, up to 18 cm. tall, light green in color. The blades more or less broadly ovate, rarely incised but at times laciniate, usually with amply ruffled margins. Blades usually about 40 µ in thickness. The cells, as seen in cross section, subquadrate. Chloroplast cup-shaped, filling outer third of a cell.

LOCAL DISTRIBUTION. Epiphytic or saxicolous. Growing between the 2.0-foot and mean low-tide levels. Point Pinos; Cypress Point; Arrowhead Point.
TYPE LOCALITY. England.
PACIFIC COAST DISTRIBUTION. Alaska (St. Michael) to Gulf of California, Mexico.

As found on the Monterey Peninsula the maximum size of blades is about a third of that attained by thalli growing along the Atlantic Coast of the United States. The blades are more transparent than those of *U. lobata* or of *U. expansa.* When a blade is spread out in the hand one's fingers are plainly visible through blades of *U. Lactuca* but not through blades of the other two species.

Ulva expansa (Setchell) Setchell and Gardner

Setchell and Gardner, 1920*A*, p. 284. Setchell and Gardner, 1920, p. 268.
Ulva fasciata forma *expansa* *Setchell in Phyc. Bor.-Amer. No. LXXVII.

Thalli, as found on the Monterey Peninsula, up to 150 cm. broad; pale grass-green in color. The blades orbicular or broadly expanded, not lobed but with deeply ruffled margins. Blades 40–45 μ in thickness at margin, 60–70 μ near the middle. Marginal cells, as seen in cross section, subquadrate, 14–17 μ tall; cells inward from margin and near base of blade, vertically elongated, 25–30 μ tall. Chloroplast laminate, usually on lateral walls of cells when seen in surface view of a blade.

LOCAL DISTRIBUTION. Found free-floating in quiet water at Monterey, the west side of Cypress Point, and Pebble Beach. Epiphytic on *Gastro-clonium Coulteri* dredged from a depth of 15–20 feet at Stillwater Cove.
TYPE LOCALITY. Near Fisherman's Wharf, Monterey.
PACIFIC COAST DISTRIBUTION. Washington (Puget Sound) to Baja California (La Paz).

U. expansa seems to be a sublittoral species and one in which the blade breaks away and continues growth if free-floating in quiet coves. It differs from the closely related *U. lobata* in size and in having entire instead of divided blades.

Ulva lobata (Kützing) Setchell and Gardner   Pl. 4, figs. 4–5

Setchell and Gardner, 1920*A*, p. 284. Setchell and Gardner, 1920, p. 268.
Phycoseris lobata Kützing, 1849, p. 477.
Ulva fasciata forma *lobata* *Setchell in Phyc. Bor.-Amer. No. 863.

Thalli, as found on the Monterey Peninsula, 10–25 cm. tall; of a rich grass-green color. The blades broadly obovate, deeply lobed or divided, with deeply ruffled margins, frequently so much divided and ruffled as to obscure the general shape. Base of blade gradually narrowed and at times stipe-like just above the hold-fast. Blades 40–50 μ in thickness at margin; up to 90 μ near the middle. Cells, as seen in cross section, vertically elongated, with a length about double the breadth. Chloroplast cup-shaped, filling outer third of a cell.

LOCAL DISTRIBUTION. Usually saxicolous, occasionally epiphytic. Most thalli growing between the 2.0- and —0.5-foot tide levels. Abundant everywhere.

TYPE LOCALITY. Chile.

PACIFIC COAST DISTRIBUTION. Central California (San Francisco) to southern California (San Diego).

This seems to be the only local species in which gametic union is anisogamous.

Ulva stenophylla Setchell and Gardner

Setchell and Gardner, 1920A, p. 282, pl. 26, fig. 2; pl. 29. Setchell and Gardner, 1920, p. 271; pl. 21, fig. 2; pl. 24.

Thalli 50–80 cm. tall. The blades linear-lanceolate, without incisions but with broadly ruffled margins, tapering abruptly at base to a short flattened cuneate stipe. The blades 5–10 cm. broad and 60–110 µ in thickness. The cells, as seen in cross section, vertically elongated, with a length 1.5–2 times the breadth. Chloroplast a thin parietal layer covering a part or the whole of a cell wall; without a pyrenoid.

LOCAL DISTRIBUTION. Monterey.

TYPE LOCALITY. As above.

PACIFIC COAST DISTRIBUTION. Central California (Bolinas to Monterey).

A rare species known locally only from the type specimens.

Ulva rigida C. A. Agardh

C. A. Agardh, 1822, p. 410. Setchell and Gardner, 1920, p. 269.

Thalli, as found on the Monterey Peninsula, up to 8 cm. tall; dark green in color. The blades at first lanceolate or ovate; later becoming broadly orbicular, ruffled, and deeply lobed. With a short, but distinct, solid stipe. The cells, as seen in cross section, vertically elongated and with a length 1.5–3 times the breadth. The gelatinous matrix of blade denser between the two cell layers and at times also denser immediately external to each of the two cell layers. Chloroplast cup-shaped, massive, filling the outer two-thirds of a cell.

LOCAL DISTRIBUTION. Growing on rocks between the 4.0- and 2.0-foot tide levels. Point Joe; Fanshell Beach; Pebble Beach.

TYPE LOCALITY. "Atlantic Ocean."

PACIFIC COAST DISTRIBUTION. Alaska (Uyak Bay) to Baja California (La Paz).

U. rigida is a darker green than other local' species and the color turns to a blackish green as thalli become dry when the tide is out. There are two structural characters distinguishing it from other species in the local flora—the small solid stipe and the denser median region in the gelatinous matrix of a blade. As found on the Monterey Peninsula the blades are 40–60 μ in thickness; according to the measurements of Setchell and Gardner the thickness of the blade is 60–110 μ.

Ulva taeniata (Setchell) Setchell and Gardner   Pl. 3, figs. 1–3

*Setchell and Gardner, 1920*A*, p. 286; pl. 28. *Setchell and Gardner, 1920, p. 273; pl. 23.
Ulva fasciata forma *taeniata* *Setchell in Phyc. Bor.-Amer. No. 862.
Ulva fasciata Harvey [not of Delile]. *Harvey, 1858, p. 58. *Anderson, 1891, p. 218.

Thalli, as found on the Monterey Peninsula, up to 150 cm. tall; yellowish-green to grass-green in color. The blades split from apex to base into several long, narrow segments. The segments twisted into close spirals, densely ruffled, and with margins more or less dentate. Segments 34–45 μ in thickness at margin, 75–140 μ near the middle. Cells, as seen in cross section, subquadrate at margins of segments, vertically elongated, and with a length double the breadth in axial portion of segments. Chloroplast cup-shaped, filling outer third of a cell.

LOCAL DISTRIBUTION. Growing on rocks between the 1.0- and −1.5-foot tide levels. Abundant at Point Pinos; Asilomar Point; Middle Reef of Moss Beach; Point Joe; Cypress Point; Midway Point; Pescadero Point; Arrowhead Point; Mission Point.

TYPE LOCALITY. Monterey, California.

PACIFIC COAST DISTRIBUTION. Central Oregon (Coos Bay) to central California (Carmel Bay).

The blades are so deeply split that a person collecting the alga often mistakes the various segments of a blade for a gregarious cluster of blades. The long, narrow, densely twisted, ruffled segments make this the most easily recognized of all species in the local flora.

Enteromorpha Link, 1820

Thallus a hollow, monostromatic, simple to profusely branched cylinder which may be in part markedly compressed. Thalli usually sessile; when mature, attached by rhizoidal outgrowths from cells in the basal region. The cells usually, but not always, paren-

chymatously arranged and embedded within a homogeneous gelatinous matrix. Chloroplast single, laminate or cup-shaped, usually
on outer face of protoplast; generally with one pyrenoid. Cells
uninucleate. The thalli multiplying vegetatively by breaking away
of proliferous branches.

With an alternation of identical sexual and asexual generations.

The asexual generation producing quadriflagellate zoospores.
All but the lowermost cells of a thallus capable of producing 4–8–
16 zoospores. The zoospores liberated through a pore in wall on
outer face of the cell.

The sexual generation producing biflagellate zoogametes. The
zoogametes formed and liberated in same manner as zoospores.
Gametic union isogamous or anisogamous. Gametes at times
germinating parthenogenetically. The zygote germinating immediately and developing directly into a thallus.

STRUCTURE AND REPRODUCTION. Hartmann, 1929, pp. 490–494. Kylin,
1930A. Moewus, 1938, pp. 374–435; figs. 5–25. Ramanthan, 1939. Yamada and
Kanda, 1941, pp. 221–225; text figs. 5–8; pls. 51–52.

KEY TO THE SPECIES IN THE LOCAL FLORA

1. Thallus freely branched 2
1. Thallus simple or sparingly branched 3
   2. Branches gradually narrowed from base to apex; with
      cells in longitudinal rows ....*E. clathrata*
   2. Branches with base narrower than apex; cells not in
      longitudinal rows ....*E. compressa*
3. Cells in more or less longitudinal rows ....*E. tubulosa*
3. Cells not in more or less longitudinal rows....................... 4
   4. Cells 10–16 μ broad...............................*E. intestinalis*
   4. Cells 4–10 μ broad 5
5. Gelatinous matrix 15–25 μ in thickness ....*E. micrococca*
5. Gelatinous matrix 8–15 μ in thickness...................*E. minima*

Enteromorpha intestinalis (Linnaeus) Link   Pl. 5, figs. 4–6

Link, 1820, p. 5. Collins, 1903, p. 23; pl. 42, figs. 6–7. Setchell and Gardner,
1920, p. 252.
   Ulva intestinalis Linnaeus, 1755, p. 418. *Anderson, 1891, p. 218.
   Ulva Enteromorpha Le Jolis, 1863, p. 42. *Anderson, 1891, p. 218. *Howe,
1893, p. 67.
   Ulva Enteromorpha var. *intestinalis* (Linnaeus) Le Jolis, 1863, p. 42. *Howe,
1893, p. 67.

Thalli, as found on the Monterey Peninsula, rarely over 20
cm. tall; yellowish-green or grass-green in color. Solitary or gre-

garious. Simple or with a few proliferous branches; frequently compressed, crisped, and contorted. The cells, as seen in surface view, not arranged in more or less longitudinal series, 10–15 μ in diameter, angular. Gelatinous matrix surrounding cells 20–40 μ in thickness.

LOCAL DISTRIBUTION. Saxicolous or epiphytic; growing between the 3.0-foot and mean low-tide levels. Point Aulon; Middle Reef of Moss Beach; Pebble Beach; rocks north of Carmel Beach.

TYPE LOCALITY. Sweden.

PACIFIC COAST DISTRIBUTION. Alaska (Kukak Bay) to Baja California (La Paz).

The forma *clavata* J. G. Agardh (J. G. Agardh, 1883, p. 131; Collins, 1903, p. 23; Setchell and Gardner, 1920, p. 253. Phyc. Bor.-Amer. No. 966) has the lower portion of the thallus narrowly cylindrical and the upper portion 10–20 times broader and often compressed. It has been found on rocks in the mid-littoral at Pebble Beach. On the Pacific Coast this form ranges from Sitka, Alaska, to Carmel Bay, California.

Enteromorpha micrococca Kützing

Kützing, 1856, p. 11; pl. 30, fig. 2. Collins, 1903, p. 20; pl. 42, figs. 1–2. Setchell and Gardner, 1920, p. 249. Phyc. Bor.-Amer. No. 66.

Thalli relatively small, gregarious, as found on the Monterey Peninsula 4–8 cm. tall, bright green in color. Simple or slightly proliferous. Frequently compressed, much curled, and twisted. The cells 4–7.5 μ broad, angular, not arranged in more or less longitudinal series. The gelatinous matrix surrounding cells 15–25 μ in thickness; typically with the cells toward the outer face.

LOCAL DISTRIBUTION. On vertical face of rocks between the 3.5- and 1.5-foot tide levels. East end of Fanshell Beach.

TYPE LOCALITY. Not stated.

PACIFIC COAST DISTRIBUTION. Alaska (Dutch Harbor) to Mexico.

Enteromorpha minima Naegeli   Pl. 5, fig. 8

Naegeli in Kützing, 1849, p. 482. Collins, 1903, p. 24; pl. 42, figs. 9–10 Setchell and Gardner, 1920, p. 250. Phyc. Bor.-Amer. No. 912.

Thalli gregarious, as found on the Monterey Peninsula 5–15 cm. tall, light green in color. Simple or slightly proliferous. The cylinder frequently compressed and with ruffled margins. The cells 5–10 μ broad, angular, not arranged in more or less longitudinal series. Gelatinous matrix surrounding cells 8–15 μ in thickness, with the cells occupying most of the space between the inner and outer surfaces.

LOCAL DISTRIBUTION. Growing in upper portion of the intertidal zone. Municipal Wharf, Monterey; Moss Beach; Pebble Beach.
TYPE LOCALITY. Helgoland, Germany.
PACIFIC COAST DISTRIBUTION. Alaska (Unalaska) to Mexico.

Enteromorpha tubulosa Kützing   Pl. 5, figs. 1–3

Kützing, 1856, p. 11; pl. 32, fig. 2. Setchell and Gardner, 1920, p. 256; pl. 14, figs. 4–5.
Enteromorpha prolifera var. *tubulosa* (Kützing) Reinbold, 1889, p. 117. Collins, 1903, p. 22. Phyc. Bor.-Amer. No. 471.

Thalli gregarious, as found on the Monterey Peninsula, 4–6 cm. tall, dark green in color. Simple or occasionally with short proliferations. Regularly cylindrical in basal half, upper half at times compressed. Cells 7–10 µ in diameter when seen in surface view; 12–14 µ tall when seen in cross section. The cells rectangular to polygonal in surface view, arranged in more or less longitudinal series. Gelatinous matrix surrounding cells 20–25 µ in thickness. Chloroplast cup-shaped, in outer half of cell; with one pyrenoid.

LOCAL DISTRIBUTION. Growing on rocks between the 2.5- and 1.0-foot tide levels. Asilomar Point; Cypress Point.
TYPE LOCALITY. Not stated.
PACIFIC COAST DISTRIBUTION. Central California (Sausalito) to southern California (Balboa).

The dimensions given above for Monterey Peninsula plants differ somewhat from those given by Collins.

Enteromorpha clathrata (Roth) Greville

Greville, 1830, p. 181. Collins, 1903, p. 28; pl. 43, fig. 4. Setchell and Gardner, 1920, p. 260. Taylor, 1937, p. 63; pl. 3, fig. 1.
Conferva clathrata Roth, 1806, p. 175.
Ulva clathrata (Roth) C. A. Agardh, 1822, p. 422. *Anderson, 1891, p. 218.

Thalli up to 40 cm. tall, light green in color. Profusely branched; with the branches gradually tapering from base to apex but the branch tips not terminating in a uniseriate row of cells. The cells, as seen in surface view, somewhat longer than broad 10–28 by 13–32 µ; arranged in more or less longitudinal series. Chloroplast not occupying entire outer face of a cell. Gelatinous matrix surrounding cells 18–28 µ in thickness.

LOCAL DISTRIBUTION. Epiphytic on other algae of mid-littoral zone. Pebble Beach.

TYPE LOCALITY. Baltic Sea.

PACIFIC COAST DISTRIBUTION. Alaska (Sitka) to central California (Carmel Bay).

Known locally only from a single collection by N. L. Gardner. The dimensions given above arc quoted from Taylor.

Enteromorpha compressa (Linnaeus) Greville   Pl. 5, fig. 7

Greville, 1830, p. 180; pl. 18. Collins, 1903, p. 25; pl. 42, figs. 11–12. Setchell and Gardner, 1920, p. 251; pl. 14, figs. 7–8; pl. 16, fig. 3.

Ulva compressa Linnaeus, 1755, p. 433. *Anderson, 1891, p. 218.

Thalli, as found on the Monterey Peninsula, 10–15 cm. tall; light green in color. Profusely branched but the branches only occasionally branched. The branches narrow at base, above this of the same diameter throughout and with a broadly rounded apex; frequently compressed. The cells as seen in surface view, 6.5–10 µ in diameter, angular, not arranged in more or less longitudinal series.

LOCAL DISTRIBUTION. Abundant at Pebble Beach on rocks between the 3.5- and 1.5-foot tide levels.

TYPE LOCALITY. Sweden.

PACIFIC COAST DISTRIBUTION. Alaska (Bering Sea) to Baja California (Magdalena Bay).

Order SCHIZOGONIALES

Thalli filamentous, foliaceous, or a solid cylinder accordingly as the cells divide in one, two, or three planes. The cells uninucleate; and cubical, angular, ellipsoidal, or disc-shaped. Chloroplast single, axial, stellate; with one pyrenoid. The thalli frequently multiplying vegetatively by fragmentation.

Reproduction by akinetes. The akinetes either developing directly into thalli or producing several aplanospores. Aplanospores also formed by division of vegetative cells in either two or three planes. Not producing zoospores.

Sexual reproduction unknown.

Family SCHIZOGONIACEAE

All Schizogoniales are placed in a single family, the Schizogoniaceae, whose characters are the same as those of the order.

1. Thalli foliaceous and monostromatic................*Prasiola* (p. 53)
1. Thallus a solid cylinder several cells in diameter......*Gayella* (p. 54)

Prasiola Meneghini, 1838

Thalli small, foliaceous, monostromatic; at times stipitate at base. Sessile and attached by rhizoids developing either at base or along lateral margins of blade. The cells cubical to rounded, at times in groups separated from one another. Cells uninucleate. Chloroplast single, axial, stellate; with one pyrenoid. Thalli multiplying vegetatively by fragmentation.

Reproduction by large akinetes. The akinetes either developing directly into thalli or producing several aplanospores. Aplanospores also formed by division of vegetative cells in two or in three planes.

Sexual reproduction by biflagellate zoogametes recorded but extremely dubious.

STRUCTURE AND REPRODUCTION. Setchell and Gardner, 1920*A*, pp. 287–290; pl. 21. Wille, 1906. Yabe, 1932.

With one species in the local flora.

Prasiola meridionalis Setchell and Gardner   Pl. 2, figs. 10–15

Setchell and Gardner, 1920*A*, p. 291; pl. 25, fig. 2. Setchell and Gardner, 1920, p. 278; pl. 20, fig. 2.

Thalli, as found on the Monterey Peninsula, up to 8 mm. tall, deep green in color. The blades broadly ovate, often with the margins curved in a hood-like manner; with a short broad stipe. Blades 40–45 μ in thickness. The cells cubical, in rectangular groups but the groups not separated from one another. The stellate chloroplast with narrow rays and with a clearly evident pyrenoid. Akinetes large, thick-walled, irregularly scattered at margin of blade.

LOCAL DISTRIBUTION. Restricted to rocks coated with the excrement of sea birds. Usually growing in the spray zone but at times growing as low as the 2.0-foot tide level. Mussel Point; Point Pinos; Pescadero Rock.

TYPE LOCALITY. Tomales Bay, Marin County, California.

PACIFIC COAST DISTRIBUTION. Washington (Friday Harbor) to central California (Carmel Bay).

There are characteristic dirty green patches just above the high-tide line on Bird Rock and on certain rocks off Cypress

Point, but it has been impossible to confirm the presumed presence of *Prasiola* on these inaccessible rocks.

Gayella Rosenvinge, 1893

Thalli small, cylindrical, and more than one cell in diameter because of cell division in three planes; simple or very sparingly branched. Sessile and attached by unicellular rhizoids formed by elongation of cells near base of thallus. Cells in multiseriate portion angular; those in uniseriate portion disc-shaped. Cells uninucleate. Chloroplasts single, axial, stellate; with one pyrenoid.

Reproduction unknown, presumably as in *Prasiola*.

STRUCTURE AND REPRODUCTION. Gardner, 1917, pp. 384–385; pl. 32, fig. 5; pl. 33, figs. 5–9.

With one species in the local flora.

Gayella constricta Setchell and Gardner   Pl. 2, figs. 8–9

Setchell and Gardner apud Gardner, 1917, p. 384; pl. 32, fig. 5; pl. 33, figs. 5–9. Setchell and Gardner, 1920, p. 280; pl. 12, figs. 5–10.

Thalli, as found on the Monterey Peninsula, up to 1.5 mm. tall; deep green in color. Thalli cylindrical, club-shaped, constricted at frequent intervals because of failure of certain cells of uniseriate juvenile stage to divide in three planes. Apical portion of thallus the broadest and up to 120 μ in diameter. Chloroplast nearly filling the cell; pyrenoid indistinct.

LOCAL DISTRIBUTION. Growing intermingled with *Prasiola meridionalis* but restricted to the lowermost portion of the *Prasiola* belt. Mussel Point.

TYPE LOCALITY. Tomales Point, Marin County, California.

PACIFIC COAST DISTRIBUTION. Known only from Friday Harbor, Washington, and the two localities mentioned above.

Order CLADOPHORALES

Thalli composed of coenocytic cells united end to end in branched or unbranched filaments. The filaments usually sessile and attached by rhizoids or by rhizoid-like branches. Chloroplast parietal, reticulate, with a few or many pyrenoids. The filaments at times multiplying vegetatively by fragmentation.

Certain genera with an alternation of identical sexual and asexual generations. Other genera presumably without such an alternation of generations.

Asexual reproduction by zoospores or by akinetes. The zoospores formed in unmodified or in slightly modified cells, never in definite sporangia. The zoospores usually quadriflagellate, rarely biflagellate; many formed within a cell and liberated through a single pore in the cell wall.

Sexual reproduction by biflagellate zoogametes formed and liberated in same manner as zoospores. Gametic union isogamous or anisogamous. Gametes at times parthenogenetic. In genera with alternating generations the zygote developing immediately into an asexual thallus.

Family CLADOPHORACEAE

All Cladophorales are placed in a single family, the Cladophoraceae, whose characters are the same as those of the order.

KEY TO THE GENERA IN THE LOCAL FLORA

1. Filaments unbranched or with short rhizoidal branches............ 2
1. Filaments profusely branched 4
   2. Filaments usually free-floating; if attached, with short
      rhizoidal branches along the entire length..*Rhizoclonium* (p. 61)
   2. Filaments sessile, rhizoids restricted to basal portion
      of filament 3
3. Rhizoids only from basal cell.................*Chaetomorpha* (p. 55)
3. Rhizoids from several cells near base..............*Urospora* (p. 63)
   4. Branches united to one another by special hooked or
      spine-like branchlets ....*Spongomorpha* (p. 64)
   4. Branches not united by special branchlets.......*Cladophora* (p. 56)

Chaetomorpha Kützing, 1845

Thallus an unbranched filament of coenocytic cells. The filaments (at least at first) sessile; the basal cell elongate, obconical, incapable of division, and with rhizoid-like processes at the lower end. Other cells of filament cylindrical to barrel-shaped and capable of dividing transversely. Chloroplast densely reticulate and with many pyrenoids; at times breaking up into a large number of small disc-shaped fragments.

One species definitely known to have an alternation of identical sexual and asexual generations; other species presumably with the same life cycle.

Asexual reproduction by means of quadriflagellate ovoid zoospores which may be formed in any cell except those at base of filament. Many zoospores formed within a cell and liberated through a single median pore in the cell wall.

Sexual reproduction by biflagellate ovoid isogametes, formed and liberated in same manner as zoospores.

STRUCTURE AND REPRODUCTION. Hartmann, 1929, pp. 485–490, fig. 1.

With one species in the local flora.

Chaetamorpha aerea (Dillwyn) Kützing   Pl. 6, figs. 4–5

Kützing, 1849, p. 379. Setchell and Gardner, 1920, p. 200; pl. 14, figs. 9–11.
Conferva aerea Dillwyn, 1809, pl. 80.
Chaetomorpha Dubyana Anderson [not of Harvey]. *Anderson, 1891, p. 219.
Chaetomorpha sutoria Anderson [not of (Berkley) Harvey]. *Anderson, 1891, p. 219. *Howe, 1893, p. 67.

Thalli, as found on the Monterey Peninsula, usually 4–8 cm. tall but at times up to 20 cm.; grass-green to yellowish-green in color. The filaments always straight, sessile, gregarious. The basal cell with a length 5–20 times the breadth. Vegetative cells in upper portion of filament cylindrical, 125–300 µ broad and with a length 0.5–2.0 times the breadth. Fertile cells barrel-shaped to subglobose, up to 450–600 µ in diameter.

LOCAL DISTRIBUTION. Growing between the 6.0- and 2.0-foot tide levels. Usually in small sandy tide pools but at times on bare or sand-covered rocks. Abundant everywhere. At Pebble Beach frequently over 10 cm. in length; elsewhere usually 4–8 cm. long.

TYPE LOCALITY. England.

PACIFIC COAST DISTRIBUTION. Central California (Santa Cruz) to southern California (San Diego).

Cladophora Kützing, 1843

Thallus a sparsely to profusely branched filament of cylindrical, barrel-shaped, or ellipsoidal coenocytic cells. The branching lateral but at times appearing as if dichotomous. The filaments sessile or free-floating; if sessile attached by rhizoidal branches from the lower cells. Erect branches not entangled by special hooked or spine-like branches. Cell division restricted to terminal and subterminal cells of the branches. The cell wall thick and often lamellate. Chloroplast reticulate, with many pyrenoids; at times breaking up into a large number of small disc-shaped fragments.

Certain species known to have an alternation of identical sexual and asexual generations.

Asexual reproduction by means of ovoid quadriflagellate zoospores formed in terminal and subterminal cells of branches. Many zoospores formed in a cell and liberated through a single pore in upper end of cell wall.

Sexual reproduction usually heterothallic; by means of biflagellate isogametes formed and liberated in same manner as zoospores. The gametes at times germinating parthenogenetically.

STRUCTURE AND REPRODUCTION. Carter, 1919. Föyn, 1934. List, 1930.

Cladophora is universally recognized as a genus in which there are few sharply marked characters separating the species one from another. The first four species in the key below have rather distinctive characters distinguishing them from others in the local flora; the remaining species do not. The occurrence of certain species in the local flora is on the authority of Collins, the only American phycologist who has attempted to master the intricacies of *Cladophora*.

KEY TO THE SPECIES IN THE LOCAL FLORA[3]

1. Thallus a dense hemispherical tuft 2
1. Thallus not a dense hemispherical tuft........................ 3
   2. Major branches 60–150 μ in diameter ....*C. hemisphaerica*
   2. Major branches 120–250 μ in diameter ....*C. trichotoma*
3. Branching predominately pectinate ....*C. microcladioides*
3. Branching not predominately pectinate 4
   4. Branches stiff, rigid; at times standing erect..........*C. graminea*
   4. Branches not stiff and erect 5
5. Major branches 150–200 μ in diameter....................*C. ovoidea*
5. Major branches less than 150 μ in diameter 6
   6. Major branches 89–120 (–160) μ in diameter ....*C. flexuosa*
   6. Major branches 46–65 μ in diameter......................... 7
7. Length of lower cells 3–6 times breadth ....*C. delicatula*
7. Length of lower cells 1.5–3 times breadth....*C. Bertolonii* var. *hamosa*

Cladophora hemisphaerica Gardner

*Gardner in Phyc. Bor.-Amer. No. 2240 (name only). *Gardner apud Collins, 1918, p. 83. *Setchell and Gardner, 1920, p. 209.

Thalli forming dense hemispherical tufts 1–3 cm. in diameter. At times with slender elongate tufts projecting beyond the hemi-

[3] *Cladophora laetevirens* (Dillwyn) Kützing has been recorded from the local flora by Harvey (1858, p. 82) and by Anderson (1891, p. 219). Collins (1909, p. 345) states that "reports of this species from the west coast are all doubtful." *Cladophora fracta* (Dillwyn) Kützing has also been recorded from the local flora by Anderson (1891, p. 219) and by Howe (1893, p. 67). These two records are extremely doubtful because *C. fracta* is a freshwater species.

spherical mass. Lower branches of thallus with cells 60–150 μ
in diameter and a length 3–6 times the breadth. Branching in
basal portion of thallus dichotomous and the dichotomies widely
divergent. Branches in outer portion of thallus 50–80 μ in diameter, straight, usually unilaterally branched and with 3–6 cells
between successive branchings.

LOCAL DISTRIBUTION. Growing on rocks between the 3.0-foot and
mean low-tide levels. At times on rocks in tide pools. Cypress Point;
Pebble Beach; north of Carmel Beach.

TYPE LOCALITY. Cypress Point.

PACIFIC COAST DISTRIBUTION. As above.

Resembling *C. trichotoma* but superficially distinguishable
from it by the absence of sand in the tufts. This species may also
be distinguished from *C. trichotoma* by differences in diameter
of branches.

Cladophora trichotoma (C. A. Agardh) Kützing   Pl. 7, fig. 2

Kützing, 1849, p. 414. Collins, 1909, p. 349. Setchell and Gardner, 1920, p.
210; pl. 16, fig. 2. *Phyc. Bor.-Amer. No. 820.
Conferva trichotoma C. A. Agardh, 1824, p. 121.
Cladophora uncinalis Anderson [not of (Müller) Harvey]. *Anderson, 1891,
p. 219. *Howe, 1893, p. 67.

Thalli at first hemispherical, later becoming laterally expanded.
As found on the Monterey Peninsula, up to 15 cm. broad and
regularly with sand accumulating between the branches until all
the thallus except the branch tips is buried in sand. Lower
branches of thallus with cells 120–250 μ in diameter and a length
4–10 times the breadth. Branching in lower portion of thallus
dichotomous or trichotomous. Branches in outer portion of thallus only slightly narrower than basal branches, somewhat curved,
unilaterally branched, and with 3–6 cells between successive
branchings.

LOCAL DISTRIBUTION. Growing on tops and sides of rocks between
the 3.0-foot and mean low-tide levels. Abundant everywhere.

TYPE LOCALITY. France.

PACIFIC COAST DISTRIBUTION. British Columbia (Vancouver Island)
to Baja California (La Paz).

C. trichotoma regularly accumulates sand between the branches
even when growing on rocks some distance from sandy beaches.
Descriptions of the species as found on the Pacific Coast state
that it grows in tide pools. On the Monterey Peninsula at least
95 per cent of the thalli are not in tide pools.

Cladophora graminea Collins

Pl. 7, fig. 1

*Collins, 1909*A*, p. 19; pl. 78, fig. 6. *Setchell and Gardner, 1920, p. 211.
Cladophora erecta *Collins in Phyc. Bor.-Amer. No. 1690 (name only).
Cladophora cartilaginea Anderson [not of (Ruprecht) Harvey]. *Anderson, 1891, p. 219. *Howe, 1893, p. 67.

Thalli, as found on the Monterey Peninsula, in tufts 4–10 cm. tall; bluish-green to blackish-green in color. The branches stiff and bending only slightly when removed from water. Lowermost cells of thallus about 300 μ in diameter and with a length 20–30 times the breadth. Primary branching of thallus dichotomous or trichotomous and the forkings diverging but slightly. Cells in upper portion of thallus 100–150 μ in diameter and with a length 4–10 times the breadth. Branching in upper portion of thallus predominately alternate, with 1–3 cells between successive branches; frequently with all branches curved in the same direction.

Local Distribution. Growing between the 0.5- and −1.5-foot tide levels. Usually on the receding vertical face of an overhanging rock. Mussel Point; Point Pinos; Point Joe; Cypress Point; Pescadero Point; rocky point at center of Pebble Beach; Mission Point.

Type Locality. Monterey, California.

Pacific Coast Distribution. Central California (Santa Cruz) to southern California (San Pedro).

Living plants have a characteristic disagreeable acrid odor. This species is also distinguishable in the field by its stiff branches and distinctive color.

Cladophora microcladioides Collins

Pl. 7, fig. 3

*Collins, 1909*A*, p. 17; pl. 78, figs. 2–3. Setchell and Gardner, 1920, p. 212; pl. 13, fig. 2.

Thalli in erect tufts 5–20 cm. tall. Primary branches more or less distinct from one another and with a few long branches. Cells at base of primary branches about 200 μ in diameter and with a length 4–6 times the breadth. The longer branches with short branchlets at frequent intervals. The branchlets acutely pointed, arcuate, and curving away from branch, pectinately branched on upper (adaxial) side. Cells at base of branchlets 80–100 μ broad and with a length 1.5–2.5 times the breadth.

Local Distribution. Growing on rocks low in the intertidal zone. Pacific Grove; Arrowhead Point.

Type Locality. San Pedro, California.

Pacific Coast Distribution. Known only from Little Torquit, Vancouver Island; from the Monterey Peninsula; and from San Pedro.

The forma *stricta* Collins (Collins in Phyc. Bor.-Amer. No. 1583. Setchell and Gardner, 1920, p. 212) differs from the type in that the branchlets are straight instead of arcuate. It has been found on rocks in a tide pool at mean low-tide level at Pebble Beach.

C. microcladioides is pectinately branched in much the same manner as *Microcladia borealis*. It may be distinguished from other species in the local flora by the succession of short tufted branches along a long branch.

Cladophora ovoidea Kützing

Kützing, 1843, p. 266. Kützing, 1853; pl. 92, fig. 1. Collins, 1909, p. 346. *Setchell and Gardner, 1920, p. 214.
    Cladophora cartilaginea Collins [not of (Ruprecht) Harvey]. *Collins in Setchell and Gardner, 1903, p. 229.

Thalli erect, tufted, 5–15 cm. tall. Branching of primary branches irregularly alternate and successive branches some distance from one another. Cells in lower portion of primary branches cylindrical, 150–200 µ in diameter and with a length 4–8 times the breadth. Branching in upper portion of thallus unilateral and on upper side of branches. Cells of upper branches barrel-shaped, about 60 µ in diameter, with a length 1.5–3 times the breadth.

LOCAL DISTRIBUTION. Growing low in the intertidal zone. Monterey; Carmel Bay.

TYPE LOCALITY. Island of Föhr, Germany.

PACIFIC COAST DISTRIBUTION. Known only from Santa Cruz, California, and from the Monterey Peninsula.

Cladophora flexuosa Harvey

Harvey, 1851, p. 353; pl. 353. Collins, 1909, p. 339. Setchell and Gardner, 1920, p. 217. *Phyc. Bor.-Amer. No. 2239.

Thalli 10–20 cm. tall, light green in color. Lower cells of major branches 80–120 µ in diameter and with a length up to six times the breadth. Branching of major branches regularly alternate and the axial filament regularly undulate. The ultimate branchlets alternate or in secund series, 40–80 µ in diameter and the cells with a length about twice the breadth.

LOCAL DISTRIBUTION. In quiet water and intermingled with *Enteromorpha*. Pebble Beach.

TYPE LOCALITY. England.

PACIFIC COAST DISTRIBUTION. Alaska (Annettee Island) to southern California (San Diego).

Known locally only from the collection distributed as No. 2239 of Phyc. Bor.-Amer.

Cladophora delicatula Montagne

Montagne, 1850, p. 302. Collins, 1909, p. 337. Setchell and Gardner, 1920, p. 220. Phyc. Bor.-Amer. No. 1582.

Thalli loosely tufted, as found on the Monterey Peninsula, up to 3 cm. tall. Lower cells of major branches 60–65 µ in diameter and with a length 3–4 times the breadth. Branching in lower portion of thallus alternate or opposite and the branches straight. The ultimate branchlets in secund series, 25–30 µ in diameter at base; with 2–15 cells, the cells with a length 1–2 times the breadth. The branches and branchlets slightly constricted at the cross walls.

LOCAL DISTRIBUTION. At the −0.5-foot tide level on piling of the Municipal Wharf, Monterey.

TYPE LOCALITY. French Guiana, South America.

PACIFIC COAST DISTRIBUTION. Known only from the Monterey Peninsula and from San Diego, California.

Cladophora Bertolonii var. hamosa (Kützing) Ardissone

Ardissone, 1886, p. 242. Collins, 1909, p. 344. *Setchell and Gardner, 1920, p. 218.
Cladophora hamosa Kützing, 1843, p. 267. Kützing, 1854; pl. 8, fig. 2.

Thalli in erect tufts 3–10 cm. tall; dark green in color. Branching of lowermost portion of thallus dichotomous or trichotomous; that of upper portion alternate, opposite, or secund. The ultimate branches feathery, unilaterally branched; the branchlets recurved and with blunt tips. Cells in lower portion of thallus not exceeding 60 µ in diameter; those in upper branches about 25 µ in diameter. Cells throughout the thallus with a length 1.5–3 times the breadth.

LOCAL DISTRIBUTION. Pacific Grove.

TYPE LOCALITY. Balearic Islands.

PACIFIC COAST DISTRIBUTION. Known only from Pacific Grove.

The cellular dimensions quoted above are those that Collins gives for Pacific Coast (Pacific Grove) plants; the species as found in European waters has cells with about double these dimensions.

Rhizoclonium Kützing, 1843

Thallus a free-floating filament of coenocytic cells and with cell division intercalary. The filaments unbranched or with tapering rhizoidal branches of one to a few cells. The cells with two to many nuclei. Chloroplasts reticulate and with many pyrenoids. The filaments multiplying vegetatively by fragmentation.

Asexual reproduction by zoospores and akinetes. The zoospores biflagellate, ovoid; many formed within a cell and liberated through a single pore in the cell wall.

Sexual reproduction by biflagellate ovoid gametes formed and liberated in same manner as zoospores. Gametic union (so far as known) anisogamous.

STRUCTURE AND REPRODUCTION. Carter, 1919. A. and G. Hamel, 1929 (as *Lola*). Wille, 1901.

KEY TO THE SPECIES IN THE LOCAL FLORA

1. Rhizoidal branches lacking or one-celled 2
1. Rhizoidal branches abundant; usually with more than
   one cell .... *R. riparium*
2. Cells less than 30 μ broad .... *R. implexum*
2. Cells 40–50 μ broad .... *R. tortuosum*

Rhizoclonium tortuosum (Dillwyn) Kützing

Kützing, 1845, p. 205. Setchell and Gardner, 1920, p. 185.
Conferva tortuosa Dillwyn, 1809, p. 46; pl. 46.

Thalli, as found on the Monterey Peninsula, in dark green yarn-like strands up to 35 cm. long. The filaments usually unbranched, occasionally with one-celled rhizoids from cells near ends, irregularly twisted and relatively rigid. The cells cylindrical, 44–50 μ broad, with a length 3–5 times the breadth.

LOCAL DISTRIBUTION. Growing between the 2.5- and 1.0-foot tide levels and usually attached to *Corallina*. Rocks at mouth of Carmel River.
TYPE LOCALITY. England.
PACIFIC COAST DISTRIBUTION. Alaska to central California (Carmel Bay).

Rhizoclonium implexum (Dillwyn) Kützing   Pl. 8, fig. 3

Kützing, 1845, p. 206. Setchell and Gardner, 1920, p. 183.
Conferva implexa Dillwyn, 1809, p. 46; pl. *B*.
Rhizoclonium riparium var. *implexum* (Dillwyn) Rosenvinge, 1893, p. 915; fig. 34. Phyc. Bor.-Amer. No. 976.

Thalli, as found on the Monterey Peninsula, in floating mats entangled with other algae. The filaments usually unbranched, very rarely with one-celled rhizoidal branches. The cells cylindrical, 35–40 μ broad, with a length 2.5–5 times the breadth.

LOCAL DISTRIBUTION. Entangled with algae growing between the 3.0- and 0.5-foot tide levels. Pebble Beach.

Type Locality. England.

Pacific Coast Distribution. Alaska (Bay of Unalaska) to central California (Carmel Bay).

Rhizoclonium riparium (Roth) Harvey   Pl. 7, fig. 4

Harvey, 1849, p. 238. Setchell and Gardner, 1920, p. 182.
Conferva riparia Roth, 1806, p. 216.
Rhizoclonium riparium var. *polyrhizum* Rosenvinge, 1893, p. 913; fig. 32.
Phyc. Bor.-Amer. No. 2238.

Thalli, as found on the Monterey Peninsula, growing in a felt-like layer on stones and woodwork. The filaments regularly with one- to five-celled tapering rhizoidal branches. The cells cylindrical, 23–27 µ broad, with a length 1–2.5 times the breadth.

Local Distribution. Growing near high-tide level. On piling of Municipal Wharf, Monterey. On dripping rocks, Pebble Beach.

Type Locality. Norderney Island, Germany.

Pacific Coast Distribution. Alaska (Uyak Bay) to central California (Carmel Bay).

Urospora Areschoug, 1866

Thallus an unbranched filament of cylindrical coenocytic cells. The filaments sessile and attached by rhizoidal outgrowths from several consecutive cells at base of filament. The rhizoids either emerging directly from a cell or growing downward for some distance between the cell walls. Cell division intercalary and occurring in all but the lowermost cells. The cells with 2–8 nuclei. The chloroplast coarsely reticulate, not fragmenting into disc-shaped fragments; with few to many pyrenoids.

Asexual reproduction by zoospores and akinetes. The zoospores quadriflagellate, obovoid, with a long posterior projection. Zoospores formed in upper cells of a filament; many formed within a cell, liberated through a single median pore in the cell wall.

Sexual reproduction by biflagellate gametes which may be formed by cells of filaments producing zoospores. The gametes formed and liberated in same manner as zoospores. Gametic union anisogamous and the two of a uniting pair different in shape. The zygote developing into a sessile *Codiolum*-like one-celled plant and this eventually producing many quadriflagellate zoospores.

Structure and Reproduction. Jorde, 1933. Printz, 1932.

With one species in the local flora.

Urospora penicilliformis (Roth) Areschoug   Pl. 6, figs. 2–3

Areschoug, 1866, p. 16.
Conferva penicilliformis Roth, 1806, p. 271.
Hormiscia penicilliformis (Roth) Fries, 1835, p. 327. Setchell and Gardner, 1920, p. 191; pl. 9, fig. 4.
Urospora incrassata Setchell and Dobie [not of Kjellman]. Setchell and Dobie in Phyc. Bor.-Amer. No. 1125.

Thalli, as found on the Monterey Peninsula, up to 4 cm. tall; dark green in color. Cells in upper portion of filament 32–55 μ broad, with a length 0.5–2 times the breadth. Rhizoids at base of filament growing downward external to the cell wall. Fertile cells barrel-shaped.

LOCAL DISTRIBUTION. Forming a dark green hair-like coating on rounded boulders between the 3.0- and 1.5-foot tide levels. Fanshell Beach; Pebble Beach.
TYPE LOCALITY. North Sea.
PACIFIC COAST DISTRIBUTION. Alaska (Port Clarence) to central California (Carmel Bay).

Spongomorpha Kützing, 1843

Thallus a profusely branched uniseriate filament in which the branches are entangled in rope-like strands or in cushion-like masses. Entanglement of branches due to special spine-like or hooked branchlets. Thalli sessile and attached by rhizoidal branches from lower cells. Terminal cells of branches longer than other cells. Cell division intercalary, not restricted to tips of branches. The cells usually multinucleate, in one species uninucleate. Chloroplast parietal, reticulate, with few to many pyrenoids.

Reproduction by biflagellate ovoid zooids which are usually considered zoospores but which in at least one species are zoogametes. The zooids formed in large numbers within intercalary cells, many formed within a cell and liberated through a single median pore in the cell wall; fertile cells solitary or in short catenate series. The single species known to produce zoogametes; heterothallic and gametic union isogamous. Structure and development of mature zygote unknown.

STRUCTURE AND REPRODUCTION. Printz, 1927, pp. 275–276; fig. 216 (as *Acrosiphonia*).

With one species in the local flora.

Spongomorpha coalita (Ruprecht) Collins — Pl. 6, fig. 1

Collins, 1909, p. 361. Setchell and Gardner, 1920, p. 230; pl. 16, fig. 4; pl. 32.
Conferva coalita Ruprecht, 1851, p. 404.
Cladophora scopaeformis (Ruprecht) Harvey, 1858, p. 75. *Anderson, 1891,
p. 219. *Howe, 1893, p. 67. Phyc. Bor.-Amer. Nos. 819, 922.
Conferva scopaeformis Ruprecht, 1851, p. 404.

Thalli, as found on the Monterey Peninsula, up to 25 cm. tall;
grass-green to dark green in color. The thallus having the appearance of a branched, much-frayed, green rope. Branching of filaments dichotomous in lower portion of thallus; irregularly
alternate or unilateral in upper portion. Union of branches into
rope-like strands due to special branchlets with 2–4 recurved
prongs. Cells in lower portion of thallus with a length less than
breadth; in upper portion of thallus with a length 3–6 or more
times the breadth. Heterothallic and with gametic union isogamous.

LOCAL DISTRIBUTION. Growing on rounded boulders between the 1.0-
and −1.5-foot tide levels. Abundant at Point Pinos; Point Joe; Cypress
Point; Midway Point; Pescadero Point; Arrowhead Point; Mission Point.
Also dredged from a depth of 20–25 feet near Point Aulon.
TYPE LOCALITY. Unalaska, Alaska.
PACIFIC COAST DISTRIBUTION. Alaska (Unalaska) to central Cali-
fornia (Carmel Bay).

Order CHLOROCOCCALES

Thallus unicellular or a nonfilamentous colony with a definite
number of cells; in either case the cells not dividing vegetatively.
The cells often of distinctive shape. The chloroplast cup-shaped
or laminate, entire or perforate, with one to many pyrenoids.
The cells uninucleate or multinucleate.

Asexual reproduction by zoospores, aplanospores, or akinetes.
The zoospores biflagellate or quadriflagellate, usually formed in
multiples of two within a cell. Aplanospores and zoospores separating from one another after liberation or all spores from a cell
aggregating to form a colony with a definite number of cells.

Sexual reproduction usually isogamous or anisogamous, in
rare cases oögamous. The zoogametes formed in same manner
as zoospores.

With one family, the Endosphaeraceae, in the local flora.

Family ENDOSPHAERACEAE

Thallus unicellular, usually endophytic. The cells globose to irregular in shape, frequently with localized thickenings of the cell wall. The chloroplasts usually parietal and perforate when mature, with one to many pyrenoids. The cells uninucleate or multinucleate.

Asexual reproduction by zoospores or akinetes. The zoospores usually quadriflagellate.

Sexual reproduction by biflagellate isogametes. The zygote enlarging to form a vegetative cell.

KEY TO THE SPECIES IN THE LOCAL FLORA

1. Cells without a basal stipe....................*Chlorochytrium* (p. 66)
1. Cells with a basal stipe...........................*Codiolum* (p. 68)

Chlorochytrium Cohn, 1872

Thallus endophytic, unicellular. The cells globose, ellipsoidal, or irregularly rounded. Not dividing vegetatively. The chloroplast at first cup-shaped, later becoming broadly expanded and perforate; with one to many pyrenoids. The cell (so far as known) uninucleate until just before the formation of zoospores or gametes and at times with the nucleus dividing reductionally.

Asexual reproduction by quadriflagellate zoospores reported for certain species. The contents of a cell dividing to form many zoospores.

Sexual reproduction by biflagellate isogametes. The number of gametes formed within a cell usually a multiple of two. The zygote eventually developing into a large vegetative cell. Gametes also germinating parthenogenetically to form vegetative cells.

STRUCTURE AND REPRODUCTION. Cohn, 1872. Gardner, 1917, pp. 379–384; pl. 32, fig. 6. Klebs, 1881, pp. 249–257; pl. 3. Kurssanow and Schemakhanova, 1927. Moore, 1900 (as *Chlorocystis*).

KEY TO THE SPECIES IN THE LOCAL FLORA

1. Cell wall with a mamillate thickening on side toward
   surface of host ....*C. inclusum*
1. Cell wall of uniform thickness throughout...............*C. Porphyrae*

Chlorochytrium inclusum Kjellman Pl. 8, fig. 2

Kjellman, 1883, p. 320; pl. 31, figs. 8–17. Setchell and Gardner, 1920, p. 147; pl. 13, fig. 1. Phyc. Bor.-Amer. No. 514.

Mature cells, as found on the Monterey Peninsula, broadly ellipsoid or somewhat angular if crowded by tissues of host. The major axis usually 75–100 µ long; always standing perpendicular to surface of host. Side of cell wall toward surface of host thickened and with a conspicuous mammillate protuberance. The chloroplast at first perforate, later without perforations and filling entire cell; with many pyrenoids.

LOCAL DISTRIBUTION. Endophytic within cortex of various foliaceous Florideae; especially *Iridophycus, Rhodoglossum,* and *Pugetia.* Point Aulon; Point Pinos; Middle Reef of Moss Beach; Point Joe; Fanshell Beach; Pescadero Point; Pebble Beach; Mission Point.

TYPE LOCALITY. Not stated.

PACIFIC COAST DISTRIBUTION. Alaska (Sitka) to central California (Carmel Bay).

Chlorochytrium Porphyrae Setchell and Gardner Pl. 8, fig. 1

Setchell and Gardner apud Gardner, 1917, p. 379; pl. 32, fig. 6. Setchell and Gardner, 1920, p. 150; pl. 15, fig. 1. Phyc. Bor.-Amer. No. 2280.

Cells oblate spheres and with the polar axis perpendicular to surface of host thallus. As found on the Monterey Peninsula, with the equatorial axis up to 50 µ. The chloroplast cup-shaped in young cells, always on side toward surface of host; with a single conspicuous pyrenoid. The chloroplast later developing finger-like projections and ultimately becoming reticulate-stellate. The pyrenoid not evident in chloroplasts of mature cells. Reproduction by fusiform biflagellate zoogametes which escape through a rounded pore in side of cell wall toward surface of host.

LOCAL DISTRIBUTION. Endophytic beneath surface of gelatinous matrix of *Porphyra perforata* and *P. lanceolata.* Asilomar end of Moss Beach; Cypress Point; north end of Carmel Beach; Mission Point.

TYPE LOCALITY. San Francisco, California.

PACIFIC COAST DISTRIBUTION. Known only from Cape Flattery, Washington, from San Francisco, California, and from the Monterey Peninsula.

As found locally this alga is usually found only in yellowish-brown hosts growing near the upper limit of the *Porphyra* belt. Here it may be present in such abundance that the host is colored green and looks like an *Ulva.*

Codiolum Braun, 1855

Thallus unicellular, free-living or endophytic. The cells globose to subcylindrical. The basal portion of the cell wall drawn out into a long stipe; apical portion of cell wall either of uniform thickness or with a spine-like thickening. The chloroplast at first cup-shaped or laminate; later becoming reticulate; with one or many pyrenoids. The number of nuclei not known.

Asexual reproduction by zoospores and aplanospores. The zoospores quadriflagellate, many formed within a cell.

Sexual reproduction unknown.[4]

STRUCTURE AND REPRODUCTION. Jorde, 1933. Kuckuck, 1894, pp. 259–261; fig. 27. Kuckuck, 1896, pp. 396–397; fig. 20.

With one species in the local flora.

Codiolum Petrocelidis Kuckuck

Kuckuck, 1894, p. 259; fig. 27. Setchell and Gardner, 1920, p. 152. Phyc. Bor.-Amer. No. 2281.

Cells endophytic within *Petrocelis* and lying erect within host. The cells ovoid to obovoid, 136–180 μ long, 20–44 μ broad. The stipe very narrow, long or short, at times lateral on basal portion of cell wall. Chloroplasts of mature cells reticulate and with up to 8 pyrenoids.

LOCAL DISTRIBUTION. Endophytic within *Petrocelis franciscana.* Cypress Point.

TYPE LOCALITY. Helgoland, Germany.

PACIFIC COAST DISTRIBUTION. Known only from Whidbey Island, Washington; San Francisco, California; and the Monterey Peninsula.

Known locally only from a single collection made by N. L. Gardner. The dimensions given above are Setchell and Gardner's measurements of specimens from San Francisco; these are somewhat larger than those given for European specimens.

Order SIPHONALES

Thallus a single coenocytic cell which does not divide vegetatively. The cell usually tubular and branched; in rare cases

---

[4] Jorde, who holds that *Codiolum gregarium* Braun is the zygotic stage in the life cycle of *Urospora,* also states that certain species of *Codiolum,* as *C. Petrocelidis,* have nothing to do with the life cycle of *Urospora.*

globose and unbranched. If tubular and branched, with or without the branches compacted to form a macroscopic structure of definite form. Tubular cells at times regularly with interior blocked off into compartments by localized ring-like thickenings of the cell wall. Chloroplasts numerous, disc-shaped, with or without a single pyrenoid. Thalli at times multiplying vegetatively by abscission of branches.

Asexual reproduction by zoospores or aplanospores. The spores usually produced within sporangia of distinctive shape. Akinetes uncommon but produced by certain genera.

Sexual reproduction anisogamous or oögamous. Anisogamous genera with or without gametangia of distinctive form. Oögamous genera with the antheridium producing a number of antherozoids and the oögonium producing a single egg.

Key to the Families in the Local Flora

1. Motile reproductive cells biflagellate 2
1. Motile reproductive cells multiflagellate.........*Derbesiaceae* (p. 71)
   2. Thallus globose, unbranched, gametangium without
      a wall ....*Halicystidaceae* (p. 69)
   2. Thallus tubular, branched, gametangium with a wall 3
3. Branches of cell not interwoven to form a macroscopic
   body of distinctive shape..................*Bryopsidaceae* (p. 72)
3. Branches of cell interwoven to form a macroscopic body
   of distinctive shape..........................*Codiaceae* (p. 74)

Family HALICYSTIDACEAE

Thallus a globose to pyriform unbranched coenocytic cell affixed by a basal rhizome-like outgrowth.

Not producing zoospores.

Sexual reproduction anisogamous. The gametes biflagellate and produced in protoplasmic areas not enclosed by gametangial walls.

With one genus, *Halicystis*.

Halicystis Areschoug, 1850

Thallus a globose to pyriform coenocytic cell with a colorless rhizome-like portion penetrating the substratum. The globose portion with the protoplasm in a thin layer just inside the cell wall and containing many minute disc-shaped chloroplasts without pyrenoids.

Not producing zoospores.

Sexual reproduction anisogamous. Heterothallic. Gametangial areas irregularly band-shaped, developing in the protoplast of the globose portion of thallus; without a cell wall at the inner face. Each gametangial area producing many biflagellate gametes. Gametes liberated through one or more pores in portion of cell wall external to a fertile area. The zygote germinating to form a tubular protonema in which certain branches penetrate the substratum. Portion of protonema external to substratum eventually disappearing; the penetrating branches persisting and developing into typical thalli.[5]

STRUCTURE AND REPRODUCTION. Hollenberg, 1935. Hollenberg, 1936. Kornmann, 1938. Kuckuck, 1909, pp. 139–157; text figs. 1–2; pl. 3. G. M. Smith, 1930, pp. 224–227; figs. 1–2. G. M. Smith, 1938, pp. 107–111; figs. 56–57.

Halicystis ovalis (Lyngbye) Areschoug   Pl. 9, fig. 1

Areschoug, 1850, p. 447. *Setchell and Gardner, 1920, p. 155; pl. 14, fig. 3. *G. M. Smith, 1930, p. 224; figs. 1–2. *Hollenberg, 1935, p. 782; text figs. 1–5; pls. 1–4.

Gastridium ovale Lyngbye, 1819, p. 72; pl. 18, fig. B.

Valonia ovalis (Lyngbye) C. A. Agardh, 1822, p. 431. *Setchell and Gardner, 1903, p. 232.

Thalli, as found on the Monterey Peninsula, with the vesicular portion 2–10 mm. in diameter, occasionally up to 15 mm.; yellowish-green in color. The vesicular portion globose to broadly pyriform. Fruiting at each series of low tides. Male plants with brownish-yellow fertile areas; female plants with blackish-green fertile areas. Perennial, but shedding the vesicular portion each fall and regenerating a new one in the spring.

LOCAL DISTRIBUTION. Epiphytic on crustose Corallinaceae, especially Lithophyllum. The host usually growing between the −0.5- and −1.5-foot tide levels and on vertical shaded sides of rocks not exposed to full force of the surf. Fairly common at Pescadero Point. Also found at Point Pinos; Asilomar Point; Cypress Point; Midway Point; Arrowhead Point; Mission Point.

PACIFIC COAST DISTRIBUTION. British Columbia (Port Renfrew, Vancouver Island) to southern California (Redondo Beach).

[5] Kornmann (1938) holds that the protonemal stage fruits in the manner characteristic of Derbesia. If this is true, Halicystis must be considered the alternate gamete-producing generation of Derbesia rather than a distinct genus.

Family DERBESIACEAE

Thallus a branched tubular coenocytic cell in which the branches are not interwoven to form a plant body of definite macroscopic shape.

Asexual reproduction by zoospores and aplanospores. The zoospores multiflagellate, the flagella lying in a transverse ring at the anterior end of the spore. The spores formed in considerable number within sporangia of distinctive shape.

Sexual reproduction unknown.

With one genus in the family.

Derbesia Solier, 1847

Thallus a branched tubular coenocytic cell in which all branches are alike and are not intertwined into a macroscopic plant body of definite shape. The thallus with the branches in erect tufts and with the branching either irregular, predominately dichotomous, or predominately unilateral. Chloroplasts minute, disc-shaped; with or without a pyrenoid.

Asexual reproduction by zoospores or aplanospores produced within sporangia formed by lateral enlargement of a young branch. The zoospores multiflagellate and with the flagella lying in a transverse whorl at anterior end of spore.

Sexual reproduction unknown.

STRUCTURE AND REPRODUCTION. Davis, 1908. Kornmann, 1938. G. M. Smith, 1938, pp. 114–116; fig. 60.

With one species in the local flora.

Derbesia marina (Lyngbye) Solier   Pl. 8, fig. 4

Solier, 1847, p. 158 (as to name only). Collins, 1909, p. 407. Setchell and Gardner, 1920, p. 165; pl. 15, fig. 3.

Vaucheria marina Lyngbye, 1819, p. 79; pl. 22, fig. *A.*

Derbesia vaucheriaeformis Saunders [not of (Harvey) J. G. Agardh]. Saunders, 1899*A*, p. 3; pl. 350, fig. 4.

Derbesia tenuissima Collins [not of (De Notaris) Crouan]. Collins in Phyc. Bor.-Amer. No. 574.

Thalli, as found on the Monterey Peninsula, about 1 cm. tall, grass-green in color. The erect filaments 50–65 µ in diameter, with the branching predominately unilateral and the branch apices gradually tapering to subacute tips. Bases of branches frequently with a colorless elongate biconcave partition. Sporangia replacing ultimate branchlets, ovoid to broadly pyriform, pedicellate and apex of pedicel with a colorless cross partition. The sporangia 150–260 μ long, 100–160 μ broad; producing 50–100 zoospores.

LOCAL DISTRIBUTION. Epiphytic on crustose Corallinaceae growing between the mean low-tide and −1.0-foot tide levels. Isolated tufts have been collected at Mussel Point; Point Pinos; and Pescadero Point. Also dredged from a depth of 30–35 feet out from Municipal Wharf, Monterey.

TYPE LOCALITY. Denmark.

PACIFIC COAST DISTRIBUTION. Alaska (Sitka) to southern California (La Jolla).

A narrow form with branches 20–25 μ in diameter has been found growing on rocks at Point Pinos. This agrees quite well with Saunders' description of Pacific Coast material that he identified as *D. vaucheriaeformis* but which, as Setchell and Gardner suggest, seems more closely related to *D. marina*.

Family BRYOPSIDACEAE

Thallus a much-branched tubular coenocytic cell in which the branches are unseptate and are not compacted to form a macroscopic plant of definite shape.

Not producing zoospores, aplanospores, or akinetes.

Sexual reproduction by a union of anisogamous biflagellate gametes. The gametes produced within gametangia formed by conversion of unmodified or of special branchlets. The zygote germinating immediately and developing into a new thallus.

With one genus, *Bryopsis,* in the local flora.

Bryopsis Lamouroux, 1809

Thallus a much-branched tubular coenocytic cell in which the branches are not compacted to form a macroscopic plant body of definite shape. Major portion of thallus erect, branched, with a percurrent axis and the branching pinnate or radial. Chloroplasts disc-shaped, with a conspicuous pyrenoid. Multiplying vegetatively by an abscission of branchlets.

Not producing zoospores, aplanospores, or akinetes.

Homothallic or heterothallic. Gametangia developing from unmodified branchlets by formation of a basal cross wall and a cleavage of the protoplasm into many biflagellate gametes.

Gametes anisogamous, liberated through several pores in wall of gametangium. The zygote developing directly into a new thallus.

STRUCTURE AND REPRODUCTION. Pringsheim, 1871. G. M. Smith, 1938, pp. 103–105; fig. 53. Zinnecker, 1935.

KEY TO THE SPECIES IN THE LOCAL FLORA

1. Erect branches pinnately branched.....................*B. corticulans*
1. Erect branches radially branched......................*B. hypnoides*

Bryopsis corticulans Setchell   Pl. 9, fig. 3

*Setchell in Phyc. Bor.-Amer. No. 626. Setchell and Gardner, 1920, p. 160; pl. 15, figs. 4–5; pl. 27. *G. M. Smith, 1930, p. 231. *G. M. Smith, 1938, p. 104; fig. 53.

Bryopsis plumosa Anderson [not of (Hudson) C. A. Agardh]. *Anderson, 1891, p. 218.

Thalli, as found on the Monterey Peninsula, usually 5–10 cm. tall but occasionally up to 16 cm.; blackish-green in color. Frequently with several erect shoots from a common base. Each shoot with a percurrent axis up to 1 mm. in diameter; base of axis without branches, upper portion of axis pinnately branched. Older branches with short blunt rhizoidal outgrowths at base. The ultimate branches (pinnules) 150–300 μ in diameter, cylindrical, abruptly constricted at base.

LOCAL DISTRIBUTION. Growing between the 2.0- and −1.5-foot tide levels on vertical sides of rocks. Usually restricted to rocks exposed to strong surf, occasionally epiphytic; rarely present in abundance. Mussel Point; Point Aulon; Point Pinos; Asilomar Point; Middle Reef of Moss Beach; Point Joe; Cypress Point; Pescadero Point; Pebble Beach; Mission Point.

TYPE LOCALITY. Pacific Grove, California.

PACIFIC COAST DISTRIBUTION. British Columbia (Victoria) to southern California (San Pedro).

Setchell and Gardner (1920) state that this species "has been observed only in winter and spring on the coast of California." On the Monterey Peninsula it is present throughout the year but is found in a fruiting condition only during the spring.

Bryopsis hypnoides Lamouroux   Pl. 9, fig. 2

Lamouroux, 1809, p. 135; pl. 5, fig. 2. Setchell and Gardner, 1920, p. 159. Phyc. Bor.-Amer. No. 1028.

Thalli, as found on the Monterey Peninsula, up to 4 cm. tall; dull green in color. Erect shoots with a percurrent axis up to 430 μ in diameter. Branching of axis profuse and radial. Bases of lower branches with long rhizoids which grow downward along the axis. The ultimate branchlets (pinnules) 2–5 mm. long, 60–75 μ in diameter; gradually tapering at upper end and abruptly constricted at base.

LOCAL DISTRIBUTION. Growing on sand-covered rocks between the 2.5- and 0.5-foot tide levels. Mussel Point; Pebble Beach.

TYPE LOCALITY. Mediterranean Sea.

PACIFIC COAST DISTRIBUTION. British Columbia (Victoria) to southern California (San Pedro).

In the two local stations where this species has been found it grows in extensive stands in quiet coves. The base of the alga is always buried in sand.

Family CODIACEAE

Thallus a much-branched tubular coenocytic cell in which the branches are organized to form a plant body of definite macroscopic shape. The thallus erect or prostrate, variously shaped, incrusted or not incrusted with lime. Branches at surface of thallus frequently organized into a palisade-like layer. Chloroplasts minute, disc-shaped, without pyrenoids.

Certain genera producing biflagellate zoospores within sporangia of distinctive shape.

Sexual reproduction anisogamous. The gametes biflagellate and produced within gametangia of distinctive shape. So far as known the zygote developing directly into a new thallus.

With one genus, *Codium,* in the local flora.

Codium Stackhouse, 1797

Thallus a much-branched tubular coenocytic cell in which the branches are compacted to form a macroscopic plant body of definite shape. The thallus not incrusted with lime; its shape crustose, globose, or cylindrical and erect. Surface of thallus with a continuous, palisade-like layer of erect inflated branch tips (utricles); interior of thallus composed of intertwined colorless filaments. Chloroplasts minute, disc-shaped, without pyrenoids; restricted to utricles.

Zoospores not formed.

Heterothallic. Gametangia club-shaped, borne laterally on utricles, male gametangia yellowish-green, female gametangia blackish-green. Gametes markedly anisogamous and many produced within a gametangium. The zygote developing directly into a new thallus.

STRUCTURE AND REPRODUCTION. Oltmanns, 1922, pp. 396–401; figs. 257–259. G. M. Smith, 1930, pp. 228–231; fig. 3. G. M. Smith, 1938, pp. 111–114; figs. 58–59.

KEY TO THE SPECIES IN THE LOCAL FLORA

1. Thallus crustose ....*C. Setchellii*
1. Thallus erect, cylindrical, dichotomously branched...........*C. fragile*

Codium Setchellii Gardner   Pl. 9, fig. 4

*Gardner, 1919, p. 489; pl. 42, figs. 10–11. *Setchell and Gardner, 1920, p. 168; pl. 9, figs. 10–11; pl. 30. *G. M. Smith, 1930, p. 227.
Codium adhaerens Anderson [not of (Cabrera) C. A. Agardh]. *Anderson, 1891, p. 218. *Howe, 1893, p. 76. *Saunders, 1899, p. 2; pl. 350, fig. 3. *Phyc. Bor.-Amer. No. 523.

Thalli crustose, irregular in outline, as found on the Monterey Peninsula up to 25 cm. in diameter; greenish-black in color. The thallus adhering firmly to substratum, usually 6–10 mm. in thickness. Internal filaments 12–30 µ broad. The utricles approximately cylindrical, 65–75 µ broad, with flattened apices. Wall at apex of utricle thickened but not mucronate. Utricles without long colorless hairs. Heterothallic. Gametangia cylindrico-conical, borne singly on utricles, 45–55 by 300–330 µ.

LOCAL DISTRIBUTION. Growing on vertical faces of rocks between the 1.0- and −1.5-foot tide levels. Rarely present in abundance. Mussel Point; Point Pinos; Asilomar Point; Point Joe; Pescadero Point; Mission Point.
TYPE LOCALITY. Pacific Grove, California.
PACIFIC COAST DISTRIBUTION. Alaska (Sitka) to central California (Carmel Bay).

Codium fragile (Suringar) Hariot   Pl. 9, fig. 5

Hariot, 1889, p. 32. Setchell and Gardner, 1920, p. 171; pls. 28–29. *G. M. Smith, 1930, p. 228; fig. 3. *G. M. Smith, 1938, p. 111; figs. 58–59.
Acanthocodium fragile Suringar, 1867.
Codium tomentosum Harvey [not of (Hudson) Stackhouse]. *Harvey, 1858, p. 29. *Anderson, 1891, p. 218. *Howe, 1893, p. 67.
Codium mucronatum var. *californicum* J. G. Agardh, 1887, p. 44; pl. 1, fig. 3. *Saunders, 1899A, p. 1; pl. 350, fig. 1. Phyc. Bor.-Amer. No. 229.

Thalli with one to several cylindrical dichotomously branched erect shoots from a crustose base. The shoots, as found on the Monterey Peninsula, 10–30 cm. tall; greenish-black in color but at times coated with whitish hairs. The utricles club-shaped, 150–350 µ broad in widest portion, with a length 5–10 times the breadth. Wall at apex of utricle thickened and with a more or less distinct spine. Utricles frequently with a pair of long tubular hair-like outgrowths near upper end. Heterothallic. Usually with two gametangia on a utricle but the two not developing simultaneously. The gametangia club-shaped, 75–150 by 250–450 μ.

LOCAL DISTRIBUTION. Growing on tops and sides of rocks between the 1.5-foot and mean low-tide levels. Abundant at Fanshell Beach; Pescadero Point; and Pebble Beach. Also found at Mussel Point; Point Pinos; Asilomar Point; Middle Reef of Moss Beach; Point Joe; Cypress Point; Arrowhead Point; and Mission Point.

TYPE LOCALITY. Japan.

PACIFIC COAST DISTRIBUTION. Alaska (Sitka) to Baja California (Ensenada).

DIVISION PHAEOPHYTA

Cells uninucleate, with the photosynthetic pigments localized in plastids (chromatophores) and masked by a brown pigment (fucoxanthin). Thalli multicellular, filamentous or nonfilamentous. Nonfilamentous thalli usually macroscopic, of definite shape, and with a differentiation between superficial and deep-lying cells. The life cycle with an alternation of a haploid sexual generation (gametophyte) and a diploid asexual generation (sporophyte), or the life cycle without a haploid sexual generation. Gametophytic and sporophytic generations either similar or dissimilar.

Gametophytes typically with multicellular (plurilocular) gametangia in which each cell produces a single gamete. The gametangia borne singly or in sori. Gametic union isogamous, anisogamous, or oögamous. Motile gametes biflagellate and with the flagella of unequal length and borne laterally.

Sporophytes producing one-celled (unilocular) sporangia containing more than one spore, the spores either zoospores or naked aplanospores. These spores each with a haploid nucleus and germinating to form gametophytes. Sporophytes at times forming multicellular (plurilocular) sporangia in which each cell produces a single zoospore. These zoospores each with a diploid nucleus and germinating to form sporophytes. Zoospores from both unilocular and plurilocular sporangia biflagellate and with the flagella of unequal length and borne laterally.

KEY TO THE CLASSES OF PHAEOPHYTA

Class ISOGENERATAE

With an alternation of vegetatively identical gametophyte and sporophyte. The thalli filamentous or nonfilamentous. Nonfilamentous thalli usually of macroscopic size and definite shape.

Sporophytes with unilocular sporangia borne singly or in sori and producing either zoospores or naked aplanospores. Sporophytes at times with plurilocular sporangia and these producing zoospores.

Gametophytes with gametangia borne singly or in sori. Gametic union isogamous, anisogamous, or oögamous.

KEY TO THE ORDERS IN THE LOCAL FLORA

1. Growth of thallus trichothallic.................*Ectocarpales* (p. 78)
1. Growth initiated by one or more apical cells...................... 2
   2. Thalli polysiphonous ....*Sphacelariales* (p. 99)
   2. Thalli not polysiphonous....................*Dictyotales* (p. 100)

Order ECTOCARPALES

Thalli monoaxial or multiaxial, with growth trichothallic and cell division intercalary. Thalli microscopic or macroscopic; the filaments uniseriate and with branches free from one another or laterally compacted into a pseudoparenchyma; pseudoparenchymatous thalli of definite shape, macroscopic, and either crustose or erect.

Sporophytes either only with unilocular sporangia or with both uni- and plurilocular sporangia. The unilocular sporangia terminal or intercalary, solitary or catenate; only rarely grouped in sori. The plurilocular sporangia identical in shape with gametangia of the species and borne in the same manner.

Gametophytes with plurilocular gametangia. The gametangia uniseriate to multiseriate, terminal or intercalary, solitary or catenate; only rarely grouped in sori. Gametic union by a fusion of biflagellate iso- or anisogametes.

KEY TO THE FAMILIES IN THE LOCAL FLORA

1. Thalli filamentous, amorphous, the branches not laterally
    adjoined ....*Ectocarpaceae* (p. 78)
1. Thalli pseudoparenchymatous, of definite macroscopic shape........ 2
   2. Thalli crustose, reproductive organs in sori......*Ralfsiaceae* (p. 94)
   2. Thalli erect, reproductive organs not
     in sori ....*Heterochordariaceae* (p. 97)

Family ECTOCARPACEAE

Thalli monoaxial, filamentous, freely to sparingly branched and the branches not laterally compacted. The branches uniseriate, but in exceptional cases biseriate in older portions. Growth trichothallic. With sporophyte and gametophyte vegetatively identical.

The sporophytes with unilocular and plurilocular sporangia. The sporangia terminal or intercalary.

Gametophytes with plurilocular gametangia. The gametangia usually pluriseriate but at times uniseriate. Gametic union isogamous or anisogamous.

Key to the Genera in the Local Flora

1. Reproductive organs terminal and solitary......................... 2
1. Reproductive organs intercalary and catenate........*Pylaiella* (p. 92)
   2. Thalli endophytic ....*Streblonema* (p. 89)
   2. Thalli epiphytic or free-living; if epiphytic, only with
      rhizoids penetrating host ....*Ectocarpus* (p. 79)

Ectocarpus Lyngbye, 1819

Thalli filamentous, freely branched, differentiated into a prostrate and an erect portion. The prostrate portion uniseriate, irregularly branched, the branches rhizoid-like and at times penetrating the substratum. Erect portion freely branched; uniseriate, but at times with the major branches corticated by descending rhizoidal filaments; the branching opposite, alternate, or secund. Growth trichothallic and cell division intercalary. The cells with parietal disc-shaped or band-shaped chromatophores. Reproductive organs terminal (in exceptional individuals intercalary) and usually borne on short lateral branchlets. Gametophyte and sporophyte identical in size and vegetative structure.

Sporophytes with the unilocular sporangia terminal. The sporophytes frequently with plurilocular sporangia identical in appearance with gametangia of the species.

Gametophytes with pluriseriate (in rare cases uniseriate) plurilocular gametangia. Gametes isogamous or anisogamous, escaping from gametangium through a single terminal pore.

Structure and Reproduction. Knight, 1929. Kylin, 1933, pp. 16–22; figs. 2–3. Papenfuss, 1935.

Key to the Species in the Local Flora

1. Major branches of erect filaments corticated...................... 2
1. All branches uncorticated.. 6
   2. Cells with band-shaped chromatophores........................ 3
   2. Cells with disc-shaped chromatophores........................ 4

3. Plurilocular organs cylindrico-conical.....................*E. acutus*
3. Plurilocular organs ovoid............................*E. corticulans*
    4. Branching predominately opposite..................*E. granulosus*
    4. Branching predominately alternate or secund...................5
5. Thalli 2–5 cm. tall, reproductive organs secund...... *E. granulosoides*
5. Thalli 7–15 cm. tall, reproductive organs in part alternate......*E. oviger*
    6. Cells with band-shaped chromatophores....................... 7
    6. Cells with disc-shaped chromatophores........................13
7. Erect filaments in branched cord-like strands............*E. tomentosus*
7. Erect filaments not in branched cord-like strands................ 8
    8. Reproductive organs both on prostrate and on erect
        filaments ....*E. confervoides* var. *pygmaeus*
    8. Reproductive organs restricted to erect filaments............... 9
9. Prostrate filaments not penetrating tissues of host.................10
9. Prostrate filaments penetrating deeply into host..................11
    10. Erect filaments usually unbranched...................*E. simulans*
    10. Erect filaments sparsely branched....................*E. variabilis*
11. Growing on *Haplogloia*.............................*E. Mesogloiae*
11. Growing on *Codium*..12
    12. Erect filaments sparsely branched.................*E. gonodioides*
    12. Erect filaments densely and fasciculately
        branched ....*E. commensalis*
13. Plurilocular organs with broadly rounded apices.........*E. cylindricus*
13. Plurilocular organs with narrowed apices.......................14
    14. Growing within conceptacles or cryptostomata of Fucales......15
    14. Not growing within conceptacles or cryptostomata of Fucales...16
15. Growing within conceptacles or cryptostomata of *Fucus*...*E. ellipticus*
15. Growing within conceptacles of *Cystoseira*............*E. acuminatus*
    16. With two kinds of plurilocular organs.............*E. chitonicola*
    16. With one kind of plurilocular organ...............*E. Saundersii*

Ectocarpus acutus Setchell and Gardner   Pl. 10, fig. 1

*Setchell and Gardner, 1922*D*, p. 404; pl. 48, figs. 36–39; pl. 49, figs. 40–41.
*Setchell and .Gardner, 1925, p. 415.
    Ectocarpus penicillatus Saunders [not of Kjellman]. *Saunders, 1898, p. 155;
pl. 21, figs. 3–4.
    Ectocarpus confervoides forma *acuminatus* Collins in Phyc. Bor.-Amer. No.
1033. Also in Phyc. Bor.-Amer. No. 1127.

Thalli epiphytic, 5–9 cm. tall. Prostrate filaments densely entangled, not penetrating deeply into host. Erect filaments with major branches corticated, profusely branched, the branching predominately alternate below and predominately secund above; the branch tips gradually attenuated. The cells cylindrical, 40–60 μ broad in lower portion of erect filaments, with a length 0.5–2.0 times the breadth. Chromatophores irregularly band-shaped, few in a cell. Unilocular sporangia unknown. Plurilocular organs only on erect filaments, very numerous, sessile or pedicellate, cylindrico-conical, 100–150 (–230) μ long, 20–35 μ broad.

LOCAL DISTRIBUTION. Epiphytic on *Desmarestia,* especially *D. herbacea.* Mussel Point; Asilomar Point; Middle Reef of Moss Beach; Cypress Point; Pebble Beach; Mission Point.

TYPE LOCALITY. Carmel, California.

PACIFIC COAST DISTRIBUTION. Puget Sound to central California (Carmel Bay).

This species is said to grow on various of the larger brown algae, but as found locally it has been noted only on *Desmarestia.* Here it is restricted to tips of leaflets.

Ectocarpus corticulans Saunders

*Saunders, 1898, p. 152; pl. 20. Setchell and Gardner, 1925, p. 418.

Ectocarpus granulosus forma *corticulans* (Saunders) Collins. Collins in Phyc. Bor.-Amer. No. 1590.

Thalli usually epiphytic, 3–30 mm. tall, tufted or feathery. Prostrate filaments forming a small compact network. Erect filaments corticated in lower portion; irregularly but rather freely branched and with branches variable in length, branch tips not tapering. Cells in lower portion of erect filaments 90–120 μ broad, barrel-shaped, the length usually less than the breadth. Chromatophores band-shaped, few in a cell. Unilocular sporangia unknown. Plurilocular organs only on erect filaments, narrowly to broadly ovoid, sessile or with short pedicels, often in secund series on short branchlets, 30–70 μ long, 12–30 μ broad.

LOCAL DISTRIBUTION. Growing on *Desmarestia.* Monterey; Pacific Grove.

TYPE LOCALITY. Pacific Grove, California.

PACIFIC COAST DISTRIBUTION. Alaska (Popof Island) to southern California (San Pedro).

Ectocarpus granulosus (J. E. Smith) C. A. Agardh
Pl. 11, figs. 1–2

C. A. Agardh, 1828, p. 45. *Anderson, 1891, p. 219. *Howe, 1893, p. 67. *Saunders, 1898, p. 156; pl. 24, figs. 3–5. Setchell and Gardner, 1925, p. 426. Phyc. Bor.-Amer. No. 1589.

Conferva granulosa J. E. Smith, 1814, p. 2351; pl. 2351.

Thalli up to 25 cm. tall, profusely branched, at times with the branches twisted in rope-like strands. Erect filaments with the major branches corticated; the branching predominately opposite, the branches gradually attenuated and with rounded apices. The ultimate branchlets frequently recurved toward branch bearing them. Cells in lower portion of major branches barrel-shaped, 50–100 µ broad, the length not exceeding the breadth. Chromatophores disc-shaped, many in a cell. Unilocular sporangia sessile, globose (not observed on plants from the Monterey Peninsula). Plurilocular organs only on erect filaments, broadly ovoid, asymmetrical, sessile, on upper side of branches and with the more rounded side toward base of branch, 60–100 µ long, 30–60 µ broad.

LOCAL DISTRIBUTION. Growing between the 0.5- and −1.5-foot tide levels; on rocks and epiphytic on various larger algae. Mussel Point; Point Pinos; Asilomar Point; Middle Reef of Moss Beach; Pebble Beach; Mission Point. Also dredged from a depth of 30–35 feet near Municipal Wharf, Monterey, and from 15 to 20 feet in Stillwater Cover.

TYPE LOCALITY. England.

PACIFIC COAST DISTRIBUTION. Puget Sound to southern California (San Pedro).

Ectocarpus granulosoides Setchell and Gardner

Pl. 11, figs. 3–4

Setchell and Gardner, 1922D, p. 410; pl. 45, figs. 7–8. Setchell and Gardner, 1925, p. 431.

Thalli epiphytic, 2–5 cm. tall. Prostrate filaments branched, wholly superficial or penetrating slightly into tissues of host. Erect filaments corticated in lower portion, profusely branched, the branching subdichotomous in basal portion and secund in upper portion. Bases of branches usually abruptly constricted; tips of branches gradually attenuated. Lower cells of erect filaments 40–80 µ broad, the length not exceeding the breadth. Chromatophores disc-shaped, many in a cell. Unilocular sporangia unknown. Plurilocular organs only on erect filaments, asymmetrically fusiform, sessile, frequently in second series on upper side of ultimate branchlets, 40–70 µ long, 10–20 µ broad.

LOCAL DISTRIBUTION. On pneumatocysts of *Nereocystis Luetkeana* cast ashore at Moss Beach. On *Calliarthron* sp. dredged from a depth of 15–20 feet in Stillwater Cove.

TYPE LOCALITY. San Pedro, California.

PACIFIC COAST DISTRIBUTION. As above.

Ectocarpus oviger Harvey

Harvey, 1862, p. 167. Setchell and Gardner, 1925, p. 428.

Ectocarpus granulosus Gardner [not of (J. E. Smith) C. A. Agardh]. *Gardner in Phyc. Bor.-Amer. No. 2242.

Thalli epiphytic, 7–15 (occasionally up to 22) cm. tall. Erect filaments with major branches densely corticated, repeatedly branched, and with the branching predominately alternate. Ultimate branchlets at times secund. Cells in lower portion of major branches 60–70 μ broad, with a length 1.5–2.5 times the breadth. Chromatophores disc-shaped, many in a cell. Unilocular sporangia not definitely known. Plurilocular organs on erect filaments, either borne alternately or borne in secund series on upper side of branches, sessile, broadly ovoid to subcylindrical, asymmetrical, 35–45 μ long, 30–35 μ broad.

LOCAL DISTRIBUTION. Growing on *Nereocystis Luetkeana*. Carmel Bay.
TYPE LOCALITY. Puget Sound.
PACIFIC COAST DISTRIBUTION. Puget Sound to central California (Carmel Bay).

Ectocarpus tomentosus (Hudson) Lyngbye

Lyngbye, 1819, p. 132; pl. 44, fig. *A*. *Saunders, 1898, p. 155; pl. 24, figs. 1–2. Setchell and Gardner, 1925, p. 417. Phyc. Bor.-Amer. No. 478.
Conferva tomentosa Hudson, 1762, p. 480.

Thalli epiphytic, as found on the Monterey Peninsula, 1–4 cm. tall. Prostrate filaments short and irregularly branched. Erect filaments uncorticated, profusely branched, and with the branches intertwined in branching cord-like strands. Branching of erect filaments alternate and with successive branches at irregular intervals, upper ends of branches gradually attenuated to an acute tip. Many of the branchlets with the upper end outwardly recurved to form hooks entangling other branches. Cells of major branches cylindrical, 8–12 μ broad, with a length 1–2.5 times the breadth. Chromatophores band-shaped, one to a few in a cell. Reproductive organs only on erect filaments. Unilocular sporangia terminal on branches, ellipsoid or ovoid, 40–52 μ long, 24–30 μ broad. Plurilocular organs usually lateral on branches but occasionally intercalary. If lateral, usually sessile but at times pedicellate, cylindrico-conical, frequently biseriate, standing erect to filament and with the upper half curved toward base of filament, 40–110 μ long, 10–15 μ broad.

LOCAL DISTRIBUTION. Growing on *Fucus, Hesperophycus,* and *Pelvetia.* Monterey; Point Aulon, north end of Carmel Beach; Mission Point.
TYPE LOCALITY. England.
PACIFIC COAST DISTRIBUTION. Alaska (Kodiak Island) to southern California (Laguna Beach).

Ectocarpus confervoides var. pygmaeus (Areschoug) Kjellman

Kjellman, 1890, p. 77. *Saunders, 1898, p. 154; pl. 15, figs. 5–9. *Setchell and Gardner, 1925, .p. 415.

Ectocarpus pygmaeus Areschoug apud Kjellman, 1872, p. 85.

Ectocarpus terminalis Gardner [not of Kützing]. Gardner in Phyc. Bor.-Amer. No. 1387.

Thalli usually epiphytic and forming a more or less extended stratum. Prostrate filaments spreading over surface of host, branched, the branches close together and with a large majority of the cells producing erect filaments. Erect filaments uncorticated, 1–3 mm. tall, simple or sparingly branched at base, slightly attenuated at apices. Cells in lower portion of erect filaments 12–25 μ broad, with a length 2–3 times the breadth. Chromatophores irregularly band-shaped, few in a cell. Unilocular sporangia ovoid to globose, pedicellate, occasionally seriate, 24–40 μ broad. Plurilocular organs borne either on prostrate or on erect filaments, with long pedicels if on prostrate filaments, with short pedicels if on erect filaments, conical to fusiform, abruptly narrowed at apex, 60–100 μ long, 20–30 μ broad.

LOCAL DISTRIBUTION. Growing on Laminariales and Desmarestiales of the lower littoral. Mussel Point; Point Aulon; Pescadero Point; Mission Point.

TYPE LOCALITY. Sweden.

PACIFIC COAST DISTRIBUTION. Alaska (Shumagin Islands) to central California (Carmel Bay).

Typical *E. confervoides* has not been found on the Monterey Peninsula.

Ectocarpus simulans Setchell and Gardner

*Setchell and Gardner, 1922D, p. 412; pl. 45, figs. 9–11. *Setchell and Gardner, 1925, p. 422.

Thalli epiphytic, tufted, 1–2 mm. tall. Prostrate filaments irregular, tortuous, forming small cushions encircling the host. Erect filaments uncorticated, usually unbranched, slightly attenuated in upper portion but with rounded tips. Cells in median portion of erect filaments 11–13 μ broad, with a length 1–2.5 times the breadth. Chromatophores band-shaped, few in a cell. Unilocular sporangia unknown. Plurilocular organs only on erect filaments, usually borne laterally but occasionally borne terminally, sessile, ellipsoidal and with blunt apices, 55–65 μ long, 15–20 μ broad.

LOCAL DISTRIBUTION. Epiphytic on *Chaetomorpha aerea.* Cypress Point.

TYPE LOCALITY. As above.

PACIFIC COAST DISTRIBUTION. As above.

Ectocarpus variabilis (Saunders) G. M. Smith Pl. 10, figs. 2–4

*G. M. Smith, 1942, p. 647; figs. 1–4.

Ectocarpus confervoides forma *variabilis* *Saunders, 1898, p. 155; pl. 15. Setchell and Gardner, 1925, p. 414; pl. 46, fig. 7. *Phyc. Bor.-Amer. No. 526.

Thalli epiphytic, tufted, as found on the Monterey Peninsula 0.5–2.0 cm. tall. Prostrate filaments freely branched, not penetrating tissues of host. Erect filaments uncorticated, sparingly branched and with the branching predominately alternate, upper ends of filaments somewhat attenuated and with rounded apices. Cells in lower portion of erect filaments 10–30 μ broad, with a length 1–3 times the breadth. Chromatophores band-shaped, elongate in lower cells, short in upper cells, several in a cell. Unilocular sporangia unknown. Plurilocular organs of two kinds and usually borne on separate erect filaments; one kind pluriseriate, 10–15 cells broad in surface view, fusiform to narrowly ovoid, pedicellate, 75–180 μ long, 15–35 μ broad, with the fertile cells about 2 μ broad; the other kind uniseriate, pedicellate, with 2–15 barrel-shaped fertile cells, 70–200 μ long, 15–35 μ broad, with the fertile cells 15–35 μ broad.

LOCAL DISTRIBUTION. Growing on various Laminariales, especially *Laminaria Andersonii* and *Lessoniopsis littoralis.* Point Pinos; Point Joe; Cypress Point; Mission Point.

TYPE LOCALITY. Point Pinos, Pacific Grove, California.

PACIFIC COAST DISTRIBUTION. Puget Sound to central California (Carmel Bay).

Ectocarpus Mesogloiae Setchell and Gardner

*Setchell and Gardner, 1922D, p. 411; pl. 45, figs. 5–6. *Setchell and Gardner, 1925, p. 423.

Thalli epiphytic, 0.75–1.5 mm. tall. Prostrate filaments branched, densely intertwined, penetrating between cells of host. Erect filaments uncorticated, sparingly and alternately branched, the branches gradually attenuated to an acute tip. Cells in lower portion of erect branches cylindrical, 15–18 μ broad, with a length 1–2 times the breadth. Chromatophores band-shaped, several in a cell. Unilocular sporangia unknown. Plurilocular organs only on erect filaments, narrowly cylindrico-conical, usually on short pedicels but occasionally sessile, 120–160 μ long, 18–22 μ broad.

LOCAL DISTRIBUTION. Epiphytic on *Haplogloia Andersonii*. Carmel Bay.

TYPE LOCALITY. As above.

PACIFIC COAST DISTRIBUTION. As above.

Ectocarpus gonodioides Setchell and Gardner

Setchell and Gardner, 1924*A*, p. 721; pl. 17, fig. 44. Setchell and Gardner, 1925, p. 439.

Thalli epiphytic on *Codium,* densely tufted, 1 mm. tall. The prostrate filaments repeatedly branched, penetrating host to a depth of 1 mm., colorless except adjacent to erect filaments. Erect filaments uncorticated, branched below, simple above, somewhat attenuated at apices. Cells in lower portion of erect filaments 8–14 μ broad, with a length 1–1.5 times the breadth. Chromatophores band-shaped, few in a cell. Unilocular sporangia unknown. Plurilocular organs restricted to base of erect filaments, narrowly fusiform, pedicellate and the pedicels with one to many cells, 70–110 μ long, 15–25 μ broad.

LOCAL DISTRIBUTION. Growing on *Codium Setchellii.* Rocks at north end of Carmel Beach.

TYPE LOCALITY. Smith Island, Gulf of California, Mexico.

PACIFIC COAST DISTRIBUTION. As above.

The dimensions given above are those of Monterey Peninsula plants and differ somewhat from those of plants from the type locality.

Ectocarpus commensalis Setchell and Gardner

*Setchell and Gardner, 1922*D*, p. 407; pl. 48, figs. 32–35. *Setchell and Gardner, 1925, p. 424.

Thalli epiphytic on *Codium,* less than 0.5 mm. tall. Prostrate filaments irregularly branched, colorless, penetrating deeply into host (often to the medulla). Erect filaments uncorticated, alternately and profusely branched near base, simple above, slightly attenuated at upper ends. Lower cells of erect filaments 12–18 μ broad, with a length 1.5–2.5 times the breadth. Chromatophores band-shaped, few in a cell. Unilocular sporangia unknown. Plurilocular organs only on erect filaments and borne near the base, pedicellate, cylindrico-conical to bluntly fusiform, 60–100 μ long, 15–20 μ broad.

LOCAL DISTRIBUTION. Growing on *Codium fragile* and *C. Setchellii.* Mussel Point; Fanshell Beach; Pebble Beach; Mission Point.

TYPE LOCALITY. Carmel Bay, California.

PACIFIC COAST DISTRIBUTION. As above.

Ectocarpus cylindricus Saunders   Pl. 12, figs. 1–2

*Saunders, 1893, p. 150; pl. 16. Setchell and Gardner, 1925, p. 432. *Phyc. Bor.-Amer. No. 1695.

Ectocarpus cylindricus forma *acmaeophilus* *Setchell and Gardner, 1922D, p. 415; pl. 49, fig. 46. *Setchell and Gardner, 1925, p. 433.

Thalli usually epiphytic and 1–2 mm. tall. Prostrate filaments irregularly branched, not penetrating tissues of host. Erect filaments uncorticated, not attenuated at apices, sparingly branched and the branches short. Cells of erect filaments 18–30 μ broad, those at apex and at base with a length 2–3 times the breadth, those in median portion with length and breadth about equal. Chromatophores disc-shaped, many in a cell. Reproductive organs only on erect filaments. Unilocular sporangia ovoid to ellipsoid, sessile or with one-celled pedicels, frequently in opposite pairs, 60–120 μ long, 30–40 μ broad. Plurilocular organs cylindrical and with broadly rounded apices, pedicellate and with the pedicel bent upward, frequently in opposite pairs, 80–200 μ long, 35–45 μ broad.

LOCAL DISTRIBUTION. Growing on various Laminariales and on *Cystoseira.* Most frequently found on pneumatocysts of *Egregia Menziesii.* Mussel Point; Point Pinos; Middle Reef of Moss Beach; Mission Point. Also on *Calliarthron* dredged from a depth of 15–20 feet at Stillwater Cove.

TYPE LOCALITY. Pacific Grove, California.

PACIFIC COAST DISTRIBUTION. As above.

The variety *codiophilus* Setchell and Gardner (*Setchell and Gardner, 1922D,* p. 415; pl. 46, fig. 14; pl. 49, figs. 42–45. *Setchell and Gardner, 1925, p. 433; pl. 51, fig. 14) has densely tufted thalli 3–5 mm. tall. The prostrate filaments are intertwined and penetrate deeply into the host. The erect filaments are fasciculately and freely branched at the base and unbranched in the upper portion. The plurilocular organs are restricted to the basal portion of erect filaments and are rarely borne in opposite pairs (pl. 11, fig. 5). This variety grows on *Codium fragile* and *C. Setchellii.* It has been found at Mussel Point; Fanshell Beach; Midway Point; Pescadero Point; Pebble Beach; and Mission Point.

Ectocarpus ellipticus Saunders

*Saunders, 1898, p. 149; pl. 14, figs. 6–9. *Setchell and Gardner, 1925, p. 436. *Phyc. Bor.-Amer. No. 527.

Thalli minute, growing in conceptacles and cryptostomata of *Fucus.* Prostrate filaments branched, colorless, penetrating tissues of host. Erect filaments uncorticated, simple or with a few one-celled lateral branches. Cells at base of erect filaments 9–12 μ broad, with a length 1–2 times the breadth. Chromatophores disc-shaped, many in a cell. Reproductive organs usually at base of the erect filaments. Unilocular sporangia ovoid to ellipsoid, sessile, 30–40 μ long, 12–18 μ broad. Plurilocular organs cylindrical to bluntly conical, uniseriate or pluriseriate, sessile or pedicellate, 70–100 μ long, 18–25 μ broad.

LOCAL DISTRIBUTION. Growing on *Fucus furcatus*. Pacific Grove; Mission Point.

TYPE LOCALITY. Pacific Grove, California.

PACIFIC COAST DISTRIBUTION. As above.

Ectocarpus acuminatus Saunders   Pl. 11, fig. 6

*Saunders, 1898, p. 149; pl. 14, figs. 1–5. Setchell and Gardner, 1925, p. 435. *Phyc. Bor.-Amer. No. 524.

Thalli minute, growing within conceptacles of *Cystoseira* and *Halidrys*. Prostrate filaments forming a compact network. Erect filaments uncorticated, up to 1 mm. tall, projecting through ostiole of host's conceptacle, simple or sparingly branched at base. Cells of erect filaments 12–14 μ broad, those in lower portion with length and breadth about equal, those in upper portion with a length 2–5 times the breadth. Chromatophores disc-shaped, many in a cell. Unilocular sporangia unknown. Plurilocular organs borne either on prostrate filaments or at base of erect filaments, cylindrico-conical and frequently arcuate, terminating in one or more sterile cylindrical cells, 90–300 μ long, 20–30 μ broad.

LOCAL DISTRIBUTION. Growing in conceptacles of *Cystoseira osmundacea*. Pacific Grove; Asilomar Point.

TYPE LOCALITY. Pacific Grove, California.

PACIFIC COAST DISTRIBUTION. Central California (Pacific Grove) to southern California (San Pedro).

Ectocarpus chitonicola Saunders

*Saunders, 1898, p. 150; pl. 15, figs. 1–4. *Setchell and Gardner, 1925, p. 436.

Thalli epizoic, 1–2 mm. tall. Prostrate filaments numerous, irregularly branched, not penetrating the host. Erect filaments uncorticated, mostly simple, occasionally sparingly branched near base, slightly attenuated in upper portion. Cells at base of erect filaments about 14 μ broad; lower cells of erect filaments with a length 0.5–2 times the breadth, upper cells with a length 2–3 times the breadth. Chromatophores disc-shaped, many in a cell.

Unilocular sporangia unknown. Plurilocular organs of two kinds; one with large fertile cells, the other with small fertile cells. The plurilocular organs borne either on prostrate or on erect filaments, sessile, subcylindrical to narrowly ovoid, 90–175 μ long, 20–35 μ broad.

LOCAL DISTRIBUTION. Growing in tufts on shells of chitons and limpets. Pacific Grove; Carmel Bay.

TYPE LOCALITY. Pacific Grove, California.

PACIFIC COAST DISTRIBUTION. As above.

Ectocarpus Saundersii Setchell and Gardner

*Setchell and Gardner, 1922D, p. 411. *Setchell and Gardner, 1925, p. 434.

Ectocarpus paradoxus var. *pacificus* *Saunders, 1898, p. 152; pl. 18, figs. 4–7. *Phyc. Bor.-Amer. No. 530.

Thalli usually epiphytic, 2–5 mm. tall. Prostrate filaments branched, densely compacted, creeping over surface of host. Erect filaments uncorticated, freely branched, the branching alternate and widely divergent, upper ends of branches tapering to an acute tip. Cells in lower portion of erect branches 25–40 μ broad, about as long as broad. Chromatophores disc-shaped, many in a cell. Reproductive organs only on erect filaments. Unilocular sporangia globose, pedicellate, occasionally intercalary, about 30 μ in diameter. Plurilocular organs cylindrical to ovoid, with obtuse or acuminate apices, pedicellate, 70–150 μ long, 25–50 μ broad.

LOCAL DISTRIBUTION. Growing on *Fucus furcatus*. Pacific Grove. Also found at mean low-tide level on piling of Municipal Wharf, Monterey.

TYPE LOCALITY. Pacific Grove, California.

PACIFIC COAST DISTRIBUTION. As above.

Streblonema Derbès and Solier, 1851

Thalli endophytic, filamentous, irregularly branched and growing between cells of host, not differentiated into a prostrate and an erect portion. The branches usually uniseriate but at times certain primary branches polysiphonous. Growth trichothallic, intercalary. The thallus at times with unbranched colorless multicellular hairs which project beyond the host; the hairs with a basal meristem. Chromatophores disc-shaped or band-shaped, few in a cell.

Presumably with an alternation of identical generations, but this not demonstrated for any species. A thallus only with unilocular sporangia, only with plurilocular organs, or with both. Reproductive organs terminal, borne singly or in clusters, sessile or pedicellate. The plurilocular organs uniseriate or pluriseriate.

STRUCTURE AND REPRODUCTION. Setchell and Gardner, 1925, p. 440.

Streblonema anomalum Setchell and Gardner Pl. 13, figs. 3–4

Setchell and Gardner, 1922C, p. 392; pl. 43, figs. 1–3. Setchell and Gardner, 1925, p. 442; pl. 52, figs. 1–3.
    Streblonema fasciculatum Saunders [not of Thuret]. Saunders, 1898, p. 148; pl. 13.

Thalli minute, not externally evident within host. The thallus an irregularly branched filament growing in various directions between host cells and with certain branches at times becoming polysiphonous. With colorless multicellular hairs projecting beyond surface of host. Chromatophores band-shaped; usually one in each cell but at times fragmenting into 2–4 disc-shaped parts. Unilocular sporangia ellipsoid, ovoid, or subglobose; sessile, 40–60 μ long, 28–35 μ broad. Plurilocular organs either terminal or lateral, usually sessile but occasionally pedicellate, cylindrico-conical and with blunt apices, 30–100 μ long, 10–16 μ broad.

LOCAL DISTRIBUTION. Growing within *Cumagloia Andersonii*. Pebble Beach.
TYPE LOCALITY. San Pedro, California.
PACIFIC COAST DISTRIBUTION. As above.

Specimens collected locally do not have the polysiphonous branches found in thalli from the type locality. Unilocular sporangia have not been observed on plants from the Monterey Peninsula.

Streblonema corymbiferum Setchell and Gardner

Pl. 13, figs. 1–2

Setchell and Gardner, 1922C, p. 391; pl. 43, fig. 8. Setchell and Gardner, 1925, p. 441; pl. 52, fig. 8.

Thalli minute, not externally evident within host. Thallus an irregularly branched filament growing in various directions between host cells. With colorless multicellular hairs. Cells 3–5 μ broad, with a length 1.5–5 times the breadth. Chromatophores band-shaped, usually one within a cell. Unilocular sporangia unknown. Plurilocular organs terminal on branches near surface of host, in corymbose clusters, uniseriate but with certain of the transverse walls diagonal, 45–55 μ long, 25–35 μ broad.

LOCAL DISTRIBUTION. Growing within *Cumagloia Andersonii* and *Nemalion lubricum*. Pebble Beach.

TYPE LOCALITY. San Pedro, California.

PACIFIC COAST DISTRIBUTION. As above.

Streblonema Porphyrae Setchell and Gardner

*Setchell and Gardner, 1922C, p. 387; pl. 44, fig. 6. *Setchell and Gardner, 1925, p. 445.

Thalli endophytic within blades and holdfast of *Porphyra naiadum*. If within blades, usually restricted to one side of blade and to portion of the matrix external to the host's cells; if within the holdfast, growing between the host cells. The thallus tortuously branched and with irregularly shaped cells 3–4 μ broad. Without colorless hairs. Unilocular sporangia unknown. Plurilocular sporangia only in portion of thallus endophytic within base of host; here terminal on outermost filaments, fusiform, uni- or biseriate, 25–35 μ long, 5–8 μ broad.

LOCAL DISTRIBUTION. Endophytic within *Porphyra naiadum*. Pacific Grove; rocks north of Carmel Beach; Mission Point.

TYPE LOCALITY. Pacific Grove, California.

PACIFIC COAST DISTRIBUTION. As above.

Streblonema evagatum Setchell and Gardner

*Setchell and Gardner, 1922C, p. 390; pl. 42, figs. 1–5. *Setchell and Gardner, 1925, p. 449.

Thalli producing externally evident, circular, colored, 1–2 cm. broad areas on sori of host. Filaments near surface of host in erect fasciculate clusters; those lying more deeply within host irregularly branched and growing in various directions. Without colorless hairs. Erect filaments 6.5–7.5 μ broad in widest portion. Chromatophores band-shaped, one or two in a cell. Unilocular sporangia unknown. Plurilocular organs borne laterally at base of erect filaments, sessile or pedicellate, cylindrical, uniseriate, 65–80 μ long, 5.5–6.5 μ broad.

LOCAL DISTRIBUTION. Growing in sori of *Laminaria Andersonii*. Cypress Point.

TYPE LOCALITY. As above.

PACIFIC COAST DISTRIBUTION. As above.

This species, known only from the type collection, is one of those which show that there are no clear-cut distinctions between

Streblonema and *Ectocarpus*. There are equally good arguments for placing it in the latter genus.

Streblonema penetrale Setchell and Gardner

*Setchell and Gardner, 1922*C*, p. 388; pl. 44, figs. 3–4. *Setchell and Gardner, 1925, p. 446.

Thalli producing externally evident colored areas of indefinite size and shape on "stipes" of host. The filaments penetrating deeply into host, tending to lie perpendicular to its surface and with the outermost branches in fasciculate clusters. Without colorless hairs. The cells 6.5–8 μ broad; those near surface of host with a length 1.5–2.5 times the breadth, those deeper within host with a length 3–5 times the breadth. Chromatophores band-shaped. Unilocular sporangia unknown. Plurilocular organs terminal on filaments at surface of host, cylindrical, uniseriate, 30–40 μ long, 8–11 μ broad.

LOCAL DISTRIBUTION. Growing on "stipes" of *Hesperophycus Harveyanus*. Pacific Grove.

TYPE LOCALITY. As above.

PACIFIC COAST DISTRIBUTION. As above.

Pylaiella Bory, 1823

Thalli filamentous, differentiated into a prostrate and an erect portion. The prostrate portion scanty or well-developed, irregularly branched. The erect portion simple to profusely branched and with the branching opposite to alternate. Growth trichothallic, intercalary. Cells with disc-shaped or band-shaped chromatophores. Gametophyte and sporophyte identical in size and in vegetative structure.

Gametophytes with pluriseriate plurilocular gametangia of approximately the same size as vegetative cells and always intercalary and catenate. Gametes isogamous and escaping from gametangium through a single lateral pore.

Sporophytes with intercalary, catenate, unilocular sporangia of approximately the same size as vegetative cells. Zoospores escaping through a lateral pore in the sporangial wall. The sporophyte frequently with plurilocular sporangia identical in appearance with gametangia but producing diploid zoospores which develop into sporophytes.

STRUCTURE AND REPRODUCTION. Knight, 1923. Kylin, 1933, pp. 5–16; fig. 1. Kylin, 1937, pp. 3–7.

Pylaiella littoralis (Linnaeus) Kjellman   Pl. 12, fig. 3

Kjellman, 1872, p. 99. Setchell and Gardner, 1925, p. 402; pl. 37, fig. 32.
Phyc. Bor.-Amer. Nos. 171, 414.
Conferva littoralis Linnaeus, 1753, p. 1165.

Thalli, as found on the Monterey Peninsula, 2–5 cm. tall, with the erect filaments twisted in cord-like strands. Erect filaments rather freely branched but the interval between successive branches irregular, branching opposite to alternate. Cells of erect filaments 25–40 μ broad, with a length 1–3 times the breadth. Chromatophores disc-shaped, many in a cell. Unilocular sporangia chiefly in lateral branchlets, intercalary, in catenate series of 5–15, barrel-shaped to subglobose, somewhat broader than vegetative cells. Plurilocular organs (not observed on Monterey Peninsula thalli) intercalary, in catenate series of 2–30, barrel-shaped.

LOCAL DISTRIBUTION. On bottom of a fishing boat, Monterey.
TYPE LOCALITY. England.
PACIFIC COAST DISTRIBUTION. Bering Sea to southern California (San Pedro).

Collected but once in the local area. As found elsewhere along the Pacific Coast the thalli are up to 60 cm. tall and the cells 20–60 μ broad.

Pylaiella Gardneri Collins   Pl. 13, figs. 5–7

Collins in Phyc. Bor.-Amer. No. 1384. Setchell and Gardner, 1925, p. 405.
Leptonema fasciculatum Saunders [not of Reinke]. *Saunders, 1899, p. 38; pl. 1, figs. 5–7.
Pylaiella Postelsiae Skottsberg, 1915, p. 158; pls. 17–19.

Thalli epiphytic on *Postelsia,* growing in dense tufts; as found on the Monterey Peninsula 1–3 mm. tall, blackish-brown in color. Prostrate filaments densely compacted into a cushion-like mass. Erect filaments sparsely branched and with the branching predominately opposite, upper portion of filaments somewhat attenuated and with rounded apices. Cells of erect filaments 10–16 μ broad, with a length 1–3.5 times the breadth. Chromatophores at first band-shaped, 1–3 in a cell, later each breaking up into 3–4 disc-shaped fragments. Unilocular sporangia unknown. Plurilocular organs intercalary, barrel-shaped, produced near upper end of erect filaments, catenate and frequently in a continuous series of a hundred or more, up to 25 μ broad.

LOCAL DISTRIBUTION. Growing on *Postelsia palmaeformis* and usually on lower portion of stipe. Appearing in midsummer and disappearing early in the winter. Cypress Point; Mission Point.

TYPE LOCALITY. Land's End, San Francisco, California.

PACIFIC COAST DISTRIBUTION. Central California (San Francisco to Carmel Highlands).

Pylaiella tenella Setchell and Gardner

Setchell and Gardner, 1922C, p. 385; pl. 42, figs. 9–11. Setchell and Gardner, 1925, p. 406.

Thalli epiphytic, in small tufts 0.5–0.75 mm. tall. Prostrate filaments short, branched. Erect filaments unbranched, with the upper end gradually attenuated to a subacute tip. Cells of erect filaments 7–10 μ broad, with a length 1–2.5 times the breadth. The cells at first with a single, lobed, band-shaped chromatophore, later the chromatophore fragmenting into several separate pieces. Unilocular sporangia intercalary, subterminal, catenate but at times biseriate, the sporangia longer than adjacent vegetative cells. Plurilocular organs intercalary, subterminal, in a continuous or a discontinuous catenate series.

LOCAL DISTRIBUTION. On blades of *Zostera* cast ashore at Monterey.

TYPE LOCALITY. Neah Bay, Washington.

PACIFIC COAST DISTRIBUTION. As above.

Family RALFSIACEAE

Thalli filamentous but with the branches laterally compacted to form a crustose pseudoparenchymatous plant body. Growth trichothallic. The thallus with a basal layer of horizontal filaments and an upper layer of erect filaments. With vegetatively identical sporophyte and gametophyte.

Sporophytes with unilocular sporangia only, and with the sporangia in sori. The sori with or without paraphyses.

Gametophytes with gametangia in sori without paraphyses. The gametangia terminal or intercalary, catenate, plurilocular. Gametic union isogamous.

KEY TO THE GENERA IN THE LOCAL FLORA

1. Sori of sporophytes with paraphyses.................*Ralfsia* (p. 95)
1. Sori of sporophytes without paraphyses.....*Hapalospongidion* (p. 96)

Ralfsia Berkeley, 1843

Thalli macroscopic, crustose; at first circular in outline, later becoming lobed at margins; with or without rhizoids on under surface. Growth trichothallic. Thallus with a basal layer of radiating, laterally adjoined, branched horizontal filaments. Uppermost cells of basal layer each with a very sparingly branched assimilating filament growing from upper side; the assimilating filaments erect throughout, or curving toward thallus margin and then bending upward. Chromatophores only in assimilating filaments; usually one in a cell and on side toward upper surface of thallus. Gametophyte and sporophyte usually vegetatively identical.

Sporophytes with fertile areas (sori) in which the terminal cell of each assimilating filament produces both a unilocular sporangium and an unbranched paraphysis. The paraphyses multicellular, erect, projecting beyond the sporangia. The sori also with small tufts of long colorless multicellular hairs.

Gametophytes with gametangia terminal on assimilating filaments and grouped in sori. The sori without paraphyses, with small tufts of long colorless multicellular hairs. The gametangia uniseriate, biseriate, or pluriseriate; the upper end of each gametangium terminating in one or more sterile cells.

STRUCTURE AND REPRODUCTION. Börgesen, 1914, pp. 33–36; figs. 20–22. Hollenberg, 1941. Kuckuck, 1894, pp. 241–246; figs. 15–15.

KEY TO THE SPECIES IN THE LOCAL FLORA

1. Paraphyses less than 130 μ long........................*R. pacifica*
1. Paraphyses over 250 μ long............................*R. hesperia*

Ralfsia pacifica Hollenberg (mss)　　　　Pl. 12, figs. 4–6

Ralfsia verrucosa Anderson [not of (Areschoug) J. G. Agardh]. *Anderson, 1891, p. 200. *Setchell and Gardner, 1925, p. 497.

Thalli, as found on the Monterey Peninsula, 2–3 cm. in diameter; brownish-black to black. Thalli irregularly circular in outline if not crowded; 0.5–1.0 mm. in thickness; with entire lower surface firmly attached to substratum. Upper surface with radial or concentric ridges. Cells in lower portion of thallus 10–16 μ broad and in upwardly curving rows; cells in upper portion of thallus 8–10 μ broad and in vertical rows. Unilocular sporangia and gametangia borne on separate plants. Unilocular sporangia sessile, oblong to pyriform, 70–90 μ long, 20–30 μ broad; paraphyses narrower at base, 90–120 μ long, with 9–12 cells. Gametangia uniseriate, up to 80 μ long, 7–9 μ broad, terminating in a single sterile cell.

LOCAL DISTRIBUTION. Growing on rocks in the upper littoral zone. Along the shore near Bird Rock; Pebble Beach; north end of Carmel Beach.

PACIFIC COAST DISTRIBUTION. Alaska (Bay of Unalaska) to Baja California.

Ralfsia hesperia Setchell and Gardner

*Setchell and Gardner, 1924, p. 2. *Setchell and Gardner, 1925, p. 498.

Thalli, as found on the Monterey Peninsula, 3–4 cm. in diameter, yellowish-brown in color. Thalli circular in outline, 1–1.5 mm. in thickness; with entire lower surface attached to substratum, at times with rhizoids from lower surface. Upper surface with concentric ridges. Cells in lower portion of thallus 16–18 μ broad and with a length 3–4 times the breadth. Thalli with unilocular sporangia only. The sporangia broadly clavate, 120–140 (–180) μ long, 28–34 μ broad. The paraphyses narrower in lower portion, 290–360 μ long, with 9–12 cells.

LOCAL DISTRIBUTION. Carmel Bay.

TYPE LOCALITY. As above.

PACIFIC COAST DISTRIBUTION. Known only from type locality and from the vicinity of Corona Del Mar, California.

According to unpublished observations of G. J. Hollenberg, this species produces only unilocular sporangia and is usually found in fruit only during the winter months. Fruiting specimens are readily distinguishable from *R. pacifica* by the length of the paraphyses.

Hapalospongidion Saunders, 1899

Thalli macroscopic, crustose, irregularly lobed, without rhizoids on the under surface. Growth trichothallic. Thallus with a distromatic (occasionally tristromatic) basal layer of horizontal, laterally adjoined, branched filaments. Upper cells of basal portion each bearing an erect unbranched filament. Erect filaments not in lateral contact and with the intervening spaces filled with gelatinous material. Certain of the erect filaments replaced by long colorless multicellular hairs. Chromatophores disc-shaped, few in a cell; in both the erect and the prostrate filaments. Gametophyte and sporophyte vegetatively identical.

Sporophytes with unilocular sporangia only; the sporangia terminal on erect filaments and borne singly.

Gametophytes with plurilocular gametangia. The gametangia subterminal of the erect filaments, catenate, biseriate. Gametic union isogamous.

STRUCTURE AND REPRODUCTION. Hollenberg, 1941. Hollenberg, 1942, pp. 528–532; figs. 1–10. Saunders, 1899, pp. 37–38; pl. 1, figs. 1–4.

Hapalospongidion gelatinosum Saunders   Pl. 14, figs. 1–2

*Saunders, 1899, p. 37; pl. 1, figs. 1–4. *Hollenberg, 1942, p. 528; figs. 1–10. *Phyc. Bor.-Amer. No. 534.

Microspongium Saundersii Setchell and Gardner, 1924, p. 12. *Setchell and Gardner, 1925, p. 492.

Thalli a few millimeters in diameter or coalescing to form irregularly shaped thalli 10 cm. or more in diameter. The erect filaments up to 750 μ tall, cylindrical in basal portion, club-shaped in upper portion; cells of basal portion cylindrical and 4–5 μ broad, those of upper portion barrel-shaped and 7–10 μ broad. Cells of basal layer and of erect filaments with numerous disc-shaped chromatophores. The gametangia 10–14 μ broad, and the rows of gametangia up to 175 μ long.

LOCAL DISTRIBUTION. Growing on rocks and either at the low- or the high-tide mark. Point Aulon; first point north of Carmel Beach.

TYPE LOCALITY. Point Aulon, Pacific Grove, California.

PACIFIC COAST DISTRIBUTION. As above.

Family HETEROCHORDARIACEAE

Thalli with erect radially branched shoots growing from a crustose base. Growth of erect shoots trichothallic and multiaxial. The erect shoots pseudoparenchymatous, differentiated into medulla and cortex. Presumably with an alternation of vegetatively identical gametophyte and sporophyte.[1]

Sporophytes with the unilocular sporangia remote from one another and lying beneath the surface of the thallus.

Gametophytes with the gametangia plurilocular, intercalary, catenate.

With one genus, *Heterochordaria*.

[1] The fact that all shoots from a single crustose base bear but one kind of reproductive organ and the fact that these may be unilocular or plurilocular indicate that the family should be placed among the Isogeneratae. Kylin (1940, p. 42) considers the plurilocular organs sporangial in nature and places the single genus in the Chordariaceae.

Heterochordaria Setchell and Gardner, 1924

Thallus with a profusely lobed and branched crustose base. The base apparently perennial and each year producing several erect annual shoots. Each shoot with a percurrent cylindrical axis clothed on all sides with short cylindrical to flattened branches with a diameter about half that of the axis. Axis and branches at first solid, later becoming hollow. Growth trichothallic. Apex of axis and branches multiaxial and with cell division intercalary but restricted to the subterminal portion. Mature portion of axis and branches pseudoparenchymatous, differentiated into medulla and cortex; the medulla composed of cylindrical, vertically elongated, colorless cells; the cortex composed of laterally adjoined four- to eight-celled unbranched assimilating filaments that stand perpendicular to the medulla. Presumably with vegetatively identical sporophyte and gametophyte.

Sporophytes with unilocular sporangia only; the sporangia remote from one another, borne on outermost cells of the medulla and standing vertically between the assimilating filaments.

Gametophytes with gametangia intercalary, catenate, pluriseriate, and formed by vertical and transverse division of all but the outermost cells of the assimilating filaments.

STRUCTURE AND REPRODUCTION. Abe, 1935, pp. 329–332; text figs. 1–3; pl. 10, fig. 1. Abe. 1935*A*. Abe, 1936. Setchell and Gardner, 1925, pp. 550–551; pl. 36, figs. 18–19; pl. 91.

Heterochordaria abietina (Ruprecht) Setchell and Gardner
Pl. 14, fig. 3

Setchell and Gardner, 1924, p. 6. Setchell and Gardner, 1925, p. 550; pl. 36, figs. 18–19; pl. 91.
Chordaria abietina Ruprecht apud Farlow, 1875, p. 357. *Anderson, 1891, p. 220. *Howe, 1893, p. 67. *Setchell and Gardner, 1903, p. 251; pl. 18, figs. 16–17.

Erect shoots (of Monterey Peninsula plants) up to 25 cm. tall and the crustose base up to 5 cm. in diameter; color varying from light tan to dark brown. Lateral branches of central axis cylindrical to sublinear, up to 3 cm. long.

LOCAL DISTRIBUTION. Growing between the 4.0- and 2.5-foot tide levels on rocks exposed to moderate or heavy surf. The erect shoots appearing early in March and disappearing early in November. Abundant at Point Pinos; Asilomar Point; the Middle Reef of Moss Beach; Fanshell Beach; Cypress Point; Pescadero Point; Arrowhead Point; Mission Point.

TYPE LOCALITY. Oregon.

PACIFIC COAST DISTRIBUTION. Alaska (St. Lawrence Island) to central California (Point Conception).

Order SPHACELARIALES

Isogeneratae, in which growth is terminal, initiated by conspicuous apical cells, and with the region posterior to each apical cell becoming polysiphonous. The thalli usually erect and branched, but at times crustose. If erect, the branching either alternate, opposite, or verticillate. Thalli with or without colorless multicellular uniseriate hairs. Chromatophores usually disc-shaped and many in a cell. The thalli at times multiplying vegetatively by an abscission of specialized branchlets (propagula).

Sporophytes usually only with unilocular sporangia; rarely producing plurilocular sporangia. The unilocular sporangia borne singly and usually pedicellate. The plurilocular sporangia identical in shape with gametangia of the species and borne in the same manner.

Gametophytes with plurilocular gametangia. The gametangia pluriseriate, terminal, solitary, and usually pedicellate. Gametic union isogamous or anisogamous.

With one family, the Sphacelariaceae, in the local flora.

Family SPHACELARIACEAE

Thalli erect or crustose. Erect thalli with branches formed from cells of the polysiphonous portion instead of from lateral initials cut off by the apical cell. The branching evidently or obscurely distichous; never verticillate. Thalli usually producing propagula. Sporophytes and gametophytes with reproductive organs as described for the order.

With one genus, *Sphacelaria,* in the local flora.

Sphacelaria Lyngbye, 1819

Thalli erect; the holdfast discoid or a loose mass of rhizoidal filaments. The erect axis freely branched, the branches cylindrical and regularly or irregularly distichous. Each branch terminating in a conspicuous cylindrical apical cell and the region posterior to the apical cell soon becoming polysiphonous. Older portions of branches at times corticated. The branches frequently with branched uniseriate hairs. Chromatophores disc-shaped, many in a cell. Thalli multiplying vegetatively by abscission of small, simple to trifurcate, specialized branchlets (propagula).

Gametophyte and sporophyte identical in size and vegetative structure.

Sporophytes usually only with unilocular sporangia but occasionally with both unilocular and plurilocular sporangia. The sporangia borne singly in polysiphonous portion of thallus. Unilocular sporangia pedicellate and with simple or branched, uniseriate or polysiphonous, pedicels. Plurilocular sporangia pluriseriate.

Gametophytes with gametangia pedicellate and borne singly on polysiphonous portion of thallus. The gametangia plurilocular, pluriseriate, and with each superficial cell forming a pore through which the enclosed gamete escapes. Gametic union isogamous or anisogamous.

STRUCTURE AND REPRODUCTION. Clint, 1927. Papenfuss, 1934. G. M. Smith, 1938, pp. 235–237; fig. 128.

Sphacelaria didichotoma Saunders   Pl. 14, fig. 4

*Saunders, 1898, p. 158; pl. 26. Setchell and Gardner, 1925, p. 397.

Thalli, as found on the Monterey Peninsula, up to 4 mm. tall, yellowish-brown in color. Branching of erect shoots predominately alternate and with the branches diverging widely from the axis. The major branches 25–35 μ in diameter and with 4–8 cells in each segment of the polysiphonous portion. Uncorticated. Propagula abundant, usually formed toward upper end of branches, frequently unilateral in arrangement. The propagula slender, 200–300 μ long, bifurcate and with the tip of each arm also bifurcate. Unilocular sporangia and gametangia unknown.

LOCAL DISTRIBUTION. Growing between mean low tide and the −1.5-foot tide levels. Municipal Wharf, Monterey; Mussel Point; Pescadero Point. Also found 10 feet below pneumatocyst of a thallus of *Nereocystis Luetkeana* cast ashore at Moss Beach. Dredged from a depth of 15–20 feet at Stillwater Cove.

TYPE LOCALITY. Carmel Bay, California.

PACIFIC COAST DISTRIBUTION. Central California (Monterey) to southern California (Clifton).

Order DICTYOTALES

With macroscopic gametophyte and sporophyte of identical size and shape. Thalli compressed; either undivided (though at times lobed or laciniate) and with a continuous marginal row of apical cells; or repeatedly dichotomous and with a single apical cell at the tip of each of the ultimate dichotomies. If dichotomous, with or without a percurrent midrib. Mature portions of thallus differentiated into medulla and cortex; the medulla one to several cells in thickness and composed of large cells; the cortex composed of small cells and usually one cell in thickness.

Sporophytes producing unilocular sporangia only and with the sporangia in small sori variously distributed on flattened faces of thallus. The sporangia producing either four or eight large non-flagellate naked aplanospores.

Gametophytes heterothallic, oögamous. Oögonia solitary or in small sori; each oögonium producing and liberating a single egg. Antheridia grouped in small sori; each antheridium plurilocular and producing uniflagellate (?) antherozoids.

Family DICTYOTACEAE

All Dictyotales are placed in a single family, the Dictyotaceae, whose characters are the same as those of the order.

With one genus, *Dictyota,* in the local flora.

Dictyota Lamouroux, 1809

Thallus with an irregularly shaped holdfast. The erect portion flattened, membranous, dichotomously branched but at times the branching appearing as if pinnate. The segments without a midrib. Tips of the ultimate dichotomies each with a single large apical cell. Mature portions of thallus differentiated into medulla and cortex; both one cell in thickness but the medulla with large cells and the cortex with small cells.

Sporophytes with unilocular sporangia only. The sporangia grouped in sori and each sporangium producing four aplanospores.

Gametophytes heterothallic, oögamous. Oögonia solitary or grouped in sori; each oögonium producing and liberating a single egg. Antheridia grouped in sori; each antheridium plurilocular, pluriseriate, producing uniflagellate (?) antherozoids.

STRUCTURE AND REPRODUCTION. Schreiber, 1935. Williams, 1904.

Dictyota flabellata (Collins) Setchell and Gardner   Pl. 15, fig. 6

Setchell and Gardner, 1924, p. 12. *Setchell and Gardner, 1925, p. 652; pl. 34, fig. 3; pl. 35, fig. 7; pl. 36, figs. 13–17.
Dilopus flabellatus Collins in Phyc. Bor.-Amer. No. 834.

Thalli, as found on the Monterey Peninsula, 8–15 cm. tall; yellowish-brown in upper portion, blackish-brown near base. The branching appearing as if alternate because of unequal growth of the two arms of each dichotomy. Segments 2–15 mm. broad; with the portion between successive dichotomies gradually broadening from bottom to top. Apex of angle between two arms of a dichotomy broadly rounded. Tips of the ultimate dichotomies broadly rounded. Sporangia, oögonia, and antheridia in minute closely aggregated sori on both flattened faces of thallus.

LOCAL DISTRIBUTION. Fifteen feet below pneumatocyst of *Nereocystis Luetkeana* growing off Mussel Point. Found free-floating near Fisherman's Wharf, Monterey. Cast ashore at Pacific Grove and at north end of Carmel Beach.

TYPE LOCALITY. La Jolla, California.

PACIFIC COAST DISTRIBUTION. Central California (Monterey) to southern California (La Jolla).

Easily distinguished from other brown algae by the conspicuous lens-shaped apical cell and the transverse rows of cells posterior to the apical cell.

Class HETEROGENERATAE

With an alternation of dissimilar gametophyte and sporophyte and one in which the sporophyte is the larger and more complex in structure. The gametophyte always filamentous and microscopic. The sporophyte filamentous or nonfilamentous, microscopic or macroscopic, and with growth trichothallic or by intercalary cell division.

Sporophytes with sporangia borne singly or in sori. Usually with unilocular sporangia only. The unilocular sporangia always producing zoospores. Sporophytes at times with plurilocular sporangia.

Gametophytes with gametangia borne singly. Gametic union isogamous, anisogamous, or oögamous.

KEY TO THE SUBCLASSES

1. Growth of sporophyte trichothallic..........*Haplostichineae* (p. 102)
1. Growth of sporophyte not trichothallic........*Polystichineae* (p. 122)

Subclass HAPLOSTICHINEAE

Sporophytes with growth trichothallic and initiated by a single axial filament or a group of axial filaments. Mature portions of sporophyte with branches of filaments free from one another, interwoven with one another, or compacted and pseudoparenchymatous.

Sporophytes usually with the sporangia borne singly. Producing unilocular sporangia only, or producing both unilocular and plurilocular sporangia.

Gametophytes filamentous and with the gametangia borne singly. Gametic union isogamous or oögamous.

Key to the Orders in the Local Flora

1. Gametic union isogamous.....................*Chordariales* (p. 103)
1. Gametic union oögamous ....*Desmarestiales* (p. 118)

Order CHORDARIALES

Heterogeneratae with growth of the sporophyte trichothallic, monoaxial or multiaxial, and with cell division of axial filaments terminal or intercalary. The sporophytes macroscopic, though at times minute. Construction of sporophyte either evidently filamentous or obscurely so because of compacting of component filaments into a pseudoparenchyma.

Sporophytes with unilocular sporangia only, or with both unilocular and plurilocular sporangia. The unilocular sporangia not borne in sori. Plurilocular sporangia uniseriate to pluriseriate, at times adjoining one another but not in true sori.

Gametophytes, so far as known, microscopic and filamentous. The gametangia plurilocular and usually uniseriate. Gametic union isogamous.

Key to the Families in the Local Flora

1. Thalli crustose, pulvinate, or globose............................2
1. Thalli erect and branched...................*Chordariaceae* (p. 116)
   2. Thalli minute; with an evident mono- or distromatic
      basal layer ....*Myrionemataceae* (p. 103)
   2. Thalli of moderate size; the basal layer,
      if present, obscure.................*Corynophloeaceae* (p. 113)

Family Myrionemataceae

Sporophytes minute, crustose, obscurely monoaxial and with cell division intercalary. The sporophyte with an evident mono- or distromatic basal layer of laterally adjoined branched filaments. All except marginal cells of basal layer (upper layer if distromatic) producing a short, simple or sparingly branched, erect filament. The erect filaments laterally adjoined or with interspaces. Sporophytes with both unilocular and plurilocular sporangia. The unilocular sporangia usually terminal on or replacing the erect filaments. The plurilocular sporangia uniseriate to pluriseriate, solitary or catenate, produced by division of cells of erect filaments.

Gametophytes, so far as known, microscopic and filamentous. Gametic union presumably isogamous.

Key to the Genera in the Local Flora

1. Basal layer of sporophyte monostromatic.......................... 2
1. Basal layer of sporophyte distromatic...........*Hecatonema* (p. 112)
   2. Plurilocular sporangia uniseriate.............*Myrionema* (p. 104)
   2. Plurilocular sporangia pluriseriate.........*Compsonema* (p. 107)

Myrionema Greville, 1827

Thalli (sporophytes) minute, crustose, circular to irregular in outline, and with a monostromatic basal layer. The basal layer composed of radiating, prostrate, laterally adjoined, branched filaments. The basal layer without rhizoidal filaments. All cells of the basal layer (except those at margin) with an erect unbranched or sparingly branched filament. The erect filaments usually laterally adjoined. Certain of the erect filaments replaced by multicellular uniseriate hairs with a basal meristematic region. Cells of both prostrate and erect filaments with 1–3 plate-like chromatophores. The unilocular sporangia borne either erect on horizontal filaments or laterally on the erect filaments. The plurilocular sporangia wholly uniseriate or uniseriate for a part of their length; either borne erect on horizontal filaments or laterally on the erect filaments.

Gametophyte a loosely and irregularly branched filament in which the branches are not laterally adjoined. Gametangia unknown.

STRUCTURE AND REPRODUCTION. Kylin, 1934, pp. 5–9, figs. 1–3.

Key to the Species in the Local Flora

1. No sporangia borne laterally on erect filaments.................... 2
1. With certain of the sporangia borne laterally on the erect filaments... 4
   2. With all of the erect filaments eventually becoming
       fertile ....*M. primarium*
   2. With intermingled sterile and fertile erect filaments............. 3
3. Erect sterile filaments with 20–30 cells.................*M. attenuatum*
3. Erect sterile filaments with less than 15 cells....*M. corunnae* var. *sterile*
   4. With unilocular sporangia.........................*M. strangulans*
   4. With plurilocular sporangia.........*M. balticum* var. *californicum*

Myrionema primarium Setchell and Gardner

Setchell and Gardner, 1922, p. 334; pl. 34, fig. 12. Setchell and Gardner, 1925, p. 456; pl. 55, fig. 12.

Myrionema primarium forma *acuminatum* *Setchell and Gardner, 1922, p. 335; pl. 32, fig. 9. *Setchell and Gardner, 1925, p. 457.

Myrionema foecundum forma *majus* *Setchell and Gardner, 1922, p. 338; pl. 32, fig. 7. *Setchell and Gardner, 1925, p. 463.

Myrionema foecundum forma *divergens* *Setchell and Gardner, 1922, p. 348; pl. 34, figs. 8-9. *Setchell and Gardner, 1925, p. 463; pl. 55, figs. 8-9.

Phycocelis foecunda Saunders [not of Strömfelt]. *Saunders, 1898, p. 148; pl. 12, figs. 1-7.

Thalli (sporophytes) more or less circular, up to 5 mm. in diameter, at times confluent with one another. The monostromatic base with regularly radiating filaments. Erect filaments at center of thallus usually 6–10 cells in height, occasionally with 12–15 cells; the erect filaments cylindrical and not tapering markedly at apex. Certain of the erect filaments replaced by multicellular hairs with a basal meristematic region. Thalli with all of the erect filaments (except the hairs) eventually becoming fertile; the thalli with adjoining groups of unilocular and plurilocular sporangia, or with plurilocular sporangia only. Unilocular sporangia cylindrical, erect, sessile or with a one-celled pedicel. Plurilocular sporangia formed by division of all cells or all but the lowermost cells of an erect filament; cylindrical to fusiform, uniseriate or with some of the median cells vertically divided.

LOCAL DISTRIBUTION. Epiphytic upon various algae but most frequently encountered on Laminariales. Found on old thalli of Laminariales practically everywhere on the Monterey Peninsula.

TYPE LOCALITY. Coos Bay, Oregon.

PACIFIC COAST DISTRIBUTION. Alaska to central California (Carmel Bay).

Several species and varieties have been described in which all of the erect filaments become fertile. These have been differentiated from one another chiefly on shape and dimensions of the plurilocular sporangia. Examination of numerous specimens from the Monterey Peninsula has led to the conclusion that these species and varieties intergraded so gradually with one another that they should be grouped in one collective species, *M. primarium*.

Myrionema attenuatum Setchell and Gardner

*Setchell and Gardner, 1922, p. 344; pl. 34, figs. 6-7. *Setchell and Gardner, 1925, p. 468; pl. 55, figs. 6-7.

Myrionema attenuatum forma *doliiforme* *Setchell and Gardner, 1922, p. 344; pl. 34, figs. 4-5. *Setchell and Gardner, 1925, p. 468; pl. 55, figs. 4-5.

Thalli (sporophytes) minute and in more or less confluent

strata on the surface of the host. Monostromatic basal layer with regularly radiating filaments. The sterile erect filaments with 20–30 or more cylindrical to barrel-shaped cells. Upper ends of erect filaments gradually attenuated. True hairs lacking. Unilocular sporangia unknown. Plurilocular sporangia borne on upper portion of erect filaments intermingled with and much shorter than sterile erect filaments. Fertile erect filaments with 2–5 of the lowermost cells sterile. Fertile portion of the filament cylindrical to slightly fusiform, uniseriate or with a few cells longitudinally divided, 30–45 μ long, 4.5–6 μ broad.

LOCAL DISTRIBUTION. On stipes of *Macrocystis pyrifera, Laminaria Farlowii,* and on sterile base of *Gigartina corymbifera.* Cypress Point; Carmel Bay.

TYPE LOCALITY. Carmel Bay.

PACIFIC COAST DISTRIBUTION. As above.

Myrionema corunnae var. sterile Setchell and Gardner

*Setchell and Gardner, 1922, p. 340; pl. 33, figs. 13–15. *Setchell and Gardner, 1925, p. 460.

Thalli (sporophytes) circular, 1.5–3 mm. in diameter. The erect filaments 6–8 cells tall. True hairs lacking. Unilocular sporangia unknown. Thalli with certain of the erect filaments not developing into plurilocular sporangia. In formation of plurilocular sporangia from cells of erect filaments the two lowermost cells frequently remaining sterile. The plurilocular sporangia cylindrical, 55–65 μ long, 4.5–5.5 μ broad.

LOCAL DISTRIBUTION. On pneumatocysts of *Nereocystis Luetkeana* cast ashore, Carmel Bay.

TYPE LOCALITY. As above.

PACIFIC COAST DISTRIBUTION. As above.

Myrionema strangulans Greville   Pl. 15, fig. 5

Greville, 1827, pl. 300. *Setchell and Gardner, 1925, p. 471; pl. 35, fig. 12; pl. 40, fig. 51.

Thalli (sporophytes) irregular in outline, 1–2 mm. in diameter. The monostromatic basal layer with radiating filaments laterally adjoined. Cells of basal layer 4–4.5 μ broad and with a length about double the breadth. Erect filaments at center of thallus 5–7 cells tall; the filaments distinctly club-shaped and with the uppermost cell 6–8 μ broad. The thallus with multicellular hairs intermingled with the erect filaments. Unilocular sporangia sessile or with a one-celled pedicel, intermingled with erect filaments; at times borne laterally at base of erect filaments; the sporangia ellipsoid to obovoid, 38–46 (–60) μ long, 18–24 μ broad. Plurilocular sporangia unknown.

LOCAL DISTRIBUTION. Abundant on *Ulva lobata* at Pebble Beach during summer months. Also found on *U. taeniata* at the Middle Reef of Moss Beach.

TYPE LOCALITY. Appin, Scotland.

PACIFIC COAST DISTRIBUTION. Alaska (Sitka) to central California (Carmel Bay).

Myrionema balticum var. californicum Setchell and Gardner

Setchell and Gardner, 1922, p. 341. Setchell and Gardner, 1925, p. 465.

Thalli (sporophytes) cushion-like, 0.5–0.75 mm. in diameter, rarely confluent with one another. Monostromatic basal layer with regularly radiating filaments. The sterile erect filaments with 10–15 cells, 75–125 μ tall, slightly attenuated at upper end. With multicellular hairs. Unilocular sporangia unknown. Plurilocular sporangia formed by division of all but the lowermost 1–3 cells of erect filaments, not infrequently formed on lateral branches close to base of erect filaments. The plurilocular sporangia 90–130 μ long, 7–9 μ broad.

LOCAL DISTRIBUTION. On the outer ends of leaves of *Phyllospadix*. Pacific Grove; Cypress Point.

TYPE LOCALITY. Point Carmel (Point Lobos), Monterey County, California.

PACIFIC COAST DISTRIBUTION. As above.

M. balticum var. *californicum* is readily distinguishable from other local members of the genus by the lateral plurilocular sporangia. It also grows in a characteristic manner on a specific host. There is some doubt as to whether this alga should be considered a variety of *M. balticum,* which, as yet, has not been found on the Pacific Coast of North America.

Compsonema Kuckuck, 1899

Sporophytes minute. The thallus crustose, circular in outline; and with a monostromatic basal layer composed of radiating, prostrate, more or less laterally adjoined, branched filaments. The basal layer at times with rhizoids. Most cells of the basal layer each bearing a single erect branched or unbranched filament. Cells of the erect filaments with one or more band-shaped chromatophores. The unilocular sporangia borne on the erect filaments, usually terminal but at times intercalary. The plurilocular sporangia either sessile on the prostrate filaments or terminal or intercalary on the erect filaments. The plurilocular sporangia pluriseriate.

Gametophytes unknown.

STRUCTURE AND REPRODUCTION. Kuckuck, 1899. Setchell and Gardner, 1922A.

KEY TO THE SPECIES IN THE LOCAL FLORA

1. Erect filaments unbranched...................................... 2
1. Erect filaments branched or with lateral fertile branches............ 7
  2. Basal layer with rhizoids............................*C. pusillum*
  2. Basal layer without rhizoids.................................. 3
3. Plurilocular sporangia both terminal and intercalary.......*C. secundum*
3. Plurilocular sporangia strictly terminal........................ 4
  4. Plurilocular sporangia sessile or with one- or two-celled pedicels... 5
  4. Plurilocular sporangia typically with pedicels of three or more cells. 6
5. Plurilocular sporangia approximately cylindrical....*C. myrionematoides*
5. Plurilocular sporangia tapering markedly in upper half..*C. coniferum*
  6. Plurilocular sporangia 8–11 µ broad....................*C. dubium*
  6. Plurilocular sporangia 16–28 µ broad...................*C. serpens*
7. Branching profuse and predominately secund............*C. ramulosum*
7. Branching sparse and irregular................................ 8
  8. Plurilocular sporangia both terminal and intercalary....*Č. intricatum*
  8. Plurilocular sporangia strictly terminal.............*C. fasciculatum*

Compsonema pusillum Setchell and Gardner

*Setchell and Gardner, 1922A, p. 356; pl. 37, fig. 3. *Setchell and Gardner, 1925, p. 477; pl. 54, fig. 3.

Thalli (sporophytes) forming irregular cushions 3–4 mm. in diameter. The prostrate basal filaments tortuous and following contour of the host; with rhizoids penetrating a short distance into host. Erect filaments 270–300 µ tall; unbranched, cylindrical, with cells 6–7 µ broad and a length 3–5 times the breadth. Unilocular sporangia spherical to ovoid, borne erect on the prostrate filaments, sessile or with pedicels of one or two cells, 18–25 (–40) µ long, 16–22 µ broad. Plurilocular sporangia borne on prostrate filaments, cylindrical to fusiform and usually two cells broad, sessile or with short pedicels, 40–60 µ long, 10–12 µ broad.

LOCAL DISTRIBUTION. On pneumatocysts of *Nereocystis Luetkeana*. Carmel Bay.

TYPE LOCALITY. As above.

PACIFIC COAST DISTRIBUTION. As above.

Compsonema secundum Setchell and Gardner Pl. 15, fig. 4

*Setchell and Gardner, 1922*A*, p. 361; pl. 37, figs. 1–2. *Setchell and Gardner, 1925, p. 483; pl. 54, figs. 1–2.
Compsonema secundum forma *terminale* *Setchell and Gardner, 1922*A*, p. 366; pl. 37, figs. 4–5. *Setchell and Gardner, 1925, p. 484; pl. 54, figs. 4–5.

Thalli (sporophytes) microscopic, more or less confluent. The prostrate basal filaments much crisped, branched, without rhizoids. Erect filaments up to 1.25 mm. long, unbranched, cylindrical and somewhat narrower near base; cells near base 5.5–6.5 µ broad and with a length up to six times the breadth, cells near apex 9.5–10.5 µ broad. Unilocular sporangia broadly clavate, borne erect on prostrate filaments, sessile or with short pedicels, 60–90 µ long, 22–28 µ broad. Plurilocular sporangia either terminal on long or short pedicels from prostrate filaments or intercalary on erect filaments. The intercalary plurilocular sporangia secund.

Local Distribution. On pneumatocysts of *Nereocystis Luetkeana.* Pacific Grove; Moss Beach; Carmel Bay.
Type Locality. Carmel Bay.
Pacific Coast Distribution. Washington (Moclips) to central California (Carmel Bay).

The plurilocular sporangia of this species are so variable that it is impossible to make a distinction between the type and the forma *terminale*.

Compsonema myrionematoides Setchell and Gardner

*Setchell and Gardner, 1922*A*, p. 361; pl. 36, fig. 1. *Setchell and Gardner, 1925, p. 474.

Thalli (sporophytes) minute, forming circular to irregular cushions 1–2.5 mm. in diameter. Basal filaments densely crowded, contorted, without rhizoids. Erect filaments 110–130 µ tall, unbranched, cylindrical, with cells 7.5–8.5 µ broad; cells near base with a length of one to two times the breadth, those near apex with a length several times the breadth. Unilocular sporangia unknown. Plurilocular sporangia borne erect on prostrate filaments, sessile or with pedicels of one or two cells, subcylindrical, 50–70 (–100) µ long, 9–12 µ broad.

Local Distribution. On stipe of *Nereocystis Luetkeana.* Pacific Grove.
Type Locality. As above.
Pacific Coast Distribution. As above.

Compsonema coniferum Setchell and Gardner

*Setchell and Gardner, 1922*A*, p. 365; pl. 38, fig. 3. *Setchell and Gardner, 1925, p. 479.

Thalli (sporophytes) minute, more or less confluent and forming a velvety coating on host. The basal filaments profusely branched and with branches contorted, without rhizoids. Erect filaments 150–200 μ tall, unbranched, tapering at upper end; cells cylindrical to somewhat barrel-shaped, 8–10 μ broad, with a length 1–1.5 times the breadth. Chromatophores band-shaped. Unilocular sporangia unknown. Plurilocular sporangia borne erect on prostrate filaments, sessile or with pedicels of one or two cells, narrowly conical, 45–65 μ long, 15–18 μ broad.

LOCAL DISTRIBUTION. On sterile base of *Gigartina corymbifera*. Cypress Point.

TYPE LOCALITY. As above.

PACIFIC COAST DISTRIBUTION. As above.

Compsonema dubium Setchell and Gardner

*Setchell and Gardner, 1922*A*, p. 465; pl. 38, fig. 6. *Setchell and Gardner, 1925, p. 479.

Thalli (sporophytes) microscopic, forming small tufts among other epiphytic algae. Monostromatic base profusely branched and with branches contorted, without rhizoids. Erect filaments 275–350 μ tall, unbranched, almost cylindrical throughout; cells 7–9 μ broad, with a length 2–3 times the breadth. Unilocular sporangia (?) ellipsoid, pedicellate and borne erect on prostrate filaments, 16–22 μ long, 12–15 μ broad. Plurilocular sporangia pedicellate on prostrate filaments and usually with pedicels of three or more cells, narrowly cylindrical, 50–75 μ long, 8–11 μ broad.

LOCAL DISTRIBUTION. On sterile base of *Gigartina corymbifera*. Cypress Point.

TYPE LOCALITY. As above.

PACIFIC COAST DISTRIBUTION. As above.

Compsonema serpens Setchell and Gardner   Pl. 15, fig. 3

*Setchell and Gardner, 1922*A,* p. 363; pl. 39, fig. 17. *Setchell and Gardner, 1925, p. 480.

Thalli (sporophytes) forming an irregularly expanded crustose stratum on surface of host. Filaments of basal monostromatic layer irregularly branched and much contorted, without rhizoids.

Erect filaments unbranched (very rarely subulately branched above), cylindrical and broadening somewhat above the base, slightly narrowed at the apex; cells cylindrical, basal cells 5.5–8.5 µ broad, median cells 10–17 µ broad. Unilocular sporangia unknown. Plurilocular sporangia borne erect on prostrate filaments, pedicellate and the pedicels usually several cells in length, cylindrico-conical, 60–130 µ long, 18–28 µ broad.

LOCAL DISTRIBUTION. On pneumatocysts of *Egregia Menziesii* and on the sterile base of *Gigartina corymbifera*. Mussel Point; Cypress Point.

TYPE LOCALITY. Cypress Point.

PACIFIC COAST DISTRIBUTION. As above.

Compsonema ramulosum Setchell and Gardner

*Setchell and Gardner, 1922*A*, p. 362; pl. 39, figs. 1–5. *Setchell and Gardner, 1925, p. 486.

Thalli (sporophytes) minute, forming circular cushions 5–7 mm. in diameter. Filaments of monostromatic basal layer contorted and irregularly branched, without rhizoids. Erect filaments up to 1 mm. tall, profusely branched and with the branching predominately secund. The branches tapering slightly. Cells near base of erect filaments 6–7.5 µ broad and with a length 1–3.5 times the breadth. Unilocular sporangia pedicellate on prostrate filaments or secundly intercalary on erect filaments, broadly clavate. Plurilocular sporangia either pedicellate on prostrate filaments, or pedicellate on erect filaments, or intercalary on erect filaments; clavate, cylindrical, or cylindrico-conical; up to 140 µ long, 16 µ broad.

LOCAL DISTRIBUTION. On pneumatocysts of *Nereocystis Luetkeana*. Carmel Bay.

TYPE LOCALITY. As above.

PACIFIC COAST DISTRIBUTION. As above.

Compsonema intricatum Setchell and Gardner

*Setchell and Gardner, 1922*A*, p. 354; pl. 35, figs. 1–3. *Setchell and Gardner, 1925, p. 482.

Thalli (sporophytes) more or less confluent and forming a velvety stratum of indefinite extent. The basal monostromatic layer with profusely branched, much-contorted filaments, without rhizoids. Erect filaments 1.5–2.5 mm. tall, unbranched or with a few short branches near base, the filaments gradually tapering to an acute point; cells cylindrical, 8–9 µ broad, with a length 1–2.5 times the breadth. Unilocular sporangia either pedicellate on prostrate filaments or sessile to pedicellate and lateral on erect filaments, ovoid to ellipsoid, 25–33 μ long, 18–22 μ broad. Plurilocular sporangia either pedicellate on prostrate and erect filaments or intercalary on erect filaments, fusiform, 80–120 μ long, 10–14 μ broad.

LOCAL DISTRIBUTION. On *Fucus furcatus*. Carmel Bay.
TYPE LOCALITY. As above.
PACIFIC COAST DISTRIBUTION. As above.

Compsonema fasciculatum Setchell and Gardner

*Setchell and Gardner, 1922*A*, p. 360; pl. 38, figs. 7–9. *Setchell and Gardner, 1925, p. 478.

Thalli (sporophytes) minute, in more or less confluent tufts. The monostromatic basal layer composed of greatly contorted filaments, without rhizoids. Erect filaments 90–130 μ tall, branched near base, with cylindrical to somewhat barrel-shaped cells; the cells 10–14 μ broad, with a length 1–2.5 times the breadth. Unilocular sporangia unknown. The plurilocular sporangia usually pedicellate and borne laterally on erect filaments, conical to fusiform, 35–45 μ long, 12–18 μ broad.

LOCAL DISTRIBUTION. On sterile base of *Gigartina corymbifera*. Pacific Grove.
TYPE LOCALITY. As above.
PACIFIC COAST DISTRIBUTION. As above.

Hecatonema Sauvageau, 1897

Sporophytes microscopic. The thallus crustose, more or less circular in outline, and with a basal layer that is wholly or in part distromatic. The basal layer composed of laterally adjoined filaments and becoming distromatic by cell divisions in a plane parallel to the substratum. Basal layer at times with rhizoids. Most cells of upper layer of basal portion each with an erect branched or unbranched filament. The unilocular sporangia clavate, sessile or pedicellate, borne erect on basal layer. The plurilocular sporangia pluriseriate, stipitate on basal layer or borne terminally on short lateral branches of the erect filaments.

Gametophytes unknown.

STRUCTURE AND REPRODUCTION. Kylin, 1937, pp. 8–9; fig. 2. Sauvageau, 1897, pp. 248–262; figs. 18–22. Setchell and Gardner, 1922*B*.

Hecatonema variabile Setchell and Gardner

*Setchell and Gardner, 1922*B*, p. 377; pl. 41, figs. 1–12. *Setchell and Gardner, 1925, p. 490.

Myrionema hecatonematoides *Setchell and Gardner, 1922, p. 343; pl. 34, fig. 11. *Setchell and Gardner, 1925, p. 467; pl. 55, fig. 11.

Thalli (sporophytes) forming circular cushions 4–7 mm. in diameter. The basal portion partly or in large part distromatic, with numerous short peg-like rhizoids 1–3 cells long. The erect filaments 240–500 μ tall, unbranched, cylindrical, somewhat narrower at the base. Unilocular sporangia clavate, sessile or pedicellate, borne on basal layer, 50–65 μ long, 20–24 μ broad. Plurilocular sporangia cylindrical to fusiform, sessile or pedicellate, borne erect on the basal layer (occasionally terminally on erect filaments), 45–120 μ long, 7–12 μ broad.

LOCAL DISTRIBUTION. On pneumatocysts of *Nereocystis Luetkeana*. Pacific Grove, Carmel Bay.

TYPE LOCALITY. Carmel Bay.

PACIFIC COAST DISTRIBUTION. As above.

Since European phycologists have shown that the major portion of the basal layer may be distromatic, *Myrionema hecatonematoides* should be referred to *Hecatonema*. There are no morphological features distinguishing it from *H. variabile*.

Family CORYNOPHLOEACEAE

Sporophytes of moderate size, crustose to globose, obscurely monoaxial and with cell division intercalary. The thallus of obvious filamentous construction and without an evident basal layer; the outermost branches modified to form assimilating filaments. With unilocular sporangia only, or with both unilocular and plurilocular sporangia. The unilocular sporangia borne near base of assimilating filaments. The plurilocular sporangia uniseriate and replacing assimilating filaments.

Gametophytes, so far as known, microscopic and filamentous. The gametangia plurilocular and uniseriate. Gametic union presumably isogamous.

KEY TO THE GENERA IN THE LOCAL FLORA

1. Unilocular sporangia ovoid to ellipsoid............*Leathesia* (p. 114)
1. Unilocular sporangia reniform..............*Petrospongium* (p. 115)

Leathesia Gray, 1821

Sporophytes macroscopic; at first subspherical and solid, later becoming irregularly convoluted and hollow. Growth trichothallic and cell division intercalary. Interior of thallus with colorless di- or trichotomously, radiately branched, filaments with progressively smaller cells upward. Outermost portion of thallus with clavate to moniliform 3- to 16-celled assimilating filaments arranged in a palisade-like manner. Thallus with fascicles of long colorless multicellular hairs projecting beyond the surface. With both unilocular and plurilocular sporangia. Unilocular sporangia isolated from one another and replacing certain of the assimilating filaments. Plurilocular sporangia uniseriate, replacing assimilating filaments, usually densely aggregated over entire surface of thallus.

Gametophytes microscopic, filamentous, with uniseriate plurilocular gametangia.

STRUCTURE AND REPRODUCTION. Damman, 1930, p. 11, fig. 3. Kylin, 1933, pp. 64–66; fig. 30. G. M. Smith, 1938, pp. 249–250; figs. 137–138.

KEY TO THE SPECIES IN THE LOCAL FLORA

1. Thalli less than 0.5 cm. in diameter..........................*L. nana*
1. Thalli up to 10 cm. in diameter.........................*L. difformis*

Leathesia difformis (Linnaeus) Areschoug   Pl. 15, fig. 2

Areschoug, 1844, p. 154 (reprint). Setchell and Gardner, 1925, p. 511; pl. 40, fig. 52; pl. 43, figs. 65–66. *Phyc. Bor.-Amer. No. 829.
Tremella difformis Linnaeus, 1755, p. 429.
Leathesia tuberiformis, S. F. Gray, 1821, p. 301. *Anderson, 1891, p. 219. *Howe, 1893, p. 67.
Leathesia amplissima *Setchell and Gardner, 1924, p. 3. *Setchell and Gardner, 1925, p. 513; pl. 43, fig. 64.

Thalli (sporophytes), as found on the Monterey Peninsula, up to 12 cm. in diameter; yellowish-brown in color. Mature thalli subspherical, hemispherical, or broadly expanded; with a much-convoluted surface and hollow at the center. Assimilating filaments 3–6 cells long, clavate, with or without the terminal cell globose. Unilocular sporangia rarely present on thalli from the Monterey Peninsula, ovoid, 40–50 μ long, 18–24 μ broad. Plurilocular sporangia of frequent occurrence, with 7–10 cells; 30–45 μ long, 4–6 μ broad. Thalli annual, appearing late in the winter and disappearing during October.

LOCAL DISTRIBUTION. Growing on rocks between the 2.5-foot and mean low-tide level. Frequently epiphytic on other algae. Abundant everywhere locally.

TYPE LOCALITY. Sweden.

PACIFIC COAST DISTRIBUTION. Alaska (Bering Sea) to southern California (San Pedro).

L. amplissima does not seem sufficiently constant in its anatomical characters to warrant recognition as distinct from *L. difformis*.

Leathesia nana Setchell and Gardner   Pl. 15, fig. 1

*Setchell and Gardner, 1924, p. 3. *Setchell and Gardner, 1925, p. 511; pl. 43, fig. 67.

Thalli (sporophytes), as found on the Monterey Peninsula, up to 0.5 cm. in diameter; yellowish-brown to dark brown. Mature thalli subspherical, surface not convoluted, not hollow at the center. Assimilating filaments 3–5 cells long, clavate, the terminal cell globose. Unilocular sporangia unknown. Plurilocular sporangia with 4–6 cells, 20–30 µ long, 3.5–4.5 µ broad. Thalli annual, appearing during the spring and disappearing during October.

LOCAL DISTRIBUTION. Epiphytic on the upper portion of leaves of *Phyllospadix*. Abundant at Pebble Beach. Also known from Monterey, Mussel Point; Point Pinos; Middle Reef of Moss Beach.

TYPE LOCALITY. Monterey, California.

PACIFIC COAST DISTRIBUTION. As above.

Continuous observation throughout summer and early fall shows that even when the thalli are not crowded they do not become more than 5 mm. in diameter.

Petrospongium Nägeli, 1858

Sporophytes macroscopic, hemispherical to crustose, with or without a convoluted surface. Growth trichothallic and cell division intercalary. Interior of thallus with loosely compacted, di- or trichotomously branched, colorless filaments with progressively smaller cells upward. The colorless filaments producing multicellular rhizoids which grow horizontally through the thallus. Outermost portion of thallus with simple or branched assimilating filaments. Chromatophores disc-shaped, several in a cell, largely restricted to assimilating filaments. With unilocular sporangia only. The sporangia isolated from one another, borne at base or just below the assimilating filaments, terminal on pedicels which are usually one-celled. The sporangia at first ellipsoid, later becoming reniform by enlargement of basal portion.

Gametophytes unknown.

STRUCTURE AND REPRODUCTION. Hauck, 1885, pp. 357–358; fig. 151.

Petrospongium rugosum (Okamura) Setchell and Gardner
Pl. 16, figs. 3–4

Setchell and Gardner, 1924, p. 12. Setchell and Gardner, 1925, p. 509; pl. 39, figs. 42–43.

Cylindrocarpus rugosa Okamura, 1907, p. 20; pl. 5, figs. 1–6.

Petrospongium Berkeleyi Setchell [not of Nägeli]. Setchell in Phyc. Bor.-Amer. No. 232.

Thalli (sporophytes), as found on the Monterey Peninsula, up to 8 cm. in diameter; usually chestnut brown in color. The thallus crustose, at first circular, later becoming irregularly lobed. Upper surface of thallus irregularly ridged and convoluted. Assimilating filaments usually unbranched, 8–11 μ broad, with 8–12 cells. Thallus with solitary colorless multicellular hairs intermingled with and projecting beyond the assimilating filaments. Unilocular sporangia reniform when mature, with one-celled pedicels, 75–90 μ long, 16–22 μ broad. Thalli annual, appearing early in the summer and disappearing during late winter.

LOCAL DISTRIBUTION. Growing on rocks between the 3.5- and 2.0-foot tide levels. Mussel Point; Asilomar Point; Middle Reef of Moss Beach; Point Joe; Fanshell Beach; Cypress Point; Pebble Beach; Mission Point.

TYPE LOCALITY. Japan.

PACIFIC COAST DISTRIBUTION. Central California (Moss Beach, San Mateo County) to southern California (San Diego).

The figures of Setchell and Gardner show sessile unilocular sporangia attached laterally below the assimilating filaments. As found on the Monterey Peninsula the sporangia have one-celled pedicels. These sporangia seem to be born laterally, but they are really borne terminally as in *P. Berkeleyi* (Grev.) Naeg. (Hauck, 1885, p. 357; fig. 151).

Family CHORDARIACEAE

Sporophytes of moderate size, erect, usually branched; monoaxial or multiaxial and with cell division intercalary. The entire thallus, or only the upper portion, clothed with long, simple or branched, assimilating filaments. With unilocular sporangia only, or with both unilocular and plurilocular sporangia. The unilocular sporangia borne at base of assimilating filaments and remote from one another. The plurilocular sporangia formed by transformation of outer ends of assimilating filaments, usually uniseriate.

Gametophytes, so far as known, microscopic and filamentous. The gametangia plurilocular and uniseriate. Gametic union isogamous.

With one genus, *Haplogloia,* in the local flora.

Haplogloia Levring, 1939

Sporophytes macroscopic, annual. The thalli cylindrical, more or less profusely branched and with the branches radial to a percurrent central axis. Branches and axis of a soft gelatinous texture and clothed with long unbranched multicellular hairs. Basal portion of axis and branches at times without hairs. Growth of axis and branches trichothallic and by intercalary cell division in a single axial filament. The axial filament with numerous lateral filaments and the basal cells of these producing descending rhizoidal filaments that corticate the axial filament. The corticating tissue eventually becoming sharply differentiated into cortex and medulla. The medulla composed of compacted vertical filaments with long cylindrical cells; the cortex composed of unbranched filaments standing perpendicular to the medulla. Cortical filaments of two kinds; one short, 5- to 9-celled, and with the upper cells moniliform; the other long, many cells in length, and with cylindrical cells. With unilocular sporangia only. The sporangia broadly obpyriform, remote from one another, uniformly distributed in cortical tissue, and each replacing a cortical filament.

Gametophytes unknown.

STRUCTURE AND REPRODUCTION. Kuckuck, 1929, p. 63; figs. 83–84 (as *Mesogloia)*. Levring, 1929. Setchell and Gardner, 1925, pp. 556–557; pl. 47, figs. 8–10; pl. 48, figs. 12–14; pl. 49, fig. 16; pl. 76 (as *Myriogloia*).

Haplogloia Andersonii (Farlow) Levring   Pl. 16, figs. 1–2

Levring, 1939, p. 50; fig. 5. Kylin, 1940, p. 21; figs. 13–14.
Mesogloia Andersonii Farlow, 1876, p. 715 (name only). Farlow, 1889, p. 9; pl. 87, fig. 2. *Anderson, 1891, p. 220.
Myriogloia Andersonii (Farlow) Kuckuck in Oltmanns, 1922, p. 22; fig. 312. Setchell and Gardner, 1925, p. 556; pl. 47, figs. 8–10; pl. 48, figs. 12–14; pl. 49, fig. 17; pl. 76.

Thalli (sporophytes), as found on the Monterey Peninsula, up to 25–40 cm. tall; light tan to dark brown in color. Frequently with several erect axes from a common base. Usually with all but the basal portion of axis and branches densely clothed with long hairs. The branches (including hairs) 1–3 mm. in diameter, portion without hairs 0.5–1 mm. in diameter. Older portions of branches hollow. The short cortical filaments broadening upward and frequently with the tip recurved. Unilocular sporangia of Monterey Peninsula thalli 24–28 μ long, 10–16 μ broad.

LOCAL DISTRIBUTION. Growing between the 0.5- and −1.5-foot tide levels on rocks in tide pools. Usually appearing late in the winter and disappearing early in June. Abundant on the Middle Reef of Moss Beach. Also collected at Point Pinos; Asilomar Point; Pescadero Point; Pescadero Rocks.

TYPE LOCALITY. Santa Cruz, California.

PACIFIC COAST DISTRIBUTION. Alaska (Sitka) to southern California (San Diego).

Order DESMARESTIALES

Heterogeneratae with a macroscopic sporophyte and a microscopic gametophyte. The sporophyte erect, pinnately branched, and with the axis and branches either cylindrical or markedly compressed. Growth, at least at first, trichothallic and initiated by a single filament. The axis and branches with deciduous or persistent branched filaments, the filaments either restricted to lateral margins or in transverse whorls.

Sporophytes with unilocular sporangia only; the sporangia isolated from one another or in small sori.

Gametophytes filamentous and with the branches free from one another. Heterothallic and oögamous. Male gametophytes with the antheridia each producing a single biflagellate antherozoid. The female gametophytes with the oögonium producing a single egg, the egg being fertilized after partially emerging from oögonial wall.

Family DESMARESTIACEAE

All Desmarestiales are placed in a single family, the Desmarestiaceae, whose characters are the same as those of the order.

With one genus, *Desmarestia,* in the local flora.

Desmarestia Lamouroux, 1813

Sporophytes macroscopic, with a single erect shoot from a discoid holdfast. The shoot pinnately branched and the branching opposite or alternate. The axis and branches slightly to markedly compressed. Growth at apex of axis and branches trichothallic and initiated by an intercalary meristematic region of a single filament. Mature portions of axis and branches solidly parenchymatous, with progressively smaller cells toward the surface and with a prominent axial uniseriate row of cells. Axis and branches fringed with filaments in upper portion but the filaments soon deciduous. Sporophytes with unilocular sporangia only. The sporangia occasionally developing from cells of filaments at tips of branches, regularly developing from superficial cells in the mature portion; in the latter case the sporangia embedded and either isolated from one another or in small sori.

Gametophytes microscopic, filamentous, heterothallic. Male gametophyte an irregularly branched filament with clusters of antheridia at tips of branches. Antheridia one-celled and each producing a single biflagellate antherozoid. Female gametophytes also branched, but with fewer and larger cells. Oögonia terminal or intercalary, one-celled, erect, cylindrical and much longer than vegetative cells. The egg extruded from, but remaining attached to, apex of oögonium. Fertilization effected while egg is perched on apex of oögonium and the young sporophyte beginning to develop there.

Structure and Reproduction. Abe, 1938. Johnson, 1891, pp. 142–143; pl. 8, figs. 12–14. Schreiber, 1932. G. M. Smith, 1938, pp. 252–256; figs. 141–142.

Key to the Species in the Local Flora

1. Branches narrow (less than 3 mm. broad).........................2
1. Branches relatively broad (over 5 mm. broad)....................4
  2. Branching opposite...3
  2. Branching alternate.................................*D. latifrons*
3. Branches hair-like, less than 0.5 mm. broad.................*D. viridis*
3. Branches flattened, about 2 mm. broad....................*D. linearis*
  4. Branches 0.5–2.0 cm. broad.........................*D. herbacea*
  4. Branches 2–10 cm. broad.............................*D. munda*

Desmarestia viridis (Müller) Lamouroux   Pl. 18, fig. 3

Lamouroux, 1813, p. 45. Taylor, 1937, p. 160; pl. 13, fig. 4. Phyc. Bor.-Amer. No. 531.
  Fucus viridis Müller, 1782*A*, p. 5; pl. 886.

Thalli (sporophytes), as found on the Monterey Peninsula, up to 45 cm. tall; light brown in color. The axis percurrent, subcylindrical, up to 1 mm. in diameter at base, oppositely branched, with an interval of 2–10 mm. between successive pairs of primary branches. The branches cylindrical, up to 25 cm. long, rebranched into 2–3 orders and with successive orders smaller in diameter.

LOCAL DISTRIBUTION. Cast ashore at south end of Carmel Beach.
TYPE LOCALITY. Denmark.
PACIFIC COAST DISTRIBUTION. Known only from Carmel Beach.

There is no evident difference between an entity found locally and the well-known *D. viridis* of the Atlantic Coast. Even so, the local alga is referred to *D. viridis* with reservations. Hundreds of thalli were found cast ashore on Carmel Beach late in June 1939. No specimens were found after July 1 of that year and, although especially sought for, the alga has not been found in succeeding years.

Desmarestia linearis Gardner mss.　Pl. 18, fig. 2

Thalli (sporophytes) up to 60 cm. tall; light brown in color. The axis percurrent, linear, 2–3 mm. broad, with opposite pairs of small aculei along the margins. Branching of axis relatively sparse, opposite, with an interval of 5–25 mm. between successive pairs of branches. Primary branches flattened, 2–3 mm. broad; the majority of them simple but certain of them rebranched into one or two orders and becoming long. Axis and branches thin, without an evident midrib. Filaments along margins of axis and branches soon deciduous.

LOCAL DISTRIBUTION. Dredged from a depth of 60 feet off Monterey. Also found cast ashore near Asilomar Point.
TYPE LOCALITY. Asilomar Point.
PACIFIC COAST DISTRIBUTION. As above.

Superficially resembling *D. herbacea* but more sparsely branched, with much thinner axis and branches, and without a midrib.

Desmarestia latifrons (Ruprecht) Kützing　Pl. 18, fig. 1

Kützing, 1859, p. 40; pl. 95. *Anderson, 1891, p. 219. Setchell and Gardner, 1925, p. 563; pl. 90. *Phyc. Bor.-Amer. No. 279.
Spinularia latifrons Ruprecht, 1851, p. 375.

Thalli (sporophytes), as found on the Monterey Peninsula, up to 1 m. tall; dark brown in color. The axis linear, becoming obscure in upper portion of thallus, flattened, 1.5–3 mm. broad. Branching of axis profuse, alternate, with an interval of 10–30 mm. between successive branches. Primary branches rebranched into 2–4 orders, flattened, at times becoming longer than the axis. Axis and major branches with a small percurrent midrib. Filaments along margins of axis and branches at times not deciduous until late in development of thallus.

LOCAL DISTRIBUTION. Growing on rocks exposed to strong surf and between mean low-tide and −1.5-foot tide levels. Point Pinos; Cypress Point; Mission Point; mouth of Carmel River. Frequently cast ashore in abundance at Pebble Beach and Carmel Beach.

TYPE LOCALITY. Fort Ross, California.

PACIFIC COAST DISTRIBUTION. Oregon (Coos Bay) to central California (Point Sur).

Desmarestia herbacea (Turner) Lamouroux   Pl. 17, fig. 2

Lamouroux, 1813, p. 45. *Setchell and Gardner, 1925, p. 566; pl. 88.
Fucus herbaceus Turner, 1808, p. 77; pl. 99.
Desmarestia ligulata Farlow [not of Lamouroux]. *Farlow, 1876, p. 710.
*Anderson, 1891, p. 219. *Howe, 1893, p. 67.
Desmarestia ligulata var. *herbacea* (Turner) J. G. Agardh, 1848, p. 169. Phyc. Bor.-Amer. No. LXXIX-*B*.

Thalli (sporophytes), as found on the Monterey Peninsula, up to 2 m. tall; light brown in color. The axis percurrent, flattened, linear, 5–10 mm. broad. Branching of axis profuse, opposite, with an interval of 5–10 mm. between successive pairs of branches. Axis and branches with a conspicuous, thick, percurrent midrib. Many of the primary branches nearly equaling the axis in length and rebranched into 2–3 orders. Branches of all orders flattened, stipitate at base and acute at apex. Filaments along margins of axis and branches soon deciduous.

LOCAL DISTRIBUTION. Growing on rocks between the 0.5- and −1.5-foot tide levels. Mussel Point; Point Aulon; Point Pinos; Asilomar Point; Middle Reef of Moss Beach; Point Joe; Fanshell Beach; Cypress Point; Pescadero Point; Mission Point. Also dredged from a depth of 30–35 feet a quarter-mile from the Municipal Wharf, Monterey.

TYPE LOCALITY. "Northwest coast of America."

PACIFIC COAST DISTRIBUTION. Alaska (Kodiak Island) to southern California (La Jolla).

Desmarestia munda Setchell and Gardner   Pl. 17, fig. 1

Setchell and Gardner, 1924, p. 7. Setchell and Gardner, 1925, p. 567; pl. 89.
Desmarestia ligulata forma *herbacea* Gardner [not of (Turner) J. G. Agardh]. Gardner in Phyc. Bor.-Amer. No. LXXIX-*A*.

Thalli (sporophytes), as found on the Monterey Peninsula, up to 4 m. tall; yellowish-brown to dark brown in color. The axis percurrent, ribbon-like, 2–10 cm. broad, with opposite pairs of aculei along the margins. Branching of axis relatively sparse, opposite, with an interval of 1–6 cm. between successive pairs of branches. Primary branches flattened, 2–8 cm. broad, rebranched into one or two orders; branches near base of thallus nearly equaling axis in length. Branches of all orders stipitate at base and with acute to rounded tips. Filaments along margins of axis and branches soon deciduous.

LOCAL DISTRIBUTION. Growing on rocks between the mean low-tide and −1.5-foot tide levels. Middle Reef of Moss Beach; Pebble Beach. Also dredged from a depth of 30–35 feet a quarter-mile from Municipal Wharf, Monterey. Frequently cast ashore in abundance at Pebble Beach.

TYPE LOCALITY. Not stated.

PACIFIC COAST DISTRIBUTION. Puget Sound to southern California (San Pedro).

Subclass POLYSTICHINEAE

Sporophytes macroscopic, of definite shape, and frequently with a differentiation of tissues. Parenchymatous throughout and with both vertical and transverse division of intercalary cells. Growth either occurring throughout a thallus, or restricted to an intercalary meristem, or initiated by an apical cell. Usually with the sporangia grouped in sori; producing unilocular sporangia only, plurilocular sporangia only, or both unilocular and plurilocular sporangia.

Gametophytes microscopic, filamentous, branched and with branches free from one another. Gametic union isogamous, anisogamous, or oögamous.

KEY TO THE ORDERS IN THE LOCAL FLORA

1. Growth not restricted to an intercalary meristem. .*Punctariales* (p. 122)
1. Growth restricted to an intercalary meristem. . . .*Laminariales* (p. 133)

Order PUNCTARIALES

With a macroscopic sporophyte and a microscopic gametophyte. The sporophytes rarely over 20 cm. tall, variously shaped, branched or unbranched. Always parenchymatous throughout and with cell division intercalary and not definitely localized in a meristem. With unilocular sporangia only, plurilocular sporangia only, or with both unilocular and plurilocular sporangia. The sporangia either remote from one another, grouped in small sori, or completely covering surface of thallus.

Gametophytes, so far as definitely known, microscopic and filamentous. The gametangia plurilocular and usually uniseriate. Gametic union isogamous or anisogamous.

Key to the Families in the Local Flora

1. Thalli of various shapes, usually unbranched, not terminating in a uniseriate filament.....................*Encoeliaceae* (p. 123)
1. Thalli cylindrical, branched, with branch tips terminating in a uniseriate filament.....................*Striariaceae* (p. 132)

Family Encoeliaceae

Sporophytes foliose, saccate, or cylindrical; usually unbranched. Thalli parenchymatous throughout and with cell division intercalary. With unilocular sporangia only, with plurilocular sporangia only, or with both unilocular and plurilocular sporangia.

Gametophytes, so far as definitely known, microscopic, filamentous, and with plurilocular gametangia.

Key to the Genera in the Local Flora

1. Sporophytes with solid blades...................................... 2
1. Sporophytes hollow and saccate................................. 4
  2. Internal cells of blade only slightly larger than surface cells ....*Punctaria* (p. 123)
  2. Internal cells of blade much larger than surface cells............. 3
3. Reproductive organs grouped in sori.............*Halorhipis* (p. 125)
3. Reproductive organs entirely covering surface of blade...*Ilea* (p. 126)
  4. Thalli globose... 5
  4. Thalli not globose...................................... 6
5. Reproductive organs in small sori..............*Soranthera* (p. 127)
5. Reproductive organs entirely covering surface of blade ....*Colpomenia* (p. 127)
  6. Tubular or a flattened tube, length at least 25 times the breadth ....*Scytosiphon* (p. 128)
  6. Flattened and blade-like, length not over 10 times the breadth ....*Coilodesme* (p. 131)

Punctaria Greville, 1830

Sporophytes macroscopic, annual. The thallus with a discoid base and one or more erect blades. The blades linear to broadly expanded, with the base tapering to a short slender stipe. Surface of blade with tufts of multicellular hairs. The blades 3–7 cells in thickness in central portion; with all cells cubical and with the interior cells only slightly larger than the superficial cells. Unilocular sporangia remote from one another, subcubical, immersed at surface of thallus, formed by metamorphosis of superficial thallus cells. Plurilocular sporangia developed simultaneously with or before development of unilocular sporangia. The plurilocular sporangia usually grouped in minute sori without paraphyses, pluriseriate, subcubical, frequently with the apex projecting beyond the thallus surface.

Gametophytes unknown.

STRUCTURE AND REPRODUCTION. Sauvageau, 1929, pp. 334–349; figs. 11–14.

KEY TO THE SPECIES IN THE LOCAL FLORA

1. Blades 1.5–2.5 cm. tall.................................*P. hesperia*
1. Blades 8–20 cm. tall.................................*P. occidentalis*

Punctaria occidentalis Setchell and Gardner   Pl. 19, fig. 3

*Setchell and Gardner, 1924, p. 4. *Setchell and Gardner, 1925, p. 520; pl. 35, fig. 6; pl. 80, fig. *B*.
Homeostroma latifolium Saunders [not of (Greville) J. G. Agardh]. *Saunders, 1898, p. 159; pl. 30, figs. 4–5.
Punctaria latifolia Setchell [not of Greville]. *Setchell in Phyc. Bor.-Amer. No. 873.

Thalli (sporophytes) up to 20 cm. tall; light brown in color. The blades up to 12 cm. broad, linear-lanceolate, oblanceolate, or broadly elliptical; with ruffled margins and with a short stipe. The blades 2–7 cells in thickness and with interior cells somewhat larger than superficial cells. The unilocular sporangia cubical to subspherical, bulging slightly above surface of blade, 30–40 (–70) μ in diameter. The plurilocular sporangia pluriseriate, cylindrical to conical, with the upper half projecting beyond surface of blade.

LOCAL DISTRIBUTION. On leaves of *Zostera* cast ashore at Monterey.
TYPE LOCALITY. Monterey, California.
PACIFIC COAST DISTRIBUTION. As above.

Punctaria hesperia Setchell and Gardner   Pl. 19, fig. 4

*Setchell and Gardner, 1924, p. 3. *Setchell and Gardner, 1925, p. 517; pl. 37, fig. 30; pl. 49, fig. 18.

Thalli (sporophytes), as found on the Monterey Peninsula, 1.5–2.5 cm. tall; light brown in color. With one to several blades; the blades lanceolate and with a very short stipe. The blades 4–6 cells in thickness and with interior cells somewhat larger than superficial cells. Unilocular sporangia numerous and intermingled with plurilocular sporangia. Plurilocular sporangia pluriseriate, conical, and with the upper half projecting beyond surface of blade, at times in small groups close to one another.

LOCAL DISTRIBUTION. Epiphytic on leaves of *Phyllospadix*. Point Pinos; Middle Reef of Moss Beach.

TYPE LOCALITY. Point Pinos, Pacific Grove, California.

PACIFIC COAST DISTRIBUTION. Known only from Victoria, British Columbia; the Monterey Peninsula; and San Pedro, California.

Halorhipis Saunders, 1898

Sporophytes macroscopic, annual. The thallus with a small discoid holdfast and a ligulate blade. Lowermost portion of blade cylindrical and stipe-like. Surface of blade with small tufts of multicellular hairs. Interior of blade composed of large cylindrical cells extending longitudinally through blade; cells at surface of blade much smaller and cubical. With unilocular sporangia only; the sporangia projecting above surface of blade; grouped in small sori. The sori usually with a tuft of multicellular hairs at center.

Gametophytes unknown.

STRUCTURE AND REPRODUCTION. Setchell and Gardner, 1925, pp. 523–525; pl. 35, fig. 8. Saunders, 1898, pp. 160–161; pl. 38.

Halorhipis Winstonii (Anderson) Saunders Pl. 20, figs. 2–3

*Saunders, 1898, p. 161; pl. 38. *Setchell and Gardner, 1925, p. 524; pl. 35, fig. 8. *Phyc. Bor.-Amer. No. 532.

Punctaria Winstonii *Anderson, 1894, p. 358.

Thalli (sporophytes) up to 35 cm. tall; of a light olive-tan color. The blades lanceolate to spatulate, up to 5 cm. broad; several blades usually arising from a common holdfast. The sori very numerous, minute (with a maximum diameter of 0.3 mm.), linear to irregular in outline. The unilocular sporangia ellipsoid to obpyriform, 30–45 µ long, 20–30 µ broad.

LOCAL DISTRIBUTION. Usually epiphytic on *Egregia laevigata;* occasionally growing on rocks. The thalli appearing late in spring and disappearing before the middle of September. Abundant every year at Pebble Beach.

TYPE LOCALITY. Pebble Beach.

PACIFIC COAST DISTRIBUTION. As above.

All published accounts of this alga state that it is epiphytic on *Egregia Menziesii. H. Winstonii* has been collected repeatedly for the past fifteen summers and in every case the host was *E. laevigata*.

Ilea Fries, 1835

Sporophytes (?) macroscopic, annual. The thallus with a small discoid holdfast and one or more erect blades. The blades linear to broadly lanceolate and with or without a stipe-like basal portion. Margins of blades at times somewhat undulate. Surface of blade with small tufts of multicellular hairs. Interior of blade composed of very large rounded cells; cells at surface of blade very much smaller and cubical. Unilocular sporangia unknown. Plurilocular reproductive organs[2] at first in localized areas, later covering entire surface of blade.

STRUCTURE AND REPRODUCTION. Kuckuck, 1912A, pp. 161–163. Kylin, 1933, pp. 44–47; fig. 17. Sauvageau, 1929, pp. 516–533; figs. 8–10. Yendo, 1919. (All as *Phyllitis*.)

Ilea Fascia (Müller) Fries   Pl. 20, fig. 4

Fries, 1835, p. 321. Setchell and Gardner, 1925, p. 535; pl. 44, figs. 68–71, 73. *Fucus Fascia* Müller, 1782, p. 7; pl. 768.
Phyllitis Fascia (Müller) Kützing, 1843, p. 342; pl. 24, fig. 3. *Anderson, 1891, p. 219. *Saunders, 1898, p. 161; pl. 30, figs. 1–3. Phyc. Bor.-Amer. No. 1131.

Thalli, as found on the Monterey Peninsula, up to 35 cm. tall; greenish-brown to dark brown in color. The blades up to 3 cm. broad, cuneate at base, above this linear to linear-lanceolate and with a somewhat pointed apex. Proportions between length and breadth of blades in a single tuft usually varying greatly. Margins of blades undulate.

LOCAL DISTRIBUTION. Growing on rocks; usually found between the 4.0- and 1.5-foot tide levels but occasionally at lower levels. Generally appearing during autumn and disappearing the following summer. Mussel Point; Asilomar Point; Middle Reef of Moss Beach; Fanshell Beach; Pebble Beach; north and south ends of Carmel Beach.

TYPE LOCALITY. Denmark.

PACIFIC COAST DISTRIBUTION. Alaska (Uyak Bay) to central California (Carmel Bay).

The variety *zosterifolia* (Reinke) Setchell and Gardner (*Setchell and Gardner, 1924, p. 13. *Setchell and Gardner, 1925, p. 537), with narrowly linear blades 10–15 cm. long and 0.5–2.0 mm. broad, has been recorded from Pebble Beach. This is the only record of its occurrence along the Pacific Coast of North America.

---

[2] Those who have investigated the reproduction of *Ilea* disagree as to whether the plurilocular reproductive organs are sporangia or gametangia.

Soranthera Postels and Ruprecht, 1840

Sporophytes macroscopic, annual. At first globose and solid; later becoming hollow and either subspherical, ellipsoid, or obpyriform. Always epiphytic and attached to host by a discoid holdfast that may seem haustorium-like because of upgrowth of adjacent host tissue. Saccate portion of thallus 5–6 cells in thickness and with superficial cells much smaller than the others. With unilocular sporangia only. The sporangia grouped in sori evenly spaced over entire surface of thallus. Each sorus with a tuft of multicellular hairs at center and with multicellular paraphyses about twice as tall as the sporangia.

Gametophytes microscopic, filamentous, irregularly branched, and with pluriseriate plurilocular gametangia at tips of certain branches. Gametic union anisogamous.

STRUCTURE AND REPRODUCTION. Angst, 1926. Angst, 1927. G. M. Smith, 1938, pp. 256–257; fig. 143.

Soranthera ulvoidea Postels and Ruprecht   Pl. 20, fig. 5

Postels and Ruprecht, 1840, p. 19. *Saunders, 1898, p. 165; pl. 29, figs. 4–5. *Setchell and Gardner, 1925, p. 525. *Phyc. Bor.-Amer. No. 417.
Soranthera ulvoidea forma *typica* Setchell and Gardner, 1903, p. 244. *Setchell and Gardner, 1925, p. 526; pl. 39, figs. 40–41; pl. 83, fig. *B*.

Thalli (sporophytes), as found on the Monterey Peninsula, usually 3–5 cm. tall and 2–4 cm. broad; olive-brown in color. Globose or ovoid when mature. The sori about 1 mm. in diameter, evenly spaced over entire thallus, much darker than vegetative areas.

LOCAL DISTRIBUTION. Epiphytic on *Rhodomela larix*. Appearing in April and disappearing in September. Asilomar Point; Middle Reef of Moss Beach.
TYPE LOCALITY. Sitka, Alaska.
PACIFIC COAST DISTRIBUTION. Alaska (Unalaska) to central California (Monterey Peninsula).

Colpomenia Derbès and Solier, 1856

Sporophytes (?) macroscopic, probably annual. Thallus more or less globose; solid when very young, later becoming a hollow water-filled sac. Mature thalli usually somewhat flattened and with more or less angular indentations. Surface of thallus with scattered tufts of multicellular hairs. Saccate portion several cells in thickness, without intercellular spaces and with progressively smaller cells to thallus surface. Unilocular sporangia unknown. Plurilocular reproductive organs[3] at first in sori developing around tufts of multicellular hairs, later spreading over entire surface of thallus. Swarmers liberated from plurilocular organs during autumn behaving as zoospores; those liberated during the spring functioning as anisogametes.

STRUCTURE AND REPRODUCTION. Kuneida and Suto, 1938. Saunders, 1898, pp. 163–164; pl. 32. Sauvageau, 1927.

Colpomenia sinuosa (Roth) Derbès and Solier Pl. 20, fig. 1

Derbès and Solier, 1856, p. 11; pl. 22, figs. 18–20. *Saunders, 1898, p. 164; pl. 32, figs. 7–8. Setchell and Gardner, 1925, p. 539; pl. 45, figs. 82–86. *Phyc. Bor.-Amer. No. 278.

Ulva sinuosa Roth, 1806, p. 327; pl. 12, fig. *B*.

Thalli, as found on the Monterey Peninsula, usually 4–6 cm. in diameter but occasionally up to 10 cm.; olive-brown to dark brown in color. Sessile and attached by a broad basal disc. Soon becoming hollow and filled with water. Globose when young, later becoming somewhat compressed and with angular indentations. The saccate portion membranous and crisp in texture. Plurilocular reproductive organs (sporangia ?) usually two cells broad.

LOCAL DISTRIBUTION. Usually epiphytic on *Gastroclonium Coulteri* but also epiphytic on various other algae growing between the 0.5- and −1.0-foot tide levels. Abundant at Pebble Beach. Rather scarce at Mussel Point; Point Pinos; Point Joe; Fanshell Beach. Also dredged from a depth of 35–40 feet near Mussel Point.

TYPE LOCALITY. Atlantic Ocean near "Gades."

PACIFIC COAST DISTRIBUTION. Alaska (Yakutat Bay) to southern California (San Pedro).

Scytosiphon C. A. Agardh, 1811

Sporophytes (?) erect and usually in gregarious clusters from a common disc-shaped base. The erect shoots tubular, unbranched, at first solid but soon becoming hollow. Hollow shoots either cylindrical and with or without constrictions at intervals or compressed and without constrictions. Portion external to central hol-

---

[3] It is uncertain whether the saccate thallus is a sporophyte or a gametophyte. It has generally been considered a sporophyte, even though it has never been found with unilocular sporangia. The recent description (Kuneida and Suto, 1938) of an anisogamous fusion of swarmers from the plurilocular organs suggests that it may be a gametophyte. However, until the sporophytic or gametophytic nature of the thallus is settled beyond all doubt it is better to follow the conventional practice of placing *Colpomenia* among the Encoeliaceae.

low space several cells in thickness, without intercellular spaces, and with progressively smaller cells to thallus surface. Surface of thallus with or without tufts of multicellular hairs. Unilocular sporangia unknown. Plurilocular reproductive organs usually uniseriate, several cells in height; intermingled with erect cylindrical unicellular paraphyses. The fertile area covering entire surface of thallus or broken up into several sori. Nature of swarmers liberated from the plurilocular organs uncertain.[4]

STRUCTURE AND REPRODUCTION. Abe, 1935, pp. 333–334; text figs. 4–5; pl. 10, fig. 2. Damman, 1930, pp. 12–13; text figs. 4–5; plate figs. 2–6. Kuckuck, 1912, pp. 158–161; pl. 8, fig. 3. Kylin, 1933, pp. 47–49; fig. 18.

KEY TO THE SPECIES IN THE LOCAL FLORA

1. Thallus (except for constrictions) the same breadth
   throughout .... *S. Lomentaria*
1. Thallus inflated midway between base and apex............ *S. bullosus*

Scytosiphon Lomentaria (Lyngbye) J. G. Agardh Pl. 19, fig. 1

J. G. Agardh, 1848, p. 126. *Anderson, 1891, p. 219. *Saunders, 1898, p. 163; pl. 31, figs. 8–10. Setchell and Gardner, 1925, p. 531; pl. 44, figs. 72, 74. *Phyc. Bor.-Amer. No. 323.

Chorda Lomentaria Lyngbye, 1819, p. 74; pl. 18, fig. E.

Scytosiphon Lomentaria forma *typica* Rosenvinge, 1893, p. 863. Setchell and Gardner, 1925, p. 533; pl. 39, fig. 45; pl. 44, fig. 75.

Scytosiphon Lomentaria forma *cylindricus major* Setchell and Gardner, 1925, p. 533.

Thalli, as found on the Monterey Peninsula, with erect shoots usually 20–30 cm. tall but occasionally up to 50 cm.; 2–6 cm. in diameter; olive-tan to dark brown in color. Typically cylindrical and with constrictions at intervals but at times without constrictions. Both constricted and unconstricted shoots often compressed and twisted in close spirals for a considerable part of their length. The plurilocular organs 10–15 cells in length.

LOCAL DISTRIBUTION. Growing on rocks between the 2.5- and −1.5-foot tide levels. Abundant at Arch Rock; Pebble Beach. Isolated tufts have been found at Mussel Point; Point Pinos; Asilomar Point; Fanshell Beach; Cypress Point; Pescadero Point; Mission Point.

TYPE LOCALITY. Denmark.

PACIFIC COAST DISTRIBUTION. Alaska (Port Clarence) to southern California (San Diego).

[4] Some investigators of this alga report a gametic union of the swarmers and a germination of the resultant zygote; others report a direct germination without gametic union. Since there is this uncertainty concerning the nature of the plurilocular organs, it is as yet uncertain whether the plant is a gametophyte or a sporophyte.

Scytosiphon Lomentaria var. complanatus Rosenvinge

Pl. 19, fig. 2

Rosenvinge, 1893, p. 863.
Scytosiphon Lomentaria forma *complanatus major* *Setchell and Gardner, 1925, p. 534.
Scytosiphon Lomentaria forma *complanatus minor* Setchell and Gardner, 1925, p. 534; pl. 44, fig. 74.
Scytosiphon Lomentaria forma *cylindricus minor* Setchell and Gardner, 1925, p. 533.

Thalli, as found on the Monterey Peninsula, with erect shoots usually 8–15 cm. tall, occasionally up to 35 cm., and 1–1.5 mm. broad; light olive-tan to dark brown in color. The shoots growing in extensive stands, not in tufts. The shoots without constrictions, usually flattened and blade-like but at times cylindrical. Frequently spirally twisted in lax spirals.

LOCAL DISTRIBUTION. Growing in dense stands on rocks between the 5.0- and 2.5-foot tide levels. Fanshell Beach; Pebble Beach.

TYPE LOCALITY. Greenland.

PACIFIC COAST DISTRIBUTION. Southern Oregon (Cape Arago) to central California (Carmel Bay).

A number of forms of *S. Lomentaria* have been described from the Pacific Coast of North America (Setchell and Gardner, 1925) but as found locally these fall into two general types: one with large broad shoots growing in isolated tufts, the other with smaller narrower shoots growing in extensive stands. The larger type (typical *S. Lomentaria*) ranges from the mid-littoral to the lower littoral. At localities where it is found in abundance, as Pebble Beach and Arch Rock, the majority of shoots in a tuft are cylindrical and with typical constrictions; but some may be without constrictions, cylindrical or flattened, and straight or spirally twisted. This is true both of tufts growing on rocks exposed by the tide and of tufts permanently submerged in tide pools. The type growing in extensive stands (the variety *complanatus*) is found in the upper littoral. Whether periodically exposed by tides or permanently submerged in high-lying tide pools, its shoots are without constrictions. The majority of them are flattened and either straight or spirally twisted.

Scytosiphon bullosus Saunders

*Saunders, 1898, p. 163; pl. 31, figs. 1–7.
Colpomenia sinuosa forma *deformans* *Setchell and Gardner, 1903, p. 242; pl. 18, figs. 13–15. Setchell and Gardner, 1925, p. 542.

Thalli, as found on the Monterey Peninsula, up to 10 cm. tall, olive-tan in color. With several erect shoots from a common crustose base but usually with only one or two of them becoming mature. Mature shoots saccate, spindle-shaped, with broadly rounded apices; usually more or less compressed; at times with one or more hollow finger-like outgrowths.

LOCAL DISTRIBUTION. Growing on rocks between the 2.0- and 1.0-foot tide levels. Mussel Point; Pacific Grove; Pebble Beach; rocks at north end of Carmel Beach.

TYPE LOCALITY. Pacific Grove, California.

PACIFIC COAST DISTRIBUTION. Alaska (Cook's Inlet) to Baja California (Gulf of California).

Setchell and Gardner refer this alga to *Colpomenia*. The fact that several erect shoots grow from a common crustose base shows that the alga is a *Scytosiphon* and not a *Colpomenia*.

Coilodesme Strömfelt, 1886

Sporophytes macroscopic, annual. Mature sporophyte a linear to obovate flattened sac, at times so markedly flattened that it seems to be a linear to obovate blade. Basal portion of sporophyte with a short solid cylindrical stipe. Attachment by means of a small disc-shaped holdfast, or, if epiphytic, by means of rhizoids penetrating the host. Saccate portion 5–15 cells in thickness and with progressively smaller cells toward the outer surface, at times with the 2–4 outermost cells in anticlinal rows. With unilocular sporangia only. The sporangia narrowly to broadly pyriform, scattered over entire saccate portion of thallus, isolated from one another and embedded just below surface of thallus.

Gametophytes microscopic, filamentous. The gametangia uniseriate and several cells in height. Gametic union isogamous.

STRUCTURE AND REPRODUCTION. Kuckuck, 1929, pp. 87–89; figs. 142–146. Saunders, 1898, pp. 159–160; pl. 29, figs. 1–3.

Coilodesme californica (Ruprecht) Kjellman   Pl. 19, fig. 5

Kjellman, 1889A, p. 8; figs. 1–8. *Saunders, 1898, p. 160; pl. 29, figs. 1–3. Setchell and Gardner, 1925, p. 579; pl. 46, figs. 1–2; pl. 86. *Phyc. Bor.-Amer. No. I.

Adenocystis californica Ruprecht, 1851, p. 291. *Howe, 1893, p. 67.

Asperococcus sinuosus Anderson [not of (Roth) Bory]. *Anderson, 1891, p. 220.

Coilodesme amplissima Setchell, 1912, p. 232.

Mature thalli (sporophytes), as found on the Monterey Peninsula, usually 25–35 cm. tall, but occasionally up to 1 m.; up to

12 cm. broad; of a light olive-tan color. Distinctly blade-like except during very early stages of development. At first smooth but soon becoming more or less wrinkled. Upper end of plant frequently becoming frayed and torn. Stipe at base of plant 1–3 mm. long.

LOCAL DISTRIBUTION. Epiphytic on *Cystoseira osmundaceae*. Sporophytes appearing in May and completely disappearing by the end of August. Abundant wherever the host is found.

TYPE LOCALITY. Fort Ross, California.

PACIFIC COAST DISTRIBUTION. Puget Sound to southern California (San Pedro).

Family STRIARIACEAE

Sporophytes erect, cylindrical, branched, with tips of branches terminating in a uniseriate filament. Portion of branch posterior to filament multiseriate, parenchymatous, and with cell division intercalary. The sporophyte producing either unilocular or plurilocular sporangia. The sporangia usually formed by superficial cells in multiseriate portion of thallus.

Gametophytes unknown. Presumably microscopic and filamentous.

With one genus, *Stictyosiphon,* in the local flora.

Stictyosiphon Kützing, 1843

Sporophytes erect and attached by a densely interwoven, crust-like mass of rhizoids. Erect portion cylindrical throughout, freely branched, and with the branching alternate or opposite. Tips of branches uniseriate, below this becoming multiseriate by vertical cell divisions. Mature portions of branches with a superficial layer of cubical cells and the cells internal to them vertically elongated and rectangular. Older portions of branches at times becoming hollow. Chromatophores in multiseriate portion restricted to superficial cells, disc-shaped or band-shaped, several in a cell. Sporophytes producing either unilocular or plurilocular sporangia. Both kinds of sporangia usually developing from superficial cells in multiseriate portion of thallus. The sporangia either isolated from one another or in small groups intermingled with vegetative cells. The sporangia either embedded or protruding above surface of thallus.

Gametophytes unknown.

STRUCTURE AND REPRODUCTION. Kuckuck, 1929, pp. 81–82; figs. 115–124. Rosenvinge, 1935, pp. 2–18; figs. 1–19.

Stictyosiphon tortilis (Ruprecht) Reinke   Pl. 20, figs. 6–7

Reinke, 1889, p. 55. Reinke, 1892, p. 47; pls. 31–32. Setchell and Gardner, 1925, p. 529. Rosenvinge, 1935, p. 3, figs. 1–8. Phyc. Bor.-Amer. No. 987.

Scytosiphon tortilis Ruprecht, 1851, p. 373.

Thalli (sporophytes), as found on the Monterey Peninsula, up to 2 cm. tall; yellowish-brown in color. Holdfast hemispherical, composed of densely interwoven rhizoids. Erect portion freely branched and with the branching almost exclusively alternate. Multiseriate portion of branches up to 65 µ broad, rarely more than ten superficial cells in circumference; the superficial cells slightly longer than broad. Cells of uniseriate portion with a length about half the breadth. Chromatophores in multiseriate portion disc-shaped to narrowly elliptical; those in uniseriate portion disc-shaped. Unilocular sporangia not observed on thalli from Monterey Peninsula. Plurilocular sporangia restricted to multiseriate portion of thallus, rarely adjoining one another, rectangular, embedded in branches but with free face bulging slightly above surface of thallus, 20–25 µ in diameter.

LOCAL DISTRIBUTION. Attached to fragments of rocks dredged from a depth of 30–35 feet a quarter-mile from Municipal Wharf, Monterey.

TYPE LOCALITY. "Anjabai."

PACIFIC COAST DISTRIBUTION. Known only from Alaska and from the Monterey Peninsula.

The foregoing description is of the plant as found locally. Specimens from Alaska distributed as No. 987 of *Phyc. Bor.-Amer.* are darker, much larger, and the superficial cells in the multiseriate portion have a length about double the breadth. There is a possibility that the Monterey plants are juvenile. This presumption is based upon the fact that specimens of other well-known algae dredged from the same station are frequently juvenile.

Order LAMINARIALES

With a macroscopic sporophyte and a microscopic gametophyte. The sporophytes relatively large (usually over a meter tall) and differentiated into holdfast, stipe, and blade or blades. The holdfast rarely disc-shaped; usually with a number of simple or branched haptera. The stipe usually cylindrical; simple or branched, with or without pneumatocysts. Blades variously shaped, entire or cleft. Growth of sporophyte by an intercalary meristem that usually lies at juncture of stipe and blade. Haptera, stipe, and blade with a medulla of parallel filaments in which the end walls may have sieve plates. The cortical region external to the medulla parenchymatous, and with progressively smaller cells toward the surface. With unilocular sporangia only. The sporangia cylindrical, overarched by unicellular paraphyses, and always borne in sori. The sori borne on the blade or restricted to special blades (sporophylls).

Gametophytes filamentous and with the branches free from one another. Heterothallic and oögamous. Male gametophytes with the antheridia each producing a single antherozoid. Female gametophytes with the oögonia each producing a single egg and the egg fertilized after partially emerging from oögonial wall.

KEY TO THE FAMILIES IN THE LOCAL FLORA

1. Stipes of sporophyte unbranched and without
   lateral blades ....*Laminariaceae* (p. 134)
1. Stipes of sporophyte either branched, or with lateral appendages, or with both.. 2
   2. Stipes branched, without lateral outgrowths...*Lessoniaceae* (p. 138)
   2. Stipes branched or unbranched, with lateral
      outgrowths ....*Alariaceae* (p. 145)

Family LAMINARIACEAE

Sporophytes always with an unbranched stipe terminating in a single blade. The blade variously shaped, simple or branched, entire or cleft, with or without longitudinal ribs, perforate or imperforate, and with a smooth or variously roughened surface. Sori always developing on blade, never on sporophylls.

With gametophytes typical for the order.

KEY TO THE GENERA IN THE LOCAL FLORA

1. Blade without longitudinal ribs.................*Laminaria* (p. 134)
1. Blade with 5 percurrent ribs.....................*Costaria* (p. 137)

Laminaria Lamouroux, 1813

Sporophytes annual or perennial. Usually with a single stipe attached either by a mass of branched haptera or by a disc-shaped holdfast; more rarely with several stipes and blades borne on a prostrate branched rhizome. The stipe cylindrical or compressed, always terminating in a single blade. Perennial species either with a persistent blade or shedding the blade each autumn and then regenerating a new blade. Blades entire or incompletely and palmately divided into a number of segments. The blades without cryptostomata; usually smooth but sometimes ruffled or bullate; without longitudinal ribs or a midrib. With unilocular sporangia only. The sporangia produced in irregularly shaped sori nearly covering both surfaces of blade; each sporangium adjoined by a unicellular paraphysis.

Gametophytes microscopic, heterothallic. Male gametophyte an irregularly branched filament with clusters of antheridia at tips of branches. Antheridia one-celled and each producing a single biflagellate antherozoid. Female gametophyte filamentous but with fewer and larger cells than male gametophyte. Oögamous, the oögonia terminal or intercalary, one-celled, erect, cylindrical, much longer than vegetative cells. The oögonium producing a single egg which is extruded from, but remains attached to, apex of oögonial wall. Fertilization effected while egg is perched on apex of oögonium and the young sporophyte beginning to develop there.

STRUCTURE AND REPRODUCTION. Kanda, 1936, pp. 242–249; text figs. 16–21; pl. 47. Kanda, 1938, pp. 87–100; text figs. 1–15; pl. 17; pl. 18, fig. 1. Myers, 1925, pp. 114–116; pl. 8, figs. 8–14; pl. 9, fig. A. Schreiber, 1930. Sauvageau, 1916. Sauvageau, 1918, pp. 126–218; figs. 42–81.

KEY TO THE SPECIES IN THE LOCAL FLORA

1. With a single stipe and blade.................................... 2
1. With several stipes borne on a branched rhizome..........*L. Sinclairii*
   2. Blade bullate ....*L. Farlowii*
   2. Blade smooth... 3
3. Holdfast disc-shaped, without haptera.................*L. ephemera*
3. Holdfast with several forked haptera..................*L. Andersonii*

Laminaria Sinclairii (Harvey) Farlow   Pl. 31, fig. 1

Farlow in Algae Exsicc. Am. Bor. No. 118. *Anderson, 1891, p. 220. *Howe, 1893, p. 67. *Setchell, 1896, p. 45. Setchell, 1905A, p. 140; pl. 15; pl. 16, figs. 12–16. Setchell and Gardner, 1925, p. 598. Phyc. Bor.-Amer. No. VII.
Lessonia Sinclairii Harvey, 1847, p. 460. Harvey, 1852, p. 87.

Sporophytes perennial, as found on the Monterey Peninsula up to 30 cm. tall; of a rich dark-brown color. With a prostrate branched rhizome bearing many erect stipes each terminating in a single blade. The stipes cylindrical, up to 10 cm. long and 5 mm. in diameter. The blades linear, not longitudinally cleft, with a smooth surface; up to 20 cm. long and 3 cm. broad.

LOCAL DISTRIBUTION. Growing on rocks between the mean low-tide and −1.0-foot tide levels. Asilomar Point and small rocky points between Asilomar Point and Point Pinos.

TYPE LOCALITY. San Francisco, California.

PACIFIC COAST DISTRIBUTION. British Columbia (Vancouver Island) to central California (San Luis Obispo County).

The most distinctive morphological feature, the rhizome, is frequently buried in sand. However, the species is easily recognized in the field because the stipes and blades are in dense clumps of 25–100.

Laminaria Farlowii Setchell   Pl. 21, fig. 2

Setchell apud *Anderson, 1891, p. 220 (name only). *Setchell, 1893, p. 355. *Howe, 1893, p. 67. *Setchell, 1896, p. 46. Setchell, 1905A, p. 146; pl. 16, fig. 17. Setchell and Gardner, 1925, p. 599; pl. 56, fig. A. *Phyc. Bor.-Amer. No. XXXI.

Sporophytes perennial, as found on the Monterey Peninsula, up to 2 m. tall; of dark chocolate-brown color. With a single stipe and blade. Holdfast with many branched haptera. The stipe cylindrical, proportionally short, up to 6 cm. long and 1.5 cm. in diameter. The blade broadly linear, up to 30 cm. broad, without longitudinal incisions, surface irregularly wrinkled and depressed. The original blade persisting throughout life of a sporophyte. The sporophyte beginning to fruit late in the summer.

LOCAL DISTRIBUTION. Growing on rocks between the 0.5- and −1.5-foot tide levels. Mussel Point; Point Pinos; Cypress Point; middle point of Pebble Beach; Mission Point.

TYPE LOCALITY. Santa Cruz, California.

PACIFIC COAST DISTRIBUTION. Central California (Santa Cruz) to southern California (La Jolla).

Laminaria ephemera Setchell   Pl. 31, fig. 2

*Setchell, 1901, p. 121. Setchell, 1908, p. 92. Setchell and Gardner, 1925, p. 603; pl. 58.

Renfrewia parvula Griggs, 1906, p. 247; pls. 16–19. Tilden Amer. Alg. Exsicc. No. 609.

Sporophytes annual, up to 50 cm. tall. With a single stipe and blade. Holdfast disc-shaped, without haptera. The stipe cylindrical, 6–10 cm. long and 2–4 mm. in diameter. The blade narrowly cuneate to broadly rounded at base, above this narrowly to broadly linear, entire or with one to three longitudinal clefts extending nearly to base, surface of blade smooth. Sori in longitudinal strips covering both surfaces of blade. The sporophytes fruiting late in the spring or very early summer and then disappearing.

LOCAL DISTRIBUTION. On rocks in tide pools of the lower littoral. Pescadero Point; Carmel Bay.

Type Locality. Pescadero Point.

Pacific Coast Distribution. Known only from the Puget Sound area and from the Monterey Peninsula.

Known locally only from the two collections mentioned in the original description and from specimens collected by N. L. Gardner in 1925 and labeled "Carmel Bay."

Laminaria Andersonii Eaton[5]   Pl. 21, fig. 1

Eaton ex Farlow, 1876, p. 715 (name only). Eaton ex Hervey, 1881, p. 98. *Anderson, 1891, p. 220. *Howe, 1893, p. 67. *Setchell, 1905A, p. 145; pl. 17, figs. 19–25. Setchell and Gardner, 1925, p. 605. *Phyc. Bor.-Amer. No. II.

Sporophytes perennial, as found on the Monterey Peninsula, up to 1.5 m. tall. With a single stipe and blade. Holdfast with many-branched haptera compacted into a conical mass 6–8 cm. tall. The stipe cylindrical, up to 50 cm. in length and 3 cm. in diameter. The blade broadly lanceolate, smooth, deeply incised into 5–10 linear segments. Blades a rich dark brown, stipes blackish-brown. Sporophytes fruiting late in the autumn and regeneration of new blades beginning before the old ones are shed.

Local Distribution. Abundant between the 0.5- and −1.5-foot tide levels on all rocky points of the Peninsula. Also collected from a depth of 10 feet below the surface at Mussel Point.

Type Locality. Santa Cruz, California.

Pacific Coast Distribution. Washington (Whidbey Island) to central California (Carmel Highlands).

Costaria Greville, 1830

Sporophytes perennial. With a single stipe attached by a mass of wide-spreading branched haptera. The stipe unbranched, cylindrical; terminating in a single perennial, undivided, broadly linear blade. The blade with five percurrent ribs and with alternate ribs projecting toward opposite surfaces of the blade. Portion of blade between the ribs bullate. With unilocular sporangia only. Sporangia on both surfaces of blade and more or less completely covering bullate portion; each sporangium adjoined by a unicellular paraphysis.

Gametophytes closely resembling those of *Laminaria*.

Structure and Reproduction. Angst, 1927A. Kanda, 1936, pp. 237–242; figs. 12–15.

[5] The universal citation of this species as *L. Andersonii* Farlow overlooks the fact that it is called *L. Andersonii* Eaton mss. by Farlow (1876) and that it is cited as *L. Andersonii* Eaton in the first published description, that of Hervey (1881).

Costaria costata (Turner) Saunders   Pl. 22, fig. 1

*Saunders, 1895, p. 57. Setchell and Gardner, 1925, p. 610; pl. 56, fig. *B*; pl. 79, fig. *A*.

Fucus costatus Turner, 1819, p. 76; pl. 226.

Costaria Turneri Greville, 1830, p. xxxix. *Anderson, 1891, p. 220. *Howe, 1893, p. 67. Phyc. Bor.-Amer. No. 631, XXXV.

Costaria Mertensii J. G. Agardh, 1848, p. 140. *Saunders, 1895, p. 57.

Sporophytes, as found on the Monterey Peninsula, usually 1.5–2 m. tall when mature, occasionally up to 3 m.; dark chocolate-brown in color. The stipe cylindrical to somewhat compressed, up to 50 cm. long. Mature blades up to 35 cm. broad; either broadly linear and with a length 8–12 times the breadth, or broadly ovate and with a length less than 4 times the breadth. In either case the basal portion of blade more or less cordate. Bullation of portion between ribs very pronounced in mature blades. The blades fruiting from midsummer until late in the autumn.

LOCAL DISTRIBUTION. Growing between the 1.0- and −1.5-foot tide levels on rocks exposed to action of surf. Mussel Point; Point Aulon; Point Pinos; Asilomar Point; Point Joe; Cypress Point; Midway Point; Pescadero Point; middle point of Pebble Beach; Arrowhead Point; Mission Point.

TYPE LOCALITY. "West coast of North America."

PACIFIC COAST DISTRIBUTION. Alaska (Shumagin Islands) to southern California (San Pedro).

Family LESSONIACEAE

Sporophytes with branched stipes and the branching regularly or obscurely dichotomous. Each branch of stipe terminating in a single blade. The sporangial sori usually on the blades but in certain genera restricted to sporophylls.

With gametophytes typical for the order.

KEY TO THE GENERA IN THE LOCAL FLORA[6]

1. Stipe in large part prostrate.................................... 2
1. Stipe wholly or in large part erect.............................. 3
   2. Blade without a midrib..................*Dictyoneurum* (p. 139)
   2. Blade with a smooth midrib.............*Dictyoneuropsis* (p. 140)

[6] *Eisenia arborea* Areschoug has been found cast ashore at Monterey after severe winter storms (Setchell, 1893, p. 349). There are unconfirmed rumors that *Pelagophycus porra* (Leman) Setchell has been found cast ashore at Carmel Beach. This occurrence is not improbable because the late C. L. Anderson is known to have found specimens of *P. porra* cast ashore at Santa Cruz, California. Neither alga is indigenous to the Monterey Peninsula, and such specimens as have been found in this vicinity have drifted up from southern California.

Dictyoneurum Ruprecht, 1852

Sporophytes perennial, gregarious. The stipe markedly flattened, prostrate, with forked haptera along lateral margins. Anterior end of stipe bending upward and branching dichotomously. Stipes rarely with more than two or three dichotomies because of progressive death and decay at posterior end. Upwardly bent ultimate dichotomies of stipe each continued in a single blade. Upper ends of ultimate dichotomies dividing dichotomously and the blade splitting longitudinally from base to apex into two blades, one borne on each arm of the newly formed dichotomy. The blades linear, without a midrib, with both flattened surfaces covered with an irregular reticulum of narrow ridges. With unilocular sporangia only. The sporangia in irregularly shaped sori produced on both flattened surfaces of blade. Each sporangium adjoined by a unicellular paraphysis.

Gametophytes unknown, presumably as in *Laminaria*.

STRUCTURE AND REPRODUCTION. Setchell and Gardner, 1925, pp. 621–623; pl. 70.

Dictyoneurum californicum Ruprecht   Pl. 22, fig. 2

Ruprecht, 1852, p. 80; pl. 7. *Anderson, 1891, p. 220. *Setchell, 1896, p. 47; pl. 1. Setchell and Gardner, 1925, p. 622; pl. 70. *Phyc. Bor.-Amer. No. XI.

Sporophytes, as found on the Monterey Peninsula, up to 65 cm. tall; color varying from light to dark yellowish-brown. Sporophytes in gregarious clumps of 25–100 individuals. The blades 4–8 cm. broad, linear, gradually tapering at both upper and lower ends, with or without marginal denticulations, reticulations on surface of blade more or less rectangular and in longitudinal series. Stages in upward splitting of a blade into two blades of frequent occurrence. Sporangial areas first appearing during midsummer; darker in color than vegetative portions of blade.

LOCAL DISTRIBUTION. Growing between the 0.5- and −1.5-tide levels on rocks more or less directly exposed to surf. Fairly common on all rocky

points of the Peninsula. Also dredged from a depth of 25 feet near Mussel
Point and from a depth of 15–20 feet at Stillwater Cove.

TYPE LOCALITY. Fort Ross, California.

PACIFIC COAST DISTRIBUTION. British Columbia (Vancouver Island)
to central California (San Luis Obispo County).

Dictyoneuropsis G. M. Smith, 1942

Sporophytes perennial. At first with an unbranched prostrate
stipe whose anterior end bends upward and terminates in a single
blade. Decumbent portion of stipe flattened and with branched
haptera along lateral margins. Blades sublinear, with a midrib;
surface of blade, except the midrib, with a coarse reticulum of
narrow ridges. Later the blade and erect portion of stipe splitting
longitudinally to form a forked stipe with each arm terminating
in a blade; this repeated until the stipe becomes three or more
times dichotomous. Longitudinal division of blade through the
midrib and followed by regeneration of a new half-blade along
exposed edge of midrib. With unilocular sporangia only. The
sporangia in irregularly shaped sori between reticulations of
blade; at times the sori covering the midrib. Each sporangium
adjoined by a unicellular paraphysis.

Gametophytes unknown, presumably as in *Laminaria*.

STRUCTURE AND REPRODUCTION. Saunders, 1895 (as *Costaria*). G. M.
Smith, 1942, pp. 651–652; figs. 9–13.

Dictyoneuropsis reticulata (Saunders) G. M. Smith
Pl. 23, figs. 1–4

*G. M. Smith, 1942, p. 651; figs. 9–13.
Costaria reticulata *Saunders, 1895, p. 58; pl. 7.

Sporophytes up to 95 cm. tall; yellowish-brown in color. Prostrate portion of stipe up to three times dichotomous; the dichotomies 4–6 mm. broad, 1 mm. in thickness; with haptera along
the lateral margins, the haptera 3–5 times dichotomous and 25–30
mm. long. Mature blades linear, slightly narrower at upper end,
broadly rounded at base; reticulation of blade restricted to portions lateral to midrib, but the entire blade at times bullate; maximum breadth of blade 15–25 cm., of midrib 1.5–3.5 cm.

LOCAL DISTRIBUTION. Dredged from a depth of 30–35 feet a quarter-
mile from Municipal Wharf, Monterey; from the same depth near Mussel
Point; from a depth of 20–25 feet near Point Aulon.

TYPE LOCALITY. "Monterey Bay near Pacific Grove, Cal."

PACIFIC COAST DISTRIBUTION. As above.

Nereocystis Postels and Ruprecht, 1840

Sporophytes annual. With a hemispherical holdfast of densely compacted branched haptera. The stipe very long, cylindrical, gradually broadening upward and terminating in a subglobose pneumatocyst; upper fourth of stipe hollow. Apex of pneumatocyst with four short flattened 4–5 times dichotomous branches. The end of each ultimate dichotomy continued in a long linear undivided blade with a smooth surface. With unilocular sporangia only. The sporangia in rectangular sori on both surfaces of blade. The sori borne at regular intervals, nearly as broad as blade, with each sporangium adjoined by a unicellular paraphysis. The fertile areas shed from blade when sporangia are mature.

Gametophytes closely resembling those of *Laminaria*.

STRUCTURE AND REPRODUCTION. Hartge, 1928. Macmillan, 1899. Setchell, 1896, p. 183.

Nereocystis Luetkeana (Mertens) Postels and Ruprecht

Pl. 24, figs. 1–2

Postels and Ruprecht, 1840, p. 9; pls. 8–9. *Farlow, 1875, p. 354. *Farlow, 1876, p. 707. *Anderson, 1891, p. 220. *Howe, 1893, p. 67. *Setchell, 1896*A*, p. 179. *Setchell, 1908*A*, p. 126. Setchell and Gardner, 1925, p. 624. *Phyc. Bor.-Amer. No. X.

Fucus Luetkeanus Mertens, 1829, p. 48.

Sporophytes usually annual but occasionally persisting until early summer of the next year; as found on the Monterey Peninsula up to 40 m. tall. The holdfast up to 40 cm. broad. Stipe of mature plant up to 36 m. long; 1–2 cm. in diameter at base, 8–10 cm. in diameter at upper end, and with pneumatocysts 9–14 cm. in diameter. Usually with 32–64 blades. The blades up to 3.5 m. long and 15 cm. broad. Some sporophytes developing sporangia as early as May.

LOCAL DISTRIBUTION. Growing in extensive beds on rocks 30–50 feet below surface of water. Upper end of stipe growing to and floating horizontally on surface of water. The beds usually developing each year at Point Pinos; Asilomar Point; Seal Rocks; Cypress Point; Stillwater Cove; Carmel Bay.

TYPE LOCALITY. Alaska.

PACIFIC COAST DISTRIBUTION. Alaska (Shumagin Islands) to southern California (Santa Barbara).

Isolated plants are also found here and there in tide pools of the intertidal belt. These plants have stipes of normal diameter, but only 1–2 m. long. The blades are of normal size and frequently produce sori.

Postelsia Ruprecht, 1852

Sporophytes annual. With a relatively small holdfast of stout branched haptera. The stipe erect, cylindrical and hollow, tapering slightly from base to apex. Apex of stipe with many short radiately disposed simple branches each terminating in a single blade. Branch and blade splitting longitudinally into two blades and branches of equal size; the splitting beginning at juncture of branch and blade. The blades narrowly linear, with dentate margins; both flattened surfaces of blade with deep, parallel, longitudinal grooves; the grooves of one surface alternate with those of the other. With unilocular sporangia only. The sporangia in linear sori lining grooves on surface of blades. Each sporangium adjoined by a unicellular paraphysis.

Gametophytes closely resembling those of *Laminaria*.

STRUCTURE AND REPRODUCTION. Myers, 1925, pp. 112–114; pl. 8, figs. 1–7; pl. 9, fig. *B*.

Postelsia palmaeformis Ruprecht   Pl. 25

Ruprecht, 1852, p. 75; pl. 6. *Anderson, 1891, p. 220. *Howe, 1893, p. 67. Setchell and Gardner, 1925, p. 625; pl. 69. *Phyc. Bor.-Amer. No. XXXVIII.

Sporophytes usually growing in extensive stands; as found on the Monterey Peninsula, up to 60 cm. tall. The stipes erect and the blades pendant when plants are exposed by recession of tide. Mature plants with 100 or more blades. The blades up to 25 cm. long. The sporophytes beginning to produce sporangia late in the spring and the blades becoming eroded as fruiting continues.

LOCAL DISTRIBUTION. Growing between the 4.0- and 1.0-foot tide levels on rocks and cliffs exposed to full force of the surf. Point Joe; Seal Rock; Cypress Point; Pescadero Point; Mission Point.

TYPE LOCALITY. Bodega Bay, California.

PACIFIC COAST DISTRIBUTION. British Columbia (Vancouver Island) to central California (San Luis Obispo County).

The only readily accessible local "groves" of *Postelsia* are at Mission Point. All other "groves" are on inaccessible, partially submerged, rocky ledges a short distance out from the shore.

Macrocystis C. A. Agardh, 1823

Sporophytes with basal portion perennial. With a conical hold-fast composed of long-branched haptera, or with a prostrate branched subligulate rhizome with short forked haptera along the lateral margins. In either case the stipe erect, cylindrical, and 2–4 times dichotomously branched near base. Branches of stipe with blades at regular intervals and all blades borne unilaterally. Each ultimate branch with a single terminal blade and new lateral blades on a branch formed by asymmetrical split-ting of terminal blade from base to apex. Mature lateral blades with a short stipe and a subglobose to spindle-shaped basal pneu-matocyst; the blade undivided and with an irregularly corrugated surface. With unilocular sporangia only. Sporangia restricted to sporophylls borne low on branches and with or without pneu-matocysts; the sporophyll at first entire, later splitting from base to apex into two equal parts, eventually becoming 4–5 times di-chotomously divided. Segments of sporophyll narrowly linear, with a short stipe, never with a pneumatocyst. The sporangia completely covering both surfaces of segments; each sporangium adjoined by a unicellular paraphysis.

Gametophytes closely resembling those of *Laminaria*.

STRUCTURE AND REPRODUCTION. Hoffmann, 1911. Howe, 1914, pp. 60–66; pl. 14, fig. *B;* pl. 18, fig. *B;* pls. 19–24. Levyns, 1933. Papenfuss, 1942, pp. 21–23; figs. 43–59. Setchell, 1932. Skottsberg, 1907, pp. 80–133; text figs. 91–170; pl. 9.

KEY TO THE SPECIES IN THE LOCAL FLORA

1. Length of terminal blade 6–10 times breadth............*M. integrifolia*
1. Length of terminal blade 3–5 times breadth...............*M. pyrifera*

Macrocystis integrifolia Bory   Pl. 26

Bory, 1826, p. 9. Howe, 1914, p. 60; pl. 18, fig. *B;* pls. 19–22. *Setchell and Gardner, 1925, p. 628; pl. 62. *Setchell, 1932, p. 447; pls. 33–38. *G. M. Smith, 1942, p. 647; figs. 5–6.

Sporophytes, as found on the Monterey Peninsula, up to 6 m. tall. With a flattened subligulate irregular subdichotomous rhi-zome with numerous branched haptera along both lateral mar-gins. The stipe usually with but 1–3 dichotomies. Terminal blade of each branch narrowly falcate and usually with but 3–6 young blades in progressive stages of differentiation by an asymmetrical splitting from base to apex. Length of terminal blade 6–10 times breadth. The mature lateral blades lanceolate, rugose, and with denticulate margins; the pneumatocysts narrowly to broadly pyriform. Lateral blades up to 40 cm. long and 5 cm. broad. Sporophylls usually without a pneumatocyst, ultimately becoming 4–5 times dichotomously divided; the ultimate segments up to 30 cm. long and 2 cm. broad.

LOCAL DISTRIBUTION. Growing in tidal channels and on gently sloping rocky ledges on rocks between the 0.5- and −0.5-foot tide levels. Mussel Point; Point Aulon; Point Pinos; Asilomar Point; Point Joe; Cypress Point; Pebble Beach; north end of Carmel Beach; Mission Point.

TYPE LOCALITY. Western coast of South America.

PACIFIC COAST DISTRIBUTION. British Columbia (Vancouver Island) to central California (Carmel Bay).

Macrocystis pyrifera (Linnaeus) C. A. Agardh   Pl. 31, figs. 3–4

C. A. Agardh, 1820, p. 47. *Harvey, 1852, p. 84. *Anderson, 1891, p. 220. *Howe, 1893, p. 67. Setchell and Gardner, 1925, p. 627; pls. 64–65. *G. M. Smith, 1942, p. 647; figs. 7–8. Phyc. Bor.-Amer. No. XXXIX.

Fucus pyriferus Linnaeus, 1771, p. 311.

Sporophytes, as found on the Monterey Peninsula,[7] up to 25 m. tall. The holdfast of old plants conical, up to 40 cm. tall, and composed of long, densely compacted, branched haptera. The stipe usually 4–5 times dichotomously divided near base. Terminal blade of each branch broadly falcate and with 10–20 young lateral blades in progressive stages of differentiation by an asymmetrical splitting from base to apex. Length of terminal blade 3–5 times breadth. The mature lateral blades lanceolate, strongly rugose, and with denticulate margins; with a stipitate base and a pyriform pneumatocyst. Lateral blades up to 80 cm. long and 40 cm. broad. Sporophylls borne near base of branches, usually with a pneumatocyst, ultimately becoming 4–5 times dichotomous. The ultimate segments up to 30 cm. long and 2 cm. broad.

LOCAL DISTRIBUTION. Growing in extensive stands on rocks 20–25 feet below surface of water. Upper ends of branches growing to surface of water. Mussel Point; Point Aulon; Point Pinos; Cypress Point; Stillwater Cove; Mission Point.

TYPE LOCALITY. South Atlantic Ocean.

PACIFIC COAST DISTRIBUTION. Alaska (Sitka) to Baja California (Magdalena Bay).

[7] The length can be determined only from plants cast ashore and when the branches are spirally twisted in a rope-like manner. Several plants were measured on Carmel Beach in the summer of 1938, and the longest of these was slightly over 25 m. The longest plant thus far discovered along the Pacific Coast of North America measured 45.7 m. (Frye, Rigg, and Crandall, p. 475).

Lessoniopsis Reinke, 1903

Sporophytes perennial. With a massive conical holdfast of compacted, repeatedly dichotomous haptera. The stipe conical, massive in lower portion, repeatedly (6–9 times) dichotomous above and with each of the ultimate dichotomies continued in a single, narrowly linear blade. New dichotomies produced by longitudinal splitting of a dichotomy and a progressively upward longitudinal splitting of the blade. Older blades with a conspicuous flattened midrib. With unilocular sporangia only. The sporangia produced on sporophylls borne laterally near base of primary dichotomies of stipe. The sporophylls without a midrib, usually shorter and broader than the sterile blades. Each sporangium adjoined by a unicellular paraphysis.

Gametophytes unknown, presumably as in *Laminaria*.

STRUCTURE AND REPRODUCTION. Griggs, 1909 (as *Lessonia*). Macmillan, 1900 (as *Lessonia*). Reinke, 1903, pp. 25–28; fig. 8.

Lessoniopsis littoralis (Farlow and Setchell) Reinke
Pl. 27, figs. 1–2

Reinke, 1903, p. 25; fig. 8. Setchell and Gardner, 1925, p. 632; pls. 67–68.

Lessonia littoralis Farlow and Setchell ex Tilden Amer. Alg. Exsicc. No. 342. *Setchell and Gardner, 1903, p. 267. *Phyc. Bor.-Amer. No. XXXVII.

Lessonia nigrescens Farlow [not of Bory]. Farlow, 1876, p. 707. *Anderson, 1891, p. 220.

Sporophytes, as found on the Monterey Peninsula, up to 2 m. tall; blackish-brown in color. Densely bushy and with up to 500 blades. The holdfast up to 15 cm. broad at base. Dichotomous portion of stipe 20–30 cm. tall, the dichotomies 4–8 mm. in diameter, and the interval between successive dichotomies 3–5 cm. The blades narrowly linear, up to 1 m. long, 6–12 mm. broad and with the flattened midribs 2–3 mm. broad.

LOCAL DISTRIBUTION. Growing between the mean low-tide and −1.5-foot tide levels on rocky ledges exposed to full force of the surf. Point Joe; Cypress Point; Pescadero Point; Arrowhead Point; Mission Point; rocks at mouth of Carmel River.

TYPE LOCALITY. Cypress Point, Monterey Peninsula, California.

PACIFIC COAST DISTRIBUTION. Alaska (Sitka) to central California (Carmel Bay).

Family ALARIACEAE

Sporophytes with branched or unbranched stipes. The meristematic region producing lateral blades that may be borne either

on the terminal blade or along the stipe. The sporangia restricted
to sporophylls.

Alaria Greville, 1830

Sporophytes perennial. With a single stipe attached by a mass
of wide-spreading branched haptera. The stipe unbranched, short,
cylindrical or flattened, terminating in a single blade. The blade
broadly expanded, undivided, with a conspicuous percurrent midrib. Surface of blade smooth or bearing cryptostomata. With
unilocular sporangia only. The sporangia produced on linear to
obovate flattened sporophylls borne on opposite sides of upper
end of stipe. The sporophylls usually with both flattened faces
each nearly covered with a single large sorus. Each sporangium
adjoined by a unicellular paraphysis.

Gametophytes closely resembling those of *Laminaria*.

STRUCTURE AND REPRODUCTION. Kanda, 1936, pp. 224–232; text figs. 1–6;
pl. 46. Printz, 1922. Sauvageau, 1916*A*. Sauvageau, 1918, pp. 219–233; figs. 82–
85.

Alaria nana Schrader

Schrader, 1903, p. 162; pls. 23–26. Setchell and Gardner, 1925, p. 636.
Alaria marginata forma *nana* (Schrader) Collins. Collins in Phyc. Bor.-
Amer. No. 1292.

Sporophytes up to 70 cm. tall. With a relatively long (4.5–7
cm.), robust, terete stipe. The blades broadly lanceolate, with a
length about 6 times the breadth; broadest (6.4–8.5 cm.) near
the base, lowermost portion of blade rather abruptly tapering,
upper portion gradually tapering. The midrib conspicuous, subrectangular in transverse section. With 25–50 linear to elliptical

sporophylls with short distinct stipes; the sporophylls 6–12 cm. long, .75–1.5 cm. broad.

LOCAL DISTRIBUTION. Mission Point.
TYPE LOCALITY. Near Port Renfrew, Vancouver Island.
PACIFIC COAST DISTRIBUTION. British Columbia (Vancouver Island) to central California (Carmel Bay).

Known locally only from a single collection made by N. L. Gardner in 1915. Elsewhere along this coast *A. nana* has been found growing relatively high in the intertidal belt and usually in association with *Postelsia palmaeformis*. There is no information available as to whether or not this is true for the local specimens collected by Gardner.

Alaria marginata Postels and Ruprecht Pl. 28

Postels and Ruprecht, 1840, p. 11. *Howe, 1893, p. 67. Setchell, 1908, p. 98. Setchell and Gardner, 1925, p. 640; pl. 66.
Alaria esculenta Farlow [not of Greville]. *Farlow, 1876, p. 707. *Anderson, 1891, p. 220.
Alaria lanceolata Nott [not of Kjellman]. *Nott in Phyc. Bor.-Amer. No. XLIV.

Mature sporophytes, as found on the Monterey Peninsula, usually 2.5–4 m. tall but occasionally up to 6 m.; light tan in color. With a relatively short (2–7 cm.) terete stipe. The blades linear–lanceolate, with a length 10–15 times the breadth; broadest (15–30 cm.) about a third the distance from base to apex, tapering gradually or somewhat abruptly below the broadest portion; all except the lowermost portion of blade with cryptostomata. The midrib conspicuous, varying considerably in breadth. With 20–40 sublinear to broadly elliptical stipitate sporophylls with broadly rounded apices; the sporophylls 10–25 cm. long, 2–6 cm. broad.

LOCAL DISTRIBUTION. Abundant between the mean low-tide and −1.5-foot tide levels on rocky points exposed to full force of waves. Mussel Point; Point Aulon; Point Pinos; Point Joe; Cypress Point; Midway Point; Pescadero Point; Arrowhead Point; Mission Point. At certain of these points also observed 5–10 feet below extreme low-tide level.
TYPE LOCALITY. Fort Ross, California.
PACIFIC COAST DISTRIBUTION. Northern California (Crescent City) to central California (Carmel Highlands).

Pterygophora Ruprecht, 1852

Sporophytes perennial. With a holdfast composed of stout branched haptera. The stipe long, erect, unbranched; cylindrical in basal portion, compressed in upper portion; woody in texture and with concentric annual growth rings. The stipe terminating in a single lanceolate blade without a midrib but with the axial portion slightly thickened, surface of the blade smooth. The blade shed and a new blade regenerated each year. The sporophylls of approximately the same size and shape as the blade but stipitate at base; borne beneath blade on both margins of flattened portion of stipe, each margin with a vertical row of 5–10 sporophylls. The sporophylls shed after fruiting and a new series developed at a higher level the next year. The sporangia in irregular patches on or nearly covering both surfaces of a sporophyll; at times also developing on terminal blade. Each sporangium adjoined by a unicellular paraphysis.

Gametophytes closely resembling those of *Laminaria*.

STRUCTURE AND REPRODUCTION. Frye, 1918. McKay, 1933. Macmillan, 1902. Setchell, 1908, pp. 95–98.

Pterygophora californica Ruprecht   Pl. 29

Ruprecht, 1852, p. 73; pl. 5. Hervey, 1881, p. 88. *Anderson, 1891, p. 220. Setchell, 1893, p. 370. *Setchell and Gardner, 1903, p. 271. Setchell and Gardner, 1925, p. 634; pl. 74. Phyc. Bor.-Amer. No. CVIII.

Sporophytes, as found on the Monterey Peninsula, up to 2.3 m. tall. The stipes up to 1.5 m. long and 4 cm. broad in upper flattened portion. The terminal blade up to 80 cm. long and 10 cm. broad. Usually beginning to fruit in October; shedding terminal blade and sporophylls later in the winter.

LOCAL DISTRIBUTION. Growing in extensive beds at a depth of 20–60 feet. Between Cypress Point and Pescadero Point; off Pescadero Rocks; off Arrowhead Point. Isolated individuals at the −1.5-foot tide level. Pescadero Point. Regularly cast ashore in considerable numbers throughout the year at Moss Beach; Fanshell Beach; Carmel Beach.

TYPE LOCALITY. Fort Ross, California.

PACIFIC COAST DISTRIBUTION. British Columbia (Vancouver Island) to northern Baja California.

The sublittoral beds of *P. californica* were discovered by Mr. Paul Bonnot while making a survey of the deep-water distribution of the abalone (*Haliotis*) for the California Fish and Game Commission. Using a regular diving suit he descended to a maximum depth of 75 feet and surveyed the area from Cypress Point to Mission Point. He did not find the alga in the sublittoral area between Monterey and Point Pinos.

Egregia Areschoug, 1876

Sporophytes perennial. With a conspicuous conical holdfast of compacted branched haptera; holdfast of old plants much abraded. The stipe subcylindrical to markedly compressed, irregularly branched and with the apex of each branch continued in a long, ligulate, blade-like rachis. Lateral margins of stipe and rachis densely fringed with short, filiform to spatulate, blades. Certain of the blades eventually developing into spindle-shaped to subspherical pneumatocysts. With unilocular sporangia only. The sporangia completely covering sporophylls that lie intermingled with and are scarcely distinguishable from sterile blades. Each sporangium adjoined by a unicellular paraphysis.

Gametophytes closely resembling those of *Laminaria*.

STRUCTURE AND REPRODUCTION. Myers, 1928. Ramaley, 1903.

KEY TO THE SPECIES IN THE LOCAL FLORA

1. Stipe and blades with many minute tubercules............*E. Menziesii*
1. Stipe and blades smooth, or relatively so.................*E. laevigata*

Egregia Menziesii (Turner) Areschoug   Pl. 30, fig. 1

Areschoug, 1876, p. 67. *Anderson, 1891, p. 221. *Howe, 1893, p. 67. Setchell and Gardner, 1925, p. 648. *Phyc. Bor.-Amer. Nos. 1741, XCII.

Fucus Menziesii Turner, 1808, p. 57; pl. 27.

Macrocystis Menziesii (Turner) C. A. Agardh, 1820, p. 49. Harvey, 1833, p. 163.

Macrocystis obtusa Harvey, 1833, p. 163.

Phyllospora Menziesii (Turner) J. G. Agardh, 1848, p. 254. *Harvey, 1852, p. 62; pl. 3, fig. B.

Mature sporophytes, as found on the Monterey Peninsula, usually up to 5 m. tall but occasionally up to 7.5 m.; deep chocolate-brown in color. Holdfasts up to 20 cm. in diameter. The stipe flattened, 2.5–3.5 cm. broad, with 6–25 branches 3–6 cm. in length. Surface of stipe densely covered with small blunt tubercules. The blades all about the same length (up to 6 cm.), stipitate at base, broadly to narrowly spatulate toward apex; surface of blade more or less covered with small tubercules. Pneumatocysts ellipsoid to subspherical, regularly tuberculate at free end.

LOCAL DISTRIBUTION. Growing on rocks between the 2.0-foot and mean low-tide levels. Except for Pebble Beach and where interrupted by sandy beaches, forming a continuous belt along the entire shore line.

TYPE LOCALITY. Nootka Sound, Vancouver Island.

PACIFIC COAST DISTRIBUTION. British Columbia (Vancouver Island) to central California (Point Conception).

Egregia laevigata Setchell   Pl. 30, fig. 2

*Setchell, 1896, p. 44. Setchell and Gardner, 1925, p. 648. Phyc. Bor.-Amer. Nos. 420, XII.
   Egregia laevigata forma *borealis* *Setchell in Phyc. Bor.-Amer. No. XL. *Setchell and Gardner, 1925, p. 649.

Mature sporophytes, as found on the Monterey Peninsula, up to 5 m. tall; light yellowish-brown in color. With holdfasts up to 15 cm. in diameter. The stipe with several long branches. Surface of stipe smooth or with a very few small pointed tubercules. The blades up to 15 cm. long, filiform to broadly ligulate or obovate. Pneumatocysts usually spindle-shaped but at times subglobose. Blades and pneumatocysts usually without minute tubercules.

LOCAL DISTRIBUTION. Growing on rocks between the 0.5- and —0.5-foot tide levels. Abundant everywhere on Pebble Beach.
TYPE LOCALITY. Pebble Beach, Monterey Peninsula, California.
PACIFIC COAST DISTRIBUTION. Except for Pebble Beach, southern California (Point Conception) to Baja California (Ensenada).

E. laevigata was founded on material collected at Pebble Beach. Because of this the subsequent segregation of the plants from this northern "island" of distribution as the forma *borealis* is illegal. Blades and pneumatocysts of living plants of *E. laevigata* are crisper and more brittle than those of *E. Menziesii*.

Class CYCLOSPOREAE

Thalli diploid; perennial; macroscopic and with height ranging from a few centimeters to several meters. The thallus flattened to cylindrical, branched, the branching dichotomous throughout or radial about a central axis. Growth of branches initiated by a single apical cell. The fertile portion of a branch or the entire branch disintegrating after reproduction.

Reproductive organs developed within conceptacles embedded at tips of branchlets and the portion of the branch tip containing conceptacles constituting a receptacle. The reproductive organs unilocular sporangia but of two kinds: macrosporangia ("oögonia") and microsporangia ("antheridia"). Thalli monoecious or dioecious. The first nuclear division in sporangia meiotic. Macrosporangia becoming 8-nucleate and then producing 1, 2, 4, or 8 uninucleate nonflagellate macrospores ("eggs"). Microsporangia producing 64 or 128 biflagellate microspores ("antherozoids"). Liberation of macro- and microspores followed by gametic union of the two to form zygotes which develop directly into new diploid thalli.

Order FUCALES

All Cyclosporeae are placed in a single order, the Fucales, whose characters are the same as those of the class.

Key to the Families of Fucales

1. Branching of thallus dichotomous and in one plane..*Fucaceae* (p. 151)
1. Branching of thallus radial to a central axis.....*Sargassaceae* (p. 155)

Family FUCACEAE

Thalli perennial, without a central axis. The portion above the holdfast dichotomously branched and with the branches in one plane.

Reproduction in the manner typical of the class and with the macrosporangium ("oögonium") producing either 1, 2, 4, or 8 macrospores ("eggs").

Key to the Genera in the Local Flora

1. Macrosporangia with eight functional spores..........*Fucus* (p. 151)
1. Macrosporangia with less than eight functional spores.............. 2
   2. With two functional spores.....................*Pelvetia* (p. 153)
   2. With one functional spore...................................... 3
3. Branches of thallus with a percurrent midrib..*Hesperophycus* (p. 152)
3. Branches of thallus without a midrib............*Pelvetiopsis* (p. 154)

Fucus Linnaeus, 1753

Thalli perennial. With a disc-shaped or irregularly shaped holdfast. Erect portion dichotomously branched, markedly flattened, with a more or less distinct percurrent midrib, at times with air-filled vesicles of definite form in pairs lateral to the midrib; with cryptostomata and caecostomata. Base of erect portion frequently becoming stipe-like through abrasion of tissues lateral to the midrib.

Heterosporous, monoecious or dioecious. The sporangia unilocular, developed within conceptacles embedded at tips of the final dichotomies. The macrosporangium ("oögonium") producing eight large nonflagellate functional macrospores ("eggs"). The microsporangium ("antheridium") producing 64 or 128 small biflagellate microspores ("antherozoids"). "Egg" and "antherozoid" uniting to form a zygote, which immediately begins to develop into a new thallus.

STRUCTURE AND REPRODUCTION. Farmer and Williams, 1898. Nienburg, 1913, pp. 7–10; fig. 2. Oltmanns, 1889, pp. 3–23; pls. 1–5. Thuret, 1854.

Fucus furcatus C. A. Agardh   Pl. 32, fig. 2

C. A. Agardh, 1820, p. 97. Gardner, 1922, p. 16; pls. 2–3. Setchell and Gardner, 1925, p. 664.
Fucus evanescens Howe [not of C. A. Agardh]. *Howe, 1893, p. 67.
Fucus evanescens forma typicus Gardner in Phyc. Bor.-Amer. No. 1338.
Fucus vesiculosus Anderson [not of Linnaeus]. *Anderson, 1891, p. 220.

Thalli, as found on the Monterey Peninsula, 20–50 cm. tall; olive-brown to dark brown in color. Regularly dichotomous, with an interval of 2.5–4 cm. between successive dichotomies; the segments 1–1.5 cm. broad and linear to cuneate; apices of segments broadly rounded. The midrib prominent and percurrent.· Caecostomata abundant. The receptacles usually flattened but at times tumid, up to 6 cm. long and generally bifurcate; conceptacles numerous. Monoecious.

LOCAL DISTRIBUTION. Growing on rocks between the 3.5- and 2.0-foot tide levels. Widely distributed on the Monterey Peninsula. Abundant at Asilomar Point and Mission Point.

TYPE LOCALITY. Given as Unalaska, Alaska, but this thought to be erroneous.

PACIFIC COAST DISTRIBUTION. Alaska (Sitka) to central California (San Luis Obispo County).

Gardner (1922) has described numerous forms of this species and all specimens of F. furcatus found on the Monterey Peninsula are to be referred to his forma luxurians.

Hesperophycus Setchell and Gardner, 1910

Thalli perennial. With a disc-shaped holdfast. Erect portion dichotomously branched, markedly flattened, with a distinct percurrent midrib; with two vertical rows of cryptostomata, one on either side of the midrib. Base of erect portion becoming stipelike through abrasion of tissues lateral to the midrib.

Heterosporous, monoecious. The sporangia unilocular and

developed within conceptacles embedded at tips of the final dichotomies. The macrosporangium ("oögonium") producing one large nonflagellate functional macrospore ("egg") and a small nonfunctional seven-nucleate macrospore. The microsporangium ("antheridium") producing 128 small biflagellate microspores ("antherozoids"). "Egg" and "antherozoid" uniting to form a zygote, which immediately begins to develop into a new thallus.

STRUCTURE AND REPRODUCTION. Gardner, 1910, pp. 129–130; pl. 16, figs. 8–10.

Hesperophycus Harveyanus (Decaisne) Setchell and Gardner
Pl. 32, fig. 1

*Setchell and Gardner apud Gardner, 1910, p. 127; pl. 16, figs. 8–10. *Gardner, 1913, p. 317; pls. 36–37. Setchell and Gardner, 1925, p. 704. *Phyc. Bor.-Amer. No. CXII.

Fucus Harveyanus Decaisne apud *Harvey 1852, p. 70 (name only). *Decaisne, 1864, p. 9; pl. 4. *Farlow, 1875, p. 354. *Farlow, 1876, p. 706. *Anderson, 1891, p. 221. *Howe, 1893, p. 67.

Thalli, as found on the Monterey Peninsula, 10–35 cm. tall; greenish-olive to yellowish-brown in color. Usually with several erect shoots from a disc-shaped base. The erect shoots regularly dichotomous and with an interval of 1–3 cm. between successive dichotomies; the segments 0.3–0.8 cm. broad, linear, apices of ultimate segments broadly rounded. The cryptostomata with conspicuous whitish hairs. The receptacles 0.5–1.2 cm. broad, tumid, simple or bifurcate, 0.5–3 cm. long.

LOCAL DISTRIBUTION. Growing on rocks between the 4.0- and 2.0-foot tide levels. Abundant on rocky headlands. Mussel Point; Point Pinos; Asilomar Point; Point Joe; Cypress Point; Pebble Beach; north end of Carmel Beach; Mission Point.

TYPE LOCALITY. Monterey, California.

PACIFIC COAST DISTRIBUTION. Central California (Santa Cruz) to Baja California (Ensenada).

Pelvetia Decaisne and Thuret, 1845

Thalli perennial. The holdfast conical, with one to several erect shoots. The shoots dichotomously branched, subcylindrical or compressed and channeled on one side, without a midrib, with or without air-filled vesicles, with inconspicuous cryptostomata.

Heterosporous, monoecious. The sporangia unilocular and developed within conceptacles at the tips of the final dichotomies. The macrosporangium ("oögonium") producing two (occasionally three to five) large nonflagellate macrospores ("eggs"). Division to form two macrospores either longitudinal or transverse. The microsporangium ("antheridium") producing 128 small biflagellate microspores ("antherozoids"). "Egg" and "antherozoid" uniting to form a zygote, which immediately begins to develop into a new thallus.

STRUCTURE AND REPRODUCTION. Gardner, 1910, pp. 130–131; pl. 17, figs. 11–16. Moore, 1928. Nienburg, 1913, pp. 16–19; fig. 6. G. M. Smith, 1938, pp. 268–273; figs. 151–154.

Pelvetia fastigiata (J. G. Agardh) DeToni   Pl. 33, fig. 2

DeToni, 1895, p. 215. *Gardner, 1910, p. 126; pl. 17, figs. 11–16. *Setchell and Gardner, 1925, p. 701. Phyc. Bor.-Amer. No. CXIII.
Fucus fastigiatus *J. G. Agardh, 1841, p. 3. *Harvey, 1852, p. 68; pl. 3, fig. *A*. *Anderson, 1891, p. 221. *Howe, 1893, p. 67.

Thalli, as found on the Monterey Peninsula, 15–40 cm. tall; dark greenish-olive to yellowish-brown in color. Frequently with several erect shoots from a holdfast. The erect shoots subcylindrical below, somewhat more compressed in upper portion; dichotomously branched throughout but generally with the two arms of a dichotomy unequal in length; the interval between successive dichotomies 3–5 cm.; the dichotomies 0.2–0.5 cm. broad. The receptacles inflated and broader than region below; fusiform; simple or bifurcate, 1–5 cm. long, 0.3–0.5 cm. broad. Division to form the two macrospores longitudinal.

LOCAL DISTRIBUTION. Growing on rocks between the 4.5- and 2.0-foot tide levels. Abundant everywhere on the Monterey Peninsula.
TYPE LOCALITY. Monterey, California.
PACIFIC COAST DISTRIBUTION. Southern Oregon (Coos Bay) to Baja California (Ensenada).

The forma *gracilis* (*Setchell and Gardner apud Gardner, 1917, p. 386) is known only from Pebble Beach, the type locality, and from Santa Catalina Island, California. It is more slender throughout, more profusely branched, and the receptacles are 1.5–3 cm. long.

Pelvetiopsis Gardner, 1910

Thalli perennial. The holdfast with one to many erect shoots. The shoots dichotomously branched throughout, cylindrical near base, flattened in upper portion, without a midrib, with inconspicuous cryptostomata.

Heterosporous, monoecious. The sporangia unilocular and developed within conceptacles at the tips of the ultimate dichotomies. The macrosporangium ("oögonium") producing one large nonflagellate uninucleate functional macrospore and a small nonfunctional seven-nucleate macrospore. The microsporangium ("antheridium") producing 128 small biflagellate microspores ("antherozoids"). "Egg" and "antherozoid" uniting to form a zygote, which immediately begins to develop into a new thallus.

STRUCTURE AND REPRODUCTION. Gardner, 1910, p. 130; pl. 16, figs. 1–7. Holz, 1903 (as *Pelvetia*).

Pelvetiopsis limitata (Setchell) Gardner   Pl. 33, fig. 1

*Gardner, 1910, p. 127; pl. 16, figs. 1–7. *Gardner, 1913, p. 321; pl. 38, figs 8–16; pl. 39. Setchell and Gardner, 1925, p. 703; pl. 46, fig. 6.
Pelvetia fastigiata forma *limitata* Setchell in Phyc. Bor.-Amer. No. 1238.

Thalli, as found on the Monterey Peninsula, 4–8 cm. tall; light tan in color. Erect shoots usually arcuate, three to five times dichotomous and with the interval between successive dichotomies 5–15 mm.; the dichotomies about 2 mm. broad. The receptacles 5–10 mm. long, inflated, somewhat broader than sterile portions of thallus, simple or bifurcate, with acute apices.

LOCAL DISTRIBUTION. Growing on rocks between the 6.0- and 3.5-foot tide levels. Usually on the tops of rocks but at times on the sides. Point Pinos; Asilomar Point; Point Joe; Fanshell Beach; Cypress Point; Pescadero Point; north end of Carmel Beach; Mission Point.

TYPE LOCALITY. Land's End, Sán Francisco, California.

PACIFIC COAST DISTRIBUTION. British Columbia (Vancouver Island) to central California (Carmel Highlands).

The forma *lata* (Gardner, 1910, p. 127. Gardner, 1913, p. 321; pl. 40) has been collected at Asilomar Point. It is taller (up to 15 cm.), has segments up to 3 mm. broad, and has larger receptacles. The shoots of the form are not arcuately curved as in typical *P. limitata*. The form has been distributed as No. CXIV of the Phycotheca Boreali-Americana.

Family SARGASSACEAE

Thalli perennial; differentiated into holdfast, stipe, and branches of various orders. Primary branches arising on all sides of stipe and usually much longer than it, at times not sharply differentiated from stipe. The branches pinnately branched, flattened to cylindrical, the ultimate branchlets frequently with air-filled vesicles. The branches disintegrating after fruiting.

Reproduction in the manner typical of the class but the macro-sporangium ("oögonium") usually producing a single macrospore ("egg").

With one genus, *Cystoseira,* in the local flora.

Cystoseira C. A. Agardh, 1820

Thalli perennial; differentiated into holdfast, stipe, and branches of various orders. The holdfast conical and woody. The stipe erect, angular, woody, terminating in a single apical cell. The branches radially arranged on stipe, cylindrical throughout or flattened in lower portion and cylindrical in upper portion. Ultimate branchlets at times with a single or a catenate row of air-filled vesicles a short distance back from the tip.

Heterosporous, monoecious or dioecious. The sporangia unilocular and developed within conceptacles at the tips of the ultimate branchlets. The macrosporangia ("oögonia") producing a single nonflagellate functional macrospore ("egg") and seven naked nuclei. The microsporangia ("antheridia") producing and liberating many (64 ?) biflagellate microspores ("antherozoids"). "Egg" and "antherozoid" uniting to form a zygote, which immediately begins to develop into a new thallus.

STRUCTURE AND REPRODUCTION. Gardner, 1910, p. 131; pl. 17, fig. 18. Nienburg, 1913, pp. 3–7; fig. 1. Valiante, 1883.

Cystoseira osmundacea (Menzies) C. A. Agardh   Pl. 34

C. A. Agardh, 1820, p. 69. Gardner, 1913, p. 333; pls. 51–52. Setchell and Gardner, 1925, p. 709. Phyc. Bor.-Amer. Nos. XCVI, CXV*A.*
    Fucus osmundaceus Menzies ex Turner, 1809, p. 91; pl. 105.
    Cystoseira expansa C. A. Agardh, 1824, p. 290. *Harvey, 1852, p. 66; pl. 1, fig. *B.*
    Cystoseira Douglasii *Harvey, 1841, p. 407.
    Halidrys osmundacea (Menzies) Harvey, 1841, p. 407. *Harvey, 1852, p. 64; pl. 2. *Anderson, 1891, p. 221. *Howe, 1893, p. 67.
    Cystoseira osmundacea forma *expansa* (C. A. Agardh) *Setchell in Phyc. Bor.-Amer. No. XLVIII. Gardner, 1913, p. 336; pl. 53. Setchell and Gardner, 1925, p. 709.

Thalli, as found on the Monterey Peninsula, up to 7.5 m. tall; blackish-brown below, light tan in upper portion. The stipe geniculate, nearly triangular in cross section; surface covered with depressions—the scars of old branches. The primary branches flattened in lower portion and the secondary branches borne on flattened portion also flattened. Upper portion of primary branches and secondary branches on it cylindrical. Ultimate branchlets of cylindrical portion with a catenate series of 5–12 small vesicles. Receptacles developing in portion of branchlets above the vesicles. Thalli dioecious.

LOCAL DISTRIBUTION. Growing on rocks between the mean low-tide and −1.5-foot tide levels. Mussel Point; Point Pinos; Asilomar Point; Cypress Point; Pescadero Point; Mission Point. Also dredged from a depth of 20–35 feet near Mussel Point and near Point Aulon.

TYPE LOCALITY. Trinidad, California.

PACIFIC COAST DISTRIBUTION. Northern Oregon (Seaside) to Baja California (Ensenada).

Although perennial, the thalli have branch tips with distinctive catenate vesicles only from late spring until early fall. The forma *expansa* intergrades so gradually with typical *C. osmundacea* that it does not seem worth while to recognize it as distinct.

DIVISION RHODOPHYTA

Cells uninucleate or multinucleate; with the photosynthetic pigments localized in one or more plastids (chromatophores) and masked by a red pigment (phycoerythrin). The thalli rarely unicellular; usually multicellular and either filamentous or nonfilamentous. Nonfilamentous thalli cylindrical, compressed or foliaceous; branched or unbranched; with or without differences between superficial and deep-lying cells.

Asexual reproduction by nonflagellate naked spores either produced by direct metamorphosis of a vegetative cell or produced within a sporangium. The sporangium either producing a single spore (monospore), four spores (tetraspores), or a small indefinite number of spores (polyspores).

Sexual reproduction by passive transportation of a small nonflagellate male gamete (spermatium) to a hair-like extension (trichogyne) of the one-celled female sex organ (carpogonium). The spermatia produced singly within one-celled male sex organs (spermatangia). The zygote either dividing to form carpospores or giving rise directly or indirectly to special filaments (gonimoblasts) all or certain of whose cells develop into carposporangia each containing a single carpospore. The mass of carpospores, or the carposporangia plus the gonimoblasts and the cell bearing them, constituting the cystocarp.

Class RHODOPHYCEAE

All Rhodophyta are placed in a single class, the Rhodophyceae, whose characters are the same as those of the division.

KEY TO THE SUBCLASSES OF RHODOPHYCEAE

1. Cells without cytoplasmic connections, cell division intercalary, carpospores formed by division of zygote......*Bangioideae* (p. 160)
1. Cells with cytoplasmic connections, cell division rarely intercalary, carpospores produced in carposporangia borne on gonimoblast filaments ....*Florideae* (p. 176)

159

Subclass BANGIOIDEAE

Cells uninucleate, usually with a single stellate chromatophore containing one pyrenoid. Thalli rarely unicellular; usually multicellular, filamentous or nonfilamentous, with cell division intercalary. Nonfilamentous thalli either cylindrical or a flattened sheet; in either case with superficial and deep-lying cells alike.

Asexual reproduction either by a direct metamorphosis of vegetative cells or by division of a vegetative cell to form spores.

Sexual reproduction definitely known for relatively few genera. The spermatia formed by division and redivision of a vegetative cell. The carpogonium with a very short trichogyne and formed by direct metamorphosis of a vegetative cell. The zygote dividing and redividing to form carpospores.

Order BANGIALES

All Bangioideae are placed in a single order, the Bangiales, whose characters are the same as those of the subclass.

Key to the Families in the Local Flora

1. Spore formation not immediately preceded by cell
   division ....*Goniotrichaceae* (p. 160)
1. Spore formation immediately preceded by cell division............. 2
   2. The division diagonal, asymmetrical, and the spore formed
      only from the smaller daughter cell...*Erythrotrichiaceae* (p. 162)
   2. The division not diagonal, the daughter cells equal in size
      and all producing spores...................*Bangiaceae* (p. 166)

Family GONIOTRICHACEAE

Thalli filamentous, branched, with the cells seriate and separated from one another by gelatinous material. The cells ovoid or cylindrical, uninucleate, each usually with a single stellate chromatophore.

Asexual reproduction by direct metamorphosis of vegetative cells into spores and the spore formation not immediately preceded by cell division.

Sexual reproduction unknown.

Key to the Genera in the Local Flora

1. Cells with a single axial stellate chromatophore..*Goniotrichum* (p. 161)
1. Cells with several parietal disc-shaped chromato-
   phores ....*Goniotrichopsis* (p. 161)

Goniotrichum Kützing, 1843

Thalli microscopic. The plant body an erect irregularly or pseudodichotomously branched filament. The filament consisting of a homogeneous gelatinous matrix within which the cells are serially embedded. The cells separated from one another by gelatinous material, cylindrical to disc-shaped, with a single stellate chromatophore.

Asexual reproduction by direct transformation of vegetative cells into spores which are liberated by dissolution or rupture of gelatinous matrix lateral to them.

Sexual reproduction unknown.

STRUCTURE AND REPRODUCTION. Rosenvinge, 1909, pp. 75–77, figs. 15–16.

Goniotrichum elegans (Chauvin) Zanardini Pl. 35, figs. 1–2

Zanardini, 1847, p. 69. Rosenvinge, 1909, p. 75; figs. 15–16. *Kylin, 1941, p. 3. Phyc. Bor.-Amer. No. 781.
Bangia elegans Chauvin, 1842, p. 33.

Filaments, as found on the Monterey Peninsula, up to 5 mm. tall; the cells olive-green to rose-red in color. The filaments frequently uniseriate, more rarely multiseriate and two or three cells broad. Branching predominately pseudodichotomous. Breadth of filaments (including sheath) 12–35 μ. Length of cells 0.5–3 times the breadth.

LOCAL DISTRIBUTION. On *Abietinaria* sp. at mean low-tide level. Mussel Point. Also dredged from a depth of 35–40 feet near Mussel Point; from 25–30 feet near Point Aulon; and from 20–25 feet near Pescadero Rock.

TYPE LOCALITY. West coast of France.

PACIFIC COAST DISTRIBUTION. Known only from Friday Harbor, Washington; the Monterey Peninsula; and San Pedro, California.

There is a rather involved nomenclatorial problem as to whether this species should be called *G. elegans* or *G. Alsidii* (Zanardini) Howe. The former name is here selected because of its widespread usage in phycological literature.

Goniotrichopsis G. M. Smith, 1943

Thalli microscopic. The plant body an erect dichotomously branched filament in which the branching resembles the false branching of Myxophyceae. The filament with a homogeneous gelatinous matrix and the cells not touching one another. Basal cells of filaments without rhizoids. The filaments at first uniseriate; later becoming multiseriate except for the branch tips and for the region below the first branching. The cells cylindrical to spherical; each with several small parietal disc-shaped chromatophores without pyrenoids. Cell division intercalary.

Reproduction unknown.

STRUCTURE AND REPRODUCTION. Smith and Hollenberg, 1943, pp. 211–213; figs. 1–5.

Goniotrichopsis sublittoralis G. M. Smith   Pl. 35, figs. 8–10

*G. M. Smith apud Smith and Hollenberg, 1943, p. 211; figs. 1–5.

Thalli up to 850 μ tall; becoming three to four times dichotomous. The branches up to 40 μ in diameter. The cells 8–12 μ in diameter and bright rose-red in color.

LOCAL DISTRIBUTION. Usually epiphytic on Florideae, especially *Callophyllis,* but occasionally growing on rocks. Repeatedly dredged from a depth of 30–35 feet a quarter-mile from Municipal Wharf, Monterey.

TYPE LOCALITY. As above.

PACIFIC COAST DISTRIBUTION. As above.

Family ERYTHROTRICHIACEAE

Thalli filamentous or nonfilamentous. Filamentous thalli branched or unbranched; nonfilamentous thalli either cylindrical, saccate, or monostromatic. The cells uninucleate and with a single stellate chromatophore.

Asexual reproduction by the formation of monospores. The monospores formed by an unequal diagonal division of a vegetative cell and a development of the smaller daughter cell into a spore.

Sexual reproduction by division and redivision of a vegetative cell into a number of spermatia and by a direct metamorphosis of a vegetative cell into a carpogonium. The zygote dividing directly into a number of carpospores.

KEY TO THE GENERA IN THE LOCAL FLORA

1. Thalli erect ....*Erythrotrichia* (p. 162)
1. Thalli prostrate, crustose, monostromatic.......*Erythrocladia* (p. 165)

Erythrotrichia Areschoug, 1850

Thalli erect, filamentous from base to apex or only filamentous in basal portion. Attached either by a basal cell, by prostrate rhizoidal filaments, or by a multicellular disc. Erect filaments branched or unbranched, the upper end when more than one cell broad either cylindrical or flattened. Cell division intercalary. Cells with a single stellate chromatophore containing one pyrenoid.

Asexual reproduction by the formation of monospores. The monospores formed by an unequal diagonal division of a vegetative cell and a development of the smaller daughter cell into a spore.

Homothallic. The spermatangia produced in same manner as spores. The carpogonium with a short trichogyne and formed by direct metamorphosis of a vegetative cell. The zygote developing directly into a single carpospore or dividing to form two or more carpospores.

STRUCTURE AND REPRODUCTION. Berthold, 1882, pp. 1-21; pl. 1, figs. 15-25.

KEY TO THE SPECIES IN THE LOCAL FLORA

1. Erect portion of thallus unbranched.............................. 2
1. Erect portion of thallus branched at base..............*E. Welwitschii*
  2. Erect portion wholly filamentous ....*E. carnea*
  2. Erect portion filamentous at base only......................... 3
3. Distal end of erect portion flattened.....................*E. pulvinata*
3. Distal end of erect portion cylindrical..................*E. californica*

Erythrotrichia Welwitschii (Ruprecht) Batters
Pl. 36, figs. 1-2

Batters, 1902, p. 55. Hamel, 1924, p. 290; fig. II-3.
Cruoria Welwitschii Ruprecht, 1851, p. 332; pl. 18, fig. 1.

Thalli, as found on the Monterey Peninsula, up to 3 mm. tall; olive-colored at base, reddish-pink in upper portion. The erect portion uniseriate from base to apex; with a few branches a short distance above point of attachment. Filaments of local plants 9–10 μ broad at base and up to 30 μ broad in upper portion. Spore formation restricted to upper part of filament; the wall cutting off a spore only slightly diagonal.

LOCAL DISTRIBUTION. On rocks in a tide pool at the 1.0-foot tide level at first point north of Carmel Beach. On stipe of *Nereocystis Luetkeana* cast ashore on south end of Carmel Beach.

TYPE LOCALITY. Lisbon, Portugal.

PACIFIC COAST DISTRIBUTION. Known only from the Monterey Peninsula.

The plants growing on *Nereocystis* had an extensive crustose monostromatic (?) base. Those growing on rock were so firmly affixed that their method of attachment is uncertain, but there is nothing indicating that the filaments had individual basal discs.

Erythrotrichia carnea (Dillwyn) J. G. Agardh   Pl. 35, figs. 3–7

J. G. Agardh, 1883, p. 15.   Taylor, 1937, p. 217; pl. 28, figs. 13–15.
Conferva carnea Dillwyn, 1809; pl. 84.

Thalli, as found on the Monterey Peninsula, up to 8 mm. tall; of a bright pink color. Attached by a lobed basal cell or by short rhizoidal outgrowths from the basal cell. Erect portion unbranched, uniseriate from base to apex. The filaments 6–10 µ broad at base, 15–25 µ broad near apex. Cells of upper portion with a breadth 2–3 times the length.

LOCAL DISTRIBUTION. Occurring sparingly on a wide variety of algae growing between the 2.0- and −1.5-foot tide levels. Municipal Wharf, Monterey; Mussel Point; Point Pinos; Middle Reef of Moss Beach; Pebble Beach; Mission Point. Also dredged from a depth of 30–35 feet a quarter-mile from Municipal Wharf, Monterey; and near Point Aulon.

TYPE LOCALITY. England.

PACIFIC COAST DISTRIBUTION. Known only from the Monterey Peninsula but probably of wide distribution.

Uniseriate unbranched plants without a basal disc are usually referred to *E. carnea*. Some of the local plants have a more extensive rhizoidal base than is usually described for the species.

Erythrotrichia pulvinata Gardner   Pl. 36, fig. 3

*Gardner, 1927, p. 238; pl. 24, figs. 1–3.

Thalli epiphytic on tips of utricles of *Codium fragile*. Attached by a multicellular, cushion-like, basal disc. The disc eventually bearing several erect shoots. The shoots uniseriate when young; older shoots uniseriate below and with upper portion monostromatic and 6–8 cells broad. The cells with a single stellate chromatophore containing one pyrenoid. Spore formation unknown.

LOCAL DISTRIBUTION. Mussel Point; Fanshell Beach; Cypress Point; Pebble Beach; Mission Point. Also on sides of branches of *Ceramium Codicola* at Mussel Point.

TYPE LOCALITY. Pebble Beach, Monterey Peninsula, California.

PACIFIC COAST DISTRIBUTION. As above.

Since the spores are unknown, there is an equal justification for considering this distinctive alga a *Porphyra*. One argument for this is the fact that its base is similar to that of *P. naiadum*. Another, though negative, argument is the fact that all other species of *Erythrotrichia* regularly form the spores characteristic of the genus, whereas *E. pulvinata* does not.

Erythrotrichia californica Kylin   Pl. 36, figs. 4–5

*Kylin, 1941, p. 3; figs. 1*A*–1*D*.

Thalli epiphytic, up to 12 mm. tall; of a bright pink color. Attached by short rhizoidal filaments in lower portion. Erect portion unbranched; uniseriate in lower portion, above this with transverse tiers of four (occasionally eight) cells. Each cell with a stellate chromatophore containing one pyrenoid. Erect portion 12–16 μ in diameter near base, up to 50 μ in diameter near apex. The rhizoidal filaments at times producing erect filaments. Spore formation restricted to multiseriate portion of thallus and the wall cutting off the spore markedly curved.

LOCAL DISTRIBUTION. Epiphytic on *Chondria decipiens*. Municipal Wharf, Monterey.

TYPE LOCALITY. As above.

PACIFIC COAST DISTRIBUTION. As above.

Erythrocladia Rosenvinge, 1909

Thalli microscopic, horizontally expanded and usually monostromatic. Growing upon other algae or upon hydroids. The thallus composed of radiately branched filaments with the branches free from one another or laterally compacted into a pseudoparenchymatous disc. Growth of thallus marginal. Cells with a single stellate chromatophore containing one pyrenoid.

Asexual reproduction by the formation of monospores. The monospores formed by an unequal diagonal division of a vegetative cell and a development of the smaller daughter cell into a spore.

Homothallic. Spermatangia apparently produced in same manner as monospores. The carpogonium with a short trichogyne and produced by direct metamorphosis of a vegetative cell. The zygote developing into a single carpospore or dividing to form more than one carpospore.

STRUCTURE AND REPRODUCTION. Howe and Hoyt, 1916, pp. 112–116; pl. 12, figs. 1–11; pl. 13. Rosenvinge, 1909, pp. 71–75; figs. 11–14.

KEY TO THE SPECIES IN THE LOCAL FLORA

1. Branches compacted into a pseudoparenchymatous disc...*E. subintegra*
1. Branches, at least at thallus margin, not laterally
     adjoined ....*E. irregularis*

Erythrocladia subintegra Rosenvinge   Pl. 36, fig. 6

Rosenvinge, 1909, p. 73; figs. 13–14. Kylin, 1925, p. 9; figs. 3C–3G. *Kylin, 1941, p. 3.

Thalli monostromatic, disc-shaped, up to 125 μ in diameter. Entire thallus with cells laterally adjoined and radiating in regular rows from the center. Central cells isodiametric or longer than broad; up to 15 μ in diameter.

LOCAL DISTRIBUTION. Growing on various algae. Mussel Point; Moss Beach; Pebble Beach.

TYPE LOCALITY. Denmark.

PACIFIC COAST DISTRIBUTION. Known only from Friday Harbor, Washington; and from the Monterey Peninsula.

This species, like others of the genus, is usually overlooked unless the host is semitransparent. This epiphyte shows up to best advantage on empty cells of *Chaetomorpha* that have discharged their zooids.

Erythrocladia irregularis Rosenvinge   Pl. 37, fig. 1

Rosenvinge, 1909, p. 72; figs. 11–12. Kylin, 1925, p. 9; figs. 3A–3B.

Thalli monostromatic, irregular in outline, up to 170 μ in diameter. Center or thallus with polygonal cells 6–7.5 μ in diameter and irregularly arranged in a pseudoparenchymatous sheet. Marginal portion of thallus with irregularly branched filaments not laterally adjoined to one another. Cells of marginal portion 3–4 μ broad and with a length 2–3 times the breadth. Cells with a single stellate chromatophore containing one pyrenoid. Monospores usually formed only in central portion of thallus.

LOCAL DISTRIBUTION. On margins of blades of *Porphyra variegata* cast ashore at Moss Beach.

TYPE LOCALITY. Denmark.

PACIFIC COAST DISTRIBUTION. Known only from Friday Harbor, Washington, and from the Monterey Peninsula.

Family BANGIACEAE

Thalli nonfilamentous; cylindrical, or flattened and monostromatic or distromatic. The cells uninucleate, with a single stellate chromatophore containing one pyrenoid.

Asexual reproduction by division of a vegetative cell into two, four, or more cells each of which becomes a spore.

Homothallic or heterothallic. Spermatangia formed by division and redivision of a vegetative cell. The carpogonia with a short trichogyne and formed by direct metamorphosis of a vegetative cell. The zygote usually dividing into 4, 8, 16, or 32 carpospores.

KEY TO THE GENERA IN THE LOCAL FLORA

1. Thalli cylindrical ....*Bangia* (p. 167)
1. Thalli flattened, monostromatic or distromatic..................... 2
   2. Carpospores in packets of 4–32................*Porphyra* (p. 168)
   2. Carpospores not in packets of 4–32...........*Porphyrella* (p. 175)

<h2>Bangia Lyngbye, 1819</h2>

Thalli erect, cylindrical, unbranched. When young, uniseriate throughout; later becoming more than one cell broad in the upper portion. Young thalli attached by the lowermost cell; older thalli with a basal disc formed by tips of intramatrical rhizoids growing down from lower cells of uniseriate portion. Cells of uniseriate portion cylindrical below, disc-shaped above; cells of multiseriate portion angular to cubical; arranged in transverse rows. Each cell with a single stellate chromatophore containing one pyrenoid.

Asexual reproduction by direct division of vegetative cells into two, four, or more spores. Spore formation of frequent occurrence and at any stage in development of thallus.

Homothallic or heterothallic. Spermatangia formed by division and redivision of vegetative cells. Carpogonia with short trichogynes and formed by direct metamorphosis of vegetative cells. The zygote dividing to form four or eight carpospores.

STRUCTURE AND REPRODUCTION. Berthold, 1882. Darbishire, 1898. Kylin, 1921, pp. 2–5; figs. 1–3.

With one species in the local flora.

Bangia vermicularis Harvey   Pl. 37, figs. 4–6

Harvey, 1858, p. 55; pl. 49, fig. *A*. *Anderson, 1891, p. 221. *Kylin, 1941, p. 4. Phyc. Bor.-Amer. No. 582.

Thalli, as found on the Monterey Peninsula, 1.5–3 cm. tall during the summer and the plant mass a rusty brown color, 6–10 cm. tall during autumn and early winter and the plant mass usually bluish-black. Uniseriate lower portion up to 70 µ in diameter and with the lowermost 10–80 cells producing intramatrical rhizoids. Multiseriate upper portion up to 250 µ in diameter, broadest at the upper end, where it may be hollow, vermiform, and constricted at intervals.

LOCAL DISTRIBUTION. Growing between the 5.0- and 2.0-foot tide levels and forming an extensive coating on rocks. Arch Rock; Point Joe; Pescadero Point; Pebble Beach; Mission Point.

TYPE LOCALITY. San Francisco, California.

PACIFIC COAST DISTRIBUTION. Central California (Bolinas to Carmel Bay).

The course of development of this alga has been followed upon the same rock for several successive years at Pebble Beach. The alga usually appears late in the spring, and throughout the summer a large majority of the plants are less than 2 cm. tall. Specimens collected during the summer resemble the common species of the Atlantic Ocean, *B. fuscopurpurea* (Dillwyn) Lyngbye. From the middle of October until early in January the plants are 6–10 cm. tall. Plants collected on the Monterey Peninsula do not have as marked an inflation of the thallus apex as is shown in the figure of Harvey.

Porphyra C. A. Agardh, 1824

Thalli with monostromatic or distromatic blades. The blades arising singly from a disc-shaped holdfast composed of rhizoids, or in gregarious clusters from a common multicellular, hemispherical, cushion-like base. The blades sessile or with a minute stipe, entire or deeply laciniate, flattened or with conspicuously ruffled margins. With the cells embedded in a colorless gelatinous matrix. Each cell with one or two stellate chromatophores containing one pyrenoid.

Asexual reproduction by spores formed by bi- or quadripartition of vegetative cells in a plane perpendicular to surface of blade.

Homothallic or heterothallic. Spermatangia in packets of 16, 32, 64, or 128 and formed by successive transverse and vertical division of vegetative cells. Spermatangial packets adjoining one another at thallus margin. Carpogonia with very short trichogynes and formed by direct metamorphosis of vegetative cells. The zygote dividing into 4, 8, 16, 32, or 64 carpospores. The packets of carpospores (cystocarps) at thallus margin and usually adjoining one another.

STRUCTURE AND REPRODUCTION. Berthold, 1882. Dangeard, 1927. G. M. Smith, 1938, pp. 302–305; fig. 165.

Porphyra naiadum Anderson   Pl. 40, fig. 1

Anderson apud Blankinship and Keeler, 1892, p. 148. *Howe, 1893, p. 67. *Hus, 1902, p. 212; pl. 21, figs. 19–22. *Kylin, 1941, p. 4. *Phyc. Bor-Amer. No. 632.

Thalli, as found on the Monterey Peninsula, 1–5 cm. tall; purplish-red to a deep purple in color. With 5–30 blades growing from a hemispherical multicellular base several cells in thickness. Young blades obovate; older blades broadly obcuneate and stipe-like in lower portion. Blades monostromatic, 25–30 μ in thickness in vegetative portion. The cells cubical, 15–20 μ in diameter; each with a single massive stellate chromatophore. Heterothallic (?). The carpospores in adjoining packets of 8 at margin of thallus.

LOCAL DISTRIBUTION. Epiphytic on leaves of *Phyllospadix*. Plants annual: appearing early in spring and disappearing late in autumn. Abundant wherever the host is present.

TYPE LOCALITY. Santa Cruz, California.

PACIFIC COAST DISTRIBUTION. British Columbia (Vancouver Island) to southern California (San Diego).

The forma *major* Hus (*Hus, 1902, p. 213. *Phyc. Bor-Amer. No. 875) with blades up to 8 cm. tall is epiphytic on *Zostera*. It has been found locally on blades of the host cast ashore at Monterey.

Porphyra lanceolata (Setchell and Hus) G. M. Smith

Pl. 38, figs. 1–2; pl. 40, fig. 3

*G. M. Smith apud Smith and Hollenberg, 1943, p. 213; figs. 8–10.

Porphyra perforata forma *lanceolata* *Setchell and Hus apud Hus, 1900, p. 65. *Hus, 1902, p. 208. Phyc. Bor.-Amer. No. 683.

With blades of male and female plants different in shape but both, as found on the Monterey Peninsula, up to 1 m. tall; steel-gray to brownish-purple in color. Blades of male plants not over 6 cm. broad, narrowly linear and usually spirally twisted, gradually attenuated at upper end and rarely with the apex longitudinally incised. Blades of female plants up to 12 cm. broad, lanceolate, deeply ruffled at margins, not gradually attenuated at apex and frequently with a deep apical incision. Blades of both male and female plants monostromatic; about 100 μ in thickness at margin, up to 200 μ in central portion just above the base. The cells ellipsoidal, 50–60 μ tall, with two stellate chromatophores each containing an indistinct pyrenoid. Cells in upper part of blade with chromatophores nearly filling cell; those at base of blade with a broad space between the chromatophores. Male plants with a continuous cream-colored margin 1–2 mm. wide and one in which every cell divides to form 128 spermatia. Female plants with the fertile margin 10–25 mm. wide, brownish-red in color, and with intermingled groups of vegetative cells and carpospores in packets of 32. As seen in surface view, the packets of carpospores frequently in hieroglyphic-like lines.

LOCAL DISTRIBUTION. Growing on rocks between the 4.0- and 2.5-foot tide levels. Appearing early in winter and persisting until late in summer. Asilomar Point; Point Joe; Fanshell Beach; Pescadero Point; Mission Point; mouth of Carmel River.

TYPE LOCALITY. Not stated.

PACIFIC COAST DISTRIBUTION. Washington (Chehalis Bay) to central California (Carmel Bay).

Porphyra pulchra Hollenberg   Pl. 39, figs. 2–3

*Hollenberg apud Smith and Hollenberg, 1943, p. 213; figs. 11–12.

Thalli up to 27 cm. tall; steel-gray to violet and at times with the color mottled. The blades sessile or with a small stipe; lanceolate to orbicular, with cells near the point of attachment producing rhizoidal outgrowths. Blades monostromatic, 50–90 μ in thickness. Gelatinous matrix of blade homogeneous. The cells 25–45 μ tall; each with two chromatophores. Homothallic. Spermatangia in packets of 64 or 128 grouped in oblong to linear sori which usually extend lengthwise at margin of blade. Carpospores in packets of 16 or 32, at margin of thallus and intermingled with vegetative cells.

LOCAL DISTRIBUTION. Epiphytic on various of the larger algae growing between the 2.5- and 0.5-foot tide levels. Pescadero Point; Mission Point; rocks at mouth of Carmel River. Also epiphytic on *Phyllospadix* cast ashore at Moss Beach.

TYPE LOCALITY. Moss Beach, Pacific Grove, California.

PACIFIC COAST DISTRIBUTION. Known only from Santa Cruz, California, and from the Monterey Peninsula.

Porphyra Nereocystis Anderson Pl. 37, p. 7

*Anderson, 1891, p. 221 (name only). Anderson apud Blankinship and Keeler, 1892, p. 149. *Howe, 1893, p. 67. *Hus, 1900, p. 65. *Hus, 1902, p. 210; pl. 20, figs. 11–12. *Phyc. Bor.-Amer. No. 583.

Thalli, as found on the Monterey Peninsula, usually 25–90 cm. tall but occasionally up to 3 m.; deep pink to a dull purplish-red in color. The blades subsessile and with a disc-shaped base; at first flattened and broadly linear to broadly ovate, later becoming concave in basal portion and ill-defined in shape because of laciniation of margins. Blades monostromatic, 25–60 μ in thickness in vegetative portion. Homothallic. The spermatangia in packets of 128 and lying in sharply defined, light-colored, spots and streaks between the packets of carpospores. The carpospores in packets of 32 adjoining one another at margin of thallus.

LOCAL DISTRIBUTION. Epiphytic on stipes of *Nereocystis Luetkeana* and usually restricted to the portion 3–6 m. below the pneumatocyst. Thalli annual and generally found only from November to June. At times present in abundance on host plants cast ashore on Moss Beach and on Carmel Beach.

TYPE LOCALITY. Santa Cruz, California.

PACIFIC COAST DISTRIBUTION. Alaska (Uyak Bay) to southern California (San Pedro).

Porphyra Thuretii Setchell and Dawson mss. Pl. 40, fig. 2

Porphyra leucosticta Hus [not of Thuret]. *Hus, 1900, p. 63. *Hus, 1902, p. 199; pl. 20, figs. 1–3.

Thalli, as found on the Monterey Peninsula, up to 75 cm. tall; of a rich rose-red color. With a disc-shaped base bearing a single blade. The blade broadly reniform, usually broader than tall, markedly cordate at base; with a short, but distinct, stipe. Blades monostromatic, 25–50 μ in thickness. Cells subcubical, with a single stellate chromatophore. Homothallic. Spermatangia in packets of 64 and the packets adjoining one another in cream-colored streaks lying diagonal to margin of blade. Carpospores in packets of 8 and lying between the diagonal streaks of spermatangia. Thalli annual and found only during the spring months.

LOCAL DISTRIBUTION. On rocks at the 1.0-foot tide level; also epiphytic on *Gracilaria Sjoestedtii*. Pacific Grove; Point Aulon; Pebble Beach; Pescadero Rocks.

TYPE LOCALITY. Pacific Grove, California.

PACIFIC COAST DISTRIBUTION. Known only from Santa Cruz, California, the Monterey Peninsula, and from the Gulf of California, Mexico.

Porphyra perforata J. G. Agardh   Pl. 39, fig. 5

J. G. Agardh, 1883, p. 69. *Hus, 1900, p. 63. *Hus, 1902, p. 202; pl. 20, figs. 4–10. *Kylin, 1941, p. 4. Phyc. Bor.-Amer. No. 682.

Porphyra vulgaris Harvey [not of C. A. Agardh]. Harvey, 1841, p. 409. *Anderson, 1891, p. 221. *Howe, 1893, p. 67.

Thalli, as found on the Monterey Peninsula, up to 150 cm. tall; steel-gray to brownish-purple in color. The blades sessile and with a disc-shaped holdfast; lanceolate when young and with deeply ruffled margins, sometimes remaining lanceolate during further development but usually becoming deeply laciniate, irregularly shaped, and about as broad as long. Blades monostromatic, 45–140 μ in thickness. The cells ellipsoidal, 40–100 μ tall, each with a single centrally located stellate chromatophore containing one pyrenoid. Homothallic. The spermatangia and carpospores in patches along thallus margin. Spermatangial areas whitish, with the spermatangia in packets of 128. Carposporic areas reddish-brown, with the carpospores in packets of 32.

LOCAL DISTRIBUTION. Common everywhere on rocks between the 3.5- and 2.0-foot tide levels; at times epiphytic on other algae.

TYPE LOCALITY. "California."

PACIFIC COAST DISTRIBUTION. Alaska (Shumagin Islands) to southern California (San Diego).

The variety *segregata* Setchell and Hus (Setchell and Hus apud Hus, 1900, p. 64. Hus, 1902, p. 207. Phyc. Bor.-Amer. No. 684) has gray to brownish-purple thalli 2–20 cm. tall. The blades are oblong-lanceolate and with a more or less umbilicate base; older blades are frequently broadly expanded and deeply laciniate. The blades are not over 60 μ in thickness. The cells are approximately cubical and with a diameter about half that of the blade. Spermatangia and carpospores are as in typical *P. perforata*. This variety has been found at the 1.5-foot tide level at Mussel Point.

Porphyra schizophylla Hollenberg   Pl. 39, fig. 4; pl. 40, fig. 4

*Hollenberg apud Smith and Hollenberg, 1943, p. 213; figs. 6–7.

Thalli up to 15 cm. tall; yellowish to light brown in color. The blades sessile, approximately oblong, more or less laciniate, and with undulate-plicate margins. The blades distromatic, 200–250 μ in thickness. Gelatinous matrix of blade with a conspicuous line of separation between the two cell layers and with concentric stratifications internal to each cell. The cells lying close to thallus surface, pyriform, with the narrower end toward center of thallus, 20–25 μ in diameter. Each cell with a pale indistinct chromatophore occupying the outer third toward thallus surface. Heterothallic. The spermatangia in packets of 16 (32?) and lying in a 1 mm. broad whitish zone at thallus margin. All cells at margin of thallus dividing to form spermatangia. The carpospores in packets of 8 and lying in a 2–3 mm. broad purplish-brown to purplish-yellow zone at thallus margin. Carposporic plants frequently with isolated vegetative cells intermingled with the packets of carpospores.

LOCAL DISTRIBUTION. Growing near high-tide level on rocks swept by heavy surf. Pescadero Point.

TYPE LOCALITY. As above.

PACIFIC COAST DISTRIBUTION. As above.

Porphyra variegata Kjellman   Pl. 38, fig. 3

Kjellman ex *Hus, 1900, p. 69. *Hus, 1902, p. 225; pl. 21, fig. 18. Phyc. Bor.-Amer. No. 930.

Diploderma variegatum Kjellman, 1889, p. 33; pl. 2, figs. 1–4.

Thalli, as found on the Monterey Peninsula, usually 15–30 cm. tall, occasionally up to 110 cm.; brick-red to brownish-red in color. The blades sessile and with a disc-shaped holdfast. Blades lanceolate, with a broadly rounded base and the upper end gradually narrowing to a rounded tip. Margins of blade slightly undulate, with a colorless zone about 1 mm. broad along the edge. Blades distromatic, 100–220 μ in thickness. The cells spherical to subspherical, 10–12 μ in diameter; each surrounded by a gelatinous sheath with concentric layers and with additional layers on side toward surface of blade. Each cell with a single olive-green stellate chromatophore with blunt rays. Heterothallic. Spermatangia unknown. Carpospores in packets of 16 or 32, intermingled with vegetative cells and scattered throughout entire blade. Chromatophores of carpospores reddish-brown.

LOCAL DISTRIBUTION. Known only from specimens cast ashore. Found at Moss Beach; along the shore in from Seal Rock; at Pebble Beach; and at Carmel Beach.

TYPE LOCALITY. Bering Island, Kamchatka.

PACIFIC COAST DISTRIBUTION. Known only from Puget Sound and from the Monterey Peninsula.

Porphyra occidentalis Setchell and Hus   Pl. 39, fig. 1

*Setchell and Hus apud Hus, 1900, p. 69. *Hus, 1902, p. 228; pl. 21, figs. 15–17.

Thalli 15–30 cm. tall; of a rich cerise color. The blades sessile and with a disc-shaped holdfast. Shape of blade varying from linear to ovate; in either case with a broadly rounded base and the apex tapering to an acute point. Margins of blade slightly undulate. Blades distromatic, 45–75 μ in thickness. Cells sub-cubical, 12–15 μ in diameter, each with a single stellate chromatophore which lies on side of the cell toward the surface of thallus. Heterothallic (?). The spermatangia in packets of 64 and forming a continuous yellowish area along margins near tip of blade. Carpospores unknown. Apparently a spring annual. ·

LOCAL DISTRIBUTION. Growing on rocks between the 0.5- and −1.5-foot tide levels. Asilomar Point; Middle Reef of Moss Beach; south end of Carmel Beach. Also found on stipes of *Pterygophora californica* cast ashore at Carmel Beach.

TYPE LOCALITY. Carmel Bay, California.

PACIFIC COAST DISTRIBUTION. As above.

When originally described the spermatangia were considered the most distinctive feature of the species. Study of living specimens shows that the position of the chromatophores is an equally distinctive character.

Porphyra miniata forma cuneiformis Setchell and Hus

*Setchell and Hus apud Hus, 1900, p. 68. *Hus, 1902, p. 218; pl. 20, fig. 14. Phyc. Bor.-Amer. No. 929.

Thalli 15–50 cm. tall, reddish-purple in color. The blades with a disc-shaped holdfast. Blades lanceolate, with a cuneate base, and with ruffled margins. Blades distromatic throughout, or distromatic at center and monostromatic at margins; 30–75 μ in thickness. Cells subcubical. Homothallic. Spermatangia in packets of 8. Carpospores in packets of 4. The packets of spermatangia and carpospores intermingled with one another at thallus margin.

LOCAL DISTRIBUTION. Found cast ashore at Pacific Grove.
TYPE LOCALITY. Not stated.
PACIFIC COAST DISTRIBUTION. Known only from the Gulf of Alaska;
Coupeville, Washington; and the Monterey Peninsula.

Porphyrella Smith and Hollenberg, 1943

Thalli with one to several blades growing from a disc-shaped
to conical holdfast. The blades monostromatic, thin and delicate,
with cells in lower portion producing rhizoids which become intertwined and form the stipitate base of blade and the holdfast. Each
cell of a blade with a single stellate chromatophore containing
one pyrenoid.

Asexual reproduction by monospores formed in a continuous
zone at margin of thallus.

Homothallic. The spermatangia in packets grouped in small
scattered sori or in irregular patches near the blade margin. The
carpogonia produced near thallus margin; the zygote not dividing
to form a packet of carpospores; the zygotes (carpospores?) re-
leased singly by disintegration of blade margins.

STRUCTURE AND REPRODUCTION. Smith and Hollenberg, 1943, pp. 215–
216; figs. 13–14.

Porphyrella Gardneri Smith and Hollenberg Pl. 37, figs. 2–3

Smith and Hollenberg, 1943, p. 215; figs. 13–14.
Porphyra Nereocystis forma. Gardner in Phyc. Bor.-Amer. No. 2297. *Kylin, 1941, p. 4.

Thalli, as found on the Monterey Peninsula, 2–3.5 cm. tall;
deep red to purplish-red in color. Usually with several blades from
a common holdfast. The holdfast disc-shaped; or somewhat conical and penetrating tissues of host. The blades cylindrically stipitate below; lanceolate when young, orbicular to cuneate when
mature. Cells of blade subcubical, 10–15 μ in diameter, with a
single stellate chromatophore. Spermatangia in packets of 64;
the packets in small scattered sori near thallus margin or in wedge-
shaped groups inwardly directed from thallus margin.

LOCAL DISTRIBUTION. Epiphytic on lateral margins of blades or *Lam-
inaria Andersonii* and on the tips of leaflets of *Egregia Menziesii*. Point
Joe; Pescadero Point; Mission Point; mouth of Carmel River.
TYPE LOCALITY. Point Joe, Monterey Peninsula, California.
PACIFIC COAST DISTRIBUTION. Known only from Cape Arago, Oregon;
Duxbury Reef, Marin County, California; and the Monterey Peninsula.

Subclass FLORIDEAE

Cells uninucleate or multinucleate, usually with several disc-shaped chromatophores. Thalli always multicellular and with cytoplasmic connections between the cells; filamentous or non-filamentous, monoaxial or multiaxial, with growth initiated by apical cells. Nonfilamentous thalli cylindrical or foliose, branched or unbranched, usually with marked differences between super-ficial and internal cells.

With a haploid sexual generation (gametophyte) that may or may not reproduce asexually by monospores produced within monosporangia or by polyspores produced several within a poly-sporangium.

The gametophyte with the spermatia produced within sperma-tangia. The spermatangia either borne in clusters, in sori, in con-ceptacles, or on special filaments. The carpogonium 1-celled and with a long trichogyne; always borne terminally on a special fila-ment—the carpogonial filament. Fertilization followed by a pro-duction of special filaments (gonimoblasts). The gonimoblasts either growing from the carpogonium or growing from a special cell (the auxiliary cell) to which has been transferred the zygote nucleus or a descendant from the zygote nucleus. The gonimo-blasts with all or certain of the cells developing into carposporan-gia. The carposporangia each usually containing a single carpo-spore but in exceptional cases containing four carpospores. The gonimoblast systems (carposporophytes or cystocarps) either borne singly, or borne adjacent to one another and in sori, in nemathecia, or in conceptacles. The cystocarps either at surface of thallus or deeply embedded within it, naked or surrounded by an enve-lope.

Division of zygote nucleus either reductional or equational. If reductional, the carpospores possessing haploid nuclei and germi-nating to form gametophytes. If equational, the carpospores pos-sessing diploid nuclei and germinating to form free-living diploid plants (tetrasporophytes) identical with gametophytes in size, form, and vegetative structure. The tetrasporophytes spore-pro-ducing. Typically with tetrasporangia each containing four spores but at times with polysporangia each containing more than four polyspores. Division of primary sporangial nuclei reductional (except in very rare cases); the tetraspores and polyspores with haploid nuclei and germinating to form gametophytes.

Order NEMALIONALES

Thalli monoaxial or multiaxial, filamentous or nonfilamentous. Filamentous thalli branched, without a true cortication. Nonfilamentous thalli usually cylindrical or compressed, rarely foliaceous, with or without the superficial cells compacted into a parenchymatous tissue.

Asexual reproduction usually by monospores; occasionally by the production of two or four spores within a sporangium.

Spermatangia usually in corymbose clusters, more rarely in sori. Carpogonial filaments 1- to 5-celled, rarely with branches from the lower cells. The gonimoblast filaments always growing directly from carpogonium; with a majority of the cells or only with the terminal cells developing into carposporangia. The cystocarps always separated from one another, superficial or deeply embedded within thallus, usually naked but sometimes surrounded by a special envelope. The carpospores always with haploid nuclei and never producing a tetrasporophytic generation.

Family CHANTRANSIACEAE

Thalli monoaxial; filamentous, uncorticated, freely branched and with the branching irregular or predominately unilateral. The cells usually with a single stellate chromatophore.

Asexual reproduction usually by monospores but at times the thalli producing sporangia containing two or four spores.

Spermatangia in loosely branched clusters. Carpogonial filaments 1- to 3-celled. The gonimoblast filaments loosely branched and with the terminal cells developing into carposporangia. The cystocarps freely exposed and without an envelope.

KEY TO THE GENERA IN THE LOCAL FLORA

1. All sporangia containing one spore............*Acrochaetium* (p. 178)
1. All or certain sporangia containing four spores. *Rhodochorton* (p. 181)

Acrochaetium Nägeli, 1862

Thalli microscopic, filamentous, epiphytic or epizoic, growing wholly external to or partially within host. Attached to host by a single basal cell, by a basal disc of a few cells, or by an extensively developed system of prostrate branches. Portion above base always erect and filamentous, uncorticated, usually unilaterally branched. Terminal cells of branches often ending in long colorless hairs. Cells of erect filaments each usually with a single stellate chromatophore.

Asexual reproduction by monospores produced within monosporangia borne laterally or terminally on erect filaments.

Sexual reproduction infrequent. Homothallic or heterothallic. Spermatangia borne in small clusters at tips of lateral branches. Carpogonial filaments one-celled, borne laterally on erect branches. Gonimoblast filaments growing directly upward from carpogonium, sparingly branched, only the terminal cells of branches developing into carposporangia.

STRUCTURE AND REPRODUCTION. Kylin, 1928, pp. 5–8; figs. 1–2. Kylin, 1930, pp. 5–6; fig. 1. Rosenvinge, 1909, pp. 80–134; figs. 18–60. (All as *Chantransia*.)

KEY TO THE SPECIES IN THE LOCAL FLORA

1. Thalli endophytic.....................................*A. Porphyrae*
1. Thalli epiphytic... 2
   2. Branching of erect filaments predominately opposite....*A. plumosum*
   2. Branching of erect filaments not predominately opposite.......... 3

3. Erect filaments with short series of branchlets, first on
   one side then on the other..........................*A. variabile*
3. Erect filaments with most branchlets on the same side............... 4
    4. Erect filaments with long branches restricted
       to basal portion ....*A. rhizoideum*
    4. Erect filaments with long branches on both upper
       and lower portions ....*A. Macounii*

Acrochaetium Porphyrae (Drew) comb. nov. Pl. 40, figs. 8–9

Rhodochorton Porphyrae Drew, 1928, p. 188; pl. 46, figs. 70–75.

Endophytic within blades of *Porphyra perforata;* restricted to basal portion of blades and forming purplish-red to brick-colored areas up to 5 cm. in diameter. Embedded within gelatinous matrix of host and the filaments lying parallel to its surface; frequently lying internal to both surfaces and with cross connecting branches. The cells cylindrical but somewhat narrower at ends; each with a stellate chromatophore containing a conspicuous pyrenoid. Monosporangia 7.5–9.5 µ broad, 8.0–14.0 µ long; borne on short unilaterally branched filaments projecting beyond surface of host.

LOCAL DISTRIBUTION. Point Aulon; Point Pinos; Point Joe; Fanshell Beach; Cypress Point; Mission Point.

TYPE LOCALITY. Land's End, San Francisco, California.

PACIFIC COAST DISTRIBUTION. Known only from San Francisco and the Monterey Peninsula.

Although present in abundance local specimens have not been found fruiting.

Acrochaetium variabile (Drew) comb. nov.

Rhodochorton variabile Drew, 1928, p. 174; pl. 38, fig. 28; pl. 39, figs. 30–31.

Thalli wholly epiphytic and not penetrating tissues of host. Basal portion growing horizontally over host and forming a layer two or more cells in thickness. Erect filaments with or without long branches, in either case with branchlets in short secund series first on one side of main filament and then on the other. Cells of main filaments 8–13 µ broad, with a length 3–4 times the breadth. Monosporangia restricted to branchlets, terminal or lateral, sessile or pedicellate, ovoid, 6–9 µ broad, 10–13 µ long.

LOCAL DISTRIBUTION. On *Laminaria Andersonii* at Cypress Point. On *Cumagloia Andersonii* at Pebble Beach. On *Pterygophora californica* cast ashore on Carmel Beach.

TYPE LOCALITY. Cypress Point, Monterey Peninsula, California.

PACIFIC COAST DISTRIBUTION. Washington (San Juan Island) to southern California (San Pedro).

Acrochaetium plumosum (Drew) comb. nov.

Rhodochorton plumosum Drew, 1928, p. 173; pl. 39, fig. 29.

Epiphytic on various Laminariales, including *Egregia Menziesii, Laminaria Andersonii,* and *Pterygophora californica.* Thalli wholly epiphytic and not penetrating tissues of host. Basal portion composed of creeping filaments. Erect filaments several millimeters tall; with many long branches borne at irregular intervals. Branchlets of axis and major branches in opposite pairs, alternate, or in short secund series. Lower cells of major branches 10–12 μ broad and with a length 3–4 times the breadth. The chromatophore parietal and with a single pyrenoid. Monosporangia terminal or lateral on branchlets, sessile or pedicellate, broadly ovoid, 7–9 μ broad, 10–13 μ long.

LOCAL DISTRIBUTION. Cypress Point.

TYPE LOCALITY. Fort Point, San Francisco, California.

PACIFIC COAST DISTRIBUTION. Central California (Tomales Bay to Carmel Bay).

Acrochaetium rhizoideum (Drew) comb. nov.

Rhodochorton rhizoideum Drew, 1928, p. 182; pl. 42, figs. 42–44.

Usually epiphytic on *Codium fragile.* Basal portion an extensively developed system of branched filaments tending to grow horizontally between utricles and cortical cells of host. Cells of basal portion irregularly shaped, 20 μ or more in diameter, with a single reticulate chromatophore or several ribbon-shaped chromatophores, with or without pyrenoids. Erect filaments occasionally unbranched, usually with several long irregularly arranged branches in lower portion. Upper portion of erect filaments with short secund branchlets. Cells of erect filaments 16–20 μ broad, with a length 2–4 times breadth, containing a parietal band-shaped chromatophore with 1–4 pyrenoids. Monosporangia terminal or lateral on branchlets, rarely sessile, ovoid, 16–25 μ broad, 22–35 μ long, the monospore with a stellate chromatophore.

Not known from the Monterey Peninsula.

The variety *patens* (Drew) comb. nov. (*Rhodochorton rhizoideum* var. *patens* *Drew, 1928, p. 183; pl. 42, fig. 45) has erect filaments that are usually unbranched. The cells of the erect filaments have a length but 1–2 times the breadth and the chromatophores have but one or two pyrenoids. This variety has been found epiphytic on *Cystoseira osmundacea* in Carmel Bay.

Acrochaetium Macounii (Collins) comb. nov.

Chantransia Macounii Collins, 1913, p. 113.
Rhodochorton Macounii (Collins) *Drew, 1928, p. 184; pl. 43, figs. 47–52; pl. 44, fig. 53.

Epiphytic on *Haplogloia Andersonii*. Young thalli with both erect and rhizoidal filaments developing directly from spore; older thalli with spore becoming obscure as the rhizoidal filaments develop into a mat running between peripheral filaments of host. Erect filaments up to 2 mm. tall, freely branched, the lower branches predominately secund and becoming many cells in length. Major branches with cells about 8 μ broad and with a length 3–4 times the breadth. Chromatophore parietal, with a pyrenoid. Monosporangia terminal and lateral on the branchlets, sometimes sessile on major branches, ovoid, 9–10 μ broad, about 14 μ long. Spermatangia terminal and lateral on densely branched branchlets. Cystocarps replacing a lateral branchlet, with 2 or 3 carposporangia, the carposporangia 10 μ broad, 15 μ long.

LOCAL DISTRIBUTION. Carmel Bay.
TYPE LOCALITY. Vancouver Island.
PACIFIC COAST DISTRIBUTION. As above.

Rhodochorton[1] Nägeli, 1862

Thalli microscopic, filamentous; epiphytic, epizoic, or free-living. Attached to substratum by a basal disc of a few cells or by prostrate filaments. Epiphytic and epizoic species with prostrate filaments penetrating host. Portion above the base, erect, filamentous, and generally unilaterally branched. Cells of erect branches usually with more than one disc- or ribbon-shaped chromatophore but sometimes with a single stellate axial chromatophore.

Asexual reproduction solely by tetraspores or by both monospores and tetraspores. Tetrasporangia and monosporangia borne laterally or terminally on the erect filaments.

---

[1] The systematic position of this genus is somewhat uncertain. The structure and development of the carposporophyte is that typical of Nemalionales, but at least two species have been described as having cystocarps and tetrasporangia produced on separate individuals. Confirmation of this presumed presence of an independent diploid tetrasporophytic generation would necessitate removal of *Rhodochorton* from the Nemalionales. Some phycologists have placed *Rhodochorton* in the Ceramiales, but this is incorrect because *Rhodochorton* does not have an auxiliary cell.

Sexual reproduction recorded for but few species. Homothallic or heterothallic. Spermatangia borne in small clusters on lateral branchlets of erect filaments. Carpogonial filaments one-celled, borne laterally on erect filaments (in exceptional cases intercalary). Gonimoblast filaments growing directly from carpogonium, rather freely branched, usually with only the terminal cells developing into carposporangia.

STRUCTURE AND REPRODUCTION. Drew, 1928. Drew, 1935. Rosenvinge, 1909, pp. 134–138, 388–397; figs. 61–64, 325–335.

KEY TO THE SPECIES IN THE LOCAL FLORA

1. Growing on rocks at high-tide level......................*R. Rothii*
1. Growing on algae or hydroids.................................. 2
   2. Growing on hydroids ....*R. concrescens*
   2. Growing on algae.. 3
3. Growing on genicula of *Calliarthron*..................*R. Amphiroae*
3. Not growing on articulated corallines.......................... 4
   4. Base of alga not penetrating host....................*R. Daviesii*
   4. Base of alga penetrating host............................... 5
5. Endophytic portion of alga unbranched.................*R. obscurum*
5. Endophytic portion of alga branched.................*R. subimmersum*

Rhodochorton Rothii (Turton) Nägeli   Pl. 41, figs. 1–2

Nägeli, 1862, p. 121; figs. 1, 3. Drew, 1928, p. 177. *Phyc. Bor.-Amer. No. LVI.
Conferva Rothii Turton, 1806, p. 1809.
Callithamnion Rothii (Turton) Lyngbye, 1819, p. 129; pl. 41, fig. *A*. *Anderson, 1891, p. 222.

Thallus forming an extensive, deep red, velvety coating on shaded rocks at extreme high-tide level. Not sharply differentiated into prostrate and erect filaments. Prostrate filaments densely interwoven and decumbent. Erect filaments sparingly and irregularly branched, length of branches almost equaling that of axis. Erect filaments at times attaining a height of 10–15 mm. and standing in penicillate tufts. Cells of erect filaments 10–20 µ broad and usually with a length 1.5–3 times the breadth. Cells with a reticulate parietal chromatophore without pyrenoids; the chromatophore frequently breaking up into several small, irregularly shaped pieces. Thalli perennial but fruiting only during winter months. Tetrasporangia borne terminally on short branchlets developing in loose clusters at tips of erect branches. Tetrasporangia, as found on the Monterey Peninsula, 15–23 µ broad, 22–26 µ long.

Growing at extreme high-tide level in caves and on the under side of ledges. Mussel Point; Point Pinos; Fanshell Beach; Pescadero Point; Pebble Beach; Mission Point.

Type Locality. France.

Pacific Coast Distribution. Alaska (St. Michael) to southern California (San Diego).

Rhodochorton concrescens Drew   Pl. 41, figs. 3–4

*Drew, 1928, p. 167; pl. 37, fig. 15.

Thalli growing on hydroids. The base an extensive monostromatic disc composed of laterally adjoined radiating filaments; cells in central portion of disc angular and 'many of them giving rise to erect filaments of 2–40 cells. The erect filaments simple, or branched and with the branching predominately unilateral; 6.5–10.5 μ in diameter, up to 275 μ tall. Cells of erect filaments cylindrical, slightly longer than broad, with 3–4 disc-shaped chromatophores that lie adjacent to the end walls. Tetrasporangia borne terminally on unbranched filaments, or at the ends of 2- or 3-celled lateral branches of erect filaments. The tetrasporangia subpyriform, 16–20 μ broad, 20–26 μ long.

Local Distribution. On *Abietinaria* sp. at mean low-tide level. Mussel Point. Also on *Abietinaria* sp. dredged from a depth of 25–30 feet near Point Aulon and from 35–40 feet near Point Pinos. On *Sertularella turgida.* Carmel Bay.

Type Locality. Carmel Bay, California.

Pacific Coast Distribution. As above.

The original description was based upon material from a single specimen of *Sertularella.* The alga has since been found to be rather common on *Abietinaria.* Here it is easily noted because of the red coloration of the host.

Rhodochorton Amphiroae Drew   Pl. 40, figs. 5–7

Drew, 1928, p. 179; pl. 40, figs. 34–37.

Thalli growing on uncalcified genicula of *Calliarthron.* Base of thallus an entangled mass of filaments some of which penetrate a short distance into host. The erect filaments about 1 mm. tall, irregularly branched in lower portion. Cells of erect filaments cylindrical, 20–25 μ broad, with a length 1–2 times the breadth. The cells with many minute parietal chromatophores. The tetrasporangia borne terminally on short lateral branchlets of erect filaments, ellipsoidal, 22–24 μ broad, 30–33 μ long.

LOCAL DISTRIBUTION. On *Calliarthron* growing at mean low-tide level. Asilomar Point; Point Joe. Also on *Calliarthron* dredged from a depth of 25–30 feet near Point Aulon.

TYPE LOCALITY. San Pedro, California.

PACIFIC COAST DISTRIBUTION. As above.

The foregoing description is of the alga as found on the Monterey Peninsula. The local plants differ from those of the type locality in breadth of erect filaments, in nature of chromatophore, and in having tetrasporangia instead of monosporangia. In spite of these differences it seems best to refer the local plant to *R. Amphiroae* because it is found in the same unique habitat as the southern plant.

Rhodochorton Daviesii (Dillwyn) Drew

*Drew, 1928, p. 172.
Conferva Daviesii Dillwyn, 1809, p. 73; pl. *F.*

Thalli epiphytic on various algae. With a basal disc of branched filaments growing prostrate on surface of host. Erect filaments with primary branching in one plane and alternate or secund. Branchlets developed on adaxial side of base of primary branches and in clusters. Cells of major branches 9–12 µ broad, with a length 2–4 times the breadth. Each cell containing a parietal chromatophore with a prominent pyrenoid. The sporangia developing in clusters on the branchlets, containing either monospores or tetraspores. The tetrasporangia 12 µ broad, 15 µ long. Monosporangia 8–12 µ broad, 14–18 µ long.

LOCAL DISTRIBUTION. On stipe of *Cystoseira osmundacea*. Carmel.

TYPE LOCALITY. Bantry Bay, England.

PACIFIC COAST DISTRIBUTION. Known only from Carmel and from La Jolla, California.

Rhodochorton obscurum Drew

Drew, 1928, p. 193; pl. 48, fig. 87.

Thalli epiphytic on other algae and with the basal portion penetrating the host. Endophytic portion unbranched, growing through and between cells of the host. Portion external to host about five cells tall, usually unbranched, with successive cells from base to apex increasing in diameter but decreasing in length. Tetrasporangia terminal on the erect filaments, subglobose, 10–13 µ broad, 13–18 µ long. Spermatangia (?) terminal and lateral on short branchlets, 3.5–4.5 µ broad, 5.5–6.5 µ long.

LOCAL DISTRIBUTION. On *Desmarestia latifrons* cast ashore at Carmel Beach.

TYPE LOCALITY. Not stated.

PACIFIC COAST DISTRIBUTION. Central California (Duxbury Reef, Marin County, to Carmel Bay).

Rhodochorton subimmersum Setchell and Gardner

Setchell and Gardner, 1903, p. 347; pl. 17, fig. 12. Drew, 1928, p. 191; pl. 47, fig. 81. Phyc. Bor.-Amer. No. 1348.

Thalli epiphytic, usually growing on *Grateloupia californica* but also found on other membranous Florideae; in patches up to 10 cm. in diameter and a darker red than the host. Prostrate filaments endophytic, growing horizontally between cortical cells of host. Cells of prostrate filaments irregularly cylindrical, 4–6 μ broad and with a length 3.5–9 times the breadth. Erect filaments standing perpendicular to blade of host, not over 10 cells in length, sometimes branching immediately above or below surface of host. Cells of erect filaments 4.5–6 μ broad and about the same in length. Chromatophore parietal, without a pyrenoid. Tetrasporangia terminal on erect filaments, ellipsoidal, 12–13 μ broad, 17–21 μ long.

LOCAL DISTRIBUTION. Forming conspicuous red patches on *Grateloupia californica*. Mussel Point; Point Aulon; Middle Reef of Moss Beach; Pebble Beach.

TYPE LOCALITY. Whidbey Island, Washington.

PACIFIC COAST DISTRIBUTION. Puget Sound to Central California (Carmel Highlands).

Family HELMINTHOCLADIACEAE

Thalli multiaxial, nonfilamentous. The thalli macroscopic, erect, sparingly to profusely branched and with cylindrical to strongly compressed branches. The thalli either gelatinous in texture or firm because of calcification. The branches with an axial core of parallel colorless filaments and with the assimilating filaments perpendicular to the axial core not laterally compacted.

Asexual reproduction by monospores infrequent.

Spermatangia in clusters at tips of assimilating filaments. The carpogonial filaments two- to five-celled, unbranched. The gonimoblast filaments branched; the branches densely compacted or widespreading, with only the terminal cells developing into carposporangia. The cystocarps deeply embedded in thallus, naked or with a loose envelope of filaments.

1. Gonimoblast filaments widely divergent and growing
    between assimilating filaments.................*Cumagloia* (p. 188)
1. Gonimoblast filaments in a compact mass and
    not growing between assimilating filaments..................... 2
  2. Cystocarps without an envelope................*Nemalion* (p. 186)
  2. Cystocarps with a loose envelope of filaments
      lying free from one another...............*Helminthora* (p. 187)

Nemalion Targioni-Tozetti, 1818

Thalli erect, growing singly or in clusters from a disc-shaped base. Erect portion a solid, sparingly or irregularly branched, cylinder of soft gelatinous texture. With a medulla of colorless longitudinal filaments more or less interwoven with one another and not very sharply delimited from the ensheathing cortex of erect, corymbosely branched, assimilating filaments. Cells of cortical tissue approximately the same diameter and those toward thallus surface each with a single stellate chromatophore.

Homothallic but at times protandrous. Spermatangia on modified three- to five-celled branch tips of assimilating filaments. Carpogonial filaments borne midway between base and apex of assimilating filaments, usually three-celled but the number of cells varying from one to five. The carpogonium dividing transversely after fertilization and the upper cell producing a dense radiately branched cluster of gonimoblast filaments in which only the terminal cells develop into carposporangia. Mature cystocarps globose, embedded with cortex, not surrounded by special filaments.

STRUCTURE AND REPRODUCTION. Cleland, 1919. Kylin, 1916*B*. G. M. Smith, 1938, pp. 315–318; fig. 169. Wolf, 1904.

With one species in the local flora.

Nemalion lubricum Duby   Pl. 41, fig. 5

Duby, 1830, p. 959. *Anderson, 1894, p. 359. Phyc. Bor.-Amer. No. 685.
Nemalion multifidum Hus [not of (Webber and Mohr) J. G. Agardh]. *Hus in Phyc. Bor.-Amer. No. 835.

Thalli with 3–8 erect cylinders from a common base; as found on the Monterey Peninsula generally 20–30 cm. tall but occasionally up to 135 cm.; light olive-brown in color. The cylinders 2–4 (–6) mm. in diameter, somewhat undulate and tapering slightly at upper end; unbranched or with 2–3 branches. Texture soft and gelatinous. Thalli annual, appearing early in April and disappearing late in October.

LOCAL DISTRIBUTION. Usually growing on rocks between the 2.5- and 1.0-foot tide levels; isolated individuals growing as high as the 5.0-foot tide level. West of Point Aulon; Arch Rock; Middle Reef of Moss Beach; eastern half of Pebble Beach.

TYPE LOCALITY. France.

PACIFIC COAST DISTRIBUTION. Alaska (Sitka) to southern California (San Diego).

N. multifidum is found on a few rocks at each of the stations on the Monterey Peninsula. It is regularly present on the same rock every summer.

Helminthora J. G. Agardh, 1852

Thalli erect, cylindrical, freely branched in an irregular manner, of a very soft, gelatinous texture. With a medulla of densely compacted longitudinal filaments; the medulla distinctly limited from the loosely and dichotomously to irregularly branched assimilating filaments, whose terminal cells are prolonged into long hyaline hairs. All cells of assimilating filaments except the hairs each with a single stellate chromatophore.

Outermost cells of assimilating filaments at times producing monosporangia.

Homothallic. The spermatangia borne in dense branching clusters at tips of assimilating filaments. Carpogonial filaments 3- or 4-celled, borne laterally low on assimilating filaments. The carpogonium dividing transversely after fertilization and the upper daughter cell producing a dense cluster of gonimoblast filaments in which the terminal cells develop into carposporangia. The cystocarp globose, embedded in cortex, enclosed by a sheath of branched filaments growing from cells of the carpogonial filament.

STRUCTURE AND REPRODUCTION. Kylin, 1928, pp. 8–10; fig. 3. Svedelius, 1917. Thuret and Bornet, 1878, pp. 63–67; pl. 32.

Helminthora Saundersii Gardner

Gardner, 1926, p. 205.

"Fronds diminutive, soft and lubricous, 2–3 cm. high, 0.5–1.0 mm. diam., branching moderately frequent, with branches mostly of the first order, but in part of the second order, all branches approximately of the same diameter; medullary filaments densely crowded, 12–16 µ diam., with cross walls inconspicuous and far apart; cortical filaments 4–5 times dichotomously branched, loosely held together, cells variable in size, mostly fusiform and the terminal ones usually the smallest; antheridia in spherical clusters on small branches arising from the terminal cells; carpogonia on three-celled carpogonial branches arising near the base of the cortical filaments and giving rise to involucral branches surrounding the cystocarp; lower cell of fertilized carpogonium remaining naked; gonimoblasts arising from the upper cell of the fertilized carpogonium, very densely crowded."

LOCAL DISTRIBUTION. On *Phyllospadix* at Monterey.
TYPE LOCALITY. As above.
PACIFIC COAST DISTRIBUTION. As above.

Known only from the original collection on which the description is based.

Cumagloia Setchell and Gardner, 1917

Thalli erect, with one or more erect axes from a small disc-shaped holdfast. Erect axes cylindrical to markedly flattened, simple or sparingly forked, densely clothed on all sides with short branchlets. The branchlets simple or branched on all sides. Axis and branchlets with a medulla of colorless longitudinal filaments more or less intertwined with one another; the medulla ensheathed by a cortex of di- or trichotomously branched assimilating filaments that stand free from one another. Cells in outer portion of assimilating filaments each with a single stellate chromatophore.

Homothallic but at times protandrous. Spermatangia borne on modified 3- to 5-celled tips of assimilating filaments. Carpogonial filaments usually 3-celled, borne low on assimilating filaments. The gonimoblast filaments growing horizontally from carpogonium and between assimilating filaments. All branching of gonimoblast filaments toward thallus surface and only the terminal cells of the branches developing into carposporangia. Mature cystocarps diffuse and intertwined with assimilating filaments.

STRUCTURE AND REPRODUCTION. Gardner, 1917, pp. 398–404; pl. 31, pl. 32, figs. 1–4. Kylin, 1928, pp. 10–11; fig. 4. G. M. Smith, 1938, pp. 318–320; figs. 170–171.

Cumagloia Andersonii (Farlow) Setchell and Gardner

Pl. 42, fig. 2

Setchell and Gardner apud Gardner, 1917, p. 399; pl. 31; pl. 32, figs. 1–4. *Kylin, 1941, p. 6.

Nemalion Andersonii Farlow, 1877, p. 240. *Anderson, 1891, p. 221. *Howe, 1893, p. 67. *Phyc. Bor.-Amer. No. 330.

Thalli, as found on the Monterey Peninsula, usually 20–40 cm. tall but occasionally up to 90 cm.; olive-brown to deep purplish-red in color. The axis cylindrical to markedly flattened, in the latter case at times becoming saccate. Cylindrical axes 2–8 mm. in diameter; flattened axes up to 5 cm. broad. Branchlets usually 20–50 mm. long and less than 2 mm. broad. Thalli soft and gelatinous but of an extremely tough consistency. Thalli annual, appearing early in February and disappearing early in November.

LOCAL DISTRIBUTION. Growing on horizontal and vertical sides of rocks between the 4.0- and 2.0-foot tide levels. Abundant at Pebble Beach. Relatively scarce at Point Aulon; Point Pinos; Middle Reef of Moss Beach; Fanshell Beach; Cypress Point; Pescadero Point; Mission Point.

TYPE LOCALITY. Santa Cruz, California.

PACIFIC COAST DISTRIBUTION. British Columbia (Vancouver Island) to southern California (San Diego).

Family CHAETANGIACEAE

Thalli multiaxial, nonfilamentous. The thalli erect, usually dichotomously branched and with cylindrical branches. The branches with an axial core or parallel filaments and with the assimilating filaments with their outer ends laterally compacted into a parenchyma.

With or without asexual reproduction by monospores.

Spermatangia scattered over surface of thallus. Carpogonial filaments 3-celled, borne laterally low on assimilating filaments. The gonimoblast filaments growing toward thallus surface and with only the terminal cells developing into carposporangia. Mature cystocarps deeply embedded in thallus and surrounded by a pericarp with a pore leading to thallus surface.

With one genus, *Gloiophloea,* in the local flora.

Gloiophloea J. G. Agardh, 1871

Thalli erect, solitary, consisting of an unconstricted, repeatedly dichotomous cylinder of a soft gelatinous texture. With a small disc-shaped holdfast. With a medulla of colorless interwoven longitudinal filaments and the medulla surrounded by dichotomously branched assimilating filaments that grow outward and obliquely upward toward thallus apex. Free ends of assimilating filaments compacted into a parenchyma. Younger portions of thallus with a continuous epidermal layer of colorless cells; older portions lacking an epidermal layer.

Homothallic or heterothallic. Spermatangia spherical to broadly ellipsoidal, borne on outermost cells of assimilating filaments and in a continuous layer over most of the thallus surface. Carpogonial filaments three-celled, borne laterally and low on cortical filaments. Prior to fertilization the cell below the carpogonium cutting off four quadrately arranged nurse cells. The zygote nucleus migrating into one of the nurse cells, dividing reductionally, and one of the daughter nuclei migrating into the gonimoblast initial growing upward through the carpogonial base. The carposporophyte branching toward thallus surface and with terminal cells developing into carposporangia. Mature cystocarp deeply embedded in thallus and surrounded by a pericarp of densely compacted filaments growing from lowermost cell of carpogonial filament. Pericarp opening to surface of thallus by a narrow carpostome.

With one species in the local flora.

Gloiophloea confusa Setchell   Pl. 42, fig. 1

Setchell, 1914, p. 118; pl. 14, figs. 44–47. *Kylin, 1941, p. 6.
Scinaia furcellata Farlow [not of (Turner) Bivona]. Farlow, 1876, p. 699 (as to Pacific Coast specimens only). *Anderson, 1891, p. 221.
Scinaia furcellata var. *undulata* Farlow, 1875, p. 367. *Phyc. Bor.-Amer. No. 422.

Thalli, as found on the Monterey Peninsula, 8–15 cm. tall; light rose-red to deep wine-red in color. Mature plants 10–15 times dichotomous, the branches 1–3 mm. broad and of the same diameter throughout. Tips of ultimate dichotomies tapering abruptly to a blunt or an acute point. Thallus of a soft gelatinous texture. Heterothallic. Cystocarps immersed in thallus and not externally evident in living plants. Pericarp broadly pyriform, 5–6 cells in thickness, 250 µ broad, 280–300 µ tall.

LOCAL DISTRIBUTION. Growing on rocks between the 0.5- and −1.5-foot tide levels. During late spring and early summer fairly common at Middle Reef of Moss Beach and at tip of Pescadero Point. Isolated individuals have been found at Monterey; foot of Eighth Street, Pacific Grove; Point Pinos; Cypress Point; Midway Point; Pebble Beach; Mission Point. Also dredged from a depth of 25 feet near Mussel Point.

TYPE LOCALITY. Monterey, California.
PACIFIC COAST DISTRIBUTION. British Columbia (Vancouver Island) to southern California (San Diego).

Family BONNEMAISONIACEAE

Thalli monoaxial, nonfilamentous. The thalli erect, freely branched, with cylindrical to compressed branches. The branches with a more or less evident axial filament and this surrounded by a compact parenchymatous cortex.

Spermatangia covering small simple branches. The carpogonial filaments three-celled and with branched sterile filaments from the two lower cells. The gonimoblast filaments freely branched and with only the terminal cells developing into carposporangia. Mature cystocarps surrounded by a pericarp and borne terminally on short simple branches.

With one genus, *Bonnemaisonia,* in the local flora.

Bonnemaisonia C. A. Agardh, 1823

Thalli erect and with a small disc-shaped holdfast. Erect portion oppositely and distichously branched into 3–5 orders of progressively smaller branches. Major branches cylindrical to markedly compressed. One of every pair of opposite branches short, simple, spine-like; the other long and with one or more orders of branching. The two kinds of branches of successive pairs regularly alternate. Tips of certain branches at times inflated and hook-like. Each branch with a single axial filament in which each cell cuts off two pericentral cells and these, in turn, cut off corticating cells. Gland cells numerous in corticating tissue.

Homothallic or heterothallic. Spermatangia borne on short simple branches and in elongate elliptical masses more or less completely covering surface of branch. Branches with spermatangia borne in a regular alternate succession. Carpogonial filaments at tips of short simple branches, three-celled and borne on a pericentral cell of axial filament. Median cell of carpogonial filament with a cluster of sterile filaments on the abaxial side. The gonimoblast filaments growing upward from the carpogonium and with only the terminal cells developing into carposporangia. The mature cystocarp terminal on a simple branch and surrounded by an ostiolate pericarp.

STRUCTURE AND REPRODUCTION. Kylin, 1916*A*. Kylin, 1928, p. 22; fig. 9. Svedelius, 1933, pp. 39–49; figs. 43–48.

KEY TO THE SPECIES IN THE LOCAL FLORA

1. Certain branches with inflated hook-like tips..........*B. californica*
1. No branches with inflated hook-like tips...............*B. geniculata*

Bonnemaisonia californica Buffham Pl. 42, figs. 3–4

Buffham, 1896, p. 181. Gardner, 1927*A*, p. 335; pl. 65; pl. 66, fig. 1. Kylin, 1928, p. 22; fig. 9.

Bonnemaisonia hamifera Howe [not of Hariot]. *Howe, 1893, p. 68. *Anderson, 1894, p. 361. Phyc. Bor.-Amer. No. 939.

Thalli, as found on the Monterey Peninsula, up to 25 cm. tall; pinkish-red in color. With 4–5 successive orders of branching and each successive order a replica of the preceding order. The major branches slightly flattened cylinders up to 2 mm. in diameter. Branching opposite, distichous, with one branch of each opposite pair simple and the other branched. Here and there the branched member of a pair replaced by a simple hook-shaped branch longer and thicker than the opposite spine-like branch.

LOCAL DISTRIBUTION. Isolated specimens have been found cast ashore at Moss Beach and at Carmel Beach.

TYPE LOCALITY. "California."

PACIFIC COAST DISTRIBUTION. British Columbia (Vancouver Island) to southern California (Ventura).

Bonnemaisonia geniculata Gardner Pl. 43, figs. 1–2

Gardner, 1927*A*, p. 336; pl. 67, fig. 1; pl. 68.

Thalli, as found on the Monterey Peninsula, up to 12 cm. tall; pinkish-red in color. The central axis percurrent, markedly flattened, 2–3 mm. broad. With 2–4 orders of branching and each successive order much reduced in size and a replica of the preceding order. The branching subopposite, distichous, with one member of each opposed pair short, simple, and spine-like, the other long and branched. The long branch of a pair markedly flattened; never with the apex inflated and bent in a hook-like manner.

LOCAL DISTRIBUTION. Epiphytic on *Erythrophyllum delesserioides* at Pescadero Point.

TYPE LOCALITY. Point Sur, Monterey County, California.

PACIFIC COAST DISTRIBUTION. Central California (Carmel Bay to Point Sur).

Order GELIDIALES

Thalli monoaxial, nonfilamentous, macroscopic. The thalli more or less freely branched and the branching distichous, the branches cylindrical to markedly compressed. The branches with a single axial filament but this frequently obscured by parallel rhizoidal filaments from inner cortical cells; the cortex parenchymatous and with progressively smaller cells toward the surface. With vegetatively identical gametophyte and tetrasporophyte.

Spermatangia in sori at surface of thallus and usually restricted to the ultimate branchlets. Carpogonial filaments 1- to 3-celled, deeply embedded within thallus. The gonimoblast filaments growing directly from carpogonium, widely divergent, lying more or less parallel to the axial filament, frequently becoming entangled with gonimoblasts from other carpogonia. With only the terminal cells developing into carposporangia or with the carposporangia in short chains. Mature cystocarps flattened, axial within a branch, the overlying cortex with a large pore at one or at both flattened faces of the branch.

Tetrasporophytes with sporangia separated from one another and embedded just beneath surface of branch tips. Fertile branchlets frequently irregularly swollen. The tetrasporangia cruciately or zonately divided.

Family GELIDIACEAE

All Gelidiales are placed in a single family, the Gelidiaceae, whose characters are the same as those of the order.

With one genus, *Gelidium,* in the local flora.

Gelidium Lamouroux, 1813

Thalli nonfilamentous; with erect, cylindrical to markedly flattened, distichously and pinnately branched axes. The branchlets alternate or opposite, usually constricted at base and bent upward in a geniculate manner near base. Growth of branches by a single apical cell that produces an axial filament in which each cell bears four quadrately arranged branching filaments. The filaments with the cells compacted into a cortex of very tough consistency. Lowermost cells of cortex frequently giving off rhizoids that lie parallel to the axial filament.

Spermatangia in elliptical sori on flattened faces of ultimate branchlets. Carpogonium sessile, borne deep within the cortex, with a long trichogyne extending to thallus surface. Gonimoblast filaments developing directly from base of carpogonium, growing parallel to axial filament, with only the terminal cells developing into carposporangia. Mature cystocarp a flattened plate at center of a thallus branch and attached to cortical region by perpendicular filaments; portion of thallus surrounding cystocarp with an ostiole on both flattened faces.

Tetrasporophytes with tetrasporangia remote from one another and borne on the ultimate branchlets, embedded just beneath surface of branchlets. The tetrasporangia cruciately divided.

STRUCTURE AND REPRODUCTION. Kylin, 1928, pp. 25–29; figs. 11–13. G. M. Smith, 1938, pp. 325–328; figs. 177–178.

KEY TO THE SPECIES IN THE LOCAL FLORA[2]

1. Thallus forming a black velvety coating on rocks...................2
1. Thallus not forming a black velvety coating on rocks...............3
  2. Tetraspores and surface cells of branch tips
    arranged in a succession of *V*'s..............*G. caloglossoides*
  2. Tetraspores and surface cells of branch tips
    not arranged in a succession of *V*'s.................*G. pusillum*
3. Thalli less than 5 cm. tall...............................*G. sinicola*
3. Thalli over 5 cm. tall..4
  4. Axis not much broader than finest branches...........*G. Coulteri*
  4. Axis considerably broader than finest branches.................5
5. Axis markedly percurrent............*G. cartilagineum* var. *robustum*
5. Axis not markedly percurrent...................................6
  6. Branches diverging widely from axis; with
    few branchlets ....*G. arborescens*
  6. Branches not diverging widely from axis; with
    many branchlets of equal length ....*G. purpurascens*

Gelidium caloglossoides Howe   Pl. 44, figs. 3–4

Howe, 1914, p. 96; pl. 34, fig. 7; pl. 35, figs. 1–12. *Hollenberg, 1942, p. 534.

Thalli, as found on the Monterey Peninsula, growing in a blackish velvety layer which may attain a diameter of 20 cm. The thallus freely branched and with the branches distinctly flattened and from .25 to .75 mm. broad. Certain branches wholly prostrate, rhizome-like, the ventral face with cylindrical to conical light-colored haptera at more or less regular intervals. These branches of the rhizome with tufts of 2–10 branches in regions lateral to the haptera and the lateral branches either prostrate or erect. If erect, the lateral branches 5–10 mm. tall, usually once pinnate, and with

[2] *Gelidium corneum* (Hudson) Lamouroux has been reported from the Monterey region by Harvey (1853, p. 116) and by Anderson (1891, p. 224), but it is extremely doubtful if this Atlantic Ocean species is present in the local flora. The *G. corneum* of Howe (1893, p. 68) is *G. purpurascens* Gardner.

the branchlets at approximately right angles. Apices of erect and prostrate branches with the surface cells subrectangular and regularly arranged in a succession of V's back from the tip. Tetrasporangia restricted to ultimate branchlets and arranged in a succession of V's.

LOCAL DISTRIBUTION. Growing on vertical face of rocks between the 0.5- and −1.0-foot tide levels. Arch Rock; Point Joe; Cypress Point; Pescadero Point.

TYPE LOCALITY. Island of San Lorenzo, Peru.

PACIFIC COAST DISTRIBUTION. Known from the Monterey Peninsula and from southern California.

Gelidium pusillum (Stackhouse) Le Jolis   Pl. 44, fig. 1

Le Jolis, 1863, p. 139. Feldmann and Hamel, 1936, p. 112; figs. 19–20.
Fucus pusillus Stackhouse, 1801, p. 17; pl. 6.

Thalli, as found on the Monterey Peninsula, growing in a blackish velvety layer which may attain a diameter of 30–40 cm. The thallus freely branched; differentiated into horizontal rhizome-like branches and erect branches. Horizontal branches cylindrical. .1 to .2 mm. in diameter, with the branching predominately opposite. Many lateral branches of rhizome bending upwards and growing to a height of 15–20 mm. The erect branches pinnately branched into one or two orders of branching, the axis and branches markedly compressed, up to 1 mm. broad, conspicuously narrowed at base. Surface cells of branches not arranged in a succession of V's back from the tip. The tetrasporangia irregularly arranged on branch tips, not arranged in V's.

LOCAL DISTRIBUTION. Growing on the vertical face of rocks between the 3.0- and −1.0-foot tide levels. Point Joe; Pescadero Point; Mission Point.

TYPE LOCALITY. England.

PACIFIC COAST DISTRIBUTION. Known only from the Monterey Peninsula.

Gelidium sinicola Gardner   Pl. 44, fig. 2

Gardner, 1927E, p. 278; pl. 47, fig. 2.

Thalli, as found on the Monterey Peninsula, forming a felty growth up to 5 cm. in diameter; purplish-red in color. With erect branches 2–3 cm. tall, cylindrical, 2–3 times pinnate, and with a percurrent axis. Branches along the erect axis constricted at base, pointed at apex, not geniculate, less than .5 mm. in diameter. Branchlets widely divergent and progressively shorter toward apex of branch. Surface cells at tips of branches angular and irregularly arranged.

LOCAL DISTRIBUTION. Growing on rocks at mean low-tide level. Pebble Beach.

TYPE LOCALITY. Point Cavalo, San Francisco Bay, California.

PACIFIC COAST DISTRIBUTION. As above.

Gelidium Coulteri Harvey   Pl. 44, fig. 5

*Harvey, 1853, p. 117. *Anderson, 1891, p. 224. *Howe, 1893, p. 68. *Kylin, 1941, p. 7. Phyc. Bor.-Amer. No. 90.

Thalli, as found on the Monterey Peninsula, 4–8 cm. tall, growing in dense stands; dark olive to olive-purple in color. Erect shoots distichously branched, 1–3 times pinnate, clothed with branchlets from base to apex. Axis and branches less than 1 mm. in diameter. The major branches flattened in lower portion, subcylindrical above. Branchlets subcylindrical, not markedly geniculate, standing at approximately an angle of 45° to the branch bearing them.

LOCAL DISTRIBUTION. Growing on rocks between the 2.5- and −0.5-foot tide levels. Frequently with the base buried in sand. Abundant everywhere.

TYPE LOCALITY. Monterey, California.

PACIFIC COAST DISTRIBUTION. Central California (San Francisco) to southern California (San Diego).

Gelidium cartilagineum var. robustum Gardner   Pl. 43, fig. 4

Gardner, 1927E, p. 280; pl. 54.
Gelidium cartilagineum Harvey [not of (Linnaeus) Gaillon]. *Harvey, 1833, p. 164. *Harvey, 1853, p. 117. *Anderson, 1891, p. 224. *Howe, 1893, p. 68. *Kylin, 1941, p. 6. Phyc. Bor.-Amer. No. 135.

Thalli growing in erect tufts 15–50 cm. tall; brownish- to purplish-red in color. Attached to substratum by a complex of prostrate branches. Erect axes unbranched in lower third; upper two-thirds repeatedly and distichously branched. Branches sub-opposite, distinctly compressed, up to 3 mm. broad. Young branchlets with the narrowed basal portion geniculate and so bent that the branchlet almost parallels the branch on which it is borne; older branchlets standing at approximately a 45° angle to the branches bearing them. Fertile plants with short profusely branched branchlets.

LOCAL DISTRIBUTION. Growing between the 0.5- and −1.5-foot tide levels on rocks exposed to surf. Not present in abundance but found on all rocky headlands of the Peninsula.

TYPE LOCALITY. Ensenada, Baja California.

PACIFIC COAST DISTRIBUTION. Central California (San Francisco) to Baja California (San Roque).

Gelidium arborescens Gardner   Pl. 43, fig. 3

*Gardner, 1927E, p. 276; pl. 42. *Kylin, 1941, p. 7.

Thalli, as found on the Monterey Peninsula, 18–25 cm. tall; of a dark purple color. Erect shoots distichously branched and with branches of 4–5 orders; the central axis frequently becoming obscure in upper portion of shoot. The branches cylindrical to subcylindrical, up to 2 mm. in diameter. Young branches geniculate at base. Older branches of the first, second, and third orders diverging widely but with the tips tending to lie parallel to the central axis. Branches with numerous rhizoidal filaments beneath the cortex.

LOCAL DISTRIBUTION. Growing on vertical and horizontal faces of rocks between the mean low-tide and −1.5-foot tide levels. Abundant at Pebble Beach. Also found at Point Pinos; Cypress Point; and at Arrowhead Point.

TYPE LOCALITY. Pebble Beach. Monterey Peninsula, California.

PACIFIC COAST DISTRIBUTION. Central California (Monterey Peninsula to Cambria).

Gelidium purpurascens Gardner   Pl. 44, fig. 6

Gardner, 1927E, p. 275; pls. 38–39. *Kylin, 1941, p. 7.
Gelidium corneum Howe [not of (Hudson) Lamouroux]. *Howe, 1893, p. 68.

Thalli, as found on the Monterey Peninsula, 10–22 cm. tall; of a deep purplish-red color. The erect shoots distichously branched, 3 or 4 times pinnate, with an obscure central axis less than 1 mm. in diameter. Major branches along axis diverging at an angle of approximately 45° and constricted at base. Throughout their entire length the major branches beset at regular and frequent intervals with much shorter branches. Many of the shorter branches markedly geniculate at base and with the upper portion more or less parallel to the branch bearing them.

LOCAL DISTRIBUTION. Growing on rocks between the mean low-tide and −1.0-foot tide levels. Cypress Point; Pebble Beach; and rocks at mouth of Carmel River.

TYPE LOCALITY. Moss Beach, San Mateo County, California.

PACIFIC COAST DISTRIBUTION. Central California (Bolinas) to southern California (San Diego).

Differing from other large species of the local flora both in the more delicate branches and in the greater number of short branches along the major branches.

Order CRYPTONEMIALES

Thalli monoaxial or multiaxial; rarely filamentous, generally nonfilamentous and either erect or crustose. Erect thalli cylindrical to foliaceous, branched or unbranched. With vegetatively identical gametophyte and tetrasporophyte.

Spermatangia in sori or borne in conceptacles. Carpogonial filaments up to a dozen or more cells in length, branched or unbranched; remote from one another, or adjoining one another and borne either in sori, in nemathecia, or in conceptacles. The gonimoblast filaments growing from auxiliary cells borne in special filaments adjacent to or remote from carpogonial filaments. Cystocarps usually deeply embedded in thallus, relatively small, and without a special envelope.

Tetrasporophytes with tetrasporangia remote from one another or grouped in sori, nemathecia, or conceptacles. The tetrasporangia zonately or cruciately divided.

Key to the Families in the Local Flora

1. Carpogonial filaments not in nemathecia or conceptacles............2
1. Carpogonial filaments borne in nemathecia or conceptacles...........8
  2. Carpogonial and auxiliary cell filaments separate
      from each other 3
  2. Carpogonial and auxiliary cell filaments borne on
      a common branched filament 5
3. Tetrasporangia intercalary, auxiliary cell
     filaments obscure ....*Cruoriaceae* (p. 216)
3. Tetrasporangia not intercalary, auxiliary cell
     filaments distinct 4
  4. Auxiliary cell filament sparingly branched,
      auxiliary cell apical or median on filament.*Dumontiaceae* (p. 199)
  4. Auxiliary cell filament profusely branched,
      auxiliary cell at base of filament........*Grateloupiaceae* (p. 237)
5. Auxiliary cell filament not subtending
     carpogonial filament ....*Gloiosiphoniaceae* (p. 208)
5. Auxiliary cell filament one-celled,
     subtending carpogonial filament 6
  6. Gonimoblast filaments growing toward
      center of thallus 7
  6. Gonimoblast filaments growing toward
      surface of thallus....................*Choreocolaceae* (p. 254)
7. Cystocarp with a pericarp...................*Endocladiaceae* (p. 210)
7. Cystocarp without a pericarp..............*Callymeniaceae* (p. 248)
  8. Carpogonial filaments borne in nemathecia..*Squamariaceae* (p. 211)
  8. Carpogonial filaments borne in conceptacles..*Corallinaceae* (p. 217)

Family DUMONTIACEAE

Thalli monoaxial, filamentous or nonfilamentous. If nonfilamentous, erect, cylindrical to foliaceous, branched or unbranched. The thalli usually with an evident percurrent axial filament and the superficial cells compacted into a parenchymatous tissue.

Carpogonial filaments up to 15 cells in length, unbranched or sparingly branched at base, sometimes with the third cell below the carpogonium functioning as a nurse cell. Auxiliary cell filaments remote from carpogonial filaments, up to 15 cells in length, unbranched or sparingly branched, the auxiliary cell usually median but at times apical. The cystocarps usually small, reniform, and deeply embedded in thallus.

Tetrasporophytes with tetrasporangia remote from one another and embedded at surface of thallus. The tetrasporangia zonately or cruciately divided.

KEY TO THE GENERA IN THE LOCAL FLORA

Cryptosiphonia J. G. Agardh, 1876

Thalli erect, solitary, or in gregarious tufts from a small disc-shaped holdfast. Erect portion cylindrical, freely and radially branched into progressively smaller branches, without a percurrent axis. Major branches of the same diameter throughout and with many short branches of approximately the same length. Ends of branches and branchlets tapering to a point. Branches with a single axial filament in which each cell bears two lateral filaments at an angle of 90° to each other; the pairs of filaments on successive axial cells alternate with one another. The lateral filaments with progressively smaller cells and the outermost cells compacted into a parenchyma. The axial filament eventually becoming enveloped by many rhizoidal filaments.

Spermatangia unknown. Carpogonial filaments 7–12 cells in length, curved, branched in lower portion; borne adaxially on second to fourth cell of a lateral filament from the axial filament. The carpogonium with a long, spirally twisted trichogyne. Auxiliary cell filament, except for carpogonium, similar to carpogonial filament; not borne adjacent to a carpogonial filament. The oöblast first growing to third cell below carpogonium and then to a median cell of an auxiliary cell filament. This becoming the auxiliary cell and producing a small dense cluster of gonimoblasts in which each cell develops into a carposporangium. Mature cystocarps globose to reniform, deeply embedded in thallus, the overlying vegetative tissue without an ostiole. Branchlets with cystocarps spindle-shaped and thicker than vegetative branchlets.

Tetrasporophytes with tetrasporangia immersed at surface of thallus. The tetrasporangia cruciately divided.

STRUCTURE AND REPRODUCTION. Kylin, 1930, pp. 23–26; figs. 13–14. Sjöstedt, 1926, pp. 4–7; figs. 1–2. G. M. Smith, 1938, pp. 329–331; figs. 179–180.

Cryptosiphonia Woodii J. G. Agardh   Pl. 45, fig. 2

J. G. Agardh, 1876, p. 251. *Anderson, 1891, p. 222. *Howe, 1893, p. 68. *Sjöstedt, 1926, p. 4; figs. 1–2. *Kylin, 1930, p. 23; figs. 13–14. *Kylin, 1941, p. 8. Phyc. Bor.-Amer. No. 449.
Pikea Woodii J. G. Agardh, 1872, p. 15.

Thalli, as found on the Monterey Peninsula, 20–25 (–35) cm. tall; olive-brown to deep blackish-purple in color. Usually profusely branched and with the major branches 1–2 mm. in diameter. Branchlets along the major branches 2–4 mm. long. The thallus firm and tough, neither gelatinous nor slimy to the touch.

LOCAL DISTRIBUTION. Growing on rocks between the 2.5- and 0.5-foot tide levels. Very abundant at Pebble Beach. Rather scarce at Point Aulon; Point Pinos; Middle Reef of Moss Beach; Point Joe; Fanshell Beach; Cypress Point.

TYPE LOCALITY. Vancouver Island.

PACIFIC COAST DISTRIBUTION. Alaska (Unalaska) to southern California (Venice).

Baylesia Setchell, 1912

Thalli growing erect from a small disc-shaped holdfast. Erect portion branched and with a subcylindrical percurrent axis. Branching of axis distichous, opposite; usually with only a few of the branches becoming long. Branches with a single axial filament in which each cell bears two lateral filaments standing at an angle of 90° to each other; the pairs of filaments on successive axial cells alternate with one another. Terminal cells of lateral filaments compacted into a parenchyma.

Spermatangia unknown. Carpogonial filament 10–12 cells long, curved, branched in lower portion; borne adaxially on lower cells of lateral filaments from axial filament. Auxiliary cell filaments resembling carpogonial filaments and borne near them. The gonimoblast filaments with all cells developing into carposporangia. Mature cystocarps reniform, deeply embedded within thallus. Branchlets containing mature cystocarps not inflated in fertile portion.

Tetrasporophytes unknown.

STRUCTURE AND REPRODUCTION. Setchell, 1912, pp. 249–250; pl. 29.

Baylesia plumosa Setchell   Pl. 45, fig. 1
  *Setchell, 1912, p. 249; pl. 29.

Thalli, as found on the Monterey Peninsula, up to 60 cm. tall; of a deep wine-red color. The axis and major branches 2–4 mm. in diameter and with the short fringing branches 1–3 cm. long.

LOCAL DISTRIBUTION. Growing on the vertical faces of rocks between the 1.0- and −0.5-foot tide levels. Isolated individuals found at foot of Eighth Street, Pacific Grove; Point Pinos; Pescadero Point; north end of Carmel Beach; Mission Point. Also dredged from a depth of 30–35 feet a quarter-mile from Municipal Wharf, Monterey.

TYPE LOCALITY. Pacific Grove, California.

PACIFIC COAST DISTRIBUTION. Known only from Santa Cruz, California, and from the Monterey Peninsula.

Superficially resembling *Dasyopsis densa* but immediately distinguishable because the short, fringing branchlets of axis and major branches are not filamentous.

Pikea Harvey, 1853

Thalli erect, usually growing singly from a small conical base. Erect portion freely and pinnately branched in a subopposite manner; with or without a percurrent axis. Lowermost branches short, above this the branches long and di- or tripinnate. Major branches somewhat compressed, with a smooth surface and without a midrib or veins. Medulla with a single conspicuous axial filament surrounded by densely intertwined rhizoidal filaments; cortex relatively narrow, composed of small cells.

Spermatangia unknown. Carpogonial filaments and auxiliary cell filaments developing at inner face of cortex, curved, with sterile branches from the lower cells. Development of carposporophyte unknown. Mature cystocarps numerous within fruiting branches, lying at inner face of cortex. Tips of branches containing cystocarps swollen.

STRUCTURE AND REPRODUCTION. Schmitz and Hauptfleisch, 1896–1897, p. 519.

KEY TO THE SPECIES IN THE LOCAL FLORA

1. Major branches up to 2 mm. broad, densely and
   regularly pinnate ....*P. pinnata*
1. Major branches not over 1 mm. broad, pinnation
   sparse and somewhat irregular.....................*P. californica*

Pikea pinnata Setchell   Pl. 45, fig. 3

Setchell in Phyc. Bor.-Amer. No. 648.

Thalli, as found on the Monterey Peninsula, up to 30 cm. tall; bright red in color. Pinnately branched and usually with all branches in the same plane; with a percurrent axis and outline of the thallus triangular. Branches near base of axis long, di- or tripinnate, the pinnation dense, regular, subopposite. Major branches with a compressed axis 1.5–2 mm. broad.

LOCAL DISTRIBUTION. Growing on rocks between the 0.5- and −1.5-foot tide levels. Usually only isolated individuals at any station. Point Aulon; Point Pinos; Asilomar Point; Middle Reef of Moss Beach; Point Joe; Cypress Point; Midway Point; north end of Carmel Beach; Mission Point. Also dredged from a depth of 30–35 feet a quarter-mile from Municipal Wharf, Monterey, and from 35–40 feet near Mussel Point.

TYPE LOCALITY. San Francisco, California.

PACIFIC COAST DISTRIBUTION. Central California (Bolinas to San Luis Obispo County).

Pikea californica Harvey   Pl. 46, fig. 3

Harvey, 1853, p. 246. Harvey, 1858, p. 131; pl. 49, fig. *B*. *Anderson, 1891, p. 222. *Howe, 1893, p. 68. *Kylin, 1941, p. 8. Phyc. Bor.-Amer. No. 897.

Erect shoots, as found on the Monterey Peninsula, up to 20 cm. tall but usually 5–10 cm. tall when growing in intertidal zone;

dark red in color. Pinnately branched but not all branches lying in the same plane. Shoots without a percurrent axis and the lower portions of major branches frequently devoid of lateral branchlets. Major branches 0.5–1 mm. broad, somewhat compressed, usually with a somewhat irregular arrangement of the simple to once-pinnate branchlets along the lateral margins.

LOCAL DISTRIBUTION. Growing on rocks between the mean low-tide and −1.5-foot tide levels. Usually only isolated individuals at any station. Mussel Point; Point Aulon; Point Pinos; Asilomar Point; Middle Reef of Moss Beach; Point Joe; Fanshell Beach; Cypress Point; Pescadero Point; north end of Carmel Beach; Mission Point. Also dredged from a depth of 20–35 feet near Point Aulon.

TYPE LOCALITY. San Francisco, California.

PACIFIC COAST DISTRIBUTION. British Columbia (Vancouver Island) to southern California (La Jolla).

Farlowia J. G. Agardh, 1876

Thalli erect, solitary or in clusters from a small disc-shaped base. Erect portion freely branched, without a percurrent axis, with branches progressively smaller toward thallus apex; the branching distichous and alternate to subopposite. Branches markedly compressed; the surface smooth or with an obscure midrib and obscure alternate veins diagonal to the midrib. Branches with a single axial filament. Branching of axial filament probably as in *Cryptosiphonia* but this difficult to determine because of early development of many parallel rhizoidal filaments around the axial filament. Cortex composed of tightly compacted, outwardly branched filaments with progressively smaller cells toward thallus surface.

Spermatangia unknown. Carpogonial filaments and auxiliary cell filaments developing at inner face of cortex, curved and with curved sterile branches from the lower cells. Development of carposporophyte unknown. Mature cystocarps globose, numerous within fertile branches, lying at juncture of cortex and medulla. Portions of branches containing mature cystocarps not swollen or otherwise modified.

STRUCTURE AND REPRODUCTION. Schmitz and Hauptfleisch, 1896–1897, pp. 519–520.

The distinctions between *Pikea* and *Farlowia* are not clear-cut. Typically *Pikea* has a more profuse and a more regular pinnate branching. Branches containing cystocarps are swollen in *Pikea* and are not swollen in *Farlowia*.

KEY TO THE SPECIES IN THE LOCAL FLORA

1. Major branches 1–2.5 cm. broad......................*F. compressa*
1. Major branches less than 0.5 cm. broad..........................2
　2. Branches with many distichous branchlets..............*F. mollis*
　2. Branches with relatively few branchlets.................*F. crassa*

Farlowia compressa J. G. Agardh   Pl. 46, fig. 2

J. G. Agardh, 1876, p. 262. *Anderson, 1891, p. 222. *Howe, 1893, p. 68.
*Kylin, 1941, p. 8. Phyc. Bor.-Amer. No. 1349.

Thalli, as found on the Monterey Peninsula, up to 40 cm.
tall; deep red in color. The branching predominately distichous
and subalternate. Major branches 1.0–2.5 cm. broad and with
more or less serrate margins, with many or few lateral branches.
Lateral branches frequently oblanceolate. The larger branches
with a very obscure midrib and parallel diagonally inserted veins.
The midrib and veins quite conspicuous after thalli have been
allowed to dry for 2–3 hours but very inconspicuous in completely dried herbarium specimens.

LOCAL DISTRIBUTION. Growing between the 0.5- and −1.5-foot tide
levels and either attached to rocks or with the base buried in sand. Common at the Middle Reef of Moss Beach. Also found at Mussel Point;
Point Aulon; Point Joe; Pescadero Point.

TYPE LOCALITY. Monterey Bay, California.

PACIFIC COAST DISTRIBUTION. Central California (Tomales Bay to
Carmel Bay).

Farlowia mollis (Harvey and Bailey) Farlow and Setchell
Pl. 47, fig. 5

Farlow and Setchell in Phyc. Bor.-Amer. No. 898. See also Phyc. Bor.-
Amer. No. 1150.
Gigartina mollis Harvey and Bailey, 1851, p. 372. Harvey, 1853, p. 175.
*Anderson, 1891, p. 223.

Thalli, as found on the Monterey Peninsula, up to 20 cm. tall;
bright red to blackish-red in color. The branches soft in texture,
and at times slimy to the touch. Branching predominately distichous, pinnate, the branches alternate or lying so close together
that they appear to be opposite. Major branches usually about
3 mm. broad, rarely 5 mm. broad. Branchlets hair-like and usually numerous. The major branches lacking an obscure midrib
and veins.

LOCAL DISTRIBUTION. Growing attached to rocks between the 0.5-
and −1.5-foot tide levels. Point Aulon; Point Pinos; Asilomar Point;

Middle Reef of Moss Beach; Fanshell Beach; Cypress Point; north end of Carmel Beach; mouth of Carmel River.

TYPE LOCALITY. Puget Sound.

PACIFIC COAST DISTRIBUTION. British Columbia (Vancouver Island) to central California (Carmel Bay).

Farlowia crassa J. G. Agardh   Pl. 46, fig. 1

J. G. Agardh, 1876, p. 262. *Anderson, 1891, p. 222.

Thalli, as found on the Monterey Peninsula, up to 25 cm. tall; dark red in color. The branching distichous, pinnate, dense or sparse. Major branches 3–5 mm. broad and with relatively few hair-like branchlets. The major branches with the same obscure midrib and diagonally inserted veins as in *F. compressa*.

LOCAL DISTRIBUTION. Growing on rocks between the 0.5- and −0.5- foot tide levels. Middle Reef of Moss Beach; north end of Carmel Beach; mouth of Carmel River.

TYPE LOCALITY. Oregon.

PACIFIC COAST DISTRIBUTION. Southern Oregon (Port Orford) to southern California (San Diego).

Leptocladia J. G. Agardh, 1892

Thalli growing erect from a disc-shaped holdfast. The erect portion flattened, repeatedly and subdichotomously divided into progressively narrower segments. Older portions of segments sparingly or profusely beset with short, flattened, proliferous outgrowths. Medulla of segments with a single axial filament ensheathed by rhizoidal filaments of smaller diameter; the cortex composed of erect filaments with progressively smaller cells and with the outermost cells compacted into a parenchyma.

Spermatangia in irregular sori. Carpogonial and auxiliary cell filaments developing at inner face of cortex, curved and with sterile branches from the lower cells. Development of carposporophyte unknown. Mature cystocarps at juncture of cortex and medulla, with the carposporangia in short rows radiating toward the thallus surface. Segments containing cystocarps not swollen or otherwise modified.

Tetrasporophytes with tetrasporangia in nemathecia scattered over surface of thallus. The tetrasporangia cruciately divided.

STRUCTURE AND REPRODUCTION. Setchell, 1912, pp. 250–254; pl. 30. Schmitz and Hauptfleisch, 1896–1897, p. 520 (the latter as *Andersoniella*).

With one species in the local flora.

Leptocladia conferta Setchell   Pl. 46, fig. 5

Setchell, 1912, p. 252; pl. 30. Phyc. Bor.-Amer. No. 1848.

Thalli 15–20 cm. tall; dark red in color. With several shoots from a common disc-shaped base. The shoots of a cartilaginous texture, markedly flattened, subdichotomously branched and frequently with one of the major dichotomies more extensively forked than the other. Major dichotomies up to 1.5 mm. broad, frequently with many relatively short fasciculate proliferous outgrowths.

LOCAL DISTRIBUTION. Growing on rocks between the 1.0-foot and mean low-tide levels. Known from the rocky point near Seal Rocks and from Carmel Bay.

TYPE LOCALITY. Dillon's Beach, Tomales Bay, California.

PACIFIC COAST DISTRIBUTION. Northern California (Crescent City) to central California (Carmel Bay).

Weeksia Setchell, 1901

Thalli with one or more stipitate blades from a disc-shaped base. The blades broadly reniform to orbicular, undivided but often laciniate, with or without marginal proliferous blades similar to the primary blade. Surface of blade unevenly flattened. Base of blade with or without veins; when present the veins radiately forked and with or without anastamoses. Medulla of blade composed of interwoven colorless filaments; the cortex with large colorless rounded cells toward the interior and vertical rows of colored cells at the exterior.

Spermatangia unknown. Carpogonial filaments several cells in length, curved; the trichogyne long, spirally twisted at base. Auxiliary cell filaments, except for carpogonium similar to carpogonial filaments. Development of carposporophyte unknown. Mature cystocarps reniform, immersed in the medulla, each lying beneath a small opening in the overlying cortical tissue; cystocarps scattered throughout the blade.

Tetrasporophytes unknown.

STRUCTURE AND REPRODUCTION. Kylin, 1925, pp. 15–16; fig. 6. Setchell, 1901, pp. 128–129. Setchell, 1912, pp. 254–255.

With one species in the local flora.

Weeksia reticulata Setchell   Pl. 46, fig. 4

*Setchell, 1901, p. 128.

Thalli up to 40 cm. tall; rose-pink to dark red in color. The blades broadly reniform to orbicular, up to 30 cm. broad. Margins of blades proliferating new blades. Base of blades with an indistinct radiating system of forked to anastamosing veins. The blades soft and fleshy in texture.

LOCAL DISTRIBUTION. Known only from specimens cast ashore. Pacific Grove; Moss Beach; Carmel Beach.

TYPE LOCALITY. "Cast ashore from deep water on several beaches near Pacific Grove."

PACIFIC COAST DISTRIBUTION. As above.

Constantinea Postels and Ruprecht, 1840

Thalli erect, solitary or in clusters from a common disc-shaped base. Erect portion with a cylindrical, simple or dichotomously branched, stipe terminating in one or more perfoliate horizontal circular blades. Lower portion of stipe with scars of old eroded blades. Blades at first entire; later frequently torn into several wedge-shaped segments. The interval between successive blades or scars of blades either shorter or longer than diameter of stipe. New blades developed on apical portion of stipe projecting through an old blade. Stipe and blade with a medulla of longitudinal filaments; cortex pseudoparenchymatous and with progressively smaller cells to the surface.

Spermatangia unknown. Carpogonial and auxiliary cell filaments several cells in length and with curved sterile branches from the lower cells; borne at inner face of the cortex. Mature cystocarps reniform, without a pericarp, deeply embedded in cortex. The cystocarps lying in a continuous zone encircling the blade some distance in from the margin.

Tetrasporophytes with the tetrasporangia in elliptical, oblong, or irregularly shaped nemathecia on upper surface of blade. The nemathecia with unicellular clavate paraphyses extending beyond the sporangia. The tetraspores zonately divided.

STRUCTURE AND REPRODUCTION. Freeman, 1899. Setchell, 1906.

With one species in the local flora.

Constantinea simplex Setchell   Pl. 47, fig. 6

*Setchell, 1901, p. 127. *Setchell, 1906, p. 171.

Constantinea sitchensis Anderson [not of Postels and Ruprecht]. *Anderson, 1891, p. 22. Phyc. Bor.-Amer. No. 450.

Thalli, as found on the Monterey Peninsula, 3–8 cm. tall; bright red to a deep dull red in color. The stipe 2–6 cm. long, 0.6–1.2 cm. in diameter; usually simple but sometimes with a single dichotomy. With one (occasionally two) horizontal, circular, saucer-shaped, perfoliate blades at apex of stipe. The interval between blade and scars of old blades less than a third the diameter of stipe. The blades up to 12 cm. in diameter, either entire or radially split into several segments.

LOCAL DISTRIBUTION. Growing on rocks at mean low-tide level. Point Douty. Also found cast ashore at Pacific Grove.

TYPE LOCALITY. Dillon's Beach, Tomales Bay, California.

PACIFIC COAST DISTRIBUTION. Northern Washington (Neah Bay) to central California (Carmel Highlands).

Family GLOIOSIPHONIACEAE

Thalli erect, filamentous or nonfilamentous. Nonfilamentous thalli branched, with cylindrical or compressed branches. The thalli monoaxial, with a percurrent axial filament, and with the cortical region loosely compacted and gelatinous.

Carpogonial and auxiliary cell filaments with a common supporting cell. The carpogonial filament three-celled, unbranched. The auxiliary cell filament three- to seven-celled, unbranched, with the auxiliary cell at or near the apex. Mature cystocarp small, globose, without an envelope.

Tetrasporophytes, so far as known, with the tetrasporangia remote from one another. The tetrasporangia cruciately divided.

With one genus, *Gloiosiphonia,* in the local flora.

Gloiosiphonia Carmichael, 1833

Thalli solitary or gregarious, with an erect profusely branched shoot. Erect shoot either with an obscure main axis bearing repeatedly divided branches; or with a conspicuous main axis bearing transverse whorls of short simple branches. Texture of branches very gelatinous to relatively firm. The branches with a single axial filament each cell of which bears four quadrately disposed branched filaments. Outer ends of lateral filaments laterally adjoined to form a fairly compact tissue. Older portion of branches with axial filament clothed with rhizoidal filaments from lower cells of lateral filaments.

Heterothallic. Spermatangia borne in extensive areas on surface of thallus. Carpogonial filament three-celled. Supporting cell of carpogonial filament borne on lowermost cell of a lateral filament from the axial filament. Supporting cell of carpogonial filament also bearing a pair of seven- or eight-celled auxiliary cell filaments in which the auxiliary cell is usually the fifth cell from the base. After fertilization the carpogonium sending out two oöblasts, one to each auxiliary cell. Gonimoblast filaments freely branched, developed on side of auxiliary cell toward thallus surface. All cells of gonimoblasts developing into carposporangia. Mature cystocarps globose, deeply embedded in thallus.

Tetrasporophytes with tetrasporangia remote from one another and embedded at surface of thallus. The tetrasporangia cruciately divided.

STRUCTURE AND REPRODUCTION. Oltmanns, 1898, pp. 109–114; pl. 5. Sjöstedt, 1926, pp. 12–15; figs. 5–6. Kylin, 1930, pp. 10–12; fig. 4.

KEY TO THE SPECIES IN THE LOCAL FLORA

1. Thalli profusely and irregularly branched..............*G. californica*
1. Thalli with transverse whorls of short branches.......*G. verticillaris*

Gloiosiphonia californica (Farlow) J. G. Agardh Pl. 47, fig. 2

J. G. Agardh, 1885, p. 10.
Nemastoma californica Farlow, 1877, p. 243. *Anderson, 1891, p. 222. *Phyc. Bor.-Amer. No. 397.

Thalli, as found on the Monterey Peninsula, usually 10–30 cm. tall but occasionally up to 60 cm.; rose-red in color. The thallus an erect, bushy, irregularly branched cylinder with the branch tips gradually narrowing to an acute point. Major branches 1–2.5 mm. in diameter. Ultimate branchlets exceedingly numerous and hair-like. The thallus very gelatinous but of a tough consistency.

LOCAL DISTRIBUTION. Growing on rocks between the 1.5- and −0.5-foot tide levels. Usually found only during spring and early summer. Mussel Point; Point Pinos; Pebble Beach.

TYPE LOCALITY. Santa Cruz, California.

PACIFIC COAST DISTRIBUTION. Alaska (Sitka) to central California (Carmel Bay).

Gloiosiphonia verticillaris Farlow Pl. 47, fig. 1

Farlow, 1889, p. 3; pl. 88, figs. 5–6, 9–10. *Phyc. Bor.-Amer. No. 100.

Thalli, as found on the Monterey Peninsula, usually 10–25 cm. tall but occasionally up to 60 cm.; of a bright rose-red color. Thalli growing in gregarious tufts from a common base, with percurrent simple cylindrical axis 0.5–1.5 mm. in diameter. The axis with transverse whorls of 3–6 lateral branches. All lateral branches in a whorl approximately the same length and up to 2 cm. long. Successive whorls on axis equidistant and at intervals of 3–5 cm. Older thalli frequently with the characteristic verticillate branching obscured by numerous short proliferous branches growing from portions of axis between verticils. Cystocarps restricted to verticillate branches of axis.

LOCAL DISTRIBUTION. Growing on sand-covered rocks between the 1.5- and 0.5-foot tide levels. Usually found only during spring and early summer. Common at Middle Reef of Moss Beach. Also found at Pebble Beach; north end of Carmel Beach; Mission Point; mouth of Carmel River.

TYPE LOCALITY. Santa Cruz, California.

PACIFIC COAST DISTRIBUTION. Alaska (Sitka) to central California (Carmel Bay).

Family ENDOCLADIACEAE

Thalli erect, nonfilamentous, freely branched and with cylindrical or compressed branches. The branches monoaxial, with a percurrent axial filament, and with the surface cells compacted into a firm parenchyma.

Carpogonial and auxiliary cell filaments borne in the same branched filament. Carpogonial filaments two-celled and two or more borne on the same filament. The auxiliary cell an enlarged cell borne low in the branched fertile filament bearing carpogonial filaments. Mature cystocarps surrounded by a pericarp.

Tetrasporophytes with the tetrasporangia borne in nemathecia. The tetrasporangia cruciately divided.

With one genus, *Endocladia,* in the local flora.

Endocladia J. G. Agardh, 1841

Thalli erect, profusely branched, without an evident central axis. The branching radial to subdichotomous; the branches cylindrical and the ultimate branchlets terete. Surface of all branches clothed with minute conical spines. Branches with a single axial filament in which each cell bears two lateral filaments at an angle of 90° to each other, the pairs of cells on successive axial cells alternate with one another. Lateral filaments from axial cells freely branched and with the outermost cells compacted into a parenchyma.

Heterothallic. Spermatangia borne in small, irregularly shaped sori on surface of the ultimate branchlets. Carpogonial and auxiliary cell filaments developing from a common cell deep within the branch. The carpogonial filament two-celled and with its supporting cell borne upon the cell that bears the auxiliary cell. The gonimoblast filaments growing toward interior of thallus and with the carposporangia developing in chains. The mature cystocarp projecting above thallus surface and surrounded by a pericarp.

Tetrasporophytes with tetrasporangia in nemathecia borne on surface of young branches. Paraphyses of nemathecia unbranched, 10–12 cells long. The tetrasporangia irregularly cruciate.

STRUCTURE AND REPRODUCTION. Kylin, 1928, pp. 41–45; figs. 22–24.

Endocladia muricata (Postels and Ruprecht) J. G. Agardh
Pl. 47, figs. 3–4

J. G. Agardh, 1847, p. 10. J. G. Agardh, 1851, p. 237. *Harvey, 1853, pl. 182; pl. 27, fig. B. *Anderson, 1891, p. 223. *Howe, 1893, p. 68. *Kylin, 1941, p. 7. *Phyc. Bor.-Amer. Nos. 136, 882.

Gigartina muricata Postels and Ruprecht, 1840, p. 16.

Thalli, as found on the Monterey Peninsula, 4–6 cm. tall, dark red to blackish-brown in color. The thalli densely bushy and with the branches about .5 mm. in diameter. Spines covering the branches about .5 mm. long and giving the thallus a very characteristic harsh texture. Pericarps of cystocarps urn-shaped, about 1 mm. tall, usually much lighter in color than branches bearing them.

LOCAL DISTRIBUTION. Growing on vertical sides of rocks between the 6.0- and 3.0-foot tide levels. Common everywhere on rocks exposed to moderate or strong surf.

TYPE LOCALITY. Alaska.

PACIFIC COAST DISTRIBUTION. Alaska (Shumagin Islands) to southern California (La Jolla).

Family SQUAMARIACEAE

Thalli nonfilamentous, prostrate, crustose. Usually with a basal layer of prostrate laterally adjoined filaments in which each cell bears an erect filament on the upper side. The erect filaments laterally compacted.

Carpogonial and auxiliary cell filaments not borne on a common cell but the two produced in numbers in the same nemathecium. The carpogonial filaments 2- to 4-celled. The auxiliary cell filaments 2- to 5-celled. The cystocarps small and globose.

Tetrasporophytes with the tetrasporangia typically produced in nemathecia. The tetrasporangia usually cruciately divided.

KEY TO THE GENERA IN THE LOCAL FLORA

1. Tetrasporangia borne in nemathecia...............................2
1. Tetrasporangia borne in conceptacles.........*Hildenbrandia* (p. 214)
  2. No vertical cell rows on lower face of thallus...................3
  2. With vertical cell rows on lower face
      of thallus ....*Asymmetria* (p. 214)
3. With rhizoids from lower surface..............*Peyssonnelia* (p. 212)
3. Without rhizoids from lower surface..........*Rhododermis* (p. 213)

Peyssonnelia Decaisne, 1841

Thalli crustose, uncalcified or somewhat calcified, circular in outline but frequently with the margin lobed, attached to the substratum by multicellular simple or branched rhizoids. Hypothallium not sharply defined, usually monostromatic. Perithallium composed of laterally adjoined vertical rows of cells.

Homothallic or heterothallic. Spermatangia developed laterally on all sides of cells of paraphyses in a nemathecium. Carpogonial filaments usually four-celled, borne on the lowermost cell of paraphyses in a nemathecium. Auxiliary cell filaments usually four-celled, borne in same manner as carpogonial filaments and in the same nemathecium. The auxiliary cell usually the second from the top of filament. The gonimoblast filaments growing upward from auxiliary cell; with all cells developing into carposporangia. Cystocarps ellipsoidal to spindle-shaped, with relatively few carposporangia.

Tetrasporangia with tetrasporangia produced in nemathecia, the sporangia intermingled with paraphyses and borne on one-celled stalks. The tetrasporangia cruciately divided.

STRUCTURE AND REPRODUCTION. Kylin, 1925, pp. 25–27; figs. 12 *B*–12 *D*, 13. Kylin, 1928, pp. 35–36; fig. 18.

With one species in the local flora.

Peyssonnelia pacifica Kylin   Pl. 48, fig. 3

Kylin, 1925, p. 25; figs. 12 *B*–12 *D*, 13. *Kylin, 1941, p. 8.
Peyssonnelia Dubyi Anderson [ñot of Crouan]. *Anderson, 1891, p. 221.

Thalli more or less circular in outline, up to 6 cm. or more in diameter, of a dark purplish-red color. Thallus 300–500 µ in thickness and with a poorly defined hypothallium. Perithallium typically with progressively smaller cells to upper surface, lower cells 15–18 μ broad, upper cells 4–6 μ broad. Paraphyses of tetrasporic nemathecia club-shaped, with 5–8 cells. Tetrasporangia 25–30 μ broad, 45–55 μ long.

LOCAL DISTRIBUTION. On shells of turban snail (*Tegula*) at mean low-tide level. Middle Reef of Moss Beach. On rocks at Cypress Point. Also dredged from a depth of 30–35 feet a quarter-mile from Municipal Wharf, Monterey, and from 20 to 25 feet at Stillwater Cove.

TYPE LOCALITY. San Juan Island, Washington.

PACIFIC COAST DISTRIBUTION. As above.

The dimensions given above are those found in specimens from the type locality.

Rhododermis Crouan, 1852

Thalli crustose, uncalcified, regularly to irregularly circular in outline, without rhizoids from the lower surface. With a monostromatic hypothallium of laterally adjoined radiately branched filaments. Perithallium with erect filaments parallel to one another. The monostromatic hypothallium usually projecting horizontally beyond the perithallium.

Spermatangia and cystocarps unknown.

Tetrasporophytes with the tetrasporangia in sori standing above upper surface of thallus. The sori with erect curved unbranched paraphyses overarching the tetrasporangia. The tetrasporangia sessile or pedicellate, cruciately divided.

STRUCTURE AND REPRODUCTION. Kuckuck, 1896*A*. Levring, 1935, pp. 42–44; fig. 9. Rosenvinge, 1917, pp. 197–202; figs. 118–120.

Rhododermis elegans Crouan

Crouan ex J. G. Agardh, 1852, p. 505.

Thalli irregularly circular, up to 5 mm. in diameter, of a bright rose-red color. Erect filaments of perithallium usually 4- to 6-celled and with cells slightly broader than long. The paraphyses usually 4- to 6-celled. The tetrasporangia 16–24 μ broad, 24–33 μ long.

LOCAL DISTRIBUTION. On sporophylls of *Pterygophora californica* cast ashore on Carmel Beach.

TYPE LOCALITY. Brest, France.

PACIFIC COAST DISTRIBUTION. Known only from Duxbury Reef, Marin County, California, and from the Monterey Peninsula.

Asymmetria Setchell and Gardner, 1927

Thallus a prostrate, uncalcified, leathery, crustose sheet more or less circular in outline and not very closely adherent to the substratum. Upper half of thallus composed of compacted erect filaments somewhat intertwined with one another. Below this a zone of closely interwoven anastamosing horizontal filaments. The thalli generally with a zone of vertical filaments below the horizontal filaments. Lower surface of thallus without rhizoids. Radial increase in diameter of thallus due to growth of the horizontal filaments.

Spermatangia and cystocarps unknown.

Tetrasporophytes with the tetrasporangia in irregularly shaped nemathecia on upper side of thallus. The nemathecia with multicellular paraphyses that are curved and clavate at the upper end. The tetrasporangia cruciately or tetrahedrally divided.

STRUCTURE AND REPRODUCTION. Gardner, 1917, pp. 396–398; pl. 33, fig. 2 (as *Coriophyllum*).

Asymmetria expansa Setchell and Gardner　Pl. 48, fig. 2

Setchell and Gardner apud Gardner, 1927*A*, p. 341.
Coriophyllum expansum Setchell and Gardner apud Gardner, 1917, p. 397; pl. 33, fig. 2.

Thalli 5–8 cm. in diameter; dark purplish-red in color; upper surface of thallus uneven and the margins irregularly lobed. The thallus 0.5–0.8 mm. in thickness and with the erect filaments of the upper half 4–6 µ in diameter. Paraphyses of nemathecia 6- to 12-celled, about 3 µ in diameter. Tetrasporangia 22–28 µ broad, 60–70 µ long.

LOCAL DISTRIBUTION. Growing on rocks just below the high-tide level. Cypress Point; Pescadero Point.

TYPE LOCALITY. Cypress Point, Monterey Peninsula, California.

PACIFIC COAST DISTRIBUTION. As above.

Hildenbrandia[3] Nardo, 1834

Thallus a prostrate, indefinitely expanded, uncalcified, crustose layer whose lower surface is closely adherent to the substratum. The hypothallium a horizontally expanded, radiately branched, filamentous layer. The perithallium consisting of erect filaments

[3] The conventional procedure is to assign this genus to the Squamariaceae pending discovery of the development and structure of the cystocarp. The production of tetrasporangia within conceptacles suggests that it belongs elsewhere.

densely compacted into a parenchymatous tissue with cells in vertical cell rows. The perithallium zonately divided into transverse layers.

Spermatangia and carposporangia unknown.

Tetrasporophytes with tetrasporangia in conceptacles scattered over entire upper surface of thallus. The conceptacles flask-shaped to subcylindrical, with many tetrasporangia. The tetrasporangia either irregularly or zonately divided.

STRUCTURE AND REPRODUCTION. Rosenvinge, 1917, pp. 202–207; figs. 121–125.

KEY TO THE SPECIES IN THE LOCAL FLORA

1. Thallus dark purplish-red, 1–3 mm. in thickness........*H. occidentalis*
1. Thallus rose-red, less than 0.5 mm. in thickness......*II. prototypus*

Hildenbrandia occidentalis Setchell   Pl. 49, fig. 4

Setchell in Phyc. Bor.-Amer. No. 2300 (name only). Setchell apud Gardner, 1917, p. 393; pl. 33, fig. 4.

Thalli indefinitely expanded and up to 70–100 cm. in diameter; moist living thalli of a dark purplish-red color, dried thalli black. The thallus 1–2 mm. in thickness. Conceptacles longer than broad, ovoid to cylindrical, with a relatively narrow ostiole. The conceptacles with or without paraphyses. The tetrasporangia elongate, zonately divided, 8–10 μ broad, 25–32 μ long.

LOCAL DISTRIBUTION. Growing on rocks slightly below the high-tide level. Widely distributed on the Monterey Peninsula. Fruiting thalli have been collected at Mussel Point; Cypress Point; Pebble Beach; north end of Carmel Beach.

TYPE LOCALITY. Land's End, San Francisco, California.

PACIFIC COAST DISTRIBUTION. Puget Sound to central California (Carmel Bay).

Hildenbrandia prototypus Nardo

Nardo, 1834, p. 675.
Hildenbrandia rosea Kützing, 1843, p. 384. *Anderson, 1891, p. 221.

Thalli indefinitely expanded, usually of a bright red color. The thallus 0.2–0.5 mm. in thickness. Conceptacles broader than long, with a broad ostiole. The tetrasporangia irregularly divided, 9–14 μ broad, 16–30 μ long.

LOCAL DISTRIBUTION. Growing on rocks in the mid-littoral. Pacific Grove.

TYPE LOCALITY. Italian shore of the Adriatic Sea.

PACIFIC COAST DISTRIBUTION. Alaska to central California (Pacific Grove).

A Pacific Coast species of *Hildenbrandia* with rose-red thalli much thinner than those of *H. occidentalis* is usually referred to *H. prototypus*. This determination is open to question because Pacific Coast specimens have not been found in fruit. The description of *H. prototypus* given above is of the species as found in the Atlantic Ocean.

Family CRUORIACEAE

Thalli nonfilamentous, prostrate, crustose. With a hypothallium several cells in thickness and composed of laterally adjoined filaments. The perithallium with erect filaments laterally separated from one another by gelatinous material.

Carpogonial and auxiliary cell filaments separated from one another and scattered through the perithallium. The carpogonial filaments 2- or 3-celled. The auxiliary cell filaments indistinguishable from erect vegetative filaments and without an evident auxiliary cell. The cystocarps small and globose.

Tetrasporophytes with the tetrasporangia intercalary or borne laterally and lying midway between base and apex of perithallial filaments. The tetrasporangia cruciately or zonately divided.

With one genus, *Petrocelis,* in the local flora.

Petrocelis J. G. Agardh, 1852

Thalli crustose, indefinitely expanded, uncalcified, many cells in thickness, and with the lower surface strongly adherent to the substratum. Lower surface of thallus without rhizoids. The hypothallium several cells in thickness, composed of horizontal branched filaments. The perithallium with erect, simple to sparingly branched filaments separated from one another by gelatinous material.

Heterothallic. The spermatangia borne on 1- or 2-celled branches at upper end of perithallial filaments. Carpogonial filaments usually 2-celled, borne laterally some distance below apices of perithallial filaments. The auxiliary cell an intercalary cell of a perithallial filament. The gonimoblast filaments growing both upward and downward from auxiliary cell; with all cells developing into carposporangia. Mature cystocarps, small, spindle-shaped, lying between perithallial filaments.

Tetrasporophytes with tetrasporangia developing from intercalary cells of perithallial filaments and lying in a horizontal zone some distance below thallus surface. Usually only one sporangium developing on each filament. The tetrasporangium cruciately divided.

STRUCTURE AND REPRODUCTION. Rosenvinge, 1917, pp. 174–180; figs. 92–99.

With one species in the local flora.

Petrocelis franciscana Setchell and Gardner   Pl. 48, fig. 1

Setchell and Gardner apud Gardner, 1917, p. 391; pl. 33, fig. 1. *Kylin, 1941, p. 17.

Petrocelis cruenta Anderson [not of J. G. Agardh]. *Anderson, 1891, p. 221. *Howe, 1893, p. 67.

Petrocelis Middendorfii Setchell [not of (Ruprecht) Kjellman]. Setchell in Phyc. Bor.-Amer. No. 900.

Thalli, as found on the Monterey Peninsula, up to a meter or more in diameter; olive-brown to brownish-red in color. The thalli 2.0–2.5 mm. in thickness. Cells of the hypothallium frequently anastamosing with one another. Perithallial filaments unbranched, of the same diameter throughout, 3.5–5 µ broad, the cells with a length up to 2.5 times the breadth. The perithallial filaments with transverse zones of anastamosing cells. Tetrasporangia borne 15–25 cells below thallus surface, 20–28 µ broad, 25–40 µ long.

LOCAL DISTRIBUTION. Growing on the vertical face of rocks between the 4.0- and 2.5-foot tide levels. Perennial but usually producing tetrasporangia only from December to February. Abundant on all rocky headlands.

TYPE LOCALITY. San Francisco, California.

PACIFIC COAST DISTRIBUTION. Puget Sound to central California (San Luis Obispo County).

Family CORALLINACEAE

Thalli nonfilamentous, calcified. The thalli wholly prostrate and crustose, or with a widely expanded crustose base bearing numerous erect shoots. The erect shoots branched, differentiated into uncalcified nodes (genicula) and broader calcified internodes (intergenicula).

Carpogonial and auxiliary cell filaments not united but the two produced in numbers in a common conceptacle. The carpogonial filaments three-celled and at center of a conceptacle; the auxiliary cell filaments two-celled and lying in a ring around the carpogonial filaments. The cystocarp with the carposporangia developing at the margin of a large disc-shaped placental cell.

Tetrasporophytes with the tetrasporangia borne in conceptacles with one or several openings. The tetrasporangia zonately divided.

Key to the Genera in the Local Flora

Melobesia Lamouroux, 1812

Thalli small, crustose, circular in outline unless densely crowded. At first one cell in thickness and composed of laterally adjoined radiating filaments. Later all cells but the marginal ones dividing horizontally into a small uncalcified cell and a large more or less calcified cell that may divide transversely to produce a vertical row of 2–15 cells. Portion of thallus more than one cell in thickness not sharply differentiated into hypothallium and perithallium.

Heterothallic. Spermatangia borne in conceptacles opening externally by a single ostiole. Carpogonial filaments borne in conceptacles with a single ostiole. All cells on floor of conceptacle functioning as supporting cells and each bearing the primordium of a single carpogonial filament. Primordia in central portion of conceptacle each developing into a 2-celled carpogonial filament; primordia at periphery of conceptacle not developing further. Supporting cells of mature and immature carpogonial filaments functioning as auxiliary cells that fuse laterally to form a single large disc-shaped placental cell. Gonimoblast filaments 2–3 cells in length, growing from margin of placental cell, usually with only the terminal cells developing into carposporangia.

Tetrasporophytes with tetrasporangial conceptacles in central portion of thallus. Young sporangia laterally separated by vertical rows of sterile cells that degenerate as the sporangia approach maturity. Roof of conceptacle developing a small pore external to each sporangium. Tetrasporangia zonately divided.

STRUCTURE AND REPRODUCTION. Kylin, 1928, pp. 37–41; figs. 19–21 (as *Epilithon*). Nichols, 1908 (as *Lithothamnion*). Suneson, 1937, pp. 59–62; fig. 36 (as *Epilithon*).

KEY TO THE SPECIES IN THE LOCAL FLORA

1. Epiphytic on *Phyllospadix*..............................*M. mediocris*
1. Epiphytic on noncalcareous Florideae.................*M. marginata*

Melobesia mediocris (Foslie) Setchell and Mason Pl. 49, fig. 1

Setchell and Mason, 1943, p. 95.
Lithophyllum zostericolum forma *mediocris* Foslie, 1900, p. 5.
Lithothamnion mediocre (Foslie) Foslie and Nichols apud Nichols, 1908, p. 347; pl. 9.
Melobesia amplexifrons Anderson [not of Harvey]. *Anderson, 1891, p. 225. Phyc. Bor.-Amer. No. 299.

Thalli, as found on the Monterey Peninsula, up to 2 mm. in diameter; light pink to deep rose-red in color. Nearly circular in outline when developing singly; usually densely crowded and angular. Two cells in thickness at margin; up to 12 cells in thickness adjacent to conceptacles. Cells in vegetative portion approximately cubical. Tetrasporangial conceptacles slightly elevated above thallus surface, 150–200 µ in diameter. The tetrasporangia 35–80 µ broad, 50–125 µ long.

LOCAL DISTRIBUTION. Epiphytic on *Phyllospadix*. Abundant wherever the host grows.

TYPE LOCALITY. Santa Cruz, California.

PACIFIC COAST DISTRIBUTION. Northern California (Fort Bragg) to central California (Carmel Bay).

Melobesia marginata Setchell and Foslie

Pl. 49, fig. 2; pl. 50, fig. 1

Setchell and Foslie apud Foslie, 1902, p. 10. Phyc. Bor.-Amer. No. 1300.
Lithothamnion marginatum (Setchell and Foslie) Foslie apud *Nichols, 1909, p. 350; pl. 10, fig. 1; pl. 11, figs. 7–9; pl. 13, fig. 25.

Thalli, as found on the Monterey Peninsula, 5–8 mm. in diameter; whitish-purple in color. Nearly circular in outline and with slightly lobed margins when developing singly; more or less angular when crowded. Two cells in thickness at margin; up to 15 cells in thickness adjacent to conceptacles. Cells in vegetative portion approximately cubical. Tetrasporangial conceptacles numerous, slightly elevated above thallus surface, 80–200 μ in diameter. The tetrasporangia 18–30 μ broad, 40–80 μ long.

LOCAL DISTRIBUTION. Of frequent occurrence on *Laurencia spectabilis, Rhodymenia,* and the larger species of *Gelidium.*

TYPE LOCALITY. Bodega Bay, Marin County, California.

PACIFIC COAST DISTRIBUTION. Washington (Whidbey Island) to southern California (La Jolla).

Lithothamnion Philippi, 1837

Thalli calcareous, wholly crustose, of limited or unlimited growth. Growing on rocks, on calcareous shells of animals, and on other algae. Lower surface entirely adherent to almost free from substratum. Upper surface smooth, tuberculate, coralloid, or with laminate projections. Thalli many cells in thickness and differentiated into hypothallium and perithallium.

Heterothallic. Spermatangia borne in conceptacles partly immersed in thallus and opening externally by a single ostiole. Carpogonial filaments in conceptacles partly immersed in thallus and opening by a single ostiole. Carpogonial filaments and development of carpospores as in *Melobesia.*

Tetrasporophytes with tetrasporangial conceptacles superficial or partly immersed in thallus. Development and structure of conceptacles as in *Melobesia.*

STRUCTURE AND REPRODUCTION. Suneson, 1937, pp. 62–68; figs. 37–41.

KEY TO THE SPECIES IN THE LOCAL FLORA

1. Thalli growing on rocks.. 2
1. Thalli epiphytic on other algae................................. 5
  2. Loosely attached to rocks.........................*L. lamellatum*
  2. Firmly attached to rocks..................................... 3
3. Upper surface smooth or almost smooth.............*L. californicum*
3. Upper surface not smooth..................................... 4
  4. Upper surface with rounded outgrowths..............*L. pacificum*
  4. Upper surface with erect coralloid outgrowths....*L. montereyicum*
5. Outline of thallus irregular...........................*L. lamellatum*
5. Outline of thallus circular to semicircular......................... 6
  6. Tetrasporic conceptacles with 60–70 pores..........*L. conchatum*
  6. Tetrasporic conceptacles with 15–25 pores............*L. parcum*

Lithothamnion californicum Foslie

*Foslie, 1900, p. 3. *Foslie, 1929; pl. 3, fig. 1. Phyc. Bor.-Amer. No. LXI.

Thalli, as found on the Monterey Peninsula, circular in outline and up to 10 cm. broad, frequently confluent with one another to form patches of indefinite extent; whitish-pink in color. Upper surface of thallus smooth except when the underlying rock has a rough surface. Lower surface firmly adherent to substratum. Thalli 0.8–1.2 mm. in thickness; the hypothallium many cells in thickness and with cells in horizontal rows; the perithallium many cells in height and with cubical cells in vertical rows. Tetrasporophytes with many conceptacles in central portion of thallus and their tops projecting slightly above thallus surface. The conceptacles 300–400 μ broad, with about 30 pores in the roof. Tetrasporangia 60–90 μ broad, 140–180 μ long.

LOCAL DISTRIBUTION. Growing on rocks between the 0.5- and −1.5-foot tide levels. Common everywhere.

TYPE LOCALITY. Point Fermin, San Pedro, California.

PACIFIC COAST DISTRIBUTION. Washington (San Juan Island) to southern California (San Diego).

Lithothamnion pacificum Foslie   Pl. 49, fig. 3

*Foslie, 1906, p. 10. *Foslie, 1929; pl. 4, fig. 14.
Lithothamnion Sonderi forma *pacifica* *Foslie, 1902, p. 4.

Thalli, as found on the Monterey Peninsula, circular or irregular in outline, 10 cm. or more in diameter, frequently confluent with one another; pinkish-purple in color. Upper surface of thallus covered with rounded to branched cylindrical outgrowths 4–6 mm. broad and 6–10 mm. tall. Lower surface firmly adherent to substratum. The thalli 2–3 mm. in thickness; the hypothallium and perithallium many cells in thickness. Tetrasporophytes with conceptacles usually restricted to outgrowths from thallus surface. The conceptacles 0.4–0.8 mm. in diameter and with the roof perforated by 100–150 pores. Tetrasporangia 40–70 μ broad, 140–170 μ long.

LOCAL DISTRIBUTION. Growing on rocks between the 0.5- and −1.5-foot tide levels. Common everywhere.

TYPE LOCALITY. Pacific Grove, California.

PACIFIC COAST DISTRIBUTION. Washington (Whidbey Island) to central California (Carmel Bay).

Lithothamnion montereyicum Foslie

*Foslie, 1906, p. 14. *Foslie, 1929; pl. 17, figs. 28–29.

Thalli consisting for the most part of erect and scantily branched coralloid branches 2–3 cm. tall. The branches about 1 cm. in diameter at base, either compressed or nearly rounded, with blunt apices. Reproductive organs unknown.

LOCAL DISTRIBUTION. Dredged from a depth of about 70 feet near Monterey.
TYPE LOCALITY. As above.
PACIFIC COAST DISTRIBUTION. As above.

This distinctive coralloid species is known only from the original collection dredged from Monterey Bay. The generic position of the species is uncertain because the tetrasporic conceptacles are as yet unknown. It is referred to *Lithothamnion* because several coralloid species are known to belong to this genus.

Lithothamnion lamellatum Setchell and Foslie

*Setchell and Foslie apud Foslie, 1903, p. 4. *Foslie, 1929; pl. 8, figs. 4–5.

Thalli forming whitish-pink crusts loosely attached either to rocks or to other algae, especially *Corallina*. The thalli irregular in outline and 2–3 cm. in diameter. Upper surface of thallus smooth. The thalli 0.3–0.5 mm. thick; the hypothallium many cells in thickness and with the cells in horizontal rows. Tetrasporophytes with conceptacles everywhere except at thallus margin. The conceptacles 350–600 μ in diameter and with the roof perforated by 40–60 pores. Tetrasporangia about 120 μ broad and 250 μ long.

LOCAL DISTRIBUTION. Growing in the lower littoral. Point Joe; Cypress Point.
TYPE LOCALITY. Cypress Point, Monterey Peninsula, California.
PACIFIC COAST DISTRIBUTION. As above.

Lithothamnion conchatum Setchell and Foslie   Pl. 50, fig. 2

*Setchell and Foslie apud Foslie, 1902, p. 6. *Foslie, 1906, p. 6. *Foslie, 1907A, p. 13. *Foslie, 1929; pl. 10, figs. 3–6. Phyc. Bor.-Amer. No. 1750.

Thalli, as found on the Monterey Peninsula, 0.5–1.5 cm. in diameter; pinkish-purple in color. The thalli circular to semicircular, attached only by middle portion of the lower face. Upper surface of thallus slightly concave or slightly convex, with small concentric ridges. The thalli 0.2–0.6 mm. in thickness and with a thick hypothallium. Tetrasporophytes with conceptacles everywhere except at periphery of thallus. The conceptacles 0.5–0.8 mm. in diameter and with the roof perforated by 60–70 pores. Tetrasporangia 100–150 μ broad, 250–350 μ long.

LOCAL DISTRIBUTION. Epiphytic on articulated Corallinaceae, especially *Calliarthron*. Common everywhere.

TYPE LOCALITY. Point Joe, Monterey Peninsula, California.

PACIFIC COAST DISTRIBUTION. Washington (San Juan Island) to central California (Carmel Bay).

This species differs from the closely related *L. parcum* in having thicker thalli, concentric ridges on upper surface of the thallus, and a larger number of pores in the roof of tetrasporic conceptacles.

Lithothamnion parcum Setchell and Foslie

*Setchell and Foslie apud Foslie, 1907*A*, p. 14. *Foslie, 1929; pl. 10, figs. 18–23. Phyc. Bor.-Amer. No. 1749.

Thalli, as found on the Monterey Peninsula, 0.5–1.0 cm. in diameter; pinkish-purple in color. Circular, semicircular, or irregular in outline; attached only by middle portion of the lower face. Upper surface of thallus slightly convex and without concentric ridges. The thalli 0.5–1.5 mm. in thickness; with a strongly developed hypothallium and a feebly developed perithallium. Tetrasporophytes with a limited number of conceptacles. The conceptacles 0.3–0.5 mm. in diameter and with the roof perforated by 15–25 pores. Tetrasporangia 50–90 μ broad, 180–240 μ long.

LOCAL DISTRIBUTION. Epiphytic on articulated Corallinaceae, especially *Calliarthron*. Common everywhere.

TYPE LOCALITY. Cypress Point, Monterey Peninsula, California.

PACIFIC COAST DISTRIBUTION. Washington (San Juan Island) to central California (Carmel Bay).

Fosliella Howe, 1920

Thalli small, crustose, more or less circular in outline and completely adherent. At first one cell in thickness and composed of laterally adjoined radiating filaments. Later all cells but the marginal ones dividing horizontally into a small uncalcified cell and a large more or less calcified cell that may divide transversely to produce a vertical row of 2–8 cells. Portion of thallus more than one cell in thickness not sharply differentiated into hypothallium and perithallium.

Heterothallic. Spermatangia borne in conceptacles opening externally by a single ostiole. Carpogonial filaments borne in conceptacles with a single ostiole. All cells on floor of conceptacle functioning as supporting cells and each bearing primordia of two carpogonial filaments. One primordium on each supporting cell in central portion of primordium developing into a 2-celled carpogonial filament; primordia at periphery of conceptacle not developing further. Supporting cells of mature and immature carpogonial filaments functioning as auxiliary cells that fuse to form a single large disc-shaped placental cell. Development of gonimoblasts and carposporangia as in *Melobesia*.

Tetrasporophytes with tetrasporangia borne in conceptacles with a single ostiole. The tetrasporangia usually developing only in peripheral portion of floor of conceptacle; zonately divided.

STRUCTURE AND REPRODUCTION. Suneson, 1937, pp. 7–19; figs. 1–10 (as *Melobesia*).

KEY TO THE SPECIES IN THE LOCAL FLORA

1. Tetrasporangia containing four spores......................... 2
1. Tetrasporangia containing two spores.................*F. intermedia*
   2. Lowermost cells below conceptacles oblique
      and with a height several times the breadth................. 3
   2. Lowermost cells below conceptacles approximately
      cubical ....*F. Nicholsii*
3. Tetrasporangial conceptacles bulging above
   surface of thallus ....*F. ascripticia*
3. Tetrasporangial conceptacles not bulging
   above surface of thallus ....*F. dispar*

Fosliella ascripticia (Foslie) comb. nov.   Pl. 50, fig. 7

Lithophyllum pustulatum forma *ascripticia* *Foslie, 1907, p. 33. Nichols, 1909*A*, p. 354; pl. 10, figs. 2–3; pl. 11, fig. 10; pl. 12, figs. 18–20; pl. 13, fig. 28.

Thalli, as found on the Monterey Peninsula, up to 1.2 cm. in diameter; of a chalky-pink color. Approximately circular if not crowded. Vegetative portion of thallus two to several cells in thickness. Cells of the lowermost layer with a height several times the breadth and vertically diagonal to the host; cells of other layers vertically oblong but shorter than those of basal layer. Tetrasporic conceptacles 200–320 µ broad, 120–140 µ tall; bulging above surface of the thallus and with the ostiole closed by a disc of gelatinous material. Central portion of floor of conceptacles sterile. Tetrasporangia 35–50 μ broad, 60–110 μ long; transversely divided and with four spores.

LOCAL DISTRIBUTION. Epiphytic on *Botryoglossum Farlowianum.* Monterey; Pacific Grove; Asilomar Point; Middle Reef of Moss Beach; Pebble Beach.

TYPE LOCALITY. Monterey, California.

PACIFIC COAST DISTRIBUTION. Central California (Monterey) to southern California (La Jolla).

Fosliella dispar (Foslie) comb. nov.   Pl. 50, fig. 6

Lithophyllum tumidulum var. *dispar* Foslie, 1907*A*, p. 27. Nichols, 1909, p. 357; pl. 10, fig. 6; pl. 11, figs. 13–14; pl. 13, fig. 26.

Lithophyllum dispar Foslie, 1909, p. 50. Phyc. Bor.-Amer. No. 1799.

Thalli, as found on the Monterey Peninsula, up to 12 mm. in diameter; of a chalky-pink color. The thalli approximately circular if on a foliaceous host and not crowded; irregularly shaped and encircling host if the latter has small cylindrical or flattened branches. Vegetative portion of thallus several cells in thickness. The cells rectangular, vertically elongated, those of the lowermost layer diagonal to the host. Tetrasporic conceptacles 200–350 μ broad, 120–215 μ tall; not bulging above surface of thallus and with the ostiole closed by a disc of gelatinous material. Central portion of floor of conceptacle sterile. Tetrasporangia 50–70 μ broad, 100–150 μ long; transversely divided and with four spores.

LOCAL DISTRIBUTION. On *Ahnfeltia plicata* near Seal Rock; on *Gelidium Coulteri* at Pacific Grove; on *Gigartina volans* at Middle Reef of Moss Beach; on *Gymnogongrus linearis* at the north end of Carmel Beach.

TYPE LOCALITY. Bolinas, California.

PACIFIC COAST DISTRIBUTION. Known only from Whidbey Island, Washington; Bolinas; and the Monterey Peninsula.

Fosliella Nicholsii (Setchell and Mason) comb. nov.
Pl. 50, fig. 8

*Heteroderma Nicholsii Setchell and Mason, 1943, p. 96.

Lithophyllum pustulatum forma *australis* Foslie, 1905, p. 117. Nichols, 1909, p. 356; pl. 10, figs. 4–5; pl. 13, figs. 21–24. Phyc. Bor.-Amer. No. 1350.

Thalli, as found on the Monterey Peninsula, up to 15 mm. in diameter; reddish-purple but semitransparent and the color modified by that of the host. Circular if not crowded. Vegetative portion of thallus monostromatic and the cells approximately square in vertical section. Tetrasporic conceptacles 170–215 μ broad, 60–95 μ tall; bulging very conspicuously above surface of thallus, the ostiole without a disc of gelatinous material. Central portion of floor of conceptacle sterile. Tetrasporangia 35–40 μ broad, 45–65 μ long; transversely divided and with four spores.

LOCAL DISTRIBUTION. Widespread on the Monterey Peninsula. Common on *Botryoglossum Farlowii, Laurencia spectabilis,* and *Stenogramme californica;* also found on *Gatroclonium Coulteri, Gelidium cartilagineum* var. *robustum, Gigartina volans,* and *Hymenena flabelligera.*

TYPE LOCALITY. La Jolla, California.

PACIFIC COAST DISTRIBUTION. Known only from the Monterey Peninsula; La Jolla; and San Diego, California.

Easily distinguished from other epiphytic crustose Corallinaceae in the local flora because of the thin semitransparent thalli with prominently bulging conceptacles.

Fosliella intermedia (Foslie) comb. nov.

Lithophyllum macrocarpum forma *intermedia* Foslie, 1905, p. 117. Nichols, 1909, p. 352; pl. 11, fig. 12; pl. 12, figs. 15–17.

Thalli up to 5 mm. in diameter; circular in outline. Vegetative portion of thallus two to several cells in thickness. Cells of the lowermost layer with a height several times the breadth and vertically diagonal to the host; cells of other layers vertically oblong but shorter than those of basal layer. Tetrasporic conceptacles 210–340 μ broad, 110–150 μ tall; bulging above surface of thallus and with the ostiole closed by a disc of gelatinous material. Entire floor of conceptacle fertile. Tetrasporangia (bisporangia) 40–60 μ broad, 75–110 μ long; transversely divided and with two spores.

LOCAL DISTRIBUTION. Epiphytic on *Corallina.* Pacific Grove.

TYPE LOCALITY. Not stated.

PACIFIC COAST DISTRIBUTION. Central California (Pacific Grove) to southern California (La Jolla).

Lithophyllum Philippi, 1837

Thalli calcareous, wholly crustose, usually of indefinite extent. With the lower surface entirely adherent or with the margins free from the substratum. Upper surface smooth, tuberculate, or with laminate outgrowths. Thalli many cells in thickness. Differentiated into hypothallium and perithallium; the hypothallium usually many cells in thickness but sometimes only one cell in thickness; the perithallium many cells in thickness and with secondary connections in vertical cell walls.

Heterothallic. Spermatangia borne in conceptacles partly immersed in thallus and opening externally by a single ostiole.

Carpogonial filaments in conceptacles partly immersed in thallus and opening by a single ostiole. Carpogonial filaments and development of carpospores as in *Fosliella*.

Tetrasporophytes with tetrasporangia borne in conceptacles partly immersed in thallus and with a single ostiole. The sporangia developing over entire floor of conceptacle or only on peripheral portion of floor. Contents of sporangia usually dividing transversely into four tetraspores but sometimes dividing transversely into two bispores.

STRUCTURE AND REPRODUCTION. Suneson, 1937, pp. 19–29; figs. 11–17.

KEY TO THE SPECIES IN THE LOCAL FLORA

1. Surface excrescences of thallus over 1 cm. tall......*L. proboscideum*
1. Surface excrescences less than 1 cm. tall........................ 2
2. Excrescences 4–8 mm. tall......................*L. grumosum*
2. Excrescences less than 2 mm. tall.................*L. neofarlowii*

Lithophyllum proboscideum Foslie

*Foslie, 1897, p. 14. *Foslie, 1909, p. 27. *Foslie, 1929; pl. 63, figs. 3–4.

Thalli irregular in outline, forming a crustose layer on rocks. With the upper surface bearing scattered to densely crowded erect cylindrical outgrowths that may grow to a height of 2 cm. The outgrowths straight or bent, sometimes subdichotomously divided; about 3 mm. broad at base, above this somewhat broader. Apices of outgrowths truncate, at times slightly depressed in center. Interior of thallus with a well-defined hypothallium and perithallium. Tetrasporophytes with the conceptacles restricted to the excrescences. The conceptacles slightly convex, 200–300 µ in diameter, with a single ostiole. Tetrasporangia 30–35 µ broad, 55–60 µ long.

LOCAL DISTRIBUTION. Dredged from a depth of 70 feet near Monterey.

TYPE LOCALITY. As above.

PACIFIC COAST DISTRIBUTION. Known only from the Monterey Peninsula and from San Pedro, California.

Lithophyllum grumosum Foslie

Foslie, 1909, p. 20. *Foslie, 1929; pl. 57, figs. 11–12.
Lithothamnion grumosum Foslie, 1897, p. 16.

Thalli, as found on the Monterey Peninsula, up to 15 or more cm. in diameter; pinkish-white in color. Circular to irregular in outline and with lobed or crenulate margins. Upper surface in central portion of thallus densely crowded with coarse, rounded to wart-like, excrescences 4–8 mm. in diameter and of about the same height. The excrescences sometimes anastamosing with one another. Thalli about 2 mm. in thickness in central portion, somewhat thinner at margins. Lower surface of thallus entirely adherent to substratum. Interior of thallus with a well-defined hypothallium and perithallium. Tetrasporophytes with conceptacles mostly restricted to excrescences; the conceptacles 200–300 μ in diameter and with a single ostiole. Tetrasporangia 35–60 μ broad, 110–120 μ long.

LOCAL DISTRIBUTION. Growing on rocks between the 0.5- and −1.5-foot tide levels. Pacific Grove, Asilomar Point; Point Joe; Pebble Beach.

TYPE LOCALITY. Pebble Beach, Monterey Peninsula, California.

PACIFIC COAST DISTRIBUTION. Central California (Pacific Grove) to southern California (San Diego).

Lithophyllum neofarlowii Setchell and Mason

Setchell and Mason, 1943, p. 95.
Lithophyllum Farlowii Foslie [not of Heydrich]. *Foslie, 1901, p. 12. *Foslie, 1929; pl. 54, figs. 5–6. Phyc. Bor.-Amer. No. XL.
Goniolithon Yendoi *Foslie, 1900, p. 25 (as to specimens from Monterey).

Thalli, as found on the Monterey Peninsula, 10 cm. or more in diameter; whitish-pink in color. Circular to irregular in outline. Upper surface tuberculate even in young plants; the tubercules hemispherical, irregular or cylindrical, up to 2 mm. tall, densely crowded and at times anastamosing with one another. Thalli about 1 mm. in thickness, with well-defined hypothallium and perithallium. Tetrasporophytes with hemispherical conceptacles about 200 μ in diameter and with a single ostiole. Tetrasporangia 50–60 μ broad, 90–100 μ long.

LOCAL DISTRIBUTION. Growing on rocks between the mean low-tide and −1.5-foot tide levels. Monterey; Pacific Grove; Pebble Beach.

TYPE LOCALITY. Monterey, California.

PACIFIC COAST DISTRIBUTION. Northern California (Fort Bragg) to central California (Carmel Bay).

Corallina Linnaeus, 1758

Thallus with a crustose base of indefinite extent. The basal portion many cells in thickness and differentiated into hypothallium and perithallium. The base bearing many erect, branched, jointed, flexible axes. Branching of axes predominately pinnate and with practically every segment of major branches bearing an opposite pair of branches or branchlets. Intergenicula of major branches relatively broad and compressed; those of branchlets and secondary branches narrow and cylindrical. Genicula uncalcified, the cells not in transverse rows. Intergenicula calcified, the medulla with cells in transverse rows. Conceptacles borne one on a branchlet and at the tip of the terminal segment.

Homothallic or heterothallic. Spermatangia borne in conceptacles with a single ostiole; the floor and sides of cavity of the conceptacle covered with spermatangia. Carpogonial filaments produced within conceptacles with a single ostiole. Floor of cavity of conceptacle with many supporting cells each bearing primordia of two or three carpogonial filaments. Primordia on peripheral supporting cells not developing further; one primordium on each supporting cell of the central region developing into a two-celled carpogonial filament. All supporting cells functioning as auxiliary cells that fuse laterally with one another to form a large disc-shaped placental cell. Gonimoblast filaments growing from margin of placental cell, 6–8 cells long, usually simple but sometimes branched, with 2–3 cells at the distal end developing into carposporangia.

Tetrasporophytes with tetrasporangia borne in conceptacles with a single ostiole; the entire floor of conceptacle fertile. The tetrasporangia zonately divided.

STRUCTURE AND REPRODUCTION. Manza, 1940, pp. 273–280; pl. 7. Suneson, 1937, pp. 29–46; text figs. 18–27; pls. 1–2.

The only fact that can be stated with certainty concerning *Corallina* as found on the Monterey Peninsula is that all specimens thus far examined fall into the subgenus *Eucorallina* of Manza (1940, p. 275). This subgenus is characterized by conceptacles without horns (antennae) and a pinnate branching of the erect shoots. Until some phycologist prepares an adequate monograph of this exceedingly difficult genus the best procedure seems to be that of following the Phycotheca Boreali-Americana and use the names it gives to Pacific Coast specimens.

KEY TO THE SPECIES IN THE LOCAL FLORA[4]

1. Branches of erect shoots short, laterally appressed,
    and all about the same length..............*C. gracilis* forma *densa*
1. Basal branches of erect shoots longer than
    upper branches ....*C. chilensis*

[4] *C. officinalis* Linnaeus has been recorded (Anderson, 1891, p. 225. Howe, 1893, p. 68) from this area, but it is extremely dubious if typical *C. officinalis* is present in the local flora. The nature of local specimens identified by Anderson (1891, p. 225) as *C. pistillaris* Montagne is wholly a matter of conjecture.

Corallina gracilis forma **densa** Collins   Pl. 50, figs. 3–5

*Collins, 1906, p. 112. *Phyc. Bor.-Amer. No. 650.

Erect shoots, as found on the Monterey Peninsula, 4–10 cm. tall; deep dull purple in color. Lower intergenicula of axis subcylindrical and about .75 mm. broad; upper intergenicula compressed and about 1 mm. broad. The axes clothed from base to apex with short lateral branches all approximately the same length. Diameter of lateral branches less than half that of axis. Branching in lower portion of axis distichously pinnate; that in upper portion of axis either distichously pinnate or verticillate and with 3–5 branchlets on each of the two flattened faces of an intergeniculum. Branchlets in lower portion of axis usually simple; those in upper portion usually pinnately branched.

LOCAL DISTRIBUTION. Growing between the 0.5- and −1.5-foot tide levels on rocks exposed to strong surf. Common on all rocky headlands.

TYPE LOCALITY. Dillon's Beach, Marin County, California.

PACIFIC COAST DISTRIBUTION. Known with certainty only from the type locality and the Monterey Peninsula but probably much more widely distributed.

The short, appressed, lateral branchlets give the erect shoots a distinctly cord-like appearance.

Corallina chilensis Decaisne   Pl. 51, fig. 4

Decaisne apud Harvey, 1847, p. 103. Phyc. Bor.-Amer. No. 499.
Corallina squamata Farlow [not of Ellis and Solander]. Farlow, 1875, p. 364. *Anderson, 1891, p. 225. *Howe, 1893, p. 68.

Erect shoots, as found on the Monterey Peninsula, 5–15 cm. tall; purplish-red in color. Lower intergenicula of axis subcylindrical and up to 1 mm. broad; upper intergenicula compressed, cuneate, up to 1.25 mm. broad. Branching of axis distichously pinnate and with progressively shorter branches toward apex of axis. The branches tending to lie in one plane and not laterally appressed. A majority of the branches pinnately branched and those toward base of axis often bipinnate. The branches robust, with a diameter equal to that of the axis.

LOCAL DISTRIBUTION. Growing on rocks between the 0.5- and −1.5-foot tide levels. Also found in tide pools at higher tidal levels. Common everywhere.

TYPE LOCALITY. Chile.

PACIFIC COAST DISTRIBUTION. British Columbia (Vancouver Island) to southern California (San Diego).

Lithothrix J. E. Gray, 1867

Thallus with a calcified crustose base of indefinite. extent. Usually growing on rocks but sometimes growing on calcified shells of animals. The basal crust bearing many erect, branched, jointed flexible shoots. Primary branching of axis of shoots dichotomous. Most segments of axis cylindrical but those in vicinity of dichotomies somewhat compressed. Secondary branching predominately alternate but sometimes opposite. Branchlets and secondary branches not tending to lie in one plane. Genicula of branches inconspicuous, not calcified, the cells not in transverse rows. Intergenicula calcified, with a medulla of parallel longitudinal filaments and the cells not in transverse rows. Conceptacles hemispherical, borne laterally on intercalary intergenicula. Intergenicula of larger branches with two or more conceptacles; those of smaller branches usually with a single conceptacle.

Spermatangial and cystocarpic plants unknown.

Tetrasporophytes with the conceptacles opening by a single ostiole. The tetrasporangia zonately divided.

STRUCTURE AND REPRODUCTION. Manza, 1940, pp. 295–297; pl. 10.

Lithothrix Aspergillum J. E. Gray   Pl. 53, fig. 3

J. E. Gray, 1867, p. 33. Manza, 1940, p. 296; pl. 10.
Amphiroa nodulosa Farlow [not of Kützing]. Farlow, 1876, p. 715. Phyc. Bor.-Amer. Nos. 498, 649.
Amphiroa Aspergillum (Gray) *Anderson, 1891, p. 225. *Howe, 1893, p. 68.

Thalli, as found on the Monterey Peninsula, 8–13 cm. tall; deep dull purple in color. Primary branching dichotomous, secondary branching alternate to opposite. Lower intergenicula of primary branches about 0.5 mm. long and 0.5–1 mm. broad; those near dichotomies and at growing tips about 1 mm. long and 1–1.5 mm. broad. Intergenicula of secondary branches about 0.5 mm. long and 0.5 mm. broad.

LOCAL DISTRIBUTION. Growing on rocks at mean low-tide level. Point Pinos; Middle Reef of Moss Beach; Point Joe.

TYPE LOCALITY. Vancouver Island, British Columbia.

PACIFIC COAST DISTRIBUTION. British Columbia (Vancouver Island) to southern California (San Diego).

Bossea Manza, 1937

Thallus with a crustose base of indefinite extent. Usually growing on rocks but sometimes growing on calcified shells of animals. The base bearing many erect, branched, jointed, flexible shoots. Branching of shoots wholly pinnate, wholly dichotomous, or partly dichotomous and partly pinnate. Intergenicula in lower part of shoot cylindrical, those in upper portion markedly compressed. Genicula uncalcified, the cells not in transverse rows. Intergenicula calcified, with a medulla of parallel longitudinal filaments in which the cells are of equal length and in transverse rows. The conceptacles borne on intercalary intergenicula, restricted to the flattened faces of the intergenicula and 2–8 on each flattened face.

Heterothallic. Spermatangial and cystocarpic conceptacles with a single ostiole. Development of spermatangia and of carposporangia unknown but presumably as in *Corallina*.

Tetrasporophytes with conceptacles opening by a single ostiole. The tetrasporangia zonately divided.

STRUCTURE AND REPRODUCTION. Manza, 1940, pp. 302–307.

KEY TO THE SPECIES IN THE LOCAL FLORA

1. Branching wholly or predominately opposite........................ 2
1. Branching wholly or predominately dichotomous................. 5
   2. Branches borne in series separated by series
      of intergenicula without branches.................*B. interrupta*
   2. Branches not borne in such series............................ 3
3. Flat sides of intergenicula usually with 4–8 conceptacles..*B. californica*
3. Flat sides of intergenicula usually with 2–4 conceptacles............ 4
   4. Upper branches with many successive pairs
      of opposite branchlets ....*B. plumosa*
   4. Upper branches with few successive pairs
      of opposite branchlets ....*B. corymbifera*
5. Branching dichotomous throughout.............................. 6
5. Branching subalternate below, dichotomous
   above ....*B. dichotoma*
   6. Upper lobes of intergenicula rounded.................*B. Gardneri*
   6. Upper lobes of intergenicula acutely
      pointed ....*B. Orbigniana*

Bossea interrupta Manza   Pl. 52, fig. 1

*Manza, 1937A, p. 563. *Manza, 1940, p. 306; pl. 16.

Erect shoots 5–20 cm. tall; purplish-red in color. Branching opposite and bi- or tripinnate. With several successive intergenicula each bearing an opposite pair of branches and then several succeeding intergenicula naked or with rudimentary branchlets. Lower intergenicula cylindrical, 2 mm. broad and 1–2 mm.

long. Intergenicula in upper portion of shoots compressed, obcordate, 2–4 mm. broad and 2 mm. long, with thin wings and with a prominent midrib. Conceptacles borne singly on each face and on midrib of an intergeniculum; or in pairs on each face of intergeniculum and one on each wing close to the midrib.

LOCAL DISTRIBUTION. Growing on rocks between the −0.5- and −1.5-foot tide levels. Pacific Grove; Middle Reef of Moss Beach.

TYPE LOCALITY. Pacific Grove, California.

PACIFIC COAST DISTRIBUTION. As above.

Bossea californica (Descaisne) Manza   Pl. 51, fig. 2

Manza, 1937*A*, p. 561. *Manza, 1940, p. 305.
Amphiroa californica *Decaisne, 1842, p. 112. *Harvey, 1853, p. 86.

Erect shoots usually 4–6 cm. tall but occasionally up to 12 cm.; reddish-pink in color. Branching dichotomous to subalternate in lower portion of shoots, opposite in upper portion. Lower intergenicula cylindrical, 2 mm. broad, 1–3 mm. long. Intergenicula in upper portion of shoot compressed, obcordate, thick and with but little differentiation between wings and midrib, 2–6 mm. broad, 2–5 mm. long. Conceptacles 2–8 (usually 6) on each of the two flattened faces of an intergeniculum, in vertical rows of 2–4 some distance in from the margin.

LOCAL DISTRIBUTION. Growing on rocks between the mean low-tide and −1.5-foot tide levels. Point Pinos; Asilomar Point; Cypress Point; Midway Point; Pescadero Point.

TYPE LOCALITY. Monterey, California.

PACIFIC COAST DISTRIBUTION. As above.

The flattened intergenicula in the upper part of a shoot are so much thicker than those of other species in the local flora that sterile plants might be mistaken for a species of *Calliarthron*. The larger number of conceptacles on an intergeniculum also distinguishes *B. californica* from other oppositely branched species in the local flora.

Bossea plumosa Manza   Pl. 51, fig. 1

Manza, 1937, p. 46. Manza, 1940, p. 303; pl. 12.

Erect shoots, as found on the Monterey Peninsula, 3–7 cm. tall; reddish-purple in color. The branching opposite and usually with every intergeniculum in upper half of major branches bearing an opposite pair of smaller branches the lowermost of which are simple and the uppermost rebranched. Intergenicula at base of shoot subcylindrical, 1 mm. broad, 1 mm. long. Intergenicula in upper part of shoot compressed, broadly obcuneate, without a sharp differentiation into wings and midrib; 1–2 mm. broad, 1 mm. long. Conceptacles 2–4 (usually 2) on each of the two flattened faces of an intergeniculum; borne in vertical rows.

LOCAL DISTRIBUTION. Growing between the 0.5- and —1.5-foot tide levels and either on rocks or on shells of animals. Mussel Point; Asilomar Point; Cypress Point; Midway Point; Pescadero Point; Pebble Beach; Mission Point.

TYPE LOCALITY. Moss Beach, San Mateo County, California.

PACIFIC COAST DISTRIBUTION. As above.

Bossea corymbifera Manza   Pl. 52, fig. 3

Manza, 1937A, p. 562. Manza, 1940, p. 305; pl. 13.

Erect shoots, as found on the Monterey Peninsula, 4–6 cm. tall; deep reddish-purple in color. The branching a mixture of unilateral and opposite, and chiefly restricted to lower two-thirds of shoot. Intergenicula toward apex of shoot at times with opposite branchlets. Intergenicula at base of shoot cylindrical, 1 mm. broad, 1–2 mm. long. Intergenicula in upper part of shoot compressed, obcordate, with a conspicuous differentiation into wings and midrib, 2–3 mm. broad, 1–2 mm. long. Conceptacles 2–4 on each of the two flattened faces of an intergeniculum; borne in vertical rows.

LOCAL DISTRIBUTION. Growing on rocks between the mean low-tide and —1.5-foot tide levels. Point Pinos; Asilomar Point; Cypress Point; Pescadero Point; Pebble Beach.

TYPE LOCALITY. Carmel Point (Point Lobos), Carmel Bay, California.

PACIFIC COAST DISTRIBUTION. As above.

Bossea dichotoma Manza   Pl. 54, fig. 1

Manza, 1937A, p. 562. Manza, 1940, p. 307; pl. 17.

Erect shoots, as found on the Monterey Peninsula, 3–8 cm. tall; of a deep reddish-purple color. Branching in lower portion of shoot alternate and pinnate, frequently from successive intergenicula; branching of upper portion dichotomous and with tips of ultimate dichotomies not tapering markedly. Intergenicula at base of shoot subcylindrical, 1.5 mm. broad, 1–2 mm. long. Intergenicula in upper part of shoot compressed, broadly cuneate to obcordate, with a conspicuous differentiation into wings and midrib and with broadly rounded wings, 2–6 mm. broad, 2–3 mm. long. Conceptacles 2–4 (usually 2) on each of the two flattened faces of an intergeniculum; borne close to the midrib and usually in vertical rows.

LOCAL DISTRIBUTION. Growing on rocks between the mean low-tide and −1.5-foot tide levels. Asilomar Point; Cypress Point; Pebble Beach.
TYPE LOCALITY. Moss Beach, San Mateo County, California.
PACIFIC COAST DISTRIBUTION. As above.

At times it is difficult to tell whether a particular specimen should be referred to *B. dichotoma* or to *B. Gardneri*. *B. dichotoma* is best distinguished by the more dense branching, the lack of a tapering of the branch tips, and by the fact that a majority of the intergenicula have but two conceptacles on each flattened face.

Bossea Gardneri Manza   Pl. 52, fig. 2

*Manza, 1937*A*, p. 536. *Manza, 1940, p. 306; pl. 15.

Erect shoots, as found on the Monterey Peninsula, 5–18 cm. tall; whitish-pink to deep purple in color. The branching dichotomous throughout but with the lower dichotomies so widely divergent that certain branches appear to be borne laterally. Tips of ultimate dichotomies gradually tapering. Intergenicula at base of shoot subcylindrical, 1 mm. broad, 1 mm. long. Intergenicula in upper part of shoot compressed, cuneate to obcordate, 1–4 mm. broad, 1–3 mm. long, with thin wings and a prominent midrib. Conceptacles 2–6 (usually 4) on each of the two flattened faces of an intergeniculum; borne close to the midrib and in vertical rows.

LOCAL DISTRIBUTION. Growing on rocks between the mean low-tide and −1.5-foot tide levels. Pacific Grove; Asilomar Point; Cypress Point; Midway Point; Pebble Beach.
TYPE LOCALITY. Pacific Grove, California.
PACIFIC COAST DISTRIBUTION. As above.

Bossea Orbigniana (Decaisne) Manza   Pl. 51, fig. 3

Manza, 1927*A*, p. 563. Manza, 1940, p. 304.
Amphiroa Orbigniana Decaisne ex Harvey, 1847, p. 100; pl. 38. Phyc. Bor.-Amer. No. 398.

Erect shoots, as found on the Monterey Peninsula, 6–8 cm. tall; reddish-pink in color. Dichotomously branched throughout and with the branches narrowly or widely divergent. Intergenicula at base of shoot cylindrical, 2 mm. broad, 1–2 mm. long. Intergenicula in upper part of shoot compressed, narrowly cuneate to cordate, rostrate at upper end, with upper margins of wings more or less acute, 2–3 mm. broad, 2 mm. long. Typically with two conceptacles on each of the two flattened faces of an intergeniculum, one on each wing and borne near the midrib.

LOCAL DISTRIBUTION. Dredged from a depth of 30–35 feet a quarter-mile from the Municipal Wharf, Monterey, and from 20 to 25 feet near Point Aulon.

TYPE LOCALITY. South America.

PACIFIC COAST DISTRIBUTION. Cape Arago, Oregon; the Monterey Peninsula; and southern California (Santa Barbara to San Diego).

As found in southern California the shoots of this species are up to 20 cm. tall, with narrowly cuneate intergenicula, and usually with but two conceptacles on each flattened face of an intergeniculum. The University of California specimen of Phycotheca Boreali-Americana No. 398 has the following annotation by Manza—"typical *Bossea Orbigniana.*" The specimens from the Monterey Peninsula are quite similar to specimens in the University of California herbarium from Cape Arago, Oregon, which have been identified by Manza as *B. Orbigniana.* The plants from these two northern stations are relatively short and have broader intergenicula, and many of the intergenicula have more than two conceptacles on a flattened face.

Calliarthron Manza, 1937

Thallus with a calcified crustose base of indefinite extent. Usually growing on rocks but sometimes growing on calcified shells of animals. The base bearing many erect, branched, jointed, flexible shoots. Branching of shoots dichotomous to pinnate and with the branches tending to lie in one plane. Intergenicula in lower portion of shoots cylindrical, those in upper portion markedly compressed. Genicula uncalcified, the cells not in transverse rows. Intergenicula calcified, with a medulla of intertwined longitudinal filaments in which the cells are not in transverse rows. Conceptacles hemispherical to conical, emergent, on both the terminal and the intercalary intergenicula. Several conceptacles on an intergeniculum and borne both on the lateral margins and the flattened faces.

Heterothallic. Spermatangial and cystocarpic conceptacles with a single ostiole. Development of spermatangia and of carposporangia unknown but presumably as in *Corallina.*

Tetrasporophytes with conceptacles opening by a single ostiole. The tetrasporangia zonately divided.

STRUCTURE AND REPRODUCTION. Manza, 1940, pp. 264–270; pls. 2–6.

KEY TO THE SPECIES IN THE LOCAL FLORA

1. Upper margins of wings of intergenicula
   with conceptacles ....*C. cheilosporioides*
1. Upper margins of wings of intergenicula
   without conceptacles ....*C. Setchelliae*

Calliarthron cheilosporioides Manza   Pl. 53, fig. 1

*Manza, 1937, p. 46. *Manza, 1940, p. 266; pl. 2.
Amphiroa Orbigniana Anderson [not of Decaisne]. *Anderson, 1891, p. 225.
*Howe, 1893, p. 68.

Erect shoots, as found on the Monterey Peninsula, 10–30 cm. tall; reddish-purple in color. The branching opposite to subalternate, lax, loosely pinnate. Intergenicula at base of shoot cylindrical, 1–2 mm. broad, 1–6 mm. long. Intergenicula in upper part of shoot markedly compressed, cuneate to obcordate, with a well-marked differentiation into wings and midrib, 2–4 mm. broad, 1–2 mm. long. Conceptacles borne on upper margin of wings, lateral margins of wings, and on flattened faces of intergenicula, conceptacles on flattened faces not in vertical rows.

LOCAL DISTRIBUTION. Growing on rocks between the 0.5- and −1.5-foot tide levels. Mussel Point; Point Aulon; Point Pinos; Asilomar Point; Middle Reef of Moss Beach; Point Joe; Cypress Point; Pebble Beach.

TYPE LOCALITY. Pebble Beach, Monterey Peninsula, California.

PACIFIC COAST DISTRIBUTION. Central California (Bolinas) to southern California (San Pedro.)

Calliarthron Setchelliae Manza   Pl. 53, fig. 2

Manza, 1937*A*, p. 566. Manza, 1940, p. 270; pl. 6.

Erect shoots, as found on the Monterey Peninsula, 6–12 cm. tall; reddish-purple in color. The branching opposite to subalternate, dense, and the branches flabellately arranged. Intergenicula at base of shoot subcylindrical, 2–3 mm. broad, 1–3 mm. long. Intergenicula in upper part of shoot markedly compressed, cuneate to obcordate, without a conspicuous differentiation into wings and midrib, 3–5 mm. broad, 2–3 mm. long. Conceptacles borne along lateral margins and on flattened faces of the intergenicula.

LOCAL DISTRIBUTION. Growing on rocks between the mean low-tide and −1.5-foot tide levels. Asilomar Point; Point Joe; Cypress Point; Pebble Beach; Mission Point. Also dredged from a depth of 20–25 feet near Point Aulon and from 30–35 feet near Point Pinos.

TYPE LOCALITY. Moss Beach, San Mateo County, California.

PACIFIC COAST DISTRIBUTION. As above.

This species is shorter and more densely branched than *C. cheilosporioides*. It also lacks conceptacles on the upper margins of the wings. Dried herbarium specimens are chalky and of a more brittle consistency than those of *C. cheilosporioides*.

Family GRATELOUPIACEAE

Thalli nonfilamentous; usually erect, compressed, and either foliaceous or much divided. The thallus multiaxial, with a medulla of parallel filaments and a cortex whose cells are progressively smaller to the thallus surface.

The carpogonial and auxiliary cell filaments separate from each other; both scattered throughout the thallus at inner face of cortex. Carpogonial filaments two-celled; borne in special bushy filaments. The auxiliary cell filament freely branched and with the auxiliary cell near the base. Mature cystocarps embedded in the thallus and with or without a special enveloping tissue.

Tetrasporophytes either with the tetrasporangia separate from one another just beneath the thallus surface or with the tetrasporangia in nemathecia. The tetrasporangia cruciately divided.

KEY TO THE GENERA IN THE LOCAL FLORA

Grateloupia C. A. Agardh, 1822

Thalli erect, with one or more blades growing from a disc-shaped holdfast. The blades usually stipitate; simple, or pinnately, palmately, or dichotomously divided. Surface of blade smooth. Lateral margins of blade frequently with small proliferous bladelets. Growth by a group of apical initials. Medulla of blade composed of colorless stellate cells with long processes, the medulla frequently with rhizoids growing from inner face of cortex; the cortex composed of compacted short-branched filaments standing perpendicular to the cortex.

Heterothallic. The spermatangia in small whitish sori on surface of blade. The carpogonial filaments two-celled, borne in special bushy filaments growing from outer face of medulla. Auxiliary cell filaments more bushy and growing from outer face of medulla, with a single cell low in the filament enlarging and becoming the auxiliary cell. After fertilization the carpogonium sending out several oöblasts each of which may grow to an auxiliary cell. Gonimoblasts branched, growing from auxiliary cell towards surface of thallus, with only the outermost cells of the branched filaments developing into carposporangia. Mature cystocarps deeply embedded in thallus, the overlying cortical tissue with an ostiole.

Tetrasporophytes with tetrasporangia remote from one another and embedded just below thallus surface. The tetrasporangia cruciately divided.

STRUCTURE AND REPRODUCTION. Kylin, 1930, pp. 19–21; figs. 9–11.

KEY TO THE SPECIES IN THE LOCAL FLORA

1. Thalli over 15 cm. tall...............................G. californica
1. Thalli less than 10 cm. tall.............................G. Setchellii

Grateloupia californica Kylin   Pl. 55, figs. 1–2

*Kylin, 1941, p. 9; text fig. 2 B; pl. 1.
Grateloupia Cutleriae Farlow [not of Kützing]. Farlow, 1876, p. 702. *Anderson, 1891, p. 222. Phyc. Bor.-Amer. No. XCIX.

Thalli, as found on the Monterey Peninsula, up to 1.5 m. tall; wine-red to olive-purple in color. Usually with several blades from a common holdfast. The blades linear-lanceolate, with a short cylindrical stipe, broadening gradually above the stipe and becoming gradually narrowed in apical portion. Upper half of blade at times longitudinally incised into 2–4 linear segments. Margins of blade with or without proliferous bladelets. Blades of a soft gelatinous texture. The cortical tissue 6–7 cells in thickness.

LOCAL DISTRIBUTION. Growing on tops of rocks between the 1.0- and −1.5-foot tide levels. At times in tide pools at higher tidal levels. Monterey; Mussel Point; Point Aulon; Middle Reef of Moss Beach; Fanshell Beach; Midway Point; north end of Carmel Beach.

TYPE LOCALITY. La Jolla, California.

PACIFIC COAST DISTRIBUTION. Puget Sound to southern California (La Jolla).

Grateloupia Setchellii Kylin   Pl. 55, fig. 3

*Kylin, 1941, p. 10; text fig. 2 D; pl. 2, fig. 5.
Grateloupia versicolor Setchell [not of J. G. Agardh]. *Setchell in Phyc.
Bor.-Amer. No. 699.

Thalli 5–10 cm., occasionally up to 15 cm. tall; of a rich rose-
red color. The blades narrowly lanceolate, with maximum breadth
of 4–6 mm., regularly with marginal proliferous bladelets and the
bladelets simple or with marginal proliferations. Base of blade
narrow, flattened, not evidently stipitate. Cortex of blade 3–4
cells in thickness; medulla of blade feebly developed.

LOCAL DISTRIBUTION. Growing at the −1.0-foot tide level on flat-
topped rocks. Point Joe; Cypress Point; Pescadero Point; rocks at mouth
of Carmel River.

TYPE LOCALITY, Point Joe, Monterey Peninsula, California.

PACIFIC COAST DISTRIBUTION. As above.

Cryptonemia J. G. Agardh, 1842

Thalli erect, with one or more blades growing from a disc-
shaped holdfast. The blades sessile or distinctly stipitate in lower
portion; entire or irregularly laciniate; without veins or a midrib;
at times with proliferous bladelets from stipe or from margin of
blade. Growth by a group of apical initials. Medulla of blade
filamentous and with many of the cells distinctly stellate; the
cortex usually but 2–4 cells in thickness and with chromatophores
restricted to the outermost cell layer.

Spermatangia unknown. Carpogonial filaments two-celled,
borne terminally on special branched bushy filaments growing
from outermost portion of medulla. Auxiliary cell filaments also
bushy but more profusely branched, with a single cell near the
base enlarging to become the auxiliary cell. Gonimoblast filaments
branched and with all branches toward thallus surface; with
practically all cells developing into carposporangia. Mature cystocarps deeply embedded in thallus, surrounded by a few persistent
sterile branches of auxiliary cell filament. Cortical tissue above
a cystocarp with a wide ostiole.

Tetrasporophytes with tetrasporangia remote from one another
and embedded just beneath thallus surface. The tetrasporangia
cruciately divided.

STRUCTURE AND REPRODUCTION. Kylin, 1925, pp. 19–21; figs. 8–9. Sjöstedt, 1926, pp. 15–19; figs. 7–9.

With one species in the local flora.

Cryptonemia ovalifolia Kylin   Pl. 54, figs. 2–3

*Kylin, 1941, p. 11; text fig. 3 *D*; pl. 3, fig. 9.

Thalli with blades up to 8 cm. tall; of a bright cherry-red color. Mature blades broadly ovate, entire, up to 6 cm. broad, stipitate, the stipe 1–2 mm. long and the portion of the blade above the stipe cuneate. The blades flaccid and membranous; with a cortex but three cells in thickness and the medulla but feebly developed.

LOCAL DISTRIBUTION. Growing on the vertical sides of rocks between the 1.0- and −0.5-foot tide levels. Point Pinos; Cypress Point; north end of Carmel Beach; Mission Point. Also dredged from a depth of 30–35 feet a quarter-mile from Municipal Wharf, Monterey, and from a depth of 30–40 feet midway between Mussel Point and Point Aulon.

TYPE LOCALITY. Point Pinos, Pacific Grove, California.

PACIFIC COAST DISTRIBUTION. As above.

As seen in its natural habitat this alga bears a very close resemblance to *Porphyra occidentalis.* It might also be mistaken for a small specimen of *Aeodes Gardneri* but is distinguishable from the latter by the structure of cortex and medulla.

Aeodes J. G. Agardh, 1876

Thalli erect, with one or more blades from a disc-shaped holdfast. The blades subsessile, ovate to lanceolate, usually entire but at times laciniate, without veins or a midrib and without proliferations from margin. Medulla of blade filamentous, the filaments loosely interwoven and tending to lie parallel to thallus surface, the cells with a length several times the breadth and frequently stellate; cortex 4–10 cells in thickness, either with all cells approximately the same size or with progressively smaller cells toward thallus surface.

Spermatangia unknown. Carpogonial filaments unknown. Auxiliary cell filaments borne on outermost medullary cells, profusely branched and branching toward thallus surface, a single cell low in the filament enlarging to become the auxiliary cell. Gonimoblast filaments branched and with all branches toward thallus surface, with practically all cells developing into carposporangia. Cystocarps surrounded by a flask-shaped, ostiolate, filamentous pericarp one to several cells in thickness.

Tetrasporophytes with tetrasporangia remote from one another and embedded just beneath thallus surface. The tetrasporangia cruciately divided.

STRUCTURE AND REPRODUCTION. Kylin, 1925, pp. 17–18; fig. 7.

With one species in the local flora.

Aeodes Gardneri Kylin   Pl. 54, figs. 4–5

Kylin, 1925, p. 17; fig. 7 *A*.
Aeodes nitidissima Setchell [not of J. G. Agardh]. *Setchell, 1901, p. 126. Phyc. Bor.-Amer. No. 946.

Thalli, as found on the Monterey Peninsula, with blades up to 50 cm. tall; of a bright cherry-red color. The blades obovate to lanceolate, up to 25 cm. broad, usually undivided, membranaceous, flaccid. The cortex 3–6 cells in thickness and with all cells approximately the same size. Pericarp of a mature cystocarp 1–2 cells in thickness and with the filaments loosely interwoven.

LOCAL DISTRIBUTION. On rocks at the −1.0-foot tide level. Pescadero Rocks. Also found cast ashore at Moss Beach.

TYPE LOCALITY. Whidbey Island, Washington.

PACIFIC COAST DISTRIBUTION. Puget Sound to southern California (San Pedro).

Halymenia C. A. Agardh, 1824

Thalli erect, with one or more blades growing from a disc-shaped holdfast. The blade usually profusely and dichotomously to irregularly divided, more rarely undivided. When divided, with or without small proliferous bladelets. The cortex composed of erect, compacted, branched filaments with progressively smaller cells to thallus surface; the medulla composed of loosely interwoven filaments, usually with many filaments running perpendicularly from inner face of one cortex to that of the opposite cortex.

The spermatangia in small whitish sori on surface of blade. Structure of carpogonial and auxiliary cell filaments unknown. The mature cystocarp lying in outermost portion of medulla, globose, with all cells developing into carposporangia. The cystocarp surrounded by a loose pericarp of medullary filaments and the overlying cortical tissue developing an ostiole.

Tetrasporophytes with the tetrasporangia remote from one another and embedded just beneath thallus surface. The tetrasporangia cruciately divided.

STRUCTURE AND REPRODUCTION. Berthold, 1884, pp. 1–18; pl. 8, figs. 1–7.

With one species in the local flora.

Halymenia californica Smith and Hollenberg

Pl. 54, fig. 6; pl. 55, fig. 4

*Smith and Hollenberg, 1943, p. 216; figs. 18–19.

Thalli 20–25 cm. tall; of a rosy-red color. The blades 4–8 cm. broad, narrowly to broadly lanceolate, at times falcate, with a cuneate base. Surface of blade resembling in appearance the surface of a finely grained leather. The cortex 2–3 cells in thickness, with cells slightly elongated anticlinally; medullary filaments rarely branched, many of the filaments extending perpendicularly from one cortex to the other.

LOCAL DISTRIBUTION. Dredged from a depth of 30–35 feet a quartermile from the Municipal Wharf, Monterey. Also found cast ashore at Moss Beach.

TYPE LOCALITY. Moss Beach, Pacific Grove, California.

PACIFIC COAST DISTRIBUTION. As above.

Although not distinctive of *Halymenia* as a whole, the medullary filaments extending straight across from cortex to cortex afford a means of distinguishing *H. californica* from other local Florideae with undivided blades.

Prionitis J. G. Agardh, 1851

Thalli erect, with one or more shoots growing from a disc-shaped holdfast. The erect shoots flattened, freely branched, the major branches of approximately the same breadth throughout, dichotomously or irregularly divided, without a midrib. Lateral margins of major branches frequently with numerous proliferous branches. The proliferous branches pinnately arranged and all lying in the same plane. Surface of branches smooth. The medulla with densely interwoven longitudinal filaments; the cortex composed of densely compacted, erect, branched filaments with progressively smaller cells toward thallus surface.

Heterothallic. The spermatangia in extensive whitish sori almost completely covering flattened faces of branches. The carpogonial filaments two-celled, borne on special bushy branched filaments at inner face of cortex. Auxiliary cell filaments also bushy but larger and more profusely branched, with a single cell low in the filament enlarging to become the auxiliary cell. Gonimoblast filaments branched and all branches toward the thallus surface; with practically all cells developing into carposporangia.

Mature cystocarps deeply embedded in thallus, surrounded by an envelope of interwoven filaments, the envelope with an ostiole.

Tetrasporophytes either with the tetrasporangia remote from one another and embedded just beneath thallus surface or with the tetrasporangia in nemathecia. The tetrasporangia cruciately divided.

STRUCTURE AND REPRODUCTION. Sjöstedt, 1926, pp. 19–22; figs. 10–12.

KEY TO THE SPECIES IN THE LOCAL FLORA

1. Branches less than 2.5 mm. broad.............................. 2
1. Branches more than 2.5 mm. broad............................ 3
   2. With numerous proliferous branchlets, all approxi-
     mately the same length............................*P. filiformis*
   2. Without or with relatively few proliferous branches......*P. linearis*
3. Branching predominately dichotomous, major
   branches with few proliferous branchlets...............*P. australis*
3. Branching irregular, major branches with many
   proliferous branchlets 4
   4. Branches 2.5–5 (rarely to 8) mm. broad.............*P. lanceolata*
   4. Branches 5–25 mm. broad.................................... 5
5. Branches deep red, firm in texture, not slippery to
   the touch ....*P. Andersonii*
5. Branches reddish-brown to olive, soft in texture,
   slippery to the touch...................................*P. Lyallii*

Prionitis filiformis Kylin   Pl. 56, fig. 1

Kylin, 1941, p. 13.
Prionitis lanceolata forma *angusta* Harvey, 1853, p. 197.
Prionitis angusta (Harvey) Setchell in Phyc. Bor.-Amer. No. XXIV.

Thalli, as found on the Monterey Peninsula, 15–45 cm. tall; reddish-brown in color. The primary branching predominately dichotomous, all dichotomies of the same breadth and about 1 mm. broad. Tips of ultimate dichotomies gradually tapering and acutely pointed. All dichotomies with numerous proliferous branchlets along the lateral margins, the branchlets all about the same length and usually but 3–5 mm. long.

LOCAL DISTRIBUTION. Growing on rocks between the 0.5- and −1.0-foot tide levels. Asilomar Point; shore in from Seal Rocks; Mission Point; mouth of Carmel River.

TYPE LOCALITY. Land's End, San Francisco, California.

PACIFIC COAST DISTRIBUTION. Southern Oregon (Cape Arago) to central California (Carmel Bay).

Prionitis linearis Kylin   Pl. 56, fig. 2

Kylin, 1941, p. 12; pl. 4, fig. 11.
Prionitis lanceolata Collins [not of Harvey]. Collins in Phyc. Bor.-Amer.
No. 199*B*.
Prionitis decipiens Setchell and Gardner [not of J. G. Agardh]. Setchell
and Gardner, 1903, p. 350.

Thalli, as found on the Monterey Peninsula, 15–25 cm. tall;
of a reddish-brown color. The branching predominately dichotomous, with all dichotomies the same breadth and 1–2 mm.
broad. Tips of ultimate dichotomies gradually tapering and
acutely pointed. The dichotomies without or with a few short
proliferous branchlets.

LOCAL DISTRIBUTION. Growing on rocks between the mean low-tide
and −1.0-foot tide levels. Middle Reef of Moss Beach; east of Fanshell
Beach.

TYPE LOCALITY. La Jolla, California.

PACIFIC COAST DISTRIBUTION. Central California (Moss Beach, San
Mateo County) to southern California (La Jolla).

Differing from *P. filiformis* in the somewhat broader segments and in the smaller number of proliferous branchlets.

Prionitis australis J. G. Agardh   Pl. 57, fig. 2

J. G. Agardh, 1851, p. 188. *Kylin, 1941, p. 12; pl. 3, fig. 10.

Thalli, as found on the Monterey Peninsula, 10–30 cm. tall;
reddish-brown in color. Branching of thallus predominately dichotomous, the flattened dichotomies 2.5–4 mm. broad and about
1 mm. in thickness. Tips of ultimate dichotomies obtusely pointed
and much lighter in color than elsewhere. Lateral margins of
thallus segments without or with relatively few proliferous branchlets.

LOCAL DISTRIBUTION. Growing between the 0.5- and −1.5-foot tide
levels on rocks exposed to heavy surf. Mussel Point; Asilomar Point;
Point Joe; Fanshell Beach; Cypress Point; Pescadero Point; Pebble
Beach; Mission Point. Also dredged from a depth of 15–20 feet at Stillwater Cove.

TYPE LOCALITY. "Pacific Ocean." Probably North America and possibly the vicinity of Monterey, California.

PACIFIC COAST DISTRIBUTION. Known with certainty only from the
Monterey Peninsula.

Although widely distributed locally this species is never present
in abundance. It has the general appearance of a *Gymnogongrus*,
but the structure of the medulla shows that it cannot be referred
to that genus. *P. australis* may be distinguished from other local

species by the light-colored blunt branch tips and the small number of proliferous branches.

Prionitis lanceolata Harvey   Pl. 57, fig. 1

*Harvey, 1853, p. 197; pl. 27, fig. *A.* *Anderson, 1891, p. 222. *Howe, 1893, p. 68. *Sjöstedt, 1926, p. 19; figs. 10–12. *Kylin, 1941, p. 12. *Phyc. Bor.-Amer. No. 199*A.*

    Gelidium lanceolatum Harvey, 1833, p. 164. *Harvey, 1841, p. 409.

Thalli, as found on the Monterey Peninsula, 15–35 cm. tall; dull brown to reddish-purple in color. Primary branching irregular; the branches flattened, linear, 3–8 mm. broad, of uniform breadth throughout except for occasional constrictions. Usually with many pinnately arranged proliferous branches along the lateral margins; the proliferous branches linear, 3–8 mm. broad, constricted at base and with tips tapering to an acute point, the branches progressively longer toward base of thallus but rarely more than 6 cm. long.

    LOCAL DISTRIBUTION. Common everywhere on rocks between the 1.0- and −1.5-foot tide levels. Also dredged from a depth of 40–60 feet near Mussel Point; and from 20–25 feet near Point Aulon and at Stillwater Cove.

    TYPE LOCALITY. Monterey, California.

    PACIFIC COAST DISTRIBUTION. British Columbia (Vaucouver Island) to southern California (San Pedro).

Prionitis Andersonii Eaton   Pl. 57, fig. 3

Eaton in Farlow, 1875, p. 372 (name only). Eaton ex J. G. Agardh, 1876, p. 159. *Anderson, 1891, p. 222. *Howe, 1893, p. 68. *Kylin, 1941, p. 11. Algae Amer.-Bor. Exsicc. No. 24.

Thalli, as found on the Monterey Peninsula, 25–75 cm. tall, of a rich dull red color. Primary branching irregular; the branches flattened, 2–3 mm. broad at base and 5–20 mm. broad in upper portion. Primary branches with many pinnately arranged proliferous branches along the lateral margins. The proliferous branches with a short cylindrical base and a long lanceolate blade 0.5–2.5 cm. broad and up to 15–25 cm. long. The blades firm in texture.

    LOCAL DISTRIBUTION. Growing between the 1.0- and −1.5-foot tide levels on sand-covered rocks in sheltered coves. Point Aulon; Point Pinos; Asilomar Point; Middle Reef of Moss Beach; Fanshell Beach; Cypress Point; north end of Carmel Beach; Mission Point.

    TYPE LOCALITY. Santa Cruz, California.

    PACIFIC COAST DISTRIBUTION. Central California (Bolinas to Carmel Bay).

Setchell and Gardner (1903, p. 350) hold that this species is typical *P. Lyallii;* Kylin (1941, p. 11) thinks that it is specifically different from *P. Lyallii. P. Andersonii* and *P. Lyallii,* which are here considered distinct, are alike in that they have broader segments than other species along the Pacific Coast of North America. As found locally, *P. Andersonii* is restricted to sand-covered rocks in sheltered coves. The thalli are of a rich red color and firm in texture. On the other hand, as found locally, *P. Lyallii* grows only on rocks exposed to the full force of the surf. Its thalli are brownish and of a soft gelatinous texture.

Prionitis Lyallii Harvey   Pl. 56, fig. 3

Harvey, 1862, p. 173. Setchell and Gardner, 1903, p. 350. Kylin, 1925, p. 19.

Thalli, as found on the Monterey Peninsula, 20–30 cm. tall; reddish-brown in color. Primary branching irregular; the primary branches flattened, not over 5 mm. broad. Primary branches with many pinnately arranged proliferous branches along the lateral margins. Proliferous branches with a cylindrical base and a long lanceolate blade 3–8 mm. broad and up to 10–20 cm. long. Proliferous branches with or without marginal proliferations. The blades of a soft gelatinous texture.

LOCAL DISTRIBUTION. Growing between the mean low-tide and −1.0-foot tide levels on rocks exposed to heavy surf. Abundant at mouth of Carmel River. Infrequent at Fanshell Beach; Cypress Point; Pescadero Point.

TYPE LOCALITY. Vancouver Island, British Columbia.

PACIFIC COAST DISTRIBUTION. British Columbia (Vancouver Island) to central California (Carmel Bay).

A number of varieties have been described for this extremely variable species, but they pass into one another by imperceptible gradations.

Lobocolax Howe, 1914

Thalli parasitic on *Prionitis,* minute, solitary or 2–5 adjacent to one another. Portion of thallus external to host irregularly globose and with a more or less convoluted surface. This portion with a medulla of loosely to tightly interwoven filaments; the cortex composed of compacted, di- or trichotomously branched, vertical filaments. Portion of thallus penetrating host massive, irregularly lobed, and composed of densely intertwined filaments.

Reproducing asexually by monospores.

Spermatangia produced at tips of cortical filaments. The carpogonial filaments one-celled, borne near tips of cortical filaments. Mature cystocarp a simple to sparingly branched row of 2–10 carposporangia.

Tetrasporophytes unknown.

STRUCTURE AND REPRODUCTION. Howe, 1914, pp. 90–93; text figs. 20–39; pl. 32, fig. A. Kylin, 1941; pp. 13–14; fig. 4.

Lobocolax deformans Howe　　　　　　Pl. 57, fig. 4

Howe, 1914, p. 91; text figs. 20–39; pl. 32, fig. A. *Kylin, 1941, p. 13; fig. 4.

The thallus growing anywhere on host except the young proliferous branches; of the same color as host or somewhat lighter in color. Portion external to host 4–5 mm. in diameter and with a convoluted surface.

LOCAL DISTRIBUTION. Parasitic on *Prionitis lanceolata* and *P. australis*. Mussel Point; Point Pinos; Middle Reef of Moss Beach; Point Joe; Fanshell Beach.

TYPE LOCALITY. Lobos de Afuera, Peru.

PACIFIC COAST DISTRIBUTION. Known only from the Monterey Peninsula.

Family CALLYMENIACEAE

Thalli nonfilamentous. Usually erect and with simple or divided blades. The blades with a nonfilamentous medulla of large cells and a relatively thin cortex.

Carpogonial and auxiliary cell filaments borne in a common branched fertile filament. The carpogonial filaments three-celled. The auxiliary cell filament reduced to a single cell and subtending the carpogonial filament. Gonimoblast filaments growing toward center of blade. Cystocarps globose, fairly massive, encircled by remains of a nutritive tissue.

Tetrasporophytes with tetrasporangia remote from one another and embedded just beneath thallus surface. The tetrasporangia cruciately divided.

KEY TO THE GENERA IN THE LOCAL FLORA

1. Thalli parasitic ....*Callocolax* (p. 252)
1. Thalli not parasitic..2
　　2. With a vertical, erect, divided blade...........*Callophyllis* (p. 249)
　　2. With a horizontal, subsessile, undivided blade......*Pugetia* (p. 253)

Callophyllis Kützing, 1843

Thalli erect, with fan-shaped, much-divided blades growing from a disc-shaped holdfast. The blades without a midrib or veins. Division of blade dichotomous, palmate, or pinnate and frequently into progressively narrower segments from base to apex. Margins of segments smooth or crisped, dentate or laciniate. Segments of blades with a single apical cell but with no evident axial filament posterior to the apical cell. The medulla composed of intermingled large and small cells; the cortex 4–5 cells in thickness and with progressively smaller cells to thallus surface.

Spermatangia unknown. Supporting cells of carpogonial filaments borne at inner face of cortex, large and irregular in shape. The supporting cell cutting off several cells, one of which divides to form a three-celled carpogonial filament. Sterile cells borne on the supporting cell and the lowermost cell of carpogonial filament large and irregular in shape. The supporting cell functioning as the auxiliary cell and the gonimoblast filaments growing toward interior of blade. The developing cystocarp surrounded by a nurse tissue. Mature cystocarps globose, with the carposporangia in small masses separated from one another by sterile tissue. Cystocarps bulging toward one side of blade and the overlying cortical tissue with one or more ostioles.

Tetrasporophytes with tetrasporangia remote from one another and embedded just beneath surface of blade. The tetrasporangia cruciately divided.

STRUCTURE AND REPRODUCTION. Kylin, 1928, pp. 56–59; figs. 34–35.

KEY TO THE SPECIES IN THE LOCAL FLORA[5]

1. Cystocarps restricted to margins of blade segments................ 2
1. Cystocarps scattered over entire blade........................... 3
  2. Blades less than 400 μ in thickness................*C. marginifructa*
  2. Blades more than 400 μ in thickness................*C. crassifolia*
3. Margins of blade segments crisped.....................*C. crenulata*
3. Margins of blade segments not crisped........................... 4
  4. Segments with obtuse tips and the tips
     frequently much dissected.......................*C. megalocarpa*
  4. Segments with acute tips and the tips
     rarely dissected into many small segments................... 5
5. Margins of segments with stipitate proliferous outgrowths..*C. pinnata*
5. Margins of segments without stipitate proliferous
  outgrowths ....*C. obtusifolia*

[5] Anderson (1891, p. 223) reports *C. laciniata* (Greville) Kützing from the Monterey region but this cannot be verified because no specimens determined as *C. laciniata* by Anderson have been found in his or other herbaria.

Callophyllis marginifructa Setchell and Swezy   Pl. 58, figs. 3–4

Setchell and Swezy apud *Setchell, 1923*A*, p. 398. *Kylin, 1941, p. 16.
Callophyllis variegata Anderson [not of (Bory) Kützing]. *Anderson, 1891,
p. 223. *Howe, 1893, p. 68 (in part).

Thalli, as found on the Monterey Peninsula, 5–15 cm. tall;
deep red in color. The blades relatively thin (less than 350 μ in
thickness) and repeatedly divided into progressively narrower
segments. Segmentation of blade flabellate-pinnate and with the
interval between successive segments usually less than 1 cm. Lower
segments of blade 2–6 mm. broad; upper segments 0.5–2 mm.
broad. Cystocarps 0.5–1.0 mm. in diameter, restricted to margins
of blade segments, densely crowded or remote from one another,
usually projecting beyond margins of blades.

LOCAL DISTRIBUTION. Growing on rocks between the mean low-tide
and −1.0-foot tide levels. Point Aulon; Cypress Point; Pescadero Point.
Also dredged from a depth of 30–35 feet a quarter-mile from Municipal
Wharf, Monterey; from 12 to 15 feet near Point Aulon; and from 15 to
20 feet at Stillwater Cove. Frequently cast ashore in abundance at Moss
Beach; Pebble Beach; Carmel Beach.

TYPE LOCALITY. San Pedro, California.

PACIFIC COAST DISTRIBUTION. Central California (Tomales .Bay) to
southern California (San Diego).

Callophyllis crassifolia Setchell and Swezy

Setchell and Swezy apud *Setchell, 1923*A*, p. 398.

Thalli, as found on the Monterey Peninsula, up to 10 cm. tall;
dull red in color. The blades over 400 μ in thickness and of a firm
fleshy texture, repeatedly and flabellately divided into progressively narrower segments. Lower segments of blade 3–5 mm.
broad, upper segments 0.5–1 mm. broad. Cystocarps about 0.5
mm. in diameter, often with a whorl of minute papillae; restricted
to margins of blade segments and usually projecting beyond the
margins.

LOCAL DISTRIBUTION. Pacific Grove; Cypress Point.

TYPE LOCALITY. Pacific Grove, California.

PACIFIC COAST DISTRIBUTION. Central California (Moss Beach, San
Mateo County, to Carmel Bay).

Callophyllis crenulata Setchell   Pl. 58, fig. 1

Setchell, 1923*A*, p. 400.

Thalli up to 20 cm. tall, deep red in color. The blades subdichotomously to flabellately divided into a relatively small num-

ber of segments. The segments narrowly to broadly cuneate and with undulate to crispate margins that are irregularly dentate or with short pinnules. The segments 2–3 cm. broad just below incisions. The cystocarps up to 1 mm. in diameter; irregularly distributed over the entire blade.

LOCAL DISTRIBUTION. Pacific Grove.
TYPE LOCALITY. Whidbey Island, Washington.
PACIFIC COAST DISTRIBUTION. As above.

Callophyllis megalocarpa Setchell and Swezy   Pl. 59, fig. 1

Setchell and Swezy apud *Setchell, 1923A, p. 401. *Kylin, 1941, p. 16.

Thalli, as found on the Monterey Peninsula, 10–20 cm. tall; deep red in color. The blades with a cylindrical stipe 1–2 cm. long; above this broadening rather abruptly. The blade repeatedly divided, the division subdichotomous to flabellate and the interval between successive divisions 2–5 cm. The ultimate segments with broadly rounded tips that are frequently incised into a number of blunt-tipped segments but 2–3 mm. long. Margins of segments in lower part of blade at times with simple or incised proliferous bladelets. The cystocarps irregularly distributed over entire blade; those in lowermost portion of old blades up to 3 mm. in diameter.

LOCAL DISTRIBUTION. Growing either in sheltered or exposed localities and on rocks between the mean low-tide and −1.5-foot tide levels. Only isolated individuals at any station. Mussel Point; Point Aulon; Arch Rock; Point Pinos; Asilomar Point; Point Joe; Fanshell Beach; Cypress Point; Arrowhead Point. Also dredged from a depth of 15–20 feet near Mussel Point and at Stillwater Cover. Frequently cast ashore at Pebble Beach and between Arrowhead Point and Carmel Beach.
TYPE LOCALITY. Carmel Bay, California.
PACIFIC COAST DISTRIBUTION. Washington (Whidbey Island) to southern California (Santa Barbara).

The character upon which the specific name is based, cystocarps of large size, is evident only on basal segments of large well-developed blades. The chief features distinguishing *C. megalocarpa* from other coarse species of the local flora are the broadly rounded tips of the ultimate segments and the frequent longitudinal incision of these tips into several short segments.

Callophyllis pinnata Setchell and Swezy   Pl. 58, fig. 2

Setchell and Swezy apud Setchell, 1923A, p. 400.

Thalli up to 40 cm. tall, deep red in color. The blades three to five times divided and with the segmentation subdichotomous to flabellate. Segments of blades narrowly to broadly cuneate; the ultimate segments relatively long and with convexly acute tips. Margins of lower segments regularly with stipitate proliferous bladelets which may be simple or two to three times divided. The cystocarps irregularly scattered over entire blade; those on lower segments up to 2 mm. in diameter.

LOCAL DISTRIBUTION. Cast ashore at Moss Beach and Pebble Beach.
TYPE LOCALITY. Duxbury Reef, Bolinas, California.
PACIFIC COAST DISTRIBUTION. Central California (Duxbury Reef to Carmel Bay).

Resembling *C. obtusifolia* but differing in the regular occurrence of stipitate proliferous bladelets along margins of the older segments.

Callophyllis obtusifolia J. G. Agardh   Pl. 59, fig. 2

J. G. Agardh, 1851, p. 297. *Kylin, 1928, p. 56; figs. 34–35. *Kylin, 1941, p. 16.
Callophyllis furcata Farlow in Algae Exsicc. Am. Bor. No. 127. *Anderson, 1891, p. 223. *Howe, 1893, p. 68. *Phyc. Bor.-Amer. No. 883.

Thalli, as found on the Monterey Peninsula, 15–45 cm. tall; of a deep red color. The blades with a flattened cuneate stipe 2–5 cm. long; above this repeatedly divided into many segments, the segmentation dichotomous throughout or dichotomous below and palmate above. The segments 1–4 cm. broad and of the same breadth from base to apex or gradually broadening upwards. The ultimate segments long, with convexly acute tips. Apices of ultimate segments rarely incised into several small segments. Lateral margins of lower segments occasionally with small proliferous outgrowths. Cystocarps numerous, scattered over entire blade; those in lower segments of old blades rarely over 1.5 mm. in diameter.

LOCAL DISTRIBUTION. Isolated individuals found on rocks between the mean low-tide and −1.0-foot tide levels. Point Pinos; Pescadero Point. Frequently cast ashore in abundance at Moss Beach.
TYPE LOCALITY. "Pacific Ocean." Probably North America and possibly the vicinity of Monterey, California.
PACIFIC COAST DISTRIBUTION. Central California (Santa Cruz) to southern California (San Pedro).

Callocolax Schmitz, 1895

Thallus filamentous and parasitic within blades of *Callophyllis*. Infected areas of host developing small, light-colored, tuberculate outgrowths of distinctive form. The tuberculate outgrowths with the epidermal layer composed exclusively of host cells; portion below the epidermal layer composed of intermingled parasite and host cells.

Spermatangia unknown. Carpogonial filaments produced on either cystocarpic or tetrasporic thalli of host. Structure of carpogonial filament as in *Callophyllis*. Mature cystocarps globose, with a few sterile cells intermingled with the carposporangia. The tissue above cystocarp without an ostiole.

Tetrasporophytes with tetrasporangia developed at tips of filaments of parasite, cruciately divided, formed deep within the host tubercules.

STRUCTURE AND REPRODUCTION. Batters, 1895, pp. 316–318; pl. 11, figs. 25–29. Kylin, 1930, pp. 31–32; fig. 19.

Callocolax neglectus Schmitz   Pl. 58, fig. 5

Schmitz in Algae Britinnicae Rariores Exsiccatae No. 154 (name only). Schmitz apud Batters, 1895, p. 318; pl. 11, figs. 25–29.

Parasite-containing tubercules of host 2–4 mm. tall and about as broad. The tubercules bilobed or palmately to irregularly lobed; usually lighter in color than host. The cystocarps occupying most of the space within the tubercules.

LOCAL DISTRIBUTION. On *Callophyllis marginifructa*. Dredged from a depth of 30–35 feet a quarter-mile from Municipal Wharf, Monterey. Cast ashore at foot of Seventh St., Pacific Grove.

TYPE LOCALITY. England (?).

PACIFIC COAST DISTRIBUTION. Known only from the Monterey Peninsula.

The description of the species as given above is based upon accounts of specimens collected in Europe because there is some doubt as to whether or not the local alga is the same species. The tubercules were about half the size of that given for European specimens. Some of the local specimens were cystocarpic; with cystocarps 100–150 μ in diameter and carposporangia 8–10 μ in diameter.

Pugetia Kylin, 1925

Thallus with a very short cylindrical stipe terminating in a single, horizontally expanded, peltate blade. The blade lying more or less closely applied to the substratum but only attached to it by the stipe. The blades without veins. The medulla composed of large colorless globose cells and between them filaments of small cells containing chromatophores.

Spermatangia and carpogonial filaments unknown. The auxiliary cell much-lobed and resembling that of *Callophyllis*. The mature cystocarp a globose mass of carposporangia, deeply embedded in blade and the overlying cortical tissue without an ostiole.

Tetrasporophytes with the tetrasporangia remote from one another and embedded just below surface of blade. The tetrasporangia cruciately divided.

STRUCTURE AND REPRODUCTION. Kylin, 1925, pp. 30–31; fig. 14.

With one species in the local flora.

Pugetia firma Kylin   Pl. 60, fig. 1

* Kylin, 1941, p. 15; pl. 4, fig. 12.
Callymenia reniformis Setchell [not of (Turner) J. G. Agardh]. *Setchell, 1901, p. 124.

Thalli, as found on the Monterey Peninsula, with blades 4–10 cm. (occasionally up to 20 cm.) in diameter; deep pink to rose-red in color. The stipe 1–3 mm. long and attached either to the center or near the margin of blade. The blades circular in outline but more or less lobed; usually becoming irregularly and deeply laciniate with age. Young blades at times shallowly cup-like. Mature blades 350–800 μ in thickness, and of a very firm crisp texture.

LOCAL DISTRIBUTION. Growing between the mean low-tide and —1.5-foot tide levels on vertical face of sheltered rocks. Abundant in favorable habitats. Mussel Point; Point Aulon; Point Pinos; Asilomar Point; Point Joe; Fanshell Beach; Cypress Point; Pescadero Point; north end of Carmel Beach; Mission Point. Also dredged from a depth of 60–75 feet near Mussel Point.

TYPE LOCALITY. Point Pinos, Pacific Grove, California.

PACIFIC COAST DISTRIBUTION. As above.

Family CHOREOCOLACEAE

Thalli nonfilamentous. The thalli parasitic, frequently colorless, minute, globose or with stubby irregularly cylindrical branches.

Carpogonial and auxiliary cell filaments borne on a common branched filament. The carpogonial filament four-celled. The auxiliary cell filament reduced to a single cell and borne immediately beneath the carpogonial filament. The gonimoblast filaments growing toward surface of the thallus.

Tetrasporophytes with the tetrasporangia remote from one

another and embedded just beneath surface of thallus. The tetrasporangia cruciately divided.

With one genus, *Choreocolax,* in the local flora.

Choreocolax Reinsch, 1875

Thalli parasitic on Ceramiales, especially *Polysiphonia.* The thallus minute, colorless, globose, attached by branched haustorial filaments ramifying among tissues of host. Portion external to host composed of radially branched, laterally compacted, filaments with somewhat smaller cells at the surface.

Heterothallic. The spermatangia borne upon outermost cells of globose portion and lying in a continuous layer. The carpogonial filaments four-celled, borne just below thallus surface; with the supporting cell functioning as the auxiliary cell. The gonimoblast filaments growing toward thallus surface and with only the terminal cells developing into carposporangia. The carposporangia elongate and lining an ostiolate conceptacle-like cavity produced by upgrowth of adjoining vegetative tissues.

Tetrasporophytes with the tetrasporangia remote from one another and embedded just below thallus surface. The tetrasporangia cruciately divided.

STRUCTURE AND REPRODUCTION. Levring, 1935, pp. 55–56; fig. 11. Richards, 1891. Sturch, 1926.

Choreocolax Polysiphoniae Reinsch

Reinsch, 1875, p. 61; pl. 49. Sturch, 1926, p. 585; figs. 1–15. Taylor, 1937, p. 278. Phyc. Bor.-Amer. No. 286.

Thalli parasitic on *Polysiphonia,* usually less than 1 mm. in diameter but sometimes up to 4 mm.; whitish to whitish-brown in color. Cystocarpic plants with several cystocarps. The tetrasporangia 15–28 µ broad, 45–80 µ long.

LOCAL DISTRIBUTION. On *Polysiphonia* sp. at the first rocky point north of Carmel Beach.

TYPE LOCALITY. "Atlantic coast of North America."

PACIFIC COAST DISTRIBUTION. Known only from Sitka, Alaska, and from the Monterey Peninsula.

The dimensions given above are those of Atlantic Coast specimens. The single local collection of *C. Polysiphoniae,* made and determined by G. J. Hollenberg, was sterile. The specimens collected in Alaska (Saunders, 1901, p. 433) were tetrasporic.

Order GIGARTINALES

Thalli monoaxial or multiaxial, nonfilamentous; usually erect, but in rare cases prostrate and crustose. Erect thalli cylindrical to foliaceous, branched or unbranched.

The spermatangia usually borne in sori. The carpogonial filaments usually separated from one another within the cortex but occasionally in nemathecia. The gonimoblast filaments growing from an auxiliary cell which is an intercalary vegetative cell and not a cell borne in a special filament. The auxiliary cell separate from or in the same cortical filament as the carpogonial filament. Gonimoblast filaments either growing toward thallus surface or toward center of thallus. The mature cystocarps usually globose, embedded in thallus, and without a special envelope.

The tetrasporophytes usually with the sporangia separate from one another and embedded just beneath the surface of the thallus. More rarely with the sporangia either in sunken nematheciumlike sori, or in true nemathecia, or in chains deep within the thallus.

KEY TO THE FAMILIES IN THE LOCAL FLORA

1. The auxiliary cell a cortical cell some distance from
   the carpogonial filament.................................... 2
1. The auxiliary cell either the supporting cell of a carpogonial
   filament or the cell immediately below......................... 3
   2. Gonimoblast filaments growing toward thallus
      surface ....*Nemastomaceae* (p. 256)
   2. Gonimoblast filaments (at least at first) growing
      toward interior of thallus..................*Soleriaceae* (p. 259)
3. The supporting cell without sterile filaments..................... 4
3. The supporting cell with sterile filaments....................... 5
   4. Gonimoblast filaments growing toward interior of
      thallus; tetrasporangia at thallus surface...*Plocamiaceae* (p. 262)
   4. Gonimoblast filaments growing toward thallus center; tetra-
      sporangia in masses deep within thallus....*Gigartinaceae* (p. 276)
5. The auxiliary cell not fusing with adjacent cells;
   tetrasporangia in nemathecia.............*Phyllophoraceae* (p. 269)
5. The auxiliary cell fusing with adjacent cells; the tetrasporangia separated from one another.......*Gracilariaceae* (p. 265)

Family NEMASTOMACEAE

Thalli erect; cylindrical, compressed, or foliaceous; simple or branched. Thalli multiaxial; the medulla with parallel longitudinal filaments and the cortex with progressively smaller cells to the thallus surface.

Carpogonial filaments 3- to 7-celled. The auxiliary cell an intercalary cortical cell remote from the carpogonial filament. The gonimoblast filaments growing toward the thallus surface and with most of the cells developing into carposporangia. Mature cystocarps embedded within thallus and without a special envelope.

Tetrasporophytes with tetrasporangia remote from one another and just beneath thallus surface. The tetrasporangia zonately divided.

With one genus, *Schizymenia,* in the local flora.

Schizymenia J. G. Agardh, 1851

Thalli with one or more blades growing erect from a small disc-shaped holdfast. Base of blade with an inconspicuous cylindrical stipe. The blade broadly ovate to broadly lanceolate, simple or divided, with more or less convoluted margins. Blades without midrib or veins and with a smooth or wrinkled surface. The medulla composed of interwoven colorless filaments; the cortex composed of erect branching filaments with progressively smaller cells to surface of blade. The cortex with numerous large colorless cylindrical to ellipsoidal gland cells standing perpendicular to surface of blade.

Heterothallic. The spermatangia in patches near margin of blade. Carpogonial filaments unknown but obviously produced remote from auxiliary cells. The auxiliary cell an enlarged intercalary cell near the base of a cortical filament. The gonimoblast filaments growing toward thallus surface, freely branched, with all cells developing into carposporangia. Mature cystocarps globose, embedded in medulla, without a special envelope, lying beneath an ostiole in the cortex.

Tetrasporophytes either with the tetrasporangia remote from one another or grouped in nemathecia. The tetrasporangia zonately divided.

STRUCTURE AND REPRODUCTION. Kylin, 1925, pp. 21–22; fig. 10. Kylin, 1930, pp. 38–40; figs. 25–26. (Both as *Turnerella.*)

KEY TO THE SPECIES IN THE LOCAL FLORA

1. Tetrasporangia not in nemathecia......................*S. pacifica*
1. Tetrasporangia in nemathecia......................*S. epiphytica*

Schizymenia pacifica Kylin   Pl. 60, fig. 4; pl. 61, fig. 1

Kylin, 1932, p. 10. *Kylin, 1941, p. 17.
Turnerella pacifica Kylin, 1925, p. 21; fig. 11. Kylin, 1930, p. 38; figs. 25–26.
Schizymenia edulis Farlow [not of (Stackhouse) J. G. Agardh]. Farlow,
1875, p. 370. *Anderson, 1891, p. 222.
Sarcophyllis californica Farlow [not of J. G. Agardh]. Farlow, 1877, p. 241.
*Anderson, 1891, p. 222. *Howe, 1893, p. 68. *Phyc. Bor.-Amer. No. 395.

Thalli, as found on the Monterey Peninsula, up to 60 cm.
tall; of a rich brownish-red color. The blades broadly ovate to
broadly lanceolate; undivided but frequently with frayed margins
and deeply laciniate. The blades soft in texture and very slimy to
the touch; when partially dried the surface becoming finely granular. Gland cells of cortex cylindrical, 8–15 µ broad, 20–60 µ
long. The tetrasporangia remote from one another and embedded
just beneath thallus surface.

LOCAL DISTRIBUTION. Growing between the mean low-tide and −1.5-
foot tide levels on top of rocks exposed to surf. Pacific Grove; Point Au-
lon; Arch Rock; Point Pinos; Middle Reef of Moss Beach; Point Joe;
Cypress Point; Midway Point; Pescadero Point; Pebble Beach; Mission
Point. Also dredged from a depth of 30–35 feet a quarter-mile from
Municipal Wharf, Monterey.

TYPE LOCALITY. Friday Harbor, Washington.

PACIFIC COAST DISTRIBUTION. Alaska (Unga Island) to southern
California (La Jolla).

Blades of thalli somewhat sheltered from waves tend to be
broader than long; blades of thalli freely exposed to waves usually
have a length double the breadth.

Schizymenia epiphytica (Setchell and Lawson) Smith and
   Hollenberg   Pl. 60, figs. 2–3

Smith and Hollenberg, 1943, p. 221; figs. 28–30.
Peyssonneliopsis epiphytica Setchell and Lawson apud *Setchell, 1905, p. 63.
*Phyc. Bor.-Amer. No. 1049.

Thalli, as found on the Monterey Peninsula, up to 30 cm.
tall; bright red in color. With one or more blades from a disc-
shaped holdfast. The blades entire, reniform-orbicular when
young; orbicular when mature and more or less roundly lobed;
edge of blade with a rim-like thickening. Older blades of a harsh
papery texture and with a much-wrinkled surface. Gland cells
numerous in cortex; ellipsoidal when young, globose when mature;
70–80 µ in diameter. With tetrasporangia in small nemathecia

standing above surface of blade. The tetrasporangia zonately divided, 10–14 µ broad, 50–58 µ long.

LOCAL DISTRIBUTION. Cast ashore at Monterey; Pacific Grove; Asilomar Point; Moss Beach; Pebble Beach; Carmel Beach.
TYPE LOCALITY. Pacific Grove, California.
PACIFIC COAST DISTRIBUTION. As above.

Family SOLERIACEAE

Thalli erect; cylindrical, compressed, or foliaceous; simple or branched. Thalli multiaxial; the medulla with parallel longitudinal filaments and the cortex with progressively smaller cells to the thallus surface.

Carpogonial filaments 3- or 4-celled. The auxiliary cell an intercalary cortical cell remote from the carpogonial filament. The gonimoblast filaments, at least at first, growing toward interior of thallus; with most of the cells developing into carposporangia. Cystocarps deeply embedded within thallus and surrounded by an envelope of nutritive filaments.

Tetrasporophytes with tetrasporangia remote from one another and just beneath the thallus surface. The tetrasporangia zonately divided.

KEY TO THE GENERA IN THE LOCAL FLORA

1. Thalli not parasitic..2
1. Thalli parasitic ....*Gardneriella* (p. 261)
  2. Thalli cylindrical, radially branched...........*Agardhiella* (p. 259)
  2. Thalli foliose, the blades thick and
    proliferating at margin....................*Opuntiella* (p. 261)

Agardhiella Schmitz, 1896

Thalli erect, with one to several shoots from a disc-shaped holdfast. Old holdfasts with prostrate cylindrical outgrowths. Erect shoots cylindrical, with a freely branched obscure central axis, the branches radially arranged or tending to lie in one plane. Branches with a medulla of parallel longitudinal filaments somewhat separated from one another and with a cortex composed of branched filaments with progressively smaller cells toward the surface; the outermost cortical cells either rounded, or angular and compacted into an angular parenchyma.

Heterothallic. The spermatangia in small sori developed on the outermost cortical cells. Carpogonial filaments borne adaxially at inner face of cortex, three-celled, with the base of the trichogyne bending sharply toward thallus surface. The auxiliary cell an intercalary cell midway between base and apex of a cortical filament. Fertilization followed by growth of an oöblast from carpogonium to auxiliary cell and a development of gonimoblast initials on the adaxial side of the auxiliary cell. The gonimoblast filaments freely branched, lying in a globose mass, with only cells at the periphery developing into carposporangia. The developing cystocarp surrounded by a thick felted layer of nutritive cells. The mature cystocarp deeply embedded in thallus, the overlying cortical tissue with an ostiole.

Tetrasporophytes with the tetrasporangia remote from one another and embedded just beneath the thallus surface. The tetrasporangia zonately divided.

STRUCTURE AND REPRODUCTION. Kylin, 1928, pp. 67–72; figs. 43–45. Osterhout, 1896 (as *Rhabdonia*). G. M. Smith, 1938, pp. 336–338; figs. 185–186.

With one species in the local flora.

Agardhiella Coulteri (Harvey) Setchell   Pl. 62, fig. 4

*Setchell in Phyc. Bor.-Amer. No. 333. *Kylin, 1941, p. 18.
"Hypriea" Coulteri *Harvey apud Harvey and Bailey, 1851, p. 371. (This cited as *Hypnea Coulteri* in Harvey, 1853, p. 154.)
Rhabdonia Coulteri *Harvey, 1853, p. 154; pl. 23, fig. *B*. *Anderson, 1891, p. 224. *Howe, 1893, p. 68.

Thalli, as found on the Monterey Peninsula, up to 35 cm. tall; bright pink to deep red in color. Primary axis of shoot cylindrical throughout, 2–3 mm. in diameter, radially branched or with the branches in one plane. Primary and secondary branches with a maximum breadth of 2–3 mm.; narrow at base and gradually tapering to an acute point at the apex. Fruiting cystocarpic plants with localized swellings marking the position of the deeply embedded cystocarps.

LOCAL DISTRIBUTION. Growing on rocks between the 1.0- and −1.5-foot tide levels. Frequently found in tide pools. Widely distributed over the entire Peninsula but never in dense stands. Also dredged from a depth of 20 feet near Mussel Point and in Stillwater Cove.

TYPE LOCALITY. Monterey, California.

PACIFIC COAST DISTRIBUTION. British Columbia (Vancouver Island) to southern California (San Diego).

Gardneriella Kylin, 1941

Thalli minute, whitish to pinkish, parasitic on *Agardhiella Coulteri*. The thalli sessile or stipitate, hemispherical to spherical, with the surface covered with tuberculations. The thallus composed of radiately branched filaments with ellipsoidal to spherical cells that become progressively smaller to the thallus surface.

Heterothallic. The spermatangia in small sori on surface of thallus. Carpogonial filaments some distance in from thallus surface, three-celled, with base of trichogyne bending sharply toward thallus surface. The auxiliary cell an undifferentiated vegetative cell some distance beneath surface of thallus. Fertilization followed by growth of an oöblast from carpogonium to the auxiliary cell, which then produces laterally a branched gonimoblast filament in which a majority of the cells develop into carposporangia.

Tetrasporophytes with tetrasporangia remote from one another and embedded just beneath thallus surface. The tetrasporangia with bispores (?).

STRUCTURE AND REPRODUCTION. Kylin, 1941, pp. 18–20; fig. 5.

Gardneriella tuberifera Kylin   Pl. 62, fig. 5

*Kylin, 1941, p. 18; fig. 5.
Janczewskia verrucaeformis Nott [not of Solms-Laubach]. *Nott, 1897, p. 83 (as to parasite on *Agardhiella Coulteri*).

Thalli 2–6 mm. in diameter; whitish to light pink in color. With the surface covered with minute hemispherical tuberculations. Parasitic on *Agardhiella Coulteri* and usually restricted to the basal 8 cm. of the host.

LOCAL DISTRIBUTION. Pacific Grove; Point Pinos; Middle Reef of Moss Beach; Pebble Beach; Mission Point.
TYPE LOCALITY. Pacific Grove, California.
PACIFIC COAST DISTRIBUTION. As above.

Opuntiella Kylin, 1925

Thallus with a single, undivided, flattened, primary blade growing erect from a disc-shaped holdfast. Margin of primary blade with stipitate proliferous blades of the same size or larger than the primary blade. The blades thick, cartilaginous in texture; the surface smooth or with minute scattered papillate outgrowths. Medulla composed of densely interwoven filaments, the cortex composed of compacted branched vertical filaments with progressively smaller cells to the blade's surface. The cortex also with large colorless cylindrical gland cells standing perpendicular to the surface of blade.

Spermatangia unknown. Carpogonial filaments usually six-celled, borne upon innermost cells of cortex. The auxiliary cell an intercalary cell of a cortical filament bearing a carpogonial filament. The gonimoblast filaments freely branched, growing toward the medulla, and with most of the cells developing into carposporangia. Mature cystocarps globose, deeply embedded in blade, not surrounded by a nutritive tissue; the overlying cystocarp with an ostiole.

Tetrasporophytes with the tetrasporangia remote from one another and embedded just beneath surface of blade. The tetrasporangia zonately divided.

STRUCTURE AND REPRODUCTION. Kylin, 1925, pp. 23–24; fig. 11. Kylin, 1934*A*, pp. 1–3; fig. 1. Leavitt, 1904 (as *Callymenia*).

Opuntiella californica (Farlow) Kylin   Pl. 61, fig. 2

Kylin, 1925, p. 23; fig. 11. *Kylin, 1932, p. 69. Kylin, 1934*A*, p. 1; fig. 1. *Kylin, 1941, p. 18.

Kallymenia (Callymenia) californica Farlow, 1877, p. 241. *Anderson, 1891, p. 222. *Howe, 1893, p. 68. *Setchell, 1901, p. 124. *Phyc. Bor.-Amer. No. 633.

Callymenia phyllophora Setchell and Gardner [not of J. G. Agardh]. Setchell and Gardner, 1903, p. 308. Leavitt, 1904, p. 291; pls. 44–45.

Thalli, as found on the Monterey Peninsula, up to 20 cm. tall and 30 cm. broad; of a deep dark-red color. Primary and proliferous blades fan-shaped to broadly obovate. The proliferous blades 2–3 mm. in thickness; up to 12 cm. tall and 15 cm. broad. Stipes of primary and proliferous blades 2–3 mm. broad, 4–8 mm. long.

LOCAL DISTRIBUTION. Isolated thalli have been found growing on rocks between the mean low-tide and −1.5-foot tide levels at Point Pinos; Point·Joe; Cypress Point; Midway Point. Thalli have been found cast ashore at Mussel Point; Point Pinos; Moss Beach; Fanshell Beach; Carmel Beach.

TYPE LOCALITY. Santa Cruz, California.

PACIFIC COAST DISTRIBUTION. Alaska (Unga Island) to southern California (San Diego).

Family PLOCAMIACEAE

Thalli erect, free-living or parasitic. The thallus sympodial and with pectinate cylindrical or compressed branches. The branches monoaxial, with a percurrent axial filament; the cortex with densely compacted cells that are progressively smaller toward the thallus surface.

Carpogonial filaments 3-celled. Supporting cell of carpogonial filament becoming the auxiliary cell and producing gonimoblast filaments on side toward thallus surface. The gonimoblast filaments branched and with most of the cells developing into carposporangia. Mature cystocarps embedded in thallus and without a special envelope.

Tetrasporophytes with tetrasporangia remote from one another and embedded just beneath the thallus surface. The tetrasporangia zonately divided.

Key to the Genera in the Local Flora

1. Thalli free-living...............................*Plocamium* (p. 263)
1. Thalli parasitic.............................*Plocamiocolax* (p. 265)

Plocamium Lamouroux, 1813

Thalli erect, attached either by a disc-shaped holdfast or by prostrate branches. The erect shoots freely branched and with subcylindrical to markedly compressed branches. The branching sympodial, distichous, pectinate; with successive pectinations alternately on the abaxial and adaxial sides of branch. Each pectination with 2–5 branches. Branches monoaxial and each cell of the axial filament bearing two lateral filaments. The lateral filaments with progressively smaller cells and the outermost cells compacted into a parenchyma.

Heterothallic. The spermatangia completely covering the ultimate branchlets. Carpogonial filaments 3-celled, borne near base of a lateral filament from axial filament of a branch. Supporting cell of carpogonial filament functioning as the auxiliary cell. The gonimoblast filaments freely branched, all directed toward thallus surface, with most of the cells developing into carposporangia. Vegetative cells adjoining the cystocarp developing into a pericarp-like structure without an ostiole.

Tetrasporophytes with tetrasporangia restricted to the ultimate branchlets. The fertile branchlets stichidium-like and inflated. The tetrasporangia zonately divided.

Structure and Reproduction. Kylin, 1923, pp. 49–53; figs. 34–35. Kylin, 1930, pp. 45–47; fig. 32.

Plocamium pacificum Kylin   Pl. 62, fig. 1

Kylin, 1925, p. 42; fig. 24*B*. *Kylin, 1941, p. 20.
Plocamium coccineum Harvey [not of (Hudson) Lyngbye]. *Harvey, 1833, p. 164. Harvey, 1853, p. 153. *Anderson, 1891, p. 224. *Howe, 1893, p. 68. Phyc. Bor.-Amer. No. 994.

Thalli, as found on the Monterey Peninsula, 10–25 cm. tall; rich rose-red in color. Erect shoots with subcylindrical branches of 4–7 orders. Lowermost branches at times smaller in diameter, more loosely branched, and growing prostrate on the substratum. The primary branches more or less zigzag, 1–2 mm. in diameter. Branches of higher orders each with 4–5 branches on the adaxial side. The lowermost of each series usually simple, 2–4 mm. long, tapering gradually to an acute point and straight or outwardly curved.

LOCAL DISTRIBUTION. Growing on rocks between the mean low-tide and −1.5-foot tide levels. Often on rocks buried in sand. Occasionally epiphytic on other algae. Mussel Point; Point Aulon; Point Pinos; Middle Reef of Moss Beach; Point Joe; Fanshell Beach; Pebble Beach; north end of Carmel Beach; Mission Point; mouth of Carmel River. Also dredged from a depth of 20–25 feet at Point Aulon and at Pescadero Rock.

TYPE LOCALITY. San Juan Island, Washington.

PACIFIC COAST DISTRIBUTION. British Columbia (Vancouver Island) to southern California (La Jolla).

There is considerable variation in density of branching of this species. Specimens from deep water are usually more laxly branched than those from the intertidal zone.

Plocamium violaceum Farlow   Pl. 62, fig. 2

Farlow, 1877, p. 240. *Anderson, 1891, p. 224. *Howe, 1893, p. 68. *Kylin, 1941, p. 20. *Phyc. Bor.-Amer. No. 542.

Thalli, as found on the Monterey Peninsula, usually 4–8 cm. tall; reddish-violet in color. Erect shoots with subcylindrical branches of 3–5 orders and with relatively few long primary branches. Branches of higher orders each with 3–4 branches on the adaxial side. The lowermost of each order usually simple, 3–6 mm. long, tapering gradually to an acute point, and strongly incurved toward the branch bearing it.

LOCAL DISTRIBUTION. Growing between the 2.5- and 0.5-foot tide levels on the vertical face of rocks exposed to heavy surf. Frequently present in abundance. Found on all rocky headlands of the Monterey Peninsula.

TYPE LOCALITY. Santa Cruz, California

PACIFIC COAST DISTRIBUTION. British Columbia (Vancouver Island) to southern California (San Pedro).

Plocamiocolax Setchell, 1923

Thallus a small pulvinate mass growing parasitically on the surface of *Plocamium*. The mass composed of radiating branches pectinately branched into one or two orders. The branches cylindrical and with blunt tips.

Spermatangia unknown. Carpogonial filaments and development of the carposporophyte unknown. The mature cystocarp a globose mass of carposporangia; the cystocarp protruding from side of a branch and surrounded by an ostiolate pericarp-like envelope.

Tetrasporophytes with tips of fertile branches somewhat inflated. The tetrasporangia zonately divided.

STRUCTURE AND REPRODUCTION. Setchell, 1923, pp. 395–396.

Plocamiocolax pulvinata Setchell   Pl. 62, fig. 3

*Setchell, 1923, p. 396.

Thalli, as found on the Monterey Peninsula, up to 5 mm. in diameter; white to light tan in color. Branches of thallus up to 2.5 mm. long and 0.25 mm. in diameter. The branches irregularly or pectinately branched, straight or twisted, cylindrical and tapering irregularly to a broadly rounded tip.

LOCAL DISTRIBUTION. Parasitic on *Plocamium pacificum* at Pebble Beach.

TYPE LOCALITY. Pebble Beach, Monterey Peninsula, California.

PACIFIC COAST DISTRIBUTION. Washington (San Juan Island) to southern California (San Pedro.)

Family GRACILARIACEAE

Thalli usually erect and free-living. Erect thalli cylindrical to compressed; more or less freely branched. The branches probably monoaxial. The medulla with large, compactly united, isodiametric cells; the cortex similar in structure but with progressively smaller cells toward the thallus surface.

Carpogonial filaments 2- or 3-celled. Supporting cell of carpogonial filament also bearing sterile filaments. The auxiliary cell formed by fusion of supporting cell, the sterile filaments it bears, and certain adjoining cortical cells. Gonimoblast filaments growing toward surface of thallus, becoming a globose mass in which all cells but those at the center develop into carposporangia. The mature cystocarp standing above thallus surface and surrounded by a thick pericarp-like envelope with an ostiole.

Tetrasporophytes with tetrasporangia remote from one another and embedded just beneath the thallus surface. The tetrasporangia cruciately divided.

KEY TO THE GENERA IN THE LOCAL FLORA

1. Thalli free-living..............................*Gracilaria* (p. 266)
1. Thalli parasitic............................*Gracilariophila* (p. 268)

Gracilaria Greville, 1830

Thalli usually with several erect branches growing from a prostrate rhizome. The erect branches subdichotomously or irregularly branched, sometimes with proliferous branchlets. The branches cylindrical to compressed, of a fleshy to cartilaginous texture. Branch tips with a single apical cell but without an evident axial filament posterior to apical cell. The branches with a parenchymatous medulla of large colorless cells and a parenchymatous cortex with progressively smaller cells to the surface.

Heterothallic. Spermatangia in superficial sori or in conceptacle-like depressions of the thallus surface. Carpogonial filaments 2-celled, flanked laterally by two special vegetative filaments borne upon the supporting cell. The carpogonium enlarging after fertilization and fusing with several neighboring cells to form a large placental cell from which gonimoblast filaments grow toward the thallus surface; the gonimoblast filaments branched, lying in a compact mass, with several cells toward the end of each branch developing into carposporangia. Mature cystocarps standing above thallus surface and the adjacent cortical tissue developing into a thick pericarp-like envelope with an ostiole.

Tetrasporophytes with tetrasporangia remote from one another and embedded just beneath the thallus surface. The tetrasporangia cruciately divided.

STRUCTURE AND REPRODUCTION. Kylin, 1930, pp. 55–59; figs. 40–44. Sjöstedt, 1926, pp. 51–64; figs. 31–41.

KEY TO THE SPECIES IN THE LOCAL FLORA

1. Branches cylindrical.. 2
1. Branches flattened......................................*G. linearis*
  2. Branches over 15 cm. long; irregularly branched.....*G. Sjoestedtii*
  2. Branches less than 10 cm. long,
     subdichotomously branched ....*G. robusta*

Gracilaria Sjoestedtii Kylin   Pl. 63, fig. 4

Kylin, 1930, p. 55. *Kylin, 1941, p. 21; pl. 7, fig. 18.
Gracilaria confervoides Farlow [as to Pacific Coast plants not of (Linnaeus) Greville]. Farlow, 1875, p. 365. *Anderson, 1891, p. 224. *Howe, 1893, p. 68. *Kylin, 1941, p. 20. *Phyc. Bor.-Amer. No. 384.
Gracilaria robusta Sjöstedt [not of Setchell]. *Sjöstedt, 1926, p. 53.
Cordylecladia conferta Anderson [not of J. G. Agardh]. *Anderson, 1891, p. 224. *Howe, 1893, p. 68.

Thalli, as found on the Monterey Peninsula, up to 2 m. tall; yellowish-brown, reddish-brown, or reddish-purple in color. With many branches growing from a disc-like holdfast and from prostrate rhizome-like branches. Erect branches cylindrical, 0.5–1.5 mm. in diameter, irregularly and sparingly branched. All branches sometimes with numerous short proliferous branchlets. Cystocarps scattered along entire branch, bulging conspicuously from surface of branch, without connecting filaments between the pericarp and mass of carposporangia.

LOCAL DISTRIBUTION. Growing half-buried in sand between rocks at the 1.0- to 1.5-foot tide levels. Occurring in abundance over the entire Monterey Peninsula. Also dredged from a depth of 30–35 feet a quarter-mile from the Municipal Wharf at Monterey; and from 40–60 feet near Mussel Point.

TYPE LOCALITY. Mussel Point, Pacific Grove, California.

PACIFIC COAST DISTRIBUTION. British Columbia (Vancouver Island) to Baja California (Ensenada).

Differing from *G. confervoides* in the lack of connecting filaments between pericarp and carposporangia. There are also minor differences in structure of cortex of the two species.

Gracilaria robusta Setchell   Pl. 63, fig. 2

*Setchell in Phyc. Bor.-Amer. No. 635. *Kylin, 1941, p. 21.

Thalli, as found on the Monterey Peninsula, up to 10 cm. tall; deep burgundy-red in color. With several branches growing erect from a disc-shaped holdfast. The erect branches cylindrical, four to five times subdichotomously branched, the branch tips terete and with blunt apices. Branches stiff and turgid, not bending when removed from water. Cystocarps irregularly scattered over branches, bulging prominently.

LOCAL DISTRIBUTION. Growing on rocks between the −0.5- and the −1.5-foot tide levels. Monterey; Mussel Point. Also dredged from a depth of 15–25 feet near Point Aulon.

TYPE LOCALITY. Monterey, California.

PACIFIC COAST DISTRIBUTION. As above.

Gracilaria linearis Kylin   Pl. 63, fig. 3

*Kylin, 1941, p. 22; pl. 7, fig. 19.

Thalli 5–8 cm. tall; dark red in color. With cartilaginous flattened. branches that are repeatedly subdichotomous. The branches usually curved in an arcuate manner. Lower segments of branches 2–4 mm. broad; the ultimate segments about 1 mm. broad.

LOCAL DISTRIBUTION. Growing on rocks in the lower littoral. Pacific Grove; Pescadero Point.

TYPE LOCALITY. Pacific Grove, California.

PACIFIC COAST DISTRIBUTION. As above.

Gracilariophila Setchell and Wilson, 1910

Thalli minute, parasitic on *Gracilaria*. Growing at surface of host and with rhizoidal filaments penetrating the host. Portion external to host globose. Medulla composed of angular thick-walled cells with granular contents; the cortex composed of small angular cells.

Heterothallic. The spermatangia in short chains on surface of thallus. Carpogonial filaments and development of carposporo-phyte unknown. Mature cystocarps embedded within and com-prising most of the volume of thallus. With carposporangia pro-duced in chains. The pericarp 10–12 cells in thickness, with con-spicuous ostiole.

Tetrasporophytes with tetrasporangia remote from one another and embedded just beneath thallus surface. Division of tetra-sporangia cruciate.

STRUCTURE AND REPRODUCTION. Wilson, 1910.

Gracilariophila oryzoides Setchell and Wilson   Pl. 63, fig. 1

Setchell and Wilson apud Wilson, 1910, p. 81; pls. 12–13.
Gracilariopsis oryzoides (Setchell and Wilson) Gardner in Phyc. Bor.-Amer. No. 2299.

Thalli, as found on the Monterey Peninsula, up to 2 mm. in

diameter; usually white but sometimes yellowish or brownish in color. Portion external to host globose but somewhat angular when thalli are crowded one against another. The parasite usually found only on lower portion of branches of host.

LOCAL DISTRIBUTION. Parasitic on *Gracilaria Sjoestedtii*. Monterey; Mussel Point; Asilomar Point; Fanshell Beach; Cypress Point.

TYPE LOCALITY. San Pedro, California.

PACIFIC COAST DISTRIBUTION. Southern Oregon (Coos Bay) to southern California (Santa Monica).

Family PHYLLOPHORACEAE

Thalli erect, branched; the branches cylindrical, markedly compressed, or foliaceous. The thalli multiaxial; the medulla with large, compactly united, isodiametric cells; the cortex also parenchymatous but with much smaller cells.

The carpogonial filaments three-celled. The supporting cell of carpogonial filament also bearing sterile filaments. The cell beneath the supporting cell or the supporting cell itself becoming the auxiliary cell; the gonimoblast filaments growing toward center of thallus. Some species with most cells of the gonimoblast filaments developing into carposporangia. Other species with cells of the gonimoblast filaments developing into tetrasporangia that lie in vertical rows in a nemathecium.

Species producing carposporangia also with a tetrasporophytic generation. The tetrasporophytes with tetrasporangia in nemathecia. The tetrasporangia cruciately divided.

KEY TO THE GENERA IN THE LOCAL FLORA

1. Thalli with cylindrical branches...................*Ahnfeltia* (p. 271)
1. Thalli with all or the ends of branches flattened.................... 2
   2. Cystocarps in long linear nemathecia........*Stenogramma* (p. 275)
   2. Cystocarps, if present, not in long linear nemathecia............ 3
3. Branches distinctly foliaceous at upper end......*Phyllophora* (p. 269)
3. Branches of the same breadth throughout.....*Gymnogongrus* (p. 272)

Phyllophora Greville, 1830

Thalli erect; with one to several erect shoots from a disc-shaped holdfast. Lower portion of erect shoot cylindrical, stipe-like, irregularly branched; above this with flattened simple or dichotomously branched blades. The blades linear, wedge-shaped, or obovate. The stipe and tips of blades frequently with small proliferous blades. Medulla with tightly compacted, large, angular cells; the cortex with small cells standing in rows perpendicular to thallus surface.

Homothallic or heterothallic. The spermatangia borne in small ovoid cavities at surface of thallus. Carpogonial filaments formed at inner face of cortex of short thick proliferous blades from stipe, three-celled and with a one-celled lateral branch from lowermost cell. The supporting cell, which functions as the auxiliary cell, also bearing a sterile branched filament. The gonimoblast filaments with most of the cells developing into carposporangia. The mature cystocarp globose and deeply embedded in thallus.

Tetrasporophytes with the tetrasporangia lying in vertical rows and borne in nemathecia. The tetrasporangia cruciately divided.

Some species without a tetrasporophytic generation. Instead, the gonimoblast filaments grow towards the thallus surface and produce an irregularly shaped nemathecium with cells in vertical rows toward the upper surface. Outermost cells of the vertical rows remaining sterile; those beneath them developing into chains of tetrasporangia. Division of primary tetrasporangial nucleus reductional and division into tetraspores cruciate.

STRUCTURE AND REPRODUCTION. Claussen, 1929. Kylin, 1928, pp. 54–56; fig. 33. Kylin, 1930, pp. 26–29; fig. 16. Rosenvinge, 1929.

With one species in the local flora.

Phyllophora Clevelandii Farlow   Pl. 63, fig. 5

Farlow, 1875, p. 368.

Thalli, as found on the Monterey Peninsula, up to 20 cm. tall; deep dull-red in color. The stipe-like portion sparingly branched, 1–2 mm. in diameter. The blades obovate to ovate-lanceolate, at times dichotomously forked at the apex; 5–10 cm. long and up to 2.5 cm. broad. Tetrasporic nemathecia oval to irregularly elongate, scattered over upper portion of blades.

LOCAL DISTRIBUTION. Occasionally found cast ashore at Moss Beach and at Carmel Beach.

TYPE LOCALITY. San Diego, California.

PACIFIC COAST DISTRIBUTION. Central California (Bolinas) to Baja California (20 miles south of Tia Juana).

Ahnfeltia Fries, 1835

Thalli erect, with numerous branches growing erect from a prostrate irregularly branched cylindrical rhizome. Erect branches cylindrical or somewhat compressed, repeatedly and dichotomously branched; at times with short proliferous branches. The branches wiry, rigid; with a medulla of narrow parallel longitudinal filaments and a cortex of sparingly branched, densely compacted, erect filaments.

Heterothallic. The spermatangia in small sori at surface of thallus. Carpogonia unknown. Cystocarps unknown, probably never formed. The fructification a conspicuous, pustule-like nemathecium whose thickness may equal the diameter of the branch bearing it. The nemathecium with a superficial layer of monospores. The nemathecia formerly considered members of a parasitic genus (*Sterrocolax*) belonging to the Florideae.

Tetrasporophytes unknown and probably absent from the life cycle.

STRUCTURE AND REPRODUCTION. Chemin, 1930. Gregory, 1934, pp. 539–549; figs. 11–25. Rosenvinge, 1931.

KEY TO THE SPECIES IN THE LOCAL FLORA

1. Branches less than 0.5 mm. in diameter...................*A. plicata*
1. Branches 0.5–1.0 mm. in diameter.................*A. gigartinoides*

Ahnfeltia plicata (Hudson) Fries   Pl. 64, figs. 2–3

Fries, 1835, p. 310. *Howe, 1893, p. 68. *Nott, 1897, p. 81. *Kylin, 1941, p. 26. Phyc. Bor.-Amer. No. 743.

Fucus plicatus Hudson, 1762, p. 470.

Sterrocolax decipiens Schmitz, 1893, p. 397. *Nott, 1897, p. 81. *Phyc. Bor.-Amer. No. 382.

Polyides rotundus Nott [not of (Gmelin) Greville]. *Nott in Phyc. Bor.-Amer. No. 382.

Thalli, as found on the Monterey Peninsula, usually 5–10 cm. tall, occasionally up to 15 cm.; deep reddish-purple to purplish-black in color. The thallus a dense, bushy, spherical mass in which the branches are more or less entangled. The branches cylindrical, 0.25–0.5 mm. in diameter, 5–10 times dichotomous, usually with an interval of 5–10 mm. between successive dichotomies. The two arms of a dichotomy often arcuate. Proliferous branches, when present, borne anywhere on branches; the proliferous branches short and not over twice dichotomous.

LOCAL DISTRIBUTION. Growing between the mean low-tide and −1.5-foot tide levels; usually growing half-buried in sand but at times on rocks free from sand. Point Aulon; Point Pinos; Middle Reef of Moss Beach; Fanshell Beach; Pebble Beach. Frequently found cast ashore at Moss Beach and at Carmel Beach.

TYPE LOCALITY. England.

PACIFIC COAST DISTRIBUTION. Alaska (St. Lawrence Island) to central California (Carmel Bay).

Ahnfeltia gigartinoides J. G. Agardh   Pl. 64, fig. 1

J. G. Agardh, 1847, p. 12. *Anderson, 1891, p. 223.

Ahnfeltia concinna J. G. Agardh, 1847, p. 12. Phyc. Bor.-Amer. No. 430.

Thalli, as found on the Monterey Peninsula, 10–30 cm. tall; deep red to purplish-black in color. The branches with successive dichotomies mostly in the same plane and the plant mass not a spherical clump. The branches cylindrical to subcylindrical, 0.5–1.0 mm. in diameter, 10–15 times dichotomous, usually with an interval of 15–30 mm. between successive dichotomies. The two arms of a dichotomy usually straight. Proliferous branches, when present, generally near base of erect branches; short and not over twice dichotomous.

LOCAL DISTRIBUTION. Growing on rocks between the 1.0- and −0.5-foot tide levels. Asilomar Point. Isolated individuals have been found cast ashore at Pacific Grove; Moss Beach; Fanshell Beach; Pebble.Beach. Also dredged from a depth of 12–15 feet near Point Aulon.

TYPE LOCALITY. St. Augustine, Mexico.

PACIFIC COAST DISTRIBUTION. British Columbia (Vancouver Island) to southern California (San Pedro).

Gymnogongrus Martius, 1833

Thalli usually with several erect branches from a common disc-shaped holdfast. The erect branches of a firm to horny texture, repeatedly dichotomous, with all dichotomies in the same plane or with the dichotomies variously twisted; at times with proliferous lateral branches. The branches cylindrical to the first or second dichotomy; above this markedly compressed. The medulla with large angular cells; the cortex with erect, sparsely branched, laterally compacted filaments.

Spermatangia uncertain. Carpogonial filaments two-celled, borne at inner face of cortex. Carpogonial thalli of certain species producing both cystocarps and tetrasporic nemathecia; those of other species producing only tetrasporic nemathecia. Development of cystocarp unknown. The mature cystocarp deeply embedded in thallus, globose, with the carposporangia in small masses separated from one another by remains of sterile cells.

The nemathecia developed from branched filaments (gonimoblasts?) growing toward thallus from supporting cell of a carpogonial filament. The filaments growing completely through the cortex and projecting beyond it in a palisade-like manner. Outermost cells of nemathecium developing into tetrasporangia; division of tetrasporangia irregularly zonate. The nemathecia formerly considered members of a parasitic genus (*Actinococcus*) belonging to the Florideae.

Tetrasporophytes unknown and probably absent from the life cycle.

STRUCTURE AND REPRODUCTION. Chemin, 1929. Chemin, 1933. Gregory, 1934, pp. 532–539; figs. 1–10.

KEY TO THE SPECIES IN THE LOCAL FLORA

1. Segments of branches less than 2 mm. broad...........*G. leptophyllus*
1. Segments of branches over 4 mm. broad........................ 2
  2. Segments less than 1 mm. in thickness.............*G. platyphyllus*
  2. Segments over 1 mm. in thickness.....................*G. linearis*

Gymnogongrus leptophyllus J. G. Agardh   Pl. 65, fig. 1

J. G. Agardh, 1876, p. 211. *Anderson, 1891, p. 223. *Kylin, 1941, p. 26. *Gymnogongrus Griffithsiae* Setchell [not of (Turner) Martius]. Setchell in Phyc. Bor.-Amer. No. 239*A*.

Thalli, as found on the Monterey Peninsula, forming dense hemispherical tufts up to 10 cm. in diameter; deep dull carmine in color. Branches of thallus curved, more or less entangled, 4–7 cm. long; with 5–8 dichotomies and with the interval between lower dichotomies about double that between the upper ones. The branches frequently with a few short lateral proliferous branchlets. The branches cylindrical or subcylindrical to the first or second dichotomy; above this markedly flattened. Uppermost dichotomies 0.75–1.25 mm. broad. Nemathecia inconspicuous. Cystocarps immersed in terminal segments, vertically ellipsoidal, up to 1.5 mm. long, bulging prominently toward both flattened faces of a segment.

LOCAL DISTRIBUTION. Growing on rocks between the 1.0- and −1.0-foot tide levels; usually accumulating sand between the branches. Asilomar Point; Middle Reef of Moss Beach; Fanshell Beach; Cypress Point; Pebble Beach.

TYPE LOCALITY. Santa Cruz, California.

PACIFIC COAST DISTRIBUTION. Central California (San Francisco) to southern California (San Diego).

Gymnogongrus linearis (Turner) J. G. Agardh   Pl. 65, fig. 3

J. G. Agardh, 1851, p. 325. Harvey, 1853, p. 167. *Anderson, 1891, p. 223
*Howe, 1893, p. 68. Phyc. Bor.-Amer. Nos. 238, 1496.
   Fucus linearis Turner, 1819, p. 59; pl. 220.
   Actinococcus latior Setchell [not of Schmitz]. Setchell, 1905, p. 59.

Thalli, as found on the Monterey Peninsula, in stands up to
40 cm. in diameter and with 50–150 erect branches attaining a
height of 10–18 cm.; light tan to brownish-purple in color. The
branches with 3–6 successive dichotomies, all lying in approximately the same plane. Portion below the first dichotomy 4–7 cm.
long and cylindrical except near the dichotomy. All dichotomies
above the first dichotomy markedly compressed, approximately
the same breadth throughout (5–8 mm.), elliptical in cross section
and over 1 mm. in thickness. Nemathecia abundant, 1–2 mm. in
diameter, bulging conspicuously from branch; produced on all but
the final dichotomies.

LOCAL DISTRIBUTION. Growing between the 1.5-foot tide level and
mean low tide on rocks partly buried in sand. Found only on rocks at ends
of long sandy beaches, but abundant at localities where it does occur. Asilomar end of Moss Beach; east end of Fanshell Beach; north end of
Carmel Beach.
   TYPE LOCALITY. Trinidad, California.
   PACIFIC COAST DISTRIBUTION. Southern Oregon (Coos Bay) to central California (San Luis Obispo County).

Gymnogongrus platyphyllus Gardner   Pl. 65, fig. 2

Gardner, 1927, p. 247; pl. 24, figs. 8–10; pl. 34.
   Gymnogongrus linearis Anderson [not of (Turner) J. G. Agardh]. Anderson in Algae Exsicc. Amer. Bor. No. 21. *Anderson, 1891, p. 223 (in part).

Thalli, as found on the Monterey Peninsula, with relatively
few erect branches from a common disc-shaped base and with the
branches 8–15 cm. tall; dull red to reddish-purple in color. The
branches with 3–5 successive dichotomies and at times with the
dichotomies twisted in various directions instead of all lying in
approximately the same plane. The branches cylindrical at extreme base but becoming markedly flattened some distance below
the first dichotomy. Portion below the first dichotomy 2–5 cm.
long. All dichotomies above the first approximately the same
breadth (4–6 mm.) and less than 1 mm. in thickness. Nemathecia
abundant, 2–3 mm. in diameter, circular to vertically elliptical,
produced on all but the final dichotomies.

LOCAL DISTRIBUTION. Isolated thalli have been found on the vertical face of rocks between the 0.5- and −1.0-foot tide levels at Point Pinos; Asilomar Point; Fanshell Beach; Pebble Beach.

TYPE LOCALITY. Bolinas, California.

PACIFIC COAST DISTRIBUTION. Central California (Bolinas) to Baja California (Ensenada).

G. platyphyllus resembles *G. linearis* but differs from the latter in that the branches are thinner and are markedly flattened a considerable distance below the first dichotomy. Differences between the two species are conspicuous when they are found growing in situ. In *G. linearis* there are frequently over a hundred erect branches from a common base and these branches are so rigid that they stand erect when exposed by recession of the tide. In *G. platyphyllus* there are relatively few branches from a common base, and when the tide is out the branches hang pendant from the rock on which the alga is growing.

Stenogramma Harvey, 1841

Thalli erect, with a small disc-shaped holdfast. Erect portion cylindrical at extreme base; above this, flattened, dichotomously branched into linear segments. Tips of ultimate dichotomies occasionally with proliferous blades. Sterile portion of segments with a medulla 1–3 cells in thickness and composed of large colorless cubical cells; the cortex 1–2 cells in thickness and composed of much smaller cubical cells.

Heterothallic. The spermatangia in large irregularly shaped sori on upper segments. Cystocarpic plants with axial linear sori superficially resembling an interrupted midrib; medulla and cortex adjacent to sori many cells in thickness. Carpogonial filaments three-celled and with a sterile one-celled filament from the lowermost cell. Supporting cell of carpogonial filament also bearing a sterile unbranched filament of 4–7 cells. The supporting cell functioning as the auxiliary cell and producing gonimoblast filaments on side toward the medulla. The gonimoblast filaments freely branched and with all cells developing into carposporangia. Mature cystocarps small, globose, deeply embedded in medulla, the overlying cortex without ostioles.

Tetrasporophytes with the tetrasporangia in small, irregularly shaped nemathecia scattered over upper segments. The nemathecia with the tetrasporangia in vertical rows of 5–10. The tetrasporangia cruciately divided.

STRUCTURE AND REPRODUCTION. Johnson, 1892. Kylin, 1928, pp. 52–54; figs. 31–32.

With one species in the local flora.

Stenogramma californica Harvey   Pl. 64, fig. 4; pl. 65, fig. 4

Harvey, 1841, p. 408. Kylin, 1925, p. 30.
Stenogramma interrupta Harvey [not of (C. A. Agardh) Montagne]. Harvey, 1853, p. 163; pl. 19, fig. C. *Anderson, 1891, p. 223. *Howe, 1893, p. 68. *Phyc. Bor.-Amer. No. 380.

Thalli, as found on the Monterey Peninsula, 10–15 cm. tall; deep red in color. Three to five times dichotomously branched and with tips of the ultimate dichotomies broadly rounded. The segments linear and 8–18 mm. broad.

LOCAL DISTRIBUTION. Growing between the 0.5- and −1.0-foot tide levels and either on rocks or in sand between rocks. Usually found only during spring and early summer. Regularly present on west side of Middle Reef of Moss Beach. Isolated thalli have been found at Pacific Grove; Asilomar Point; Cypress Point; Pebble Beach; north end of Carmel Beach; and Mission Point. Also dredged from a depth of 30–55 feet a quarter-mile from Municipal Wharf, Monterey, and from 20–25 feet near Point Aulon.

TYPE LOCALITY. San Francisco, California.

PACIFIC COAST DISTRIBUTION. Puget Sound (San Juan Island) to southern California (San Diego).

Family GIGARTINACEAE

Thalli usually erect; branched or unbranched; cylindrical, compressed or foliaceous. The thalli multiaxial; with a medulla of parallel longitudinal filaments and a cortex or erect branched filaments.

Carpogonial filament three-celled, its supporting cell without sterile·filaments. The supporting cell becoming the auxiliary cell and producing gonimoblast filaments on side toward thallus interior. Most cells of gonimoblast filaments eventually developing into carposporangia. Mature cystocarps globose, deeply embedded in thallus, and with or without a special enveloping tissue.

Tetrasporophytes with the tetrasporangia in globose masses adjacent to or embedded within the medulla. The tetrasporangia developing from innermost cortical cells or from special filaments borne on medullary filaments. The tetrasporangia cruciately divided.

Gigartina Stackhouse, 1809

Thalli with one or more shoots from a disc-shaped holdfast. The shoots cylindrical to foliaceous, undivided to dichotomously, irregularly, or pinnately divided. Surface of thallus sooner or later developing many small papillate or ligulate outgrowths. Multiaxial. The medulla composed of interwoven colorless filaments; the cortex composed of erect, laterally compacted, branching filaments with progressively smaller cells toward the surface. Fructifications generally restricted to outgrowths from surface of thallus.

Heterothallic. The spermatangia in irregular sori on surface of thallus. Carpogonial filaments three-celled, borne near base of cortical filaments and restricted to cortical filaments of outgrowths from surface of thallus. Supporting cell of carpogonial filament functioning as auxiliary cell and producing gonimoblast filaments only on side toward interior of thallus. The developing carposporophyte becoming invested by, and with some of the gonimoblast filaments penetrating into, an ensheathing nutritive zone of medullary filaments rich in food reserves. The cystocarp globose, with only the peripheral cells developing into carposporangia. The cystocarp bulging above surface of thallus and the overlying cortical tissue with an ostiole.

Tetrasporophytes with the tetrasporangia in globose masses at inner face of cortex. The tetrasporangia developing from the innermost cortical cells and cruciately divided.

STRUCTURE AND REPRODUCTION. Kylin, 1928, pp. 51–52; fig. 30. Sjöstedt, 1926, pp. 46–50; figs. 28–30.

Gigartina canaliculata Harvey   Pl. 69, fig. 3

Harvey, 1841, p. 409. *Harvey, 1853, p. 174; pl. 27, fig. *C*. *Anderson, 1891, p. 223. *Howe, 1893, p. 68. Setchell and Gardner, 1933, p. 264. *Kylin, 1941, p. 25. Phyc. Bor.-Amer. No. 1395.
Gelidium corniculatum Harvey, 1833, p. 164.

Thalli, as found on the Monterey Peninsula, up to 25 cm. tall; deep olive to olive-purple in color. With several erect shoots from a disc-shaped base. Erect shoots cylindrical, profusely branched in upper two-thirds and with the branches less than 2 mm. in diameter. The branching distichous, irregular in lower portion, regularly pinnate in upper portion. Thalli usually not developing pinnules until fully grown. The pinnules more or less thorn-like, borne singly or in clusters near the tips of branchlets in the pinnately branched portion. Cystocarps large and usually borne singly near base of a pinnule.

LOCAL DISTRIBUTION. Growing on rocks between the 2.0- and −1.0-foot tide levels. Widespread and abundant over the entire Monterey Peninsula.

TYPE LOCALITY. San Francisco, California.

PACIFIC COAST DISTRIBUTION. Southern Oregon (Coos Bay) to Baja California (Ensenada).

Gigartina leptorhynchos J. G. Agardh — Pl. 70, fig. 3

J. G. Agardh, 1885, p. 28. Setchell and Gardner, 1933, p. 267; pl. 46.
Gigartina microphylla var. *horrida* Farlow, 1875, p. 370.
Gigartina horrida Farlow apud *Anderson, 1891, p. 223. *Howe, 1893, p. 68.
Phyc. Bor.-Amer. No. 137.

Thalli, as found on the Monterey Peninsula, up to 20 cm. tall; dark reddish-brown in color. With one or more erect shoots from a disc-shaped holdfast. The shoots profusely and irregularly branched. The major branches somewhat flattened, up to 8 mm. broad, with many long or short cylindrical proliferous branches. Major and proliferous branches with pinnules on flattened faces and lateral margins. The pinnules cylindrical, branched, up to 6 mm. long, the branches so densely crowded with pinnules that the entire surface is bristly.

LOCAL DISTRIBUTION. Growing on rocks between the 1.5-foot and mean low-tide levels. Abundant everywhere.
TYPE LOCALITY. Santa Barbara, California.
PACIFIC COAST DISTRIBUTION. Central California (Santa Cruz) to Baja California (Ensenada).

Gigartina Boryi Setchell and Gardner — Pl. 68, fig. 1

Setchell and Gardner, 1933, p. 268; pls. 48–49.

Thalli, as found on the Monterey Peninsula, up to 55 cm. tall; rose-red to dark red in color. With one or more blades from a disc-shaped holdfast. The blades stipitate in lower portion, the stipe gradually broadening in upper part and at times once or twice dichotomous in upper portion. Upper end of stipe, or of each dichotomy, continued in a long (not over 6 cm. broad) blade that is gradually attenuated at apex. Lateral margins of blade with numerous, oblanceolate, proliferous, blade-like outgrowths; the outgrowths at times large and making the blade appear as if pinnately divided. Flattened faces and margins of blade with numerous fertile pinnules; the blades frequently with an intramarginal zone destitute of pinnules. The pinnules spindle-shaped, with a length several times the breadth.

LOCAL DISTRIBUTION. Growing on rocks between the 1.0- and −0.5-foot tide levels. Mussel Point; Cypress Point; Pebble Beach. Also dredged from a depth of 12–15 feet near Point Aulon.
TYPE LOCALITY. Pacific Grove, California.
PACIFIC COAST DISTRIBUTION. Central California (Pacific Grove) to southern California (San Diego).

Gigartina spinosa (Kützing) Harvey   Pl. 68, fig. 2

Harvey, 1853, p. 177; pl. 28, fig. *B.* *Anderson, 1891, p. 223. *Howe, 1893, p. 68. *Setchell and Gardner, 1933, p. 271. *Kylin, 1941, p. 25. *Phyc. Bor.-Amer. No. XX.
   Mastocarpus spinosus Kützing, 1847, p. 24.

Thalli, as found on the Monterey Peninsula, up to 40 cm. tall; greenish-purple to brownish-red in color. With one or more blades from a disc-shaped holdfast. Lowermost 2–4 cm. cylindrical and stipe-like; above this gradually broadening into a thick blade 3–8 cm. broad. The blades frequently dichotomously divided either in apical portion or in portion above stipe. Blades, or segments of blades, broadly lanceolate to narrowly obcuneate; with many marginal proliferous bladelets some of which may approach the size of the blade. Blades with large proliferous bladelets frequently appearing as if pinnately divided. Fertile pinnules on margins and flattened faces of blade; cylindrical, acutely pointed, simple or forked, up to 5 mm. long; with cystocarps in the middle or toward the tip.

LOCAL DISTRIBUTION. Growing between the mean low-tide and −1.5-foot tide levels on rocks more or less directly exposed to strong surf. Abundant on all rocky headlands.

TYPE LOCALITY. Monterey, California.

PACIFIC COAST DISTRIBUTION. Central California (Monterey) to southern California (La Jolla).

Gigartina californica J. G. Agardh   Pl. 67, fig. 1

J. G. Agardh, 1899, p. 39. *Setchell and Gardner, 1933, p. 272; pl. 52. *Kylin, 1941, p. 25.

Thalli, as found on the Monterey Peninsula, up to 70 cm. tall; usually of a dark red color. With one or more blades from a disc-shaped holdfast. The blades obovate-lanceolate; simple or with a single broad forking at the apex; base of blade stipe-like and this portion at times once or twice dichotomous and with each dichotomy terminating in a blade. Basal portion of a blade cuneate and gradually broadening upward; apical portion of blade rounded but tapering to an acute point. Margins of blade usually without proliferous bladelets. Fertile pinnules on margins and on flattened faces of blade; lacking on cuneate basal portion. Cystocarpic pinnules short, verrucose, acutely pointed, generally with one cystocarp.

LOCAL DISTRIBUTION. Growing between the mean low-tide and −1.5-foot tide levels on rocks more or less directly exposed to surf. Abundant on all rocky headlands.

TYPE LOCALITY. Santa Cruz, California.

PACIFIC COAST DISTRIBUTION. Central California (Bolinas to Carmel Bay).

Until quite recently phycologists have confused this species and *G. corymbifera* with *G. radula,* a species not found on the Pacific Coast of North America. *G. californica* may be distinguished from *G. corymbifera* by the pointed instead of broadly rounded blade apices. Most specimens of *G. californica* also have blades thinner than those of *G. corymbifera.*

Gigartina corymbifera (Kützing) J. G. Agardh Pl. 66

J. G. Agardh, 1876, p. 202. *Setchell and Gardner, 1933, p. 275; pls. 53–54. *Kylin, 1941, p. 25.

Mastocarpus corymbiferus *Kützing, 1847, p. 24.

Iridaea papillata Harvey [not of (C. A. Agardh) Greville]. *Harvey, 1833, p. 165. Harvey, 1841, p. 409.

Iridaea radula Harvey [not of (Esper) Greville]. *Harvey, 1841, p. 409.

Gigartina radula Harvey [not of (Esper) J. G. Agardh]. *Harvey, 1853, p. 178. *Anderson, 1891, p. 223. *Howe, 1893, p. 68.

Gigartina radula forma *exasperata* *Setchell in Phyc. Bor.-Amer. No. XVIII.

Thalli, as found on the Monterey Peninsula, up to 50 cm. tall; yellowish-red to wine-red in color. With one or more blades from a disc-shaped holdfast. The blades simple, broadly obovate, with a broadly rounded apex. Base of blade stipe-like, above this broadening gradually for a short distance and then broadening abruptly. Length of blade 1.5–3 times breadth of widest portion. Fertile pinnules on margins and both flattened faces but frequently lacking on an intramarginal zone; the pinnules either short and blunt; or long, acutely pointed, branched or unbranched cylinders. Cystocarpic pinnules generally with three or more cystocarps.

LOCAL DISTRIBUTION. Growing between the mean low-tide and −1.5-foot tide levels on rocks more or less directly exposed to surf. Abundant on all rocky headlands. Also dredged from a depth of 20–25 feet near Mussel Point and at Stillwater Cove.

TYPE LOCALITY. Monterey, California (presumably).

PACIFIC COAST DISTRIBUTION. Central California (Fort Ross) to southern California (San Diego).

Gigartina Harveyana (Kützing) Setchell and Gardner

Pl. 67, fig. 2

Setchell and Gardner, 1933, p. 276. *Kylin, 1941, p. 25.
Mastocarpus Harveyanus *Kützing, 1849, p. 734.
Rhodymenia ciliata var. *microphylla* Harvey, 1833, p. 164.
Gigartina microphylla *Harvey, 1853, p. 176; pl. 28, fig. *A*. *Anderson, 1891,
p. 223. *Howe, 1893, p. 68.
Gigartina radula forma *microphylla* (Harvey) *Setchell in Phyc. Bor.-Amer.
No. XIX.

Thalli, as found on the Monterey Peninsula, up to 90 cm.
tall; brownish-red to rose-red in color. With one or more blades
from a disc-shaped holdfast. The blades simple, linear-lanceolate, 2–8 cm. broad, very gradually attenuated to a sharp point
at the apex. Base of blade stipe-like and the stipitate portion at
times once or twice dichotomous and each dichotomy terminating
in a blade. Margins of blades frequently with many small proliferous bladelets but these rarely becoming more than 2 cm. long.
Fertile pinnules on margins and flattened faces of blade, frequently
lacking on an intramarginal zone; the pinnules short, cylindrical,
acutely pointed.

LOCAL DISTRIBUTION. Growing between the 1.0- and −1.5-foot tide
levels on rocks more or less covered with sand. Very abundant in sandy
coves. Also dredged from a depth of 25 feet near Point Aulon.

TYPE LOCALITY. Monterey, California.

PACIFIC COAST DISTRIBUTION. Central California (Santa Cruz) to
southern California (San Diego).

This species is found chiefly in quiet sandy coves. Here it
grows in great abundance and usually with the base buried in
sand. The blades are thinner than those of other species with
large undivided blades.

Gigartina volans (C. A. Agardh) J. G. Agardh   Pl. 70, fig. 1

J. G. Agardh apud C. A. Agardh, 1846; pl. 18. *Anderson, 1891, p. 223.
*Howe, 1893, p. 68. *Setchell and Gardner, 1933, p. 279; pls. 56–57. Phyc. Bor.-
Amer. No. XXI.
Sphaerococcus volans C. A. Agardh, 1821; pl. 18.
Gigartina velifera J. G. Agardh, 1899, p. 41. *Setchell and Gardner, 1933,
p. 280; pl. 58.

Thalli, as found on the Monterey Peninsula, up to 40 cm. tall;
usually purplish-brown in color. With one or more blades from
a disc-shaped holdfast. The blades stipitate; the stipe either short
(4–8 cm.) or long (up to 20 cm.); apex of stipe frequently dichotomously branched and each dichotomy terminating in a blade.

Base of stipe cylindrical, upper half flattened and narrowly ob-ovate, above this narrowly cylindrical just below the blade. The blades ligulate, 10–25 cm. long, 3–8 cm. broad, with a broadly cuneate to broadly rounded base, the apex rather abruptly nar-rowed to an acute or rounded tip. Lateral margins of blade and stipe with many small proliferous bladelets. Fertile pinnules markedly flattened and borne on flattened faces of blade. All fer-tile pinnules spermatangial or cystocarpic. Tetrasporangial sori borne immersed in blade, not in pinnules.

LOCAL DISTRIBUTION. Growing on rocks between the 1.5- and —0.5-foot tide levels. Point Aulon; Middle Reef of Moss Beach; Fanshell Beach; Pescadero Point; north end of Carmel Beach; Mission Point; mouth of Carmel River.

TYPE LOCALITY. Listed as Cape of Good Hope, South Africa, in the original description, but now thought to be somewhere along the coast of California.

PACIFIC COAST DISTRIBUTION. Southern Oregon (Coos Bay) to south-ern California (La Jolla).

Gigartina papillata (C. A. Agardh) J. G. Agardh   Pl. 70, fig. 2

J. G. Agardh apud C. A. Agardh, 1846; pl. 19. *Anderson, 1891, p. 223. *Howe, 1893, p. 68. Setchell and Gardner, 1933, p. 287; pl. 61.
Sphaerococcus papillatus C. A. Agardh, 1821; pl. 19.
Gigartina papillata var. *subsimplex* Setchell in Phyc. Bor.-Amer. No. 425.

Thalli, as found on the Monterey Peninsula, up to 15 cm. tall; dull brownish-red in color. With one or more blades from a disc-shaped holdfast. The blades dichotomously divided and with rela-tively broad more or less cuneate segments; margins of segments without a ridge and usually without proliferous bladelets. Pin-nules restricted to flattened faces of blade; short, blunt, usually with a single cystocarp.

LOCAL DISTRIBUTION. Growing on rocks between the 3.5- and 1.0-foot tide levels. Abundant everywhere.

TYPE LOCALITY. Listed as Ouaihee (Hawaii) in the original descrip-tion, but now thought to be somewhere along the coast of California.

PACIFIC COAST DISTRIBUTION. Central California (Tomales Bay to Carmel Bay).

Gigartina cristata (Setchell) Setchell and Gardner   Pl. 69, fig. 1

*Setchell and Gardner, 1933, p. 289; pl. 63. *Kylin, 1941, p. 26.
Gigartina papillata forma *cristata* *Setchell in Phyc. Bor.-Amer. No. 426.

Thalli, as found on the Monterey Peninsula, up to 18 cm. tall; dark reddish-brown in color. With one or more blades from a disc-shaped holdfast. The blades 3–5 times dichotomously divided, the segments sublinear, 6–15 mm. broad, the ultimate segments usually with acute tips. Lateral margins of segments with a thickened ridge and with numerous small proliferous lanceolate to cuneate bladelets which frequently arise just within the thickened margin. Surface of blade at first smooth, later becoming covered with irregularly globose papillae.

LOCAL DISTRIBUTION. Growing on rocks between the 2.0-foot and mean low-tide levels. Arch Rock; Point Pinos; Asilomar Point; Middle Reef of Moss Beach; Point Joe; Fanshell Beach; Cypress Point; north end of Carmel Beach.

TYPE LOCALITY. Point Joe, Pacific Grove, California.

PACIFIC COAST DISTRIBUTION. Central Washington (Westport) to central California (Point Sur).

Setchell and Gardner (1933, pl. 63) give a photograph of the type of this species, but this is not characteristic of a majority of the specimens in the University of California herbarium, which they have determined as *G. cristata*. The most distinctive feature of the species is the thickened, selvage-like margin of the segments.

Gigartina Agardhii Setchell and Gardner   Pl. 69, fig. 2

Setchell and Gardner, 1933, p. 290; pl. 64. *Kylin, 1941, p. 26.
Gigartina papillata forma *dissecta* *Setchell in Phyc. Bor.-Amer. No. 427.

Thalli, as found on the Monterey Peninsula, up to 15 cm. tall; dark reddish-brown in color. With one or more blades from a disc-shaped holdfast. The blades 3–5 times dichotomously divided into linear segments 2–5 mm. broad, the ultimate segments usually acutely pointed at tips. Lateral margins of segments lacking a thickened ridge and usually without proliferous bladelets. Fertile pinnules restricted to flattened faces of segments, acutely pointed, at times bifurcate and somewhat flattened.

LOCAL DISTRIBUTION. Growing on rocks between the 3.5- and 1.0-foot tide levels. Abundant everywhere.

TYPE LOCALITY. Point Joe, Pacific Grove, California.

PACIFIC COAST DISTRIBUTION. Central California (Fort Ross) to southern California (Laguna).

Rhodoglossum J. G. Agardh, 1876

Thalli with one or more blades growing erect from a disc-shaped holdfast. The blades sessile or stipitate; simple or dichotomously divided into many segments. Multiaxial. The medulla composed of interwoven colorless longitudinal filaments;

the cortex composed of laterally adjoined, erect, branching filaments with progressively smaller cells to the thallus surface.

Heterothallic. The spermatangia in extensive sori on flattened faces of the blade. Carpogonial filaments 3-celled, borne
near the base of cortical filaments. Supporting cell of the carpogonial filament functioning as the auxiliary cell and producing
gonimoblast filaments only on side toward interior of thallus.
Gonimoblast filaments with many short lateral branches in which
each cell develops into a carposporangium. The mature cystocarp
globose, deeply embedded in blade, surrounded by a nutritive
layer of medullary cells.

Tetrasporophytes with the tetrasporangia in compressed globose masses at juncture of cortex and medulla. The tetrasporangia developing from the innermost cortical cells and cruciately
divided.

STRUCTURE AND REPRODUCTION. Kylin, 1928, pp. 49–52; figs. 28–29.

KEY TO THE SPECIES IN THE LOCAL FLORA

1. Blades simple... 2
1. Blades dichotomously divided................................. 3
   2. Blades linear...................................*R. americanum*
   2. Blades elliptical to subcordate.........................*R. roseum*
3. Blades one to three times dichotomous..................*R. parvum*
3. Blades several times dichotomous..........................*R. affine*

Rhodoglossum americanum Kylin   Pl. 71, fig. 1

*Kylin, 1941, p. 24; pl. 9, fig. 23.
Rhodoglossum polycarpum Setchell [not of J. G. Agardh]. *Setchell in
Phyc. Bor.-Amer. No. 538.

Thalli, as found on the Monterey Peninsula, generally 25–40
cm. tall but occasionally up to 70 cm.; light to deep rose-red in
color. With one or more blades from a small disc-shaped holdfast. The blades with a short cylindrical stipe 1–2 cm. long; the
stipe at times with a single dichotomy and each arm terminating
in a blade. The blades linear-lanceolate, 5–10 cm. broad when
mature, with the upper end gradually tapering to an acute or to
a rounded tip. Blades of cystocarpic thalli usually entire; those
of tetrasporic thalli frequently with a deep longitudinal incision
at the apex. Margins of blades but slightly ruffled; occasionally
with proliferous outgrowths near the base.

LOCAL DISTRIBUTION. Growing on rocks between the 2.0- and 0.5-
foot tide levels in sheltered coves. Very abundant at Pebble Beach. Also

collected at Point Pinos; Asilomar Point; Middle Reef of Moss Beach; Fanshell Beach; Mission Point.

TYPE LOCALITY. Pebble Beach, Carmel Bay, California.

PACIFIC COAST DISTRIBUTION. Central California (Bolinas to Carmel Bay).

Rhodoglossum roseum (Kylin) G. M. Smith   Pl. 71, fig. 3

*G. M. Smith apud Smith and Hollenberg, 1943, p. 216; fig. 17.

Iridaea rosea *Kylin, 1941, p. 24; pl. 9, fig. 22.

Thalli, as found on the Monterey Peninsula, 8–15 cm. tall but occasionally up to 20 cm.; deep rose-red to purplish-red in color. With one or more blades from a disc-shaped holdfast. Stipe of blade cylindrical, 2–3 mm. long, not dichotomously divided at apex. The blades 5–8 cm. broad, simple, elliptical to subcordate, broadly rounded at apex, with somewhat ruffled margins. Cystocarps 0.5–1 mm. in diameter; tetrasporangial sori compressed, up to 0.5 mm. broad.

LOCAL DISTRIBUTION. Growing on the tops of rounded boulders between the mean low-tide and −1.5-foot tide levels. Restricted to boulders exposed to strong surf and usually growing intermingled with *Ulva*. Pacific Grove; Arch Rock; Asilomar Point; Point Joe; Fanshell Beach; Cypress Point; Pescadero Point; Mission Point.

TYPE LOCALITY. Pacific Grove, California.

PACIFIC COAST DISTRIBUTION. As above.

Rhodoglossum parvum G. M. Smith and Hollenberg

Pl. 70, figs. 4–5

*Smith and Hollenberg, 1943, p. 216; figs. 15–16.

Thalli, as found on the Monterey Peninsula, 3–6 cm. tall; brownish-red in color. With one or more blades from a disc-shaped holdfast. The blades with a cylindrical stipe 8–12 mm. long; upper portion of stipe gradually broadening into the once to thrice dichotomously divided cuneate blade in which all segments are flattened and lie in the same plane. Ultimate segments of blade 0.5–2.0 cm. broad and with broadly rounded tips. Cystocarps about 0.5 mm. in diameter. Tetrasporangial sori flattened, about 0.5 mm. broad.

LOCAL DISTRIBUTION. Growing on rocks at mean low-tide level. Cypress Point.

TYPE LOCALITY. As above.

PACIFIC COAST DISTRIBUTION. As above.

Differing from *R. affine* in the proportionally longer stipe, smaller amount of dissection of blades, and in the lack of curvature of blade segments.

Rhodoglossum affine (Harvey) Kylin Pl. 71, fig. 2

Kylin, 1928, p. 49. *Kylin, 1941, p. 24.
Chondrus affinis *Harvey, 1841, p. 408. *Harvey, 1853, p. 181. *Anderson, 1891, p. 223. *Phyc. Bor.-Amer. No. 424.
Chondrus canaliculatus Farlow [not of Greville]. Farlow, 1876, p. 701. *Anderson, 1891, p. 223. *Howe, 1893, p. 68.

Thalli, as found on the Monterey Peninsula, 5–15 cm. tall; greenish-olive to reddish-purple in color. Usually with several blades from a common disc-shaped holdfast. The blade with a very short cylindrical stipe; above this more or less broadly cuneate and repeatedly dichotomous. Segments of blade linear, narrow or broad, usually concave on one side and convex on the other. Apices of ultimate segments acute to obtuse. Margins of basal segments at times with small proliferous bladelets. Cystocarps 1–2.5 mm. in diameter.

LOCAL DISTRIBUTION. Growing on vertical face of rocks between the 2.0-foot and mean low-tide levels. Abundant at Point Pinos; Asilomar Point; Point Joe; Fanshell Beach; Cypress Point; Arrowhead Point; Mission Point.

TYPE LOCALITY. Monterey, California.

PACIFIC COAST DISTRIBUTION. Central California (Santa Cruz) to southern California (La Jolla).

Iridophycus Setchell and Gardner, 1936

Thalli with one or more blades growing erect from a disc-shaped holdfast. The blades with a short cylindrical stipe; the apophysis (the transition region from stipe to blade) flattened, simple or dichotomously divided, smooth or with variously shaped outgrowths from lateral margins. The blades broad or narrow, simple or deeply cleft, usually with an acute apex and a rounded base; markedly iridescent when submerged. Multiaxial. Medulla composed of interwoven colorless longitudinal filaments; the cortex composed of laterally adjoined, erect, branching filaments with progressively smaller cells to the thallus surface.

Heterothallic. The spermatangia in extensive sori on flattened faces of blade. Carpogonial filaments three-celled, borne near the base of cortical filaments. Supporting cell of the carpogonial filament functioning as the auxiliary cell and producing gonimoblast filaments only on side toward interior of thallus. The gonimoblast filaments with many short lateral branches in which each cell develops into a carposporangium. The mature cystocarp globose, deeply embedded in blade, surrounded by a nutritive layer of medullary cells; the cortical tissue external to the cysto-carp with an ostiole.

The tetrasporophytes with the tetrasporangia developing from cells of special filaments borne upon the medullary filaments. The mature tetrasporangia lying in globose masses embedded in the medulla. The tetrasporangia cruciately divided.

STRUCTURE AND REPRODUCTION. Kylin, 1928, pp. 45–49; figs. 25–27. G. M. Smith, 1938, pp. 334–336; figs. 183–184. (Both as *Iridaea*.)

KEY TO THE SPECIES IN THE LOCAL FLORA

1. Blades usually irregularly and deeply cleft into
     a number of segments ....*I. heterocarpum*
1. Blades usually simple but sometimes divided into 2–4 segments...... 2
     2. Blades spirally twisted...............................*I. lineare*
     2. Blades not spirally twisted................................. 3
3. Color of blade blood-red...........................*I. sanguineum*
3. Color of blade not blood-red................................... 4
     4. Blades 1–1.5 mm. in thickness, leathery in texture.....*I. coriaceum*
     4. Blades less than 0.75 mm. in thickness, not leathery in texture.... 5
5. Color of blade usually greenish........................*I. flaccidum*
5. Color of blade usually purplish........................*I. splendens*

Iridophycus flaccidum Setchell and Gardner   Pl. 72, fig. 2

*Setchell and Gardner, 1937, p. 171.
     Iridaea minor J. G. Agardh [not of Endlicher]. J. G. Agardh, 1849, p. 86.
     Iridaea laminarioides Harvey [not of Bory]. *Harvey, 1853, p. 179. *Anderson, 1891, p. 223. *Howe, 1893, p. 68.
     Iridophycus Agardhianum *Setchell and Gardner, 1937, p. 170.
     Iridaea Agardhianum (Setchell and Gardner) Kylin, 1941, p. 23; pl. 8, fig. 21.
     Iridaea cordata Kylin [not of (Turner) Bory]. *Kylin, 1941, p. 22.

Thalli, as found on the Monterey Peninsula, usually 30–60 cm. tall but occasionally up to 120 cm.; greenish-olive if growing in the midlittoral, deep purple if growing in lower littoral. Usually with several blades from a disc-shaped holdfast. Stipe of blade relatively short, the apophysis narrowly cuneate. The blades ovate-lanceolate, with apex gradually tapering to a point, length of blade 3–6 times the maximum breadth; usually entire but occasionally with one or two longitudinal incisions halfway from apex to base; margins of blades more or less ruffled. The blades less than .5 mm. in thickness; relatively soft in texture. Cysto-carps very numerous, rarely over 1 mm. in diameter.

LOCAL DISTRIBUTION. Abundant everywhere on rocks in the mid-littoral zone. Also found between the 0.5- and —0.5-foot tide levels at Point Pinos; Pebble Beach; Arrowhead Point.

TYPE LOCALITY. Carmel, California.

PACIFIC COAST DISTRIBUTION. Northern California (Crescent City) to central California (Point Sur).

This is the abundant greenish-colored *Iridophycus* of the mid-littoral; thalli growing in the lower littoral have purple blades. Herbarium specimens from both the mid-littoral and lower littoral have blades that are a deep purple near the base and of a lighter color above. This affords a means of distinguishing between herbarium specimens of *I. flaccidum* and *I. splendens* because blades of the latter are of a uniform purple color.

Kylin (1941; pl. 8, fig. 21) has published a photograph of the type of *I. Agardhianum*. This seems to be nothing more than a juvenile specimen of *I. flaccidum*.

Iridophycus splendens Setchell and Gardner   Pl. 72, fig. 1

*Setchell and Gardner, 1937, p. 170.

Thalli, as found on the Monterey Peninsula, 80–120 cm. tall; of a rich purple color. Usually with several blades from a disc-shaped holdfast. Stipe of blade not over 1 cm. long; the apophysis broadly cuneate. The blades lanceolate, with a broadly rounded base and a gradually tapering apex; margins of blades more or less amply ruffled. The blades usually entire but sometimes deeply incised into 2–4 lobes. The length frequently 10 or more times the maximum breadth. Thickness of blades 0.5–0.7 mm.

LOCAL DISTRIBUTION. Growing between the 1.0- and —1.0-foot tide levels on rocks somewhat sheltered from the surf. Middle Reef of Moss Beach; Cypress Point; Pebble Beach; first point north of Carmel Beach.

TYPE LOCALITY. First point north of Carmel Beach, Carmel, California.

PACIFIC COAST DISTRIBUTION. Oregon (Cape Kiawandi) to southern California.

Living specimens may be confused with low-littoral specimens of *I. flaccidum,* but herbarium specimens are distinguishable because of their uniform color.

Iridophycus sanguineum Setchell and Gardner

Setchell and Gardner, 1937, p. 172.

Thalli with blades up to 40 cm. long and 20 cm. broad; blood-red in color. The blades ovate, usually entire, and with a cuneate base.

LOCAL DISTRIBUTION. Known locally only from a single specimen N. L. Gardner found cast ashore at Pacific Grove.

TYPE LOCALITY. Duxbury Reef, Bolinas, California.

PACIFIC COAST DISTRIBUTION. Southern Oregon (Cape Arago) to central California (Pacific Grove).

This imperfectly known species is known only from specimens cast ashore, apparently from the sublittoral. Its blood-red color is the most striking macroscopic character. The maximum breadth of medullary filaments (25 µ) is nearly double the maximum breadth of medullary filaments of *I. flaccidum* and *I. splendens*.

Iridophycus coriaceum Setchell and Gardner   Pl. 71, fig. 4

*Setchell and Gardner, 1937, p. 170.

Thalli, as found on the Monterey Peninsula, up to 125 cm. tall; reddish-brown in color. Usually with several blades from a disc-shaped holdfast. The stipes fairly conspicuous, up to 2 cm. long; the apophysis narrowly cuneate, up to 5 cm. long. The blades ovate, usually entire but sometimes deeply incised into 2–4 segments, with an acute apex, the margins not ruffled. The blades leathery in texture, 1.0–1.4 mm. in thickness. The cystocarps inconspicuous, not bulging above surface of blade, 1.0–1.5 mm. in diameter.

LOCAL DISTRIBUTION. Growing between the 1.0- and −1.0-foot tide levels on rocks exposed to strong surf. Mussel Point; Arch Rock; Point Pinos; Asilomar Point; Middle Reef of Moss Beach; Cypress Point; Pebble Beach; first point north of Carmel Beach.

TYPE LOCALITY. First point north of Carmel Beach, Carmel, California.

PACIFIC COAST DISTRIBUTION. Northern Washington (Neah Bay) to central California (Carmel Bay).

Differing from other local species in the much thicker blades. The blades of dried herbarium specimens are horny in texture.

Iridophycus lineare Setchell and Gardner   Pl. 72, fig. 3

*Setchell and Gardner, 1937, p. 171.

Iridaea dichotoma Anderson [not of Hooker and Harvey]. *Anderson, 1891, p. 223. *Howe, 1893, p. 68.

Iridaea lineare (Setchell and Gardner) *Kylin, 1941, p. 23.

Thalli, as found on the Monterey Peninsula, usually 40–60 cm. tall but occasionally up to 1 m.; brownish-red to reddish-purple in color. Regularly with several blades from a disc-shaped holdfast. Stipe of blade conspicuous, 2–5 cm. long; the apophysis very narrowly cuneate, up to 5 cm. long, frequently with a single dichotomy at the apex and each arm terminating in a blade. The blades linear-lanceolate, 3.5–7 cm. broad, spirally twisted and with amply ruffled margins. Thickness of blades 0.5–7.5 mm. Cystocarps densely crowded, inconspicuous, less than 1 mm. in diameter.

LOCAL DISTRIBUTION. Growing between the 1.0- and −1.0-foot tide levels on rocks exposed to heavy surf. Mussel Point; Point Pinos; Asilomar Point; Point Joe; Cypress Point; Arrowhead Point; first point north of Carmel Beach; Mission Point; mouth of Carmel River.

TYPE LOCALITY. First point north of Carmel Beach, Carmel, California.

PACIFIC COAST DISTRIBUTION. Oregon (Sunset Bay) to southern California (Ventura).

The spiral twisting of the blades, so characteristic of living plants, is not usually evident in herbarium specimens. Both living and dried specimens are easily distinguishable because of the long, narrow blades and the long stipes.

Iridophycus heterocarpum (Postels and Ruprecht) Setchell and Gardner   Pl. 73, fig. 3

Setchell and Gardner, 1937, p. 170.
Iridaea heterocarpum Postels and Ruprecht, 1840, p. 18. *Kylin, 1941, p. 23.

Thalli, as found on the Monterey Peninsula, usually 10–15 cm. tall but at times up to 30 cm.; reddish-brown in color. Frequently with a single blade from the disc-shaped holdfast. The stipe very short; the apophysis broadly cuneate. The blades cuneate in outline, usually broader than tall; irregularly cleft into a number of segments, the depth of the incision variable and sometimes extending down to the apophysis. The segments ovate-lanceolate, with acutely pointed tips. Thickness of blades 0.5–7.5 mm. Cystocarps large, up to 3 mm. in diameter but variable in size, bulging prominently above surface of blade.

LOCAL DISTRIBUTION. Growing between the 2.0-foot tide and mean low-tide levels on rocks exposed to considerable surf. Point Pinos; Asilomar Point; Point Joe; Fanshell Beach; Cypress Point; Pebble Beach; Arrowhead Point; Mission Point.

TYPE LOCALITY. "North Pacific Ocean."

PACIFIC COAST DISTRIBUTION. British Columbia (Vancouver Island) to central California (Point Sur).

This is the only species in the local flora in which the blades are always divided and in which the cystocarps are over 2 mm. in diameter.

Erythrophyllum J. G. Agardh, 1871

Thalli with one or more blades growing erect from a disc-shaped holdfast. The blades with a conspicuous percurrent midrib and with the lower portion becoming stipe-like through abrasion of portions lateral to the midrib. The blades simple or branched from the margin, with conspicuous or inconspicuous forked veins diagonal to the midrib; old blades usually with portion lateral to the midrib diagonally lacerated. Multiaxial. The medulla composed of colorless longitudinal filaments; the cortex with rounded cells that are progressively smaller to the thallus surface. Fructifications restricted to papillate outgrowths from surface of blade.

Spermatangia unknown. The carpogonial filaments borne at inner face of the cortex. The gonimoblast filaments growing toward the medulla of the fertile papillate outgrowths and with many of the cells eventually developing into carposporangia. Mature cystocarps embedded in medulla of fertile papillae and consisting of intermingled carposporangia and sterile filaments.

Tetrasporophytes with the tetrasporangia remote from one another and embedded just beneath surface of fertile papillae. The tetrasporangia cruciately divided.

Structure and Reproduction. Twiss, 1911.

Erythrophyllum delesserioides J. G. Agardh   Pl. 73, fig. 4

J. G. Agardh, 1872, p. 11. *Anderson, 1891, p. 224. *Howe, 1893, p. 68. *Kylin, 1941, p. 17. *Phyc. Bor.-Amer. Nos. 50, 588.

Erythrophyllum Gunningii *Anderson, 1891, p. 224 (name only).

Thalli, as found on the Monterey Peninsula, usually 30–35 cm. tall but occasionally up to 50 cm.; deep purplish-red in color. The blades lanceolate, 6–14 cm. broad; the percurrent midrib always conspicuous, the veins conspicuous or inconspicuous. Older blades always lacerated and branched. Fruiting papillae usually not developing until late in the autumn, densely aggregated on the midrib and on persistent portion of blade lateral to midrib. In midwinter the blades usually with all parts eroded away except the midrib.

Local Distribution. Growing between the mean low-tide and −1.5-foot tide levels on rocks exposed to heavy surf. Present on every rocky headland but especially abundant at Point Pinos; Point Joe; Cypress Point; Pescadero Point; and Mission Point.

Type Locality. Vancouver Island, British Columbia.

Pacific Coast Distribution. Alaska (Departure Bay) to central California (San Luis Obispo County).

Besa Setchell, 1912

Thalli prostrate, crustose, many cells in thickness and indefinitely expanded. Uncalcified and with a horizontal layer of cells bearing erect filaments. The erect filaments laterally adjoined and compacted into a parenchymatous tissue.

Spermatangia unknown. Carpogonial filaments and gonimoblast filaments unknown. The mature cystocarps deeply embedded within conspicuous papillate outgrowths standing above upper surface of thallus. The cystocarps globose and with the carposporangia in groups intermingled with sterile cells.

Tetrasporophytes unknown.

STRUCTURE AND REPRODUCTION. Gardner, 1917, pp. 395–396. Setchell, 1912, pp. 236–238; pl. 25, figs. 5–6.

The validity of this genus is open to question because there is a possibility that it may be the cystocarpic generation of *Hildenbrandia,* a genus well known to phycologists but one in which only the tetrasporic generation has been found. *Besa* has been placed in the Gigartinaceae because the cystocarps lie within papillae resembling those of *Gigartina.*

Besa papillaeformis Setchell

Setchell, 1912, p. 237; pl. 25, figs. 5–6. *Gardner, 1917, p. 395. Phyc. Bor.-Amer. No. 1849.

Crustose portion of thallus several centimeters in diameter. Fruiting papillae 250–500 μ tall and up to 400 μ broad.

LOCAL DISTRIBUTION. Cypress Point.

TYPE LOCALITY. Land's End, San Francisco, California.

PACIFIC COAST DISTRIBUTION. As above.

Order RHODYMENIALES

Thalli multiaxial and with a ring of apical cells; nonfilamentous and usually erect, cylindrical to foliaceous, branched or unbranched. Medulla solid or hollow, never composed of longitudinal filaments; the cortex usually parenchymatous.

The spermatangia borne in small or in extensive sori. The carpogonial filaments three- or four-celled. The gonimoblast filaments growing from an auxiliary cell which is the terminal cell of a two-celled filament borne on supporting cell of carpogonial filament. The auxiliary cell always formed before fertilization. The gonimoblast filaments growing toward thallus surface and with most of the cells developing into carposporangia. The mature cystocarp standing above thallus surface and surrounded by a pericarp derived from overlying cortical tissue.

Tetrasporophytes with the tetrasporangia embedded just beneath thallus surface, usually with them remote from one another but occasionally with them in nemathecium-like patches. The tetrasporangia cruciately or tetrahedrally divided.

Key to the Families in the Local Flora

1. Carpogonial filament three-celled; auxiliary cell not fusing
     with other cells after fertilization.........*Rhodymeniaceae* (p. 294)
1. Carpogonial filament four-celled; auxiliary cell fusing
     with adjoining cells to form large placental cell. *Champiaceae* (p. 302)

Family Rhodymeniaceae

Thalli cylindrical to foliose, branched or unbranched, solid or hollow, not transversely septate if hollow.

Carpogonial filament three-celled. With one or with two two-celled auxiliary cell filaments on supporting cell of carpogonial filament. The auxiliary cell not fusing with other cells after fertilization. The gonimoblast filaments growing toward thallus surface, many-celled, radiately branched, with most of the cells developing into carposporangia. The cystocarp with many angular carposporangia and the mass surrounded by a pericarp.

Tetrasporophytes with the tetrasporangia separated from one another or in nemathecium-like groups. The tetrasporangia usually cruciately divided, more rarely tetrahedrally divided.

Key to the Genera in the Local Flora

1. Thalli free-living................................ 2
1. Thalli parasitic ....*Faucheocolax* (p. 296)
    2. Thallus wholly saccate or saccate at tips of branches............ 3
    2. Thallus foliaceous, with divided blades........................ 4
3. Thallus unbranched........................*Halosaccion* (p. 297)
3. Thallus a branched cylinder and each branch tip
       a hollow sac.............................*Botryocladia* (p. 296)
    4. Blade dichotomously divided at least in stipe-like
         basal portion ....*Rhodymenia* (p. 298)
    4. Blade not dichotomously divided................*Fauchea* (p. 295)

Fauchea Montagne, 1846

Thalli with blades growing erect from a small disc-shaped base. The blades sessile, more or less flabellately divided, lower dichotomies several times broader than the upper ones. Growing tips with several apical cells. Medulla two or three cells in thickness, composed of very large cells and without filaments between the cells; the cortex 4–6 cells in thickness, composed of laterally adjoined vertical rows of small cells.

Spermatangia unknown. Carpogonial filaments three-celled, developing over entire blade or only along margins of dichotomies. The auxiliary cell borne at base of a filament arising from supporting cell of carpogonial filament. The gonimoblast filaments growing toward thallus surface, aggregated in a compact spherical mass, with most of the cells developing into carposporangia. The mature cystocarp standing above surface of blade, surrounded by a pericarp formed from adjoining cortical cells, the pericarp with a small ostiole.

Tetrasporophytes with the tetrasporangia in small nemathecium-like sori. The sori small, irregularly shaped, densely scattered over both flattened faces of blade. The tetrasporangia cruciately divided.

STRUCTURE AND REPRODUCTION. Kylin, 1930, pp. 33–35; figs. 20–21. Sjöstedt, 1926, pp. 25–30; figs. 15–18½A.

With one species in the local flora.

Fauchea media Kylin   Pl. 73, fig. 1

*Kylin, 1941, p. 27; pl. 10, fig. 24.
Fauchea laciniata Kylin [not of J. G. Agardh]. *Kylin, 1931, p. 9 (as to Pacific Grove specimens).

Thalli 3–5 cm. tall, deep rose-red in color. The blades about as broad as tall, flabellately to subdichotomously divided into progressively narrower segments. The primary segments 10–15 mm. broad, the ultimate segments 2–4 mm. broad. The cystocarps irregularly scattered over most of flattened surface of blade; the pericarps coronate.

LOCAL DISTRIBUTION. Growing on rocks between the mean low-tide and −1.5-foot tide levels. Isolated specimens have been found at Mussel Point; Point Pinos; Middle Reef of Moss Beach; Pescadero Point; Pebble Beach.

TYPE LOCALITY. Point Pinos, Pacific Grove, California.

PACIFIC COAST DISTRIBUTION. As above.

Fauchea laciniata J. G. Agardh has been recorded from the Monterey Peninsula by Setchell (1901, p. 124), but in a conversation shortly before his death he stated that these specimens were a species of *Callophyllis* rather than *F. laciniata*.

Faucheocolax Setchell, 1923

Thalli parasitic on *Fauchea*. The thallus minute, with a solid basal cushion bearing many short, wart-like, fertile branches. Vegetative structure, cystocarps, and tetrasporangia as in *Fauchea*.

STRUCTURE AND REPRODUCTION. Setchell, 1923, p. 394.

Faucheocolax attenuata Setchell   Pl. 73, fig. 2
*Setchell, 1923, p. 394.

Thalli about 2 mm. in diameter; whitish to pinkish in color. With simple or forked fertile branches. Cystocarpic thalli with cystocarps at tips of fertile branches. Tetrasporophytes with fertile branches inflated at base and attenuated at tips. The tetrasporangia cruciately divided.

LOCAL DISTRIBUTION. Parasitic on *Fauchea media*. Carmel Bay; Pescadero Point.

TYPE LOCALITY. Carmel Bay, California.

PACIFIC COAST DISTRIBUTION. As above.

Botryocladia Kylin, 1931

Thalli with a disc-shaped holdfast bearing an erect, solidly parenchymatous, monopodially branched cylinder in which the branching appears as if dichotomous or alternate. Each branch tip terminating in a large, hollow, spherical to pyriform vesicle 10–30 times broader than the branch on which it is borne. The vesicles at times borne in abundance on all sides of major branches. Apex of a branch with several apical cells. The vesicles with very large cells adjoining the central cavity and with progressively smaller cells to the surface.

Heterothallic. The spermatangia in small sori on the vesicles. Carpogonial filaments three-celled, borne on vesicular portion of thallus. The auxiliary cell terminal on a two-celled filament from supporting cell of carpogonial filament. The gonimoblast filaments growing toward thallus surface, with all cells developing into carposporangia; the auxiliary cell not fusing with adjoining cells. The mature cystocarp with angular carposporangia; surrounded by an ostiolate pericarp developed from adjoining cortical cells.

The tetrasporophytes with tetrasporangia isolated from one another and embedded just beneath surface of vesicles. The tetrasporangia cruciately divided.

STRUCTURE AND REPRODUCTION. Bliding, 1928, pp. 51–59; figs. 42–51. Kuckuck, 1912A. (Both as *Chrysymenia*.)

With one species in the local flora.

Botryocladia pseudodichotoma (Farlow) Kylin   Pl. 73, fig. 5

Kylin, 1931, p. 18.
Chrysymenia pseudodichotoma Farlow, 1889, p. 1; pl. 88, figs. 7–8. *Anderson, 1891, p. 222. *Howe, 1893, p. 68. Phyc. Bor.-Amer. No. 139.
Chrysymenia (misprinted *Cryptonemia*) *obovata* Farlow [not of Sonder]. Farlow, 1877, p. 242. *Anderson, 1891, p. 222.

Thalli, as found on the Monterey Peninsula, up to 15 cm. tall; deep rose-red in color. Branching of the cylindrical portion widely divergent and appearing as if dichotomous. The vesicles large, elongate-pyriform, 4–7 cm. long and 1.5–2.5 cm. broad when fully developed.

LOCAL DISTRIBUTION. Epiphytic on holdfasts of *Macrocystis pyrifera* growing off Mussel Point. Various collectors have found plants cast ashore between Mussel Point and Point Pinos. Most of these plants have been collected after winter gales.

TYPE LOCALITY. Santa Cruz, California.

PACIFIC COAST DISTRIBUTION. British Columbia (Vancouver Island) to southern California (San Diego).

Halosaccion Kützing, 1843

Thalli erect, with one or more unbranched hollow sacs growing erect from a disc-shaped holdfast. The sacs with a very short, cylindrical, solidly parenchymatous stipe. Saccate portion above the stipe cylindrical but often markedly compressed at maturity. The saccate portion frequently with hollow cylindrical proliferous outgrowths. The saccate portion with large colorless cells next to the central cavity and progressively smaller cells outward, cells near the surface in anticlinal rows and containing chromatophores.

Spermatangia and cystocarps unknown. The tetrasporophytes with tetrasporangia remote from one another, embedded just beneath thallus surface, scattered over entire thallus. The tetrasporangia cruciately divided.

STRUCTURE AND REPRODUCTION. Schmitz and Hauptfleisch, 1896–1897, p. 405.

With one species in the local flora.

Halosaccion glandiforme (Gmelin) Ruprecht　Pl. 73, figs. 6–7

Ruprecht, 1851, p. 279; pl. 16, figs. *A–Q.* Setchell and Gardner, 1903, p. 317.
*Kylin, 1941, p. 27. Phyc. Bor.-Amer. No. CXXI.
　　Ulva glandiformis Gmelin, 1768, p. 232.
　　Halosaccion hydrophora (Postels and Ruprecht) J. G. Agardh, 1852, p. 358.
*Anderson, 1891, p. 223. *Howe, 1893, p. 68. Phyc. Bor.-Amer. No. 249.
　　Halosaccion fucicola (Postels and Ruprecht) J. G. Agardh, 1852, p. 358.
*Harvey, 1853, p. 194.

Thalli, as found on the Monterey Peninsula, up to 25 cm. tall;
yellowish-brown, olive-brown, or reddish-purple in color. Regularly with several sacs borne on a single holdfast. Young thalli
with the saccate portion cylindrical, up to 3 cm. in diameter, with
an intact broadly rounded apex, and filled with water. Somewhat
older thalli with the saccate portion more or less compressed but
filled with water. Old thalli with the saccate portion completely
flattened and with the rounded tip eroded away.

LOCAL DISTRIBUTION. Growing on rocks between the 2.5- and 1.0-
foot tide levels. Present in abundance at Asilomar end of Moss Beach;
Middle Reef of Moss Beach; Fanshell Beach. Isolated thalli found on all
rocky points of the Peninsula.

TYPE LOCALITY. Okhotsk Sea, Kamchatka, U.S.S.R.

PACIFIC COAST DISTRIBUTION. Alaska (westernmost Aleutian Islands)
to Mexico.

Rhodymenia Greville, 1830

Thalli with a disc-shaped holdfast or with a cylindrical,
branched, rhizome-like, prostrate holdfast. The holdfast bearing
erect blades with conspicuous to inconspicuous stipes. The blade
usually dichotomously or irregularly divided, more rarely entire;
without midrib or veins; margins of blade with or without proliferous outgrowths. The medulla composed of large, compactly
arranged, cubical to brick-shaped, colorless cells; the cortex 2–3
cells in thickness and with small rounded cells in vertical rows.

Heterothallic. The spermatangia in small irregularly shaped
sori on flattened faces of blade. Carpogonial filaments three-
celled, borne on innermost cortical cells. The auxiliary cell the
terminal cell of a two-celled filament borne on supporting cell of
a carpogonial filament. The gonimoblast filaments growing toward
thallus surface, lying in a compact globose mass, with almost all
cells developing into carposporangia. Mature cystocarps scattered
over entire blade or restricted to tips of blade, globose, overarched
by a thick pericarp with an ostiole.

Tetrasporophytes with the tetrasporangia restricted to tips of blade segments or scattered over entire blade; the tetrasporangia embedded just beneath surface of blade, remote from one another or in small nemathecium-like sori. The tetrasporangia cruciately divided.

STRUCTURE AND REPRODUCTION. Kylin, 1930, pp. 35–37; figs. 22–23. Sjöstedt, 1926, pp. 30–36; figs. 18½B–21.

KEY TO THE SPECIES IN THE LOCAL FLORA

1. Segments of blade less than 5 mm. broad........................ 2
1. Segments of blade 5–30 mm. broad............................. 5
   2. Stipe with 2–5 sympodial branchings..................*R. lobata*
   2. Stipe usually unbranched................................. 3
3. Thalli up to 20 cm. tall..............................*R. lobulifera*
3. Thalli less than 10 cm. tall................................. 4
   4. Tetrasporangial sori not nemathecoid...............*R. californica*
   4. Tetrasporangial sori nemathecoid..................*R. attenuata*
5. Blade segments with marginal proliferations....*R. palmata* var. *mollis*
5. Blade segments without marginal proliferations..........*R. pacifica*

Rhodymenia lobata Dawson   Pl. 74, fig. 3

*Dawson, 1941, p. 147; pl. 19, figs. 12–13; pl. 28, fig. 41.

Thalli 20–25 cm. tall; bright red in color. The blades with a slightly flattened sympodially branched stipe that is 10–15 cm. long. The blades terminating branches of stipe 3–5 times dichotomously divided, the segments about 3 mm. broad and diverging at an angle of 30°–45°. The stipe and lower segments of blade at times with small proliferous bladelets. Tetrasporophytes with tetrasporangia in rounded sori on broadly expanded apices of ultimate blade segments. Cortical tissue of sorus nemathecoid.

LOCAL DISTRIBUTION. Cast ashore at Pebble Beach.
TYPE LOCALITY. As above.
PACIFIC COAST DISTRIBUTION. As above.

Rhodymenia lobulifera Dawson   Pl. 74, fig. 4

*Dawson, 1941, p. 137; pl. 25, fig. 36.

Thalli up to 20 cm. tall; deep red in color. With an unbranched stipe 2–7 cm. long and the stipe broadening gradually at the upper end. The blade 3–5 times divided, the division usually dichotomous but sometimes palmate, segments of blade 3–5 mm. broad. Ends of ultimate segments narrowed to an acute tip. Tetrasporophytes with the tetrasporangia in sori borne on proliferous pedicellate bladelets growing from lateral margins of ultimate segments of blade. Cortical tissue of sorus nemathecoid. The cystocarps also produced on proliferous bladelets from ultimate segments of blade.

LOCAL DISTRIBUTION. Carmel Bay.

TYPE LOCALITY. San Pedro, California.

PACIFIC COAST DISTRIBUTION. Known only from California (Bolinas, Carmel Bay, San Pedro).

Rhodymenia attenuata Dawson   Pl. 74, fig. 1

*Dawson, 1941, p. 139; pl. 19, figs. 10–11; pl. 24, fig. 35.

Thalli. 5–8 cm. tall, deep red in color. The stipe unbranched, 5–8 mm. long. The blade 3–5 times dichotomously divided and with segments 1.5–2.5 mm. broad. Apices of ultimate segments frequently attenuated in sterile plants. Tetrasporophytes with tetrasporangia in small rounded sori on broadened apices of the ultimate segments or in small proliferous outgrowths from blade segments. Cortical tissue of tetrasporangial sori nemathecoid. Cystocarps on terminal segments of blade or on proliferations from terminal segments.

LOCAL DISTRIBUTION. Cast ashore at Pebble Beach.

TYPE LOCALITY. San Pedro, California (for tetrasporophytes).

PACIFIC COAST DISTRIBUTION. As above.

Tips of segments of *R. californica* may have an attenuation approaching that characteristic of *R. attenuata*. When tetrasporophytes are available the two species are readily distinguishable by the nemathecoid or non-nemathecoid organization of tetrasporangial sori.

Rhodymenia californica Kylin   Pl. 74, fig. 2

*Kylin, 1931, p. 21; pl. 9, fig. 22. *Kylin, 1941, p. 27. *Dawson, 1941, p. 135. *Rhodymenia corallina* Farlow [not of (Bory) Greville]. Farlow, 1875, p. 367. *Anderson, 1891, p. 223. Phyc. Bor.-Amer. No. 692.

Thalli, as found on the Monterey Peninsula, usually 3–5 cm. tall but occasionally up to 7.5 cm.; bright red in color. With a branching cylindrical rhizome attached to substratum by cylindrical root-like branches. The blades 2–5 times dichotomously divided and with a stipe-like base 2–6 mm. long. Segments of blade somewhat rigid, narrowly linear, 3–5 mm. broad; the ultimate segments with broadly rounded to acutely pointed tips. Lateral margins of segments without proliferations. Tetrasporophytes with tetrasporangia in small oval sori at tips of the ultimate dichotomies. Cortical tissue of sorus not nemathecoid.

LOCAL DISTRIBUTION. Growing on the vertical face of sheltered rocks between the mean low-tide and —1.5-foot tide levels. Common at Mussel Point; Point Aulon; Point Pinos; Asilomar Point; Middle Reef of Moss Beach; Fanshell Beach; Cypress Point; Midway Point; Pescadero Point; Arrowhead Point; Mission Point. Also dredged from a depth of 20–25 feet near Point Aulon and in Stillwater Cove.

TYPE LOCALITY. Mussel Point, Pacific Grove, California.

PACIFIC COAST DISTRIBUTION. Central California (Half Moon Bay) to southern California (San Diego).

Rhodymenia pacifica Kylin   Pl. 76, fig. 1

*Kylin, 1931, p. 21; pl. 9, fig. 21. *Kylin, 1941, p. 27. Dawson, 1941, p. 142; pl. 20, fig. 14.

Rhodymenia palmata Anderson [not of (Linnaeus) Greville]. *Anderson, 1891, p. 223.

Rhodymenia pulmettiformis *Dawson, 1941, p. 140; pl. 22, fig. 29.

Thalli, as found on the Monterey Peninsula, 8–13 cm. tall; deep dull red in color. With a branching cylindrical rhizome attached to the substratum by cylindrical root-like branches. Stipe of blade 5–20 mm. long, usually unbranched. The blades 2–5 times dichotomously divided; the segments crisp and rigid, wedge-shaped to linear, 5–12 mm. broad; the ultimate segments with broadly rounded tips. Lateral margins of segments without proliferations but the tips of the ultimate segments occasionally with proliferous bladelets. Tetraspores and cystocarps unknown.

LOCAL DISTRIBUTION. Growing on the vertical face of rocks between the mean low-tide and —1.5-foot tide levels. Fairly common at Mussel Point; Point Aulon; Point Pinos; Asilomar Point; Middle Reef of Moss Beach; Fanshell Beach; Cypress Point; Mission Point. Also dredged from a depth of 60–75 feet near Mussel Point and from 15–20 feet at Stillwater Cove.

TYPE LOCALITY. Mussel Point, Pacific Grove, California.

PACIFIC COAST DISTRIBUTION. Central California (Pacific Grove) to southern California (San Diego).

Rhodymenia palmata var. mollis Setchell and Gardner

*Setchell and Gardner, 1903, p. 315. Phyc. Bor.-Amer. No. 934.

Thalli 20–40 cm. tall; dull reddish-purple in color. The blade with a very inconspicuous stipe that gradually broadens upward. The blades subdichotomously to palmately divided, with segments 15–30 cm. broad. Margins of segments with numerous proliferous blades but these rarely becoming of large size. The tetrasporangia grouped in indistinct sori scattered over surface of blade.

LOCAL DISTRIBUTION. On rocks in a tide pool at mean low-tide level, Mission Point. Fifteen feet below pneumatocyst of a thallus of *Nereocystis Luetkeana* off Mussel Point. Also cast ashore at Pacific Grove.

TYPE LOCALITY. Puget Sound.

PACIFIC COAST DISTRIBUTION. Alaska (Agattu Island) to central California (Pacific Grove).

This variety has thicker and less papery blades than the type and the proliferous blades are relatively smaller.

Family CHAMPIACEAE

Thalli more or less branched. The branches cylindrical or somewhat compressed; hollow (at least in upper part) and with delicate transverse septa.

Carpogonial filament four-celled, its supporting cell bearing either one or two two-celled auxiliary cell filaments. The auxiliary cell terminal on auxiliary-cell filament. After fertilization the auxiliary cell or cells uniting with the cell beneath and with the supporting cell to form a large, irregularly shaped, placental cell. The placental cell with many short gonimoblast filaments growing toward thallus surface. If the gonimoblast filaments are more than one-celled, only the terminal cells developing into carposporangia. The mature cystocarp standing above thallus surface and surrounded by a pericarp.

Tetrasporophytes with the tetrasporangia separated from one another and embedded just beneath thallus surface. The tetrasporangia tetrahedrally divided.

KEY TO THE GENERA IN THE LOCAL FLORA

1. Lateral branches bending toward substratum.......*Coeloseira* (p. 304)
1. Lateral branches not bending toward substratum *Gastroclonium* (p. 302)

Gastroclonium Kützing, 1843

Thalli erect, cylindrical, with irregularly to subdichotomously branched major branches, the major branches with many short branchlets. With all branches or only the branchlets constricted at regular intervals. Basal portion of major branches solid; branchlets and upper part of major branches hollow and transversely septate. The hollow branches with a ring of elongate medullary cells; the cortex parenchymatous and with progressively smaller cells toward the surface.

Heterothallic. The spermatangia in irregularly shaped sori borne on bladder-like terminal branchlets. Carpogonial filaments four-celled, the supporting cell a cell at inner face of cortex. The carpogonial filament flanked right and left by a two-cell auxiliary-cell filament. Fertilization followed by a development of one-celled gonimoblast filaments from both auxiliary cells and a fusion of carpogonial filament, supporting-cell, and auxiliary-cell filaments into a two-lobed placental cell. Mature cystocarp standing above thallus and surrounded by an urn-shaped pericarp with a wide ostiole.

The tetrasporophytes with the tetrasporangia remote from one another and embedded just beneath surface of thallus, the tetrasporangia borne only on ultimate branchlets of thallus. The tetrasporangia tetrahedrally divided. Tetrasporophytes at times with polysporangia containing 15–20 spores.

STRUCTURE AND REPRODUCTION. Bliding, 1928, pp. 23–41; figs. 14–32 (as *Chylocladia*). G. M. Smith, 1938, pp. 339–342; figs. 187–189.

Gastroclonium Coulteri (Harvey) Kylin   Pl. 75

*Kylin, 1931, p. 30. *Kylin, 1941, p. 27.
Lomentaria ovalis var. *Coulteri* *Harvey, 1853, p. 78; pl. 19, fig. *A*. Phyc. Bor.-Amer. No. 433.
Chylocladia ovalis var. *Coulteri* (Harvey) Farlow, 1876, p. 695. *Anderson, 1891, p. 225. *Howe, 1893, p. 68.

Thalli, as found on the Monterey Peninsula, up to 25 cm. tall; generally dark olive or olive-brown but sometimes bright green in color. With several shoots from a disc-shaped holdfast. The shoots cylindrical, sparingly branched in an irregular or subdichotomous manner; lower portion of branches generally naked, upper portion with numerous short lateral branchlets. The branchlets 1–2.5 cm. long, club-shaped, with broadly rounded apices, slightly constricted at regular intervals; interior of branchlets hollow, transversely septate at regular intervals.

LOCAL DISTRIBUTION. Growing on rocks between the 2.0- and −1.5-foot tide levels. Common everywhere. Also dredged from a depth of 20–25 feet near Mussel Point and from 15–20 feet at Stillwater Cove.

TYPE LOCALITY. Monterey, California.

PACIFIC COAST DISTRIBUTION. Central California (Fort Ross) to southern California (San Diego).

Coeloseira Hollenberg, 1940

Thalli small; with a short, erect, solid, cylindrical axis bearing alternately disposed cylindrical or somewhat compressed branches; the branches frequently appearing as if borne in a transverse whorl at apex of axis. The branches standing more or less horizontally to the axis, with or without their tips recurving to the substratum and becoming stoloniferous. The branches hollow, transversely septate, externally constricted at each septation. Portions of branch external to central hollow region 1–3 cells in thickness.

Spermatangia unknown. Carpogonial filaments unknown. The developing cystocarp with a two-lobed placental cell formed by fusion of two auxiliary cells, a supporting cell, and adjoining vegetative cells. Each lobe of placental cell bearing many wedge-shaped carposporangia. The mature cystocarp surrounded by a pericarp without an ostiole.

Tetrasporophytes with polysporangia only. The polysporangia globose, containing 12–16 polyspores, embedded just beneath tips of branches.

STRUCTURE AND REPRODUCTION. Hollenberg, 1940, pp. 871–876; figs. 7–17.

With one species in the local flora.

Coeloseira compressa Hollenberg   Pl. 76, fig. 2

Hollenberg, 1940, p. 874; figs 7C–7D, 13–17.

Thalli, as found on the Monterey Peninsula, up to 0.8 cm. tall and 2.5 cm. broad; bright red in color. The branches frequently with their apices recurving toward the substratum and at times with stoloniferous tips. The branches distinctly compressed, about 1 mm. broad, with 5–15 well-defined constrictions, simple or with branchlets on the side away from the substratum. Stoloniferous portion of branches much smaller in diameter but with definite constrictions.

LOCAL DISTRIBUTION. Growing three feet below the water line on the receiving hopper of a sardine cannery near Mussel Point. Also dredged from a depth of 25–30 feet off Point Aulon.

TYPE LOCALITY. Corona del Mar, Orange County, California.

PACIFIC COAST DISTRIBUTION. Known only from Pacific Grove; Corona del Mar; and Punta Banda, Baja California.

Order CERAMIALES

Thalli monoaxial, filamentous or nonfilamentous, erect or prostrate. If filamentous, either uncorticated, with only the major branches corticated, or with all branches corticated from base to apex. Nonfilamentous thalli polysiphonous or foliaceous. Polysiphonous thalli uncorticated or partially to completely corticated.

The spermatia either in corymbose clusters, in compact masses along special filaments (trichoblasts), or in sori. Carpogonial filament always four-celled; its supporting cell with or without sterile filaments. The gonimoblast filaments growing from an auxiliary cell formed after fertilization and cut off directly from supporting cell of the carpogonial filament. The gonimoblast filaments with all or with only the terminal cells developing into carposporangia. The mature cystocarps either naked, partly surrounded by filaments, or with a true pericarp.

Tetrasporophytes with the tetrasporangia freely exposed or embedded in thallus; and either borne singly, in sori, or on special branches (stichidia). The tetrasporangia usually tetrahedrally divided.

Key to the Families in the Local Flora

1. Thalli filamentous, uncorticated to wholly
   corticated .... *Ceramiaceae* (p. 305)
1. Thalli not filamentous... 2
   2. Polysiphonous, uncorticated to wholly corticated................ 3
   2. Not polysiphonous, more or less foliaceous..*Delesseriaceae* (p. 334)
3. Growth of thallus not sympodial............. *Rhodomelaceae* (p. 357)
3. Growth of thallus sympodial.................... *Dasyaceae* (p. 355)

Family CERAMIACEAE

Thalli filamentous. Wholly uncorticated, with only the major branches corticated, or with all branches corticated. Wholly corticated thalli sometimes with flattened branches. The corticating cells never polysiphonous and always shorter than the cell they encircle.

Carpogonial filaments four-celled. The supporting cell usually forming a single auxiliary cell after fertilization but at times forming one on either side of the carpogonial filament. The gonimoblast filaments with most of the cells or with only the terminal cells developing into carposporangia. The mature cystocarp naked or partly to completely enclosed by an involucre of incurved filaments.

Tetrasporophytes with the sporangia separated from one another and borne freely exposed or embedded in the corticating tissue. The tetrasporangia cruciately or tetrahedrally divided.

KEY TO THE GENERA IN THE LOCAL FLORA

1. The final orders of branches uncorticated...................... 2
1. The final orders of branches incompletely or completely corticated... 7
   2. Branching opposite or verticillate.......................... 3
   2. Branching not opposite or verticillate...................... 4
3. Branching opposite or if verticillate with all branches
   of a verticil the same length...............*Antithamnion* (p. 306)
3. Branching verticillate, each verticil with two long and
   two short branches.....................*Platythamnion* (p. 314)
   4. Branching regularly alternate................................ 5
   4. Branching not regularly alternate............................ 6
5. Tetrasporophytes with tetrasporangia.........*Callithamnion* (p. 317)
5. Tetrasporophytes with polysporangia.........*Pleonosporium* (p. 320)
   6. Branching predominately dichotomous; cells
     large and visible to naked eye...............*Griffithsia* (p. 323)
   6. Branching irregular or predominately unilateral,
     cells cylindrical and of microscopic size..*Spermothamnion* (p. 322)
7. Cortication of branches differentiated into nodes and internodes..... 8
7. Cortication homogeneous from base to apex of a branch............ 9
   8. Corticating cells rectangular and in vertical
     rows ....*Centroceras* (p. 327)
   8. Corticating cells polygonal and irregularly
     arranged ....*Ceramium* (p. 324)
9. Branching opposite and the two opposite branches
   unlike ....*Ptilota* (p. 331)
9. Branching alternate or pectinate................*Microcladia* (p. 329)

Antithamnion Nägeli, 1847

Thalli filamentous, profusely branched and with erect uncorticated branches attached by a disc-shaped holdfast or by a branched filamentous holdfast. If filamentous the holdfast wholly superficial or penetrating the substratum. Erect branches with secondary branches and branchlets in opposite pairs or in verticils of three or four and with all members of a verticil the same length. Portions of branches at times alternately branched because of suppression of one of an opposite pair of branches. Branchlets with or without hyaline gland cells. Cells of branches with many small elliptical or band-shaped chromatophores.

Heterothallic. The spermatangia in loose to dense clusters on upper side of branchlets. Carpogonial filament 4-celled and with trichogyne directed toward branch apex; its supporting cell the lowermost cell of a lateral branchlet. Supporting cell cutting off a single auxiliary cell from side opposite the carpogonial filament, the interval between carpogonium and auxiliary cell becoming bridged by a small cell cut off from base of carpogonium. Gonimoblast filaments growing upward from auxiliary cell, branched and with all but the lowermost cells developing into carposporangia. Mature cystocarp a freely exposed mass without an involucre.

Tetrasporophytes with the tetrasporangia borne on the adaxial side of branchlets. The tetrasporangia sessile or pedicellate, cruciately divided but at times appearing as if tetrahedrally divided.

STRUCTURE AND REPRODUCTION. Capt, 1930. Kylin, 1923, pp. 61–62; fig. 41. Kylin, 1925, pp. 45–51; figs. 27–31. Phillips, 1897, pp. 356–357; pl. 18, figs. 11–12. Westbrook, 1931.

KEY TO THE SPECIES IN THE LOCAL FLORA

1. Branchlets in opposite pairs 2
1. Branchlets in verticils of three or four........................ 8
  2. Branchlets pectinate on adaxial side......................... 3
  2. Branchlets not pectinate.................................... 5
3. No branchlet opposite a major branch.......................... 4
3. With a branchlet opposite a major branch................*A. Kylinii*
  4. Tips of branchlets broadly rounded.................*A. defectum*
  4. Tips of branchlets acutely pointed.................*A. pygmaeum*
5. With gland cells... 6
5. Without gland cells.. 7
  6. Branchlets tapering abruptly at tips.............*A. dendroideum*
  6. Branchlets not tapering abruptly at tips.........*A. glanduliferum*
7. Many branchlets curved and entangling major
    branches in rope-like strands......................*A. uncinatum*
7. Few branchlets curved and the major branches not
    entangled in rope-like strands......................*A. pacificum*
8. Tips of branchlets rounded......................*A. occidentale*
8. Tips of branchlets acutely pointed........................... 9
9. Branchlets tapering abruptly at tips...........................10
9. Branchlets not tapering abruptly at tips...............*A. subulatum*
  10. Successive verticils overlapping ....*A. densiusculum*
  10. Successive verticils not overlapping................*A. Baylesiae*

Antithamnion Kylinii Gardner   Pl. 77, fig. 1; pl. 78, fig. 5

Gardner, 1927C, p. 411; pl. 89, fig. 1.

Thalli, as found on the Monterey Peninsula, up to 2 cm. tall. With a percurrent axis bearing several major branches and with a simple branchlet opposite each major branch. Cells in lower portion of axis 75–125 µ broad and with a length 2–3 times the breadth. The axis and branches with an opposite pair of branchlets from the upper end of each cell. The branchlets pectinately branched on adaxial side and with the pectinating filaments bending away from tip of the branchlet; basal cell of branchlet much shorter than others and not bearing a pectinating filament. Branchlets and filaments borne on them gradually tapering to an acute tip. Filaments of branchlets with a single gland cell borne either at the base or the apex. Tetrasporangia with one-celled pedicels; either replacing a pectinating filament or borne laterally at base of a filament. The tetrasporangia pyriform, cruciately divided, 65–70 µ long, 46–52 µ broad.

LOCAL DISTRIBUTION. On piling of Municipal Wharf, Monterey, and about ten feet below surface of water.

TYPE LOCALITY. Victoria, British Columbia.

PACIFIC COAST DISTRIBUTION. As above.

Antithamnion defectum Kylin   Pl. 78, figs. 1–2

Kylin, 1925, p. 46; fig. 27.

Thalli, as found on the Monterey Peninsula, up to 1.5 cm. tall. With an obscure axis bearing numerous major branches and without a branchlet opposite a major branch. Cells in lower portion of axis 35–50 µ broad and with a length 2–3 times the breadth. The axis and branches with an opposite pair of branchlets from the upper end of each cell. The branchlets pectinately branched on adaxial side and with the pectinating filaments bending toward tip of branchlet. The lowermost two or three filaments on a branchlet at times with a gland cell at the tip. The apices of branchlets and the pectinating filaments broadly rounded. The tetrasporangia pedicellate, replacing the lowermost two or three filaments of a branchlet. The tetrasporangia pyriform, cruciately divided, 32–45 µ long, 30–40 µ broad.

LOCAL DISTRIBUTION. On stipe of *Nereocystis Luetkeana* cast ashore at Pebble Beach and at south end of Carmel Beach. Dredged from a depth of 30–35 feet near Point Pinos.

TYPE LOCALITY. Friday Harbor, Washington.

PACIFIC COAST DISTRIBUTION. As above.

The somewhat smaller dimensions recorded for local plants may be due to the fact that the few plants collected were not fully developed.

Antithamnion pygmaeum Gardner   Pl. 78, fig. 4; pl. 80, fig. 1

Gardner, 1927C, p. 413; pls. 91–93.

Thalli, as found on the Monterey Peninsula, 4–8 mm. tall and attached by a branched, disc-shaped holdfast. With a conspicuous percurrent axis bearing a few major branches and without a branchlet opposite a major branch. Cells in lower portion of axis 50–75 µ broad and with a length 3–4 times the breadth. The axis and branches with an opposite pair of branchlets from the upper end of each cell. The branchlets pectinately branched on adaxial side and with the pectinating filaments bending sharply toward tip of branchlet. The lowermost two or three filaments on a branchlet frequently with one or two gland cells. The apices of filaments and branchlet acutely pointed. The tetrasporangia pedicellate, borne singly on the lowermost two or three filaments of a branchlet. The tetrasporangia ellipsoidal, cruciately divided, 75–80 µ long, 48–54 µ broad.

LOCAL DISTRIBUTION. Growing at mean low-tide level. On a sponge at Middle Reef of Moss Beach. Forming low creeping patches on rocks at Pescadero Point.

TYPE LOCALITY. La Jolla, California.

PACIFIC COAST DISTRIBUTION. Central California (Pacific Grove) to southern California (San Diego).

Antithamnion dendroideum Smith and Hollenberg

Pl. 77, figs. 2–3

*Smith and Hollenberg, 1943, p. 217; figs. 20–21.

Thalli up to 2 cm. tall. With a percurrent axis bearing two or three major branches and with a simple branchlet opposite each major branch. Cells in lower portion of axis 100–150 µ broad and with a length 3.5 times the breadth. Basal cells of axis with long colorless descending rhizoids. The axis and branches with an opposite pair (very rarely a verticil of three) branchlets from the upper end of each cell. The branchlets usually simple, 10- to 14-celled, and with the terminal three or four cells tapering abruptly to form an acute tip. Occasional branchlets pectinately branched on adaxial side; the pectinating filaments either long and without gland cells or short and with gland cells. Simple branchlets occasionally but three- or four-celled and with a gland cell. Cells of branchlets up to 80 µ broad and with a length 2.5 times the breadth. Spermatangia, cystocarps, and tetrasporangia unknown.

LOCAL DISTRIBUTION. Dredged from a depth of 30–35 feet a quarter-mile from Municipal Wharf, Monterey.

TYPE LOCALITY. As above.

PACIFIC COAST DISTRIBUTION. As above.

Easily recognized by the distinctive branchlets. To the naked eye the alga resembles *Pterosiphonia dendroidea* but when lifted from the water is much less rigid than the latter.

Antithamnion glanduliferum Kylin   Pl. 77, fig. 4

Kylin, 1925, p. 47; figs. 28 *E*–28 *G*.

Thalli, as found on the Monterey Peninsula, 2–5 cm. tall. With a fairly conspicuous percurrent axis bearing many major branches and with a branchlet opposite each major branch. Cells in lower portion of axis up to 100 µ broad and with a length 3–5 times the breadth. The axis and major branches with an opposite pair of branchlets from the upper end of each cell. The branchlets usually simple but occasionally with one or more short filaments from cells near base. Many branchlets with one or more gland cells. The tetrasporangia sessile, borne on the two or three lowermost cells of a branchlet. The tetrasporangia ellipsoidal, cruciately divided but often appearing as if tetrahedrally divided, up to 80 µ long and 30 µ broad.

LOCAL DISTRIBUTION. Growing on rocks or on other algae between mean low-tide level and the −1.5-foot tide level. Mussel Point; Middle Reef of Moss Beach; Mission Point. Frequently found on stipes (10–20 feet below pneumatocyst) of *Nereocystis Luetkeana*. Also dredged from a depth of 30–35 feet a quarter-mile from Municipal Wharf, Monterey.

TYPE LOCALITY. Friday Harbor, Washington.

PACIFIC COAST DISTRIBUTION. Puget Sound to central California (Carmel Highlands).

Antithamnion pacificum (Harvey) Kylin

Kylin, 1925, p. 47; figs. 28 *C*–28 *D*, 29.

Callithamnion floccosum var. *pacificum* Harvey, 1862, p. 176.

Callithamnion floccosum Anderson [not of (Müller) Kleen]. *Anderson, 1891, p. 222.

Antithamnion floccosum var. *pacificum* (Harvey) Setchell and Gardner, 1903, p. 341. Phyc. Bor.-Amer. No. 147.

Thalli, as found on the Monterey Peninsula, up to 10 cm. tall. With a very obscure axis bearing numerous major branches and with a branchlet opposite each major branch. Cells in lower portions of axis and major branches up to 100 µ broad and with a length five or more times the breadth. The axis and branches with an opposite pair of branchlets at the upper end of each cell. The branchlets simple, curved upward toward apex of branch bearing them; with a length 2–3 times that of cells bearing them. Branchlets without gland cells. The tetrasporangia pedicellate, in fasciculate clusters of 2–4 on adaxial side of basal cells of the branchlets. The tetrasporangia broadly ellipsoidal, cruciately divided, up to 50 μ long and 40 μ broad.

LOCAL DISTRIBUTION. On stipes and pneumatocysts of *Nereocystis Luetkeana* cast ashore at Moss Beach and at Carmel Beach. Usually found only from late autumn to late spring.

TYPE LOCALITY. Either Orcas Island, Washington, or Esquimalt, British Columbia.

PACIFIC COAST DISTRIBUTION. Alaska (Yakutat Bay) to southern California (La Jolla).[6]

Antithamnion uncinatum Gardner   Pl. 76, fig. 4

Gardner, 1927D, p. 408; pl. 89, fig. 2; pl. 90.

Thalli, as found on the Monterey Peninsula, 15–20 cm. tall. Freely branched and with the general appearance of the thallus resembling a branched frayed rope. The major branches with a percurrent axis but this obscured by the many long branches. Major branches with a branchlet opposite each long branch. Cells in lower portion of major branches 125–150 μ broad and with a length up to ten times the breadth. The branches with an opposite pair of branchlets from the upper end of each cell. The branchlets simple; those on mature cells 3–4 times longer than the cell bearing them. The branchlets without gland cells. Certain of the branchlets elongate and with the tips uncinately or circinately curved around a long branch. The tetrasporangia pedicellate, borne singly or in fasciculate clusters of 2–4 on adaxial side of lower cells of branchlets. The tetrasporangia ellipsoidal, cruciately divided, 75–85 μ long, 42–48 μ broad.

LOCAL DISTRIBUTION. On stipe and pneumatocyst of *Nereocystis Luetkeana* cast ashore at Moss Beach. On *Macrocystis pyrifera* cast ashore at Pebble Beach.

TYPE LOCALITY. Dillon's Beach, Tomales Bay, California.

PACIFIC COAST DISTRIBUTION. Puget Sound to central California (Carmel Bay).

[6] The range given here is based upon University of California herbarium specimens labeled *Callithamnion floccosum* var. *pacificum* or *Antithamnion floccosum* var. *pacificum*. These determinations are open to question because they were made before *A. glanduliferum* and *A. uncinatum* were recognized as distinct from *A. pacificum*.

Closely related to *A. pacificum* but differing in the entwining of major branches into rope-like strands through an entangling of the curved branchlets with larger branches. In this respect *A. uncinatum* and *A. pacificum* stand in much the same relationship to each other as do *Spongomorpha* and *Cladophora*.

Antithamnion occidentale Kylin

Kylin, 1925, p. 47; figs. 30 *A*–30 *D*.

Thalli, as found on the Monterey Peninsula, up to 5 cm. tall. With a percurrent axis bearing a few long branches and with a branchlet opposite each long branch. Cells in lower portion of axis and major branches 125–175 µ broad and with a length 3–4 times the breadth. Older portions of axis and major branches with verticils of three or four branchlets on upper end of each cell; all branchlets of a verticil the same length. Successive verticils overlapping and hence not giving the branch a zonate appearance when observed without magnification. Upper portions of branches at times with a pair of opposite branchlets at upper end of each cell. Branchlets of a verticil 15–20 µ broad at base. The branchlets rather freely branched, the branching irregular or pectinate; tips of branchlets and the filaments on them distinctly rounded. The branchlets with gland cells. Tetrasporangia sessile on filaments of branchlets. The tetrasporangia ellipsoidal, cruciately divided.

LOCAL DISTRIBUTION. Growing at mean low-tide level on rocks partly buried in sand at foot of Twelfth Street, Carmel. On stipe of *Nereocystis Luetkeana* cast ashore at Pebble Beach and at south end of Carmel Beach.

TYPE LOCALITY. Friday Harbor, Washington.

PACIFIC COAST DISTRIBUTION. Known only from Puget Sound and from Carmel.

Antithamnion subulatum (Harvey) J. G. Agardh Pl. 78, fig. 3

J. G. Agardh, 1892, p. 20. Kylin, 1925, p. 50; fig. 31.
Callithamnion subulatum Harvey, 1862, p. 175.

Thalli, as found on the Monterey Peninsula, up to 3 cm. tall. With many erect shoots growing from a common base. Erect shoots with a percurrent axis bearing many major branches of moderate length and with each cell bearing a major branch also bearing one or more branchlets. Cells in lower portion of axis 90–125 µ broad and with a length 4–6 times the breadth. Older portions of axis and major branches with verticils of three or four branchlets on upper end of each cell; all branchlets of a verticil equal in length and successive verticils overlapping one another. Upper portions of branches at times with a pair of opposite branchlets. The branchlets 25–50 μ broad at base, rather freely branched, and with the filaments gradually tapering to an acute tip. The branchlets with gland cells. The tetrasporangia sessile on the branchlets; tetrahedrally divided (?).

LOCAL DISTRIBUTION. Growing at mean low-tide level on piles of Municipal Wharf, Monterey.

TYPE LOCALITY. Esquimalt, British Columbia.

PACIFIC COAST DISTRIBUTION. Known only from the Puget Sound area and from Monterey.

Antithamnion densiusculum Gardner   Pl. 76, fig. 3

Gardner, 1927B, p. 374; pl. 75, fig. 2.

Thalli, as found on the Monterey Peninsula, up to 25 cm. tall. With a percurrent axis bearing numerous branches rebranched into two or three orders of branching. Cells in lower portion of axis about 250 μ broad and with a length 5–7 times the breadth. Axis and branches with a verticil of three or four upwardly bent branchlets at upper end of each cell and with successive verticils overlapping. The lowermost cell of a branchlet with a whorl of three or four filaments; the other cells without filaments. The branchlets and the filaments borne on them abruptly narrowed 3–4 cells from tip and with a gland cell at the juncture of broad and narrow portions. Cells in broad portion of branchlets barrel-shaped and the lowermost cells 40–60 μ broad. The tetrasporangia sessile or with one-celled pedicles; borne adaxially on filaments at base of branchlets. The tetrasporangia broadly ellipsoidal to subspherical, cruciately divided, 75–100 μ long, 65–85 μ broad.

LOCAL DISTRIBUTION. Epiphytic on *Calliarthron* at Asilomar Point.

TYPE LOCALITY. Point Defiance, Tacoma, Washington.

PACIFIC COAST DISTRIBUTION. Known only from Vancouver Island, British Columbia; Puget Sound; and Pacific Grove.

Antithamnion Baylesiae Gardner

Gardner, 1927B, p. 375; pl. 75, fig. 1.

Thalli 7–10 cm. tall. With several erect shoots growing from a common base. Erect shoots with a conspicuous percurrent axis and many branches of moderate length. Cells in lower portion of axis 200–350 μ broad and with a length 5–6 times the breadth. Axis and branches with cells from base to apex each bearing a verticil of four (rarely three) branchlets at upper end of each cell. Verticils on older portions of branches not overlapping and giving the branch a *Platythamnion* - like zonate appearance. Branchlets with 2–4 orders of branching all directed toward apex of branchlet. Cells of branchlets barrel-shaped, those in each successive order about half the diameter of those in preceding order; the ultimate order tapering to an acute point. Gland cells hemispherical, conspicuous, borne singly at base of ultimate order of branches of a branchlet. The tetrasporangia usually sessile but occasionally pedicellate, borne near base of branchlets; cruciately divided, 80–90 μ long, 60–70 μ broad.

LOCAL DISTRIBUTION. Pacific Grove. Cast ashore at Carmel Beach.
TYPE LOCALITY. Pacific Grove.
PACIFIC COAST DISTRIBUTION. As above.

Platythamnion J. G. Agardh, 1892

Thalli filamentous, erect, profusely branched and with branches uncorticated. Attached by rhizoidal filaments from lowermost cells. Erect shoots with a percurrent axis bearing distichous long branches either in a regularly alternate or an irregular succession. Each cell of axis and branches with a verticil of four quadrately arranged branchlets and with branchlets of one opposed pair more than double the length of the other opposed pair. The branchlets bearing filaments and these usually branched and verticillate. The branchlets with or without gland cells.

Heterothallic. The spermatangia in loose fasciculate clusters on filaments of the branchlets. Carpogonial filament 4-celled; its supporting cell the lowermost cell of a branchlet. The supporting cell cutting off a single auxiliary cell adjacent to the carpogonium. The gonimoblast filaments growing upward from the auxiliary cell; branched and with all but the lowermost cells developing into carposporangia. Mature cystocarps freely exposed, globose to lobed, without an involucre.

Tetrasporophytes with the tetrasporangia sessile or pedicellate, borne at base of filaments of branchlets. The tetrasporangia cruciately divided.

STRUCTURE AND REPRODUCTION. Kylin, 1925, pp. 51–54; figs. 32–34.

1. Older branchlets with four quadrately arranged
    rows of filaments...........................*P. heteromorphum*
1. Older branchlets with two or with three rows of filaments......... 2
   2. With three rows of filaments, two above, one below.....*P. villosum*
   2. With two rows of filaments on upper side and
       none below...................................*P. pectinatum*

Platythamnion heteromorphum J. G. Agardh   Pl. 79, fig. 3

J. G. Agardh, 1892, p. 23. Kylin, 1925, p. 51; fig. 32 C.
Callithamnion heteromorphum J. G. Agardh, 1876, p. 23. Algae Exsicc.
Amer. Bor. No. 154.

Thalli, as found on the Monterey Peninsula, up to 2.5 cm.
tall. With major branches along the percurrent axis distichous,
alternate, and usually on every fourth cell of the axis. The
branches relatively short but branched in the same manner as
the axis. Cells in lower portion of axis 220–250 μ broad and
with a length about 1.5 times the breadth. Each cell of axis and
branches with a verticil of four branchlets; two long and two
short. The long branchlets of a verticil 10–12 cells in length and
each cell bearing four quadrately disposed filaments; the top and
bottom filaments long and branched, the lateral filaments short
and usually simple. The short branchlets of a verticil 3–5 cells
in length and with filaments restricted to the basal cell. Gland
cells on the long filaments of a branchlet. Tetrasporangia restricted to upper and lower filaments of long branchlets. The
tetrasporangia subglobose, cruciately divided, 28–30 μ long, 24–27
μ broad.

LOCAL DISTRIBUTION. Dredged from a depth of 30–35 feet a quarter-
mile from Municipal Wharf, Monterey.
TYPE LOCALITY. Santa Cruz, California.
PACIFIC COAST DISTRIBUTION. Central California (San Francisco) to
southern California (San Pedro).

Platythamnion villosum Kylin   Pl. 79, fig. 2

Kylin, 1925, p. 51; figs. 32 A–32 B, 33 A–33 D.

Thalli, as found on the Monterey Peninsula, up to 4 cm. tall.
With major branches along the percurrent axis distichous, alternate, and usually borne on every fourth cell of the axis. The
branches short but branching in same manner as axis. Cells in
lower portion of axis 150–300 μ broad and with a length 2–3

times the breadth. Each cell of axis and branches with a verticil of four branchlets; two long and two short. The long branchlets of a verticil 6–8 cells in length and each cell bearing three branched filaments; two on the upper side and one on the lower. All three filaments approximately the same length. The short branchlets of a verticil 3–4 cells in length and with all or only the lower cells bearing an opposite pair of filaments. Gland cells usually restricted to filaments of long branchlets. Tetrasporangia restricted to long branchlets of a verticil. The tetrasporangia broadly ellipsoidal, cruciately divided, 25–34 μ long, 18–25 μ broad.

LOCAL DISTRIBUTION. Growing between the mean low-tide and −1.5-foot tide levels. On piling of Municipal Wharf, Monterey. On rocks at Asilomar Point and at Mission Point. Also dredged from a depth of 30–35 feet a quarter-mile from Municipal Wharf, Monterey, and from 25–30 feet near Point Aulon.

TYPE LOCALITY. Friday Harbor, Washington.

PACIFIC COAST DISTRIBUTION. Known from Sitka, Alaska; Puget Sound; and the Monterey Peninsula.

Platythamnion pectinatum Kylin   Pl. 79, fig. 1

Kylin, 1925, p. 53; figs. 32 *D*, 33 *E*, 34 *A*–34 *C*. *Kylin, 1941, p. 28.
Platythamnion heteromorphum Setchell [not of J. G. Agardh]. *Setchell in Phyc. Bor.-Amer. No. 343.

Thalli, as found on the Monterey Peninsula, up to 5 cm. tall. With major branches along the percurrent axis distichously and alternately arranged. The branches relatively long, branched into 2–4 orders of branching, and with the branching in same manner as axis. Cells in lower portion of axis 140–220 μ broad and with a length 1.5–3 times the breadth. Each cell of axis and branches with a verticil of four branchlets; two long and two short. The long branches of a verticil 8–10 cells in length and each cell bearing two filaments on the upper side. The lowermost cell of a long branchlet also at times with a single filament on the under side. The short branchlets of a verticil usually 4 cells in length. Gland cells large, frequently replacing a filament on a branchlet. Tetrasporangia usually restricted to long branchlets of a verticil. The tetrasporangia sessile or pedicellate, broadly ellipsoidal, cruciately divided, 32–36 μ long, 20–23 μ broad.

LOCAL DISTRIBUTION. Growing between the mean low-tide and −1.0-foot tide levels. On piling of Municipal Wharf, Monterey, and on rocks at foot of Twelfth Street, Carmel. On *Polyneura latissima* cast ashore at Moss Beach. Also on rocks dredged from a depth of 30–35 feet a quarter-mile from Municipal Wharf, Monterey.

TYPE LOCALITY. Friday Harbor, Washington.

PACIFIC COAST DISTRIBUTION. Puget Sound to southern California (San Pedro).

Callithamnion Lyngbye, 1819

Thalli filamentous, growing erect from a compact, disc-shaped base or from a branched, filamentous holdfast. Filamentous holdfasts either growing superficially upon or penetrating the substratum. Axis of erect portion obscure to percurrent, alternately branched throughout. The axis (and major branches) corticated from base to apex, corticated only at base, or uncorticated. The branches rebranched into 2–7 orders of branching and with successive orders distichous or lying in various planes. Cells of axis and major branches usually multinucleate and with many small rounded or band-shaped chromatophores.

Homothallic or heterothallic. The spermatangia borne in loose fasciculate clusters or in dense ovoid masses on adaxial side of ultimate branchlets. Certain intercalary cells of major branches forming two opposed supporting cells. One supporting cell producing a laterally borne, 4-celled, carpogonial filament and, after fertilization, a large auxiliary cell at its upper end; the other supporting cell forming only a large auxiliary cell at its upper end. This followed by formation of a small cell between each auxiliary cell and base of carpogonium. The gonimoblast filaments branching upward from auxiliary cells and with all but the basal cells developing into carposporangia. Mature cystocarps 2- or 4-lobed; without an involucre.

Tetrasporophytes with the tetrasporangia borne on adaxial side of ultimate branchlets; usually one on a cell but at times in clusters of two or three. The tetrasporangia tetrahedrally divided.

STRUCTURE AND REPRODUCTION. Kylin, 1923, pp. 56–57; fig. 37. Levring, 1937, pp. 115–118; figs. 18–19. Oltmanns, 1898, pp. 114–119; pl. 6, figs. 1–13; pl. 7, figs. 11–20. Westbrook, 1930.

KEY TO THE SPECIES IN THE LOCAL FLORA

1. Axis and main branches densely corticated..............*C. Pikeanum*
1. Axis and main branches uncorticated........................... 2
　2. Apices of branchlets acutely pointed..............*C. californicum*
　2. Apices of branchlets broadly rounded........................ 3
3. Ultimate branchlets long, with downwardly curved tips...*C. rupicolum*
3. Ultimate branchlets short, with incurved tips...........*C. biseriatum*

Callithamnion Pikeanum Harvey   Pl. 81, fig. 2

Harvey, 1853, p. 230. Gardner, 1927C, p. 405; pl. 87, fig. 1. *Kylin, 1941, p. 28.

Callithamnion arbuscula var. *pacifica* Anderson [not of Harvey]. *Anderson, 1891, p. 222. *Howe, 1893, p. 68.

Ceratothamnion Pikeanum (Harvey) J. G. Agardh, 1892, p. 35. *Phyc. Bor.-Amer. No. 390.

Thalli, as found on the Monterey Peninsula, usually 10–20 cm. tall but occasionally up to 40 cm.; brownish-purple in color. The axis conspicuous, percurrent, corticated from base to apex; clothed on all sides with relatively short (1–5 cm. long) primary branches bearing very short secondary and tertiary branches. All branches to the third order corticated from base to apex. All corticated branches of the second and higher orders densely clothed with alternately branched uncorticated filaments, with the branches recurved and the ultimate branchlets acutely pointed. The tetrasporangia borne on adaxial side of ultimate branchlets, sessile, subspherical, 80–90 μ in diameter.

LOCAL DISTRIBUTION. Growing on vertical face of rocks between the 3.5- and 1.0-foot tide levels. Common everywhere.

TYPE LOCALITY. Golden Gate, San Francisco, California.

PACIFIC COAST DISTRIBUTION. Southeastern Alaska (Vallenar Point) to central California (Carmel Bay).

Callithamnion californicum Gardner   Pl. 80, figs. 2–3

*Gardner, 1927B, p. 378; pl. 78, fig. 4.

Thalli 3–5 cm. tall. With an obscure percurrent axis alternately branched into 5 or 6 orders of branching and the final branchlets irregularly pinnate. Cells in lower portion of axis 45–100 μ broad and with a length up to 10 times the breadth. The axis and major branches uncorticated. Branches of each successive order progressively smaller and each order of branching arising on adaxial side of a branch of the previous order. The ultimate branchlets 4–7 cells in length and gradually tapering to an acute tip. Tetrasporangia borne on adaxial side of branchlets and restricted to the lowermost 1–3 cells, sessile, 65–105 μ long, 40–56 μ broad.

LOCAL DISTRIBUTION. Growing on rocks between the 1.0- and −0.5-foot tide levels. Asilomar Point; foot of Twelfth Street, Carmel; Mission Point; Carmel Bay.

TYPE LOCALITY. Carmel Bay, California.

PACIFIC COAST DISTRIBUTION. As above.

Callithamnion rupicolum Anderson   Pl. 81, fig. 3

Anderson, 1894, p. 360; figs. *A–B*. Phyc. Bor.-Amer. No. 1648.

Thalli with many prostrate branches and growing in felt-like patches. The erect branches, as found on the Monterey Peninsula, up to 2 cm. tall. The axis conspicuous, percurrent. Cells in lower portion of axis 80–110 μ broad and with a length 5–8 times the breadth. The axis pinnately and alternately branched into 2–4 orders of branching; the lower primary branches at times with a few descending rhizoidal filaments incompletely corticating basal portion of axis. Branches of all orders borne on middle of a cell. The ultimate branchlets 8–12 cells in length, widely divergent from branch bearing them and with downwardly curved tips. Cells of branchlets barrel-shaped and the terminal cell with a broadly rounded apex. Tetrasporangia borne on adaxial side of a branchlet, the lowermost 6–8 cells of branchlet frequently with tetrasporangia. The tetrasporangia sessile, ellipsoidal, 56–72 μ long, 52–60 μ broad.

LOCAL DISTRIBUTION. Growing between the 4.5- and −0.5-foot tide levels. Thalli of higher tide levels usually on rocks; those from lowermost levels frequently on articulated corallines. Mussel Point; Point Pinos; Asilomar Point; Point Joe; Cypress Point; Pebble Beach; Mission Point.

TYPE LOCALITY. Monterey Bay, California.

PACIFIC COAST DISTRIBUTION. Central California (Fort Ross) to southern California (Laguna Beach).

Callithamnion biseriatum Kylin   Pl. 80, fig. 4

Kylin, 1925, p. 54; figs. 35, 36 *A*–36 *C*.

Thalli usually epiphytic on membranous Florideae and with multicellular rhizoidal branches penetrating deeply into tissues of host. The erect branches, as found on the Monterey Peninsula, 1–2 cm. tall. The axis conspicuous, percurrent, alternately branched into 2–4 successive orders of branching. Cells in lower portion of axis 50–150 μ broad and with a length 2–4 times the breadth. Branches of some thalli regularly with branchlets from the two lowermost cells on the adaxial side; branches of other thalli alternately branched throughout. The branchlets curved toward tip of branch bearing them, tapering slightly, with broadly rounded apices. Tetrasporangia on adaxial side of branchlets, pedicellate, the pedicels sometimes branched and with 2–3 tetrasporangia. The tetrasporangia pyriform, 46–52 μ long, 42–46 μ broad.

LOCAL DISTRIBUTION. Epiphytic on *Schizymenia epiphytica* cast ashore at Moss Beach and at Carmel Beach.

TYPE LOCALITY. Friday Harbor, Washington.

PACIFIC COAST DISTRIBUTION. Known only from Friday Harbor and vicinity, and from the Monterey Peninsula.

Pleonosporium Nägeli, 1862

Thalli filamentous, erect, alternately branched. With a conspicuous percurrent axis; the axis with branches of 3–7 orders of branching. The axis and primary branches corticated nearly to apex, corticated only at base, or uncorticated.

Heterothallic. The spermatangia in corymbose or in dense ellipsoidal clusters on ultimate branchlets; restricted to adaxial side or borne alternately on abaxial and adaxial sides. Female plants with subterminal cells of certain branches producing two supporting cells, one of which bears a 4-celled carpogonial filament. Formation of auxiliary cells and development of cystocarp presumably as in *Callithamnion.* The mature cystocarp globose or bilobed, naked or with a rudimentary involucre.

The tetrasporophytes producing polysporangia only. The polysporangia sessile or pedicellate, restricted to adaxial side of branchlets or borne in alternate abaxial and adaxial succession on branchlets.

STRUCTURE AND REPRODUCTION. Kylin, 1925, pp. 56–58; fig. 37. Newton, 1931, pp. 373–374; fig. 225.

KEY TO THE SPECIES IN THE LOCAL FLORA

1. Axis and major branches corticated...................*P. dasyoides*
1. Axis and major branches uncorticated............*P. vancouverianum*

Pleonosporium dasyoides (J. G. Agardh) DeToni
Pl. 81, fig. 1; pl. 83, fig. 1

DeToni, 1903, p. 1310. *Kylin, 1941, p. 28.
Callithamnion dasyoides J. G. Agardh, 1876, p. 31. *Anderson, 1891, p. 222.
*Howe, 1893, p. 68. *Phyc. Bor.-Amer. No. 96.

Thalli, as found on the Monterey Peninsula, usually 5–10 cm. tall but occasionally up to 20 cm. The thallus alternately branched and with primary branches along upper half of percurrent axis much longer than those in lower half. The axis and branches of first and second orders heavily corticated except near the apices; the axis about 1 mm. broad near the base. The branches diverging widely from axis or branch bearing them. The branchlets 12–16 cells in length, distichously plumose; successive branchlets on a branch overlapping one another. The spermatangia on simple filaments borne alternately along a branchlet and the lowermost filament with spermatangia always on the abaxial side of a branchlet. The polysporangia pedicellate, terminating simple or branched filaments borne near base of a branchlet. The filament bearing polysporangia usually on adaxial side of second cell from base of a branchlet but at times on abaxial side of basal cell. The polysporangia broadly obpyriform, 75–85 μ long, 55–70 μ broad.

LOCAL DISTRIBUTION. Epiphytic on various Florideae, especially *Ptilota densa,* growing between the mean low-tide and −1.5-foot tide levels. Asilomar Point; Middle Reef of Moss Beach; Point Joe; Pebble Beach. Also dredged from a depth of 30–50 feet near Point Aulon and from 15–20 feet at Stillwater Cove.

TYPE LOCALITY. "California."

PACIFIC COAST DISTRIBUTION. Central California (Tomales Bay) to southern California (San Pedro).

Pleonosporium vancouverianum J. G. Agardh Pl. 82, figs. 1–2

J. G. Agardh, 1892, p. 37. Kylin, 1925, p. 57; figs. 37*A*–37*C*.
Callithamnion vancouverianum J. G. Agardh, 1876, p. 30.

Thalli, as found on the Monterey Peninsula, 1.5–2.5 cm. tall. Alternately and distichously branched into two or three orders of branching and with the primary branches progressively longer toward base of thallus. The axis percurrent, uncorticated; with cells in the lower portion 200–300 μ broad and slightly longer than broad. The branches not diverging widely from axis or from branch bearing them. The branchlets 15–20 cells in length, distichously and densely plumose; successive branchlets on a branch not overlapping one another. The spermatangia on branched filaments borne alternately along a branchlet. The spermatangia borne alternately on the filament and the lowermost always on the abaxial side. Polysporangia sessile and borne alternately along simple filaments on a branchlet; the lowermost always on abaxial side of a filament. The polysporangia obpyriform, 58–85 μ long, 28–45 μ broad.

LOCAL DISTRIBUTION. Dredged from a depth of 30–35 feet a quarter-mile from Municipal Wharf, Monterey. Found both on rocks and on tube worms.

TYPE LOCALITY. Esquimalt, British Columbia.

PACIFIC COAST DISTRIBUTION. Known only from Vancouver Island, British Columbia; Puget Sound; and the Monterey Peninsula.

Spermothamnion Areschoug, 1877

Thalli strictly filamentous, freely branched, uncorticated; differentiated into prostrate and erect filaments. Prostrate filaments irregularly branched and with branches creeping over the substratum. Cells of prostrate filament multinucleate, frequently with the ventral face bearing a unicellular rhizoid terminating in an expanded disc. Many cells of prostrate filaments also with an erect branched filament on the dorsal side. Branching of erect filaments predominately unilateral to opposite. Cells of erect filaments uninucleate and with many small disc-shaped chromatophores.

Homothallic or heterothallic. Sometimes also with sex organs on diploid tetrasporophytes. The spermatangia in dense ellipsoid masses on adaxial side of short branchlets borne near base of the erect filaments. Female thalli with reproductive organs borne on subterminal cell of a three- or four-celled branch of an erect filament. This subterminal cell dividing vertically to cut off three supporting cells of equal size. The abaxial (median) supporting cell functionless. One of the other two supporting cells producing a laterally borne sterile cell, a laterally borne, four-celled carpogonial filament, and (after fertilization) an auxiliary cell. The remaining supporting cell forming only an auxiliary cell. The formation of auxiliary cell followed by intercalation of a small cell between each auxiliary cell and base of the carpogonium. The gonimoblast filaments branching upward from the auxiliary cells and with only the terminal cells developing into carposporangia. The mature cystocarp naked or with a loose involucre of incurved filaments.

According to the species the tetrasporophytes with tetrasporangia or with polysporangia. Both types of sporangium produced in loose clusters at the ends of short branches borne near base of erect filaments.

STRUCTURE AND REPRODUCTION. Drew, 1934. Drew, 1937. Kylin, 1930, pp. 60–66; figs. 46, 49. Rosenvinge, 1923, pp. 298–305; figs. 202–211.

With one species in the local flora.

Spermothamnion Snyderae Farlow   Pl. 82, figs. 3–5

Farlow, 1899, p. 74. Drew, 1937, p. 463; text figs. 1–12; pl. 21. Phyc. Bor.-Amer. No. 598.

Thalli, as found on the Monterey Peninsula, 2–5 cm. tall. The erect filaments with most branches unilateral and rarely with more than three orders of branching. Successive orders of branching approximately the same breadth. Cells of erect filaments 70–100 μ broad and with a length 10–20 times the breadth. The cysto-carps without an involucre. Tetrasporophytes with polysporangia only, and borne terminally on short branches near base of erect filaments. The polysporangia broadly ellipsoidal, 95–110 μ long, 75–90 μ broad; with 8–32 (usually 12 or 16) polyspores. Thalli perennial but rarely fruiting during spring and summer.

LOCAL DISTRIBUTION. Growing on the vertical face of rocks between the 0.5- and −1.5-foot tide levels. Usually in extensive tufted masses. Mussel Point; Point Pinos; Middle Reef of Moss Beach; Point Joe; Cypress Point; Pescadero Point; Pebble Beach; Mission Point. Also dredged from a depth of 30–35 feet a quarter-mile from Municipal Wharf, Monterey; from 35 to 40 feet near Mussel Point; from 30 to 35 feet near Point Pinos; and from 20 to 25 feet near Arrowhead Point.

TYPE LOCALITY. Santa Cruz, California.

PACIFIC COAST DISTRIBUTION. Central California (Bolinas) to southern California (San Diego).

Griffithsia C. A. Agardh, 1817

Thalli erect, freely branched, bushy filaments. The branching usually dichotomous. The cells visible to the naked eye, usually broadening gradually from base to apex. Upper ends of cells with or without delicate repeatedly branched multicellular hairs. The cells with an immense number of nuclei and chromatophores. Cell division by the abstriction of a small, lens-shaped, daughter cell at the distal end of a cell.

Heterothallic. The spermatangia borne terminally on simple or repeatedly branched filaments from upper end of a large vegetative cell. The spermatangial masses with or without an involucre of sterile filaments. Female thalli with a special three-celled branch whose median cell bears one or two supporting cells; the supporting cell (or cells) producing a four-celled carpogonial filament. After fertilization the supporting cell (or cells) cutting off an auxiliary cell from which grow gonimoblast filaments most of whose cells develop into carposporangia. The mature cystocarp embedded in a gelatinous matrix and partially enveloped by an involucre of incurved rays (filaments).

The tetrasporophytes with the tetrasporangia developing terminally on sparsely branched filaments. The tetrasporangial filaments borne in sori at upper end of large vegetative cells. The tetrasporangia tetrahedrally divided.

STRUCTURE AND REPRODUCTION. Kylin, 1916. Kylin, 1925, pp. 58–60; figs. 38–39. Lewis, 1909.

With one species in the local flora.

Griffithsia pacifica Kylin   Pl. 83, fig. 2

Kylin, 1925, p. 58; figs. 38–39. *Kylin, 1941, p. 28.
Griffithsia opuntioides Anderson [not of J. G. Agardh]. *Anderson, 1891, p. 222.
Griffithsia sp. *Howe, 1893, p. 68.

Thalli, as found on the Monterey Peninsula, up to 5 cm. tall; reddish-pink in color. The branching regularly dichotomous. The cells cylindrical, slightly inflated at upper end, up to 4 cm. long and 0.5 mm. broad, without branched filaments at the upper end. Spermatangia on profusely branched filaments without involucres. Tetrasporangial filaments with one-celled involucral rays.

LOCAL DISTRIBUTION. Growing upon rocks between the 0.5- and −1.5-foot tide levels. Isolated tufts have been found at Mussel Point; Point Aulon; Arch Rock; Point Pinos; Middle Reef of Moss Beach; Fanshell Beach; Cypress Point; Pescadero Point; Pebble Beach; Mission Point. Also dredged from a depth of 25–30 feet near Point Aulon; from 30 to 35 feet near Point Pinos; and from 20 to 25 feet near Pescadero Rock.

TYPE LOCALITY. Friday Harbor, Washington.

PACIFIC COAST DISTRIBUTION. Puget Sound to southern California (San Diego).

Fruiting specimens of this species are of extremely rare occurrence locally irrespective of the time of year at which collections are made.

Ceramium Roth, 1797

Thalli usually erect but at times partially or wholly prostrate. Erect portion cylindrical, freely branched, with branches of all orders corticated and with the corticating cells either in transverse belts or in a continuous layer. The branching either alternate, predominately unilateral, or irregular; frequently appearing as if dichotomous. Branch tips usually forcipate. Axial filament of a branch composed of large cells and with each cell cutting off a transverse band of corticating cells at the upper end. The interval between successive bands remaining uncorticated or becoming corticated by an upward and downward growth of the corticating tissue.

Heterothallic. The spermatangia forming a continuous layer on the corticating cells. Carpogonial filament four-celled, its supporting cell a corticating cell of a branch. Certain species with the supporting cell producing two carpogonial filaments. In either case the supporting cell cutting off a single auxiliary cell after fertilization. The gonimoblast filaments growing upward from the auxiliary cell and with practically all cells developing into carposporangia. The mature cystocarp intercalary on a branch; usually surrounded by an involucre composed of a few incurved branches.

Tetrasporophytes regularly with tetrasporangia and sometimes also with polysporangia containing several spores. The sporangia sessile; either standing above, partially enclosed by, or completely enclosed by surrounding cells. The tetrasporangia tetrahedrally divided.

STRUCTURE AND REPRODUCTION. Kylin, 1923, pp. 62–64; fig. 42. Phillips, 1897, p. 361; pl. 18, fig. 19. Rosenvinge, 1923, pp. 371–387; figs. 308–324.

KEY TO THE SPECIES IN THE LOCAL FLORA

1. Branches completely covered by corticating cells.................. 2
1. Branches with transverse uncorticated bands.............C. Gardneri
　　2. Older portions of major branches with many
　　　　short lateral branches ....C. pacificum
　　2. Older portions of major branches lacking or with
　　　　few short lateral branches................................ 3
3. Epiphytic on Codium...................................C. codicola
3. Epiphytic on various algae or saxicolous.............C. Eatonianum

Ceramium Gardneri Kylin　　　　　　　　　　Pl. 84, fig. 2

*Kylin, 1941, p. 29.
Ceramium diaphanum Anderson [not of (Lightfoot) Roth]. *Anderson, 1891, p. 221. *Howe, 1893, p. 67.
Ceramium californicum Gardner [not of J. G. Agardh]. *Gardner in Phyc. Bor.-Amer. No. 2248.

Thalli, as found on the Monterey Peninsula, 1–3 cm. tall; bright salmon pink in color. The branching dichotomous and with the branches diverging 35°–45°. Lower portion of major dichotomies without or with a few lateral branchlets of much smaller diameter. All branches with corticating tissue restricted to nodes and lying in sharply delimited transverse bands. Lower portion of thallus with the colorless uncorticated internodes 3–4 times longer than the colored corticated nodes. Cystocarps unknown. The tetrasporangia partly embedded in the corticating tissue and usually restricted to inner face of the dichotomies.

LOCAL DISTRIBUTION. Growing on rocks between the mean low-tide and 1.0-foot tide levels. Usually on rocks exposed to heavy surf but at times in sheltered tide pools. Monterey; Cypress Point; Pescadero Point.

TYPE LOCALITY. Pescadero Point, Monterey Peninsula, California.

PACIFIC COAST DISTRIBUTION. Southern Oregon (Coos Bay) to central California (Carmel Highlands).

This is the only incompletely corticated species in the local flora. The closely related *C. californicum* J. G. Agardh, a rather common alga at the type locality (Santa Cruz, California), has not been collected on the Monterey Peninsula.

Ceramium pacificum (Collins) Kylin   Pl. 83, fig. 3

Kylin, 1925, p. 61. *Kylin, 1941, p. 29.
Ceramium rubrum var. *pacificum* *Collins in Phyc. Bor.-Amer. No. 893.
Ceramium rubrum Anderson [not of (Hudson) C. A. Agardh]. *Anderson, 1891, p. 221. *Howe, 1893, p. 67.

Thalli, as found on the Monterey Peninsula, 5–18 cm. tall; deep carmine in color. The branching dichotomous and with the branches diverging 50°–80°. Ultimate dichotomies less widely divergent and forcipate. The branches beset with numerous simple or forked proliferous branchlets, most of which are less than 5 mm. in length. All branches and branchlets completely corticated and with the zonate differentiation of the nodal and internodal portions of corticating tissue indistinct. Cystocarps surrounded by involucral branches and borne at the last two or three forkings of branches. The tetrasporangia immersed in the corticating tissue; irregularly distributed.

LOCAL DISTRIBUTION. Growing on sheltered rocks between the 0.5- and −1.0-foot tide levels. Monterey; Point Pinos; Middle Reef of Moss Beach. Occasionally cast ashore in abundance on beach at Monterey and at Pebble Beach.

TYPE LOCALITY. Monterey, California.

PACIFIC COAST DISTRIBUTION. British Columbia (Vancouver Island) to southern California (Santa Barbara).

Easily distinguished from other local species by size of thallus and by the numerous short proliferous branchlets along the branches.

Ceramium codicola J. G. Agardh   Pl. 84, fig. 1

J. G. Agardh, 1894, p. 23. Setchell, 1905, p. 2. *Kylin, 1941, p. 29. Phyc. Bor.-Amer. No. 248.

Thalli, as found on the Monterey Peninsula, usually 1–2.5

cm. tall but at times up to 4 cm.; dull red in color. The branching predominately dichotomous and with the branches diverging 50°–70°. Ultimate dichotomies not markedly forcipate. Major branches at times with a few short proliferous branchlets. The branches and branchlets completely corticated and with the zonate differentiation between nodal and internodal portions of corticating tissue inconspicuous. The thalli always epiphytic and attached to host by means of rhizoids with inflated bulbous tips. Cystocarps surrounded by involucral branches and borne at the last two or three dichotomies of branches.

LOCAL DISTRIBUTION. On the Monterey Peninsula found only on *Codium fragile*. Abundant locally wherever the host is present.

TYPE LOCALITY. Santa Cruz, California.

PACIFIC COAST DISTRIBUTION. Alaska (Sitka) to southern California (San Diego).

Ceramium Eatonianum (Farlow) DeToni   Pl. 84, figs. 3–4

DeToni, 1903, p. 1493.
Centroceras Eatonianum Farlow, 1875, p. 373. *Anderson, 1891, p. 222. *Howe, 1893, p. 67. *Kylin, 1941, p. 30. Algae Exsicc. Amer. Bor. No. 30.

Thalli, as found on the Monterey Peninsula, usually 4–10 cm. tall but at times up to 15 cm.; generally purplish-black in color. The branching dichotomous but appearing as if distichously pinnate; divergence of branches 20°–40°. Without short proliferous branchlets. All branches completely corticated, somewhat constricted at nodes, and with the internodal corticating cells tending to lie in vertical rows. Nodal portion of the corticating tissue with gland cells. Cystocarps lateral, without involucral branches. The tetrasporangia completely immersed in the corticating tissue.

LOCAL DISTRIBUTION. Growing between the 2.5- and −1.0-foot tide levels. Usually on rocks but occasionally on other algae. Mussel Point; Point Pinos; Middle Reef of Moss Beach; Pescadero Point; Pebble Beach; Mission Point. Also dredged from a depth of 20–25 feet near Arrowhead Point.

TYPE LOCALITY. Not stated.

PACIFIC COAST DISTRIBUTION. Southern Oregon (Coos Bay) to southern California (San Diego).

Centroceras Kützing, 1841

The thalli usually erect but sometimes in prostrate mats. The erect portion cylindrical, freely branched, and with branches of all orders corticated by rectangular cells regularly arranged in vertical rows. The branching usually dichotomous, the dichotomies equal or unequal and resembling a sympodium; more rarely the branching lateral. Branch tips forcipate. Each branch with an axial filament of large cylindrical cells and with each cell cutting off a transverse ring of corticating cells at the upper end. The corticating cells dividing transversely and developing into a tissue ensheathing the entire axial cell. The uppermost corticating cells encircling each axial cell frequently with a transverse ring of 1- to 3-celled spines at the upper end.

Spermatangia unknown. Carpogonial filaments and development of cystocarp unknown. The mature cystocarps globose, sessile, surrounded by an involucre of a few curved branches.

Tetrasporophytes with tetrasporangia developing from corticating cells and at times with them borne on short somewhat specialized branches. The tetrasporangia lying in a transverse ring encircling the apex of a node and projecting beyond the adjoining corticating cells. The tetrasporangia tetrahedrally divided.

Centroceras clavulatum (C. A. Agardh) Montagne

Pl. 84, figs. 5–6

Montagne apud Durieu, 1846, p. 140. Harvey, 1853, p. 211; pl. 33, fig. C. *Anderson, 1891, p. 222. *Howe, 1893, p. 67. *Kylin, 1941, p. 30. Phyc. Bor.-Amer. No. 148B.

Ceramium clavulatum C. A. Agardh apud Kunth, 1822, p. 2.

Thalli, as found on the Monterey Peninsula, up to 8 cm. tall; blackish-red in color. Dichotomously branched and with the two arms of each dichotomy equal in length and diverging 10°–15°. The ultimate dichotomies distinctly forcipate. Each segment of the upper dichotomies with a transverse whorl of one- or two-celled spines at the upper end; the spines on segments of lower dichotomies persistent or disappearing. The lower dichotomies, as found locally, 130–180 μ in diameter and with segments 350–450 μ long.

LOCAL DISTRIBUTION. Growing on rocks between the 2.0-foot and mean low-tide levels. Abundant at certain stations. Monterey; Mussel Point; Point Pinos; Middle Reef of Moss Beach; Fanshell Beach; Cypress Point; Pebble Beach; Mission Point.

TYPE LOCALITY. Callao, Peru.

PACIFIC COAST DISTRIBUTION. Central California (Santa Cruz) to Baja California (La Paz).

Branches of the type specimen from Callao are 85–110 μ in diameter (Howe, 1911, p. 509) or somewhat narrower than those of Monterey Peninsula specimens.

Microcladia Greville, 1830

Thalli erect, freely branched, with or without prostrate rhizome-like branches. The erect portion branched into 5–7 orders of branching and with cylindrical to slightly compressed branches. The branching distichous and regularly alternate or appearing to be unilateral and alternately pectinate. Apices of ultimate branchlets forcipate. Each branch with an axial filament of large cells and all cells corticated by irregularly shaped cells. Older portions of branches with the corticating tissue several cells in thickness and with progressive smaller cells toward the branch surface.

Heterothallic. The spermatangia developing in a continuous layer on the ultimate branches. Carpogonial filaments and development of cystocarp unknown. The mature cystocarps globose, with or without an involucre of 3–6 curved corticated branches.

Tetrasporophytes with tetrasporangia borne upon branches of the last three orders. The tetrasporangia embedded among surface cells of cortex; either in a vertical row on abaxial side of branch or densely crowded on all sides of a branch. The tetrasporangia tetrahedrally divided.

STRUCTURE AND REPRODUCTION. Schmitz and Hauptfleisch, 1896–1897, p. 502.

KEY TO THE SPECIES IN THE LOCAL FLORA

1. Branching distichous and alternate.............................. 2
1. Branching appearing as if unilateral and pectinate.........*M. borealis*
    2. Cystocarps with an involucre......................*M. Coulteri*
    2. Cystocarps without an involucre.................*M. californica*

Microcladia Coulteri Harvey   Pl. 86, figs. 1–2

*Harvey, 1853, p. 209; pl. 33, fig. *A*. *Anderson, 1891, p. 222. *Howe, 1893, p. 67. *Kylin, 1941, p. 30. Phyc. Bor.-Amer. No. 1448.

Thalli epiphytic and with an irregularly branched holdfast completely embedded in host. As found on the Monterey Peninsula, up to 35 cm. tall and deep rose-red in color. With a percurrent axis branched into 5–7 orders of branching. The branching regularly alternate, distichous, and with all branches lying in one plane. Lower third of axis usually with long branches and outline of the entire shoot pyramidate. Branches of the first, second, and third orders usually straight; those of the ultimate orders curved and forcipate. Cystocarps restricted to branches of the final orders; with an involucre of 3–6 curved corticated branchlets. The tetrasporangia densely crowded on all sides of branches of the last three orders.

LOCAL DISTRIBUTION. Epiphytic on the larger membranous Florideae, especially *Gigartina, Prionitis,* and *Grateloupia.* Occasionally found on Laminariales. Abundant over the entire Peninsula on hosts growing between the 1.0- and −1.5-foot tide levels. Also found on Florideae dredged from a depth of 20–25 feet near Mussel Point and at Stillwater Cove.

TYPE LOCALITY. Monterey, California.

PACIFIC COAST DISTRIBUTION. British Columbia (Vancouver Island) to southern California (San Diego).

Microcladia californica Farlow   Pl. 85, figs. 9–10

Farlow, 1875, p. 372. *Anderson, 1891, p. 222. *Phyc. Bor.-Amer. No. 548.

Thalli epiphytic. Size and vegetative structure as in *M. Coulteri.* The cystocarps naked and without an involucre of branchlets.

LOCAL DISTRIBUTION. Usually found epiphytic on *Egregia.* Monterey; Point Pinos; Middle Reef of Moss Beach; Pescadero Point; Pebble Beach.

TYPE LOCALITY. Santa Cruz, California.

PACIFIC COAST DISTRIBUTION. Central California (San Francisco) to southern California (San Diego).

M. californica and *M. Coulteri* resemble each other so closely in vegetative structure that cystocarpic plants must be available before the two can be distinguished with certainty. On the Monterey Peninsula *M. californica* is a very rare plant as compared with *M. Coulteri.*

Microcladia borealis Ruprecht   Pl. 85, fig. 11

Ruprecht, 1851, p. 259. Harvey, 1853, p. 210. *Anderson, 1891, p. 222. *Howe, 1893, p. 67. *Kylin, 1941, p. 30. *Phyc. Bor.-Amer. No. 48.

Thalli, as found on the Monterey Peninsula, up to 18 cm. tall; dark olive-gray to deep red in color. With tufts of erect branches growing from a prostrate rhizome-like system of branches. The erect branches with 5–6 orders of branching but without branches in the lower third. The branching unilateral, pectinate, and with the pectination in successive orders of branching alternate. Branches of the first and second orders arcuate and curving away from apex or axis or branch bearing them; branches of higher orders incurved and with forcipate tips. The tetrasporangia densely crowded on somewhat inflated branch tips.

LOCAL DISTRIBUTION. Growing between the 2.5- and 0.5-foot tide levels on vertical face of rocks more or less exposed to surf. Common everywhere and at times present in abundance.

TYPE LOCALITY. Unalaska Island, Alaska.

PACIFIC COAST DISTRIBUTION. Alaska (Unalaska) to central California (San Simeon).

Ptilota C. A. Agardh, 1817

Thalli relatively large, erect, profusely and distichously branched, with branches of all orders more than one cell in thickness. The branching opposite and with one of each pair of branches much longer than the opposite branch or branchlet. The long and the short branch of each successive pair alternate with the corresponding branch in the pair below. The major branches more or less compressed; the ultimate branchlets markedly compressed and resembling minute leaflets. Each branch with an axial filament completely corticated from base to apex; the corticating tissue in mature portions of branches more than one cell in thickness.

Heterothallic. The spermatangia in a continuous layer on surface of the ultimate branchlets. Carpogonial filaments 4-celled borne on a supporting cell cut off from the subterminal axial cell of a branchlet; the supporting cell also producing three 3-celled sterile filaments superficially resembling carpogonial filaments. The supporting cell, after fertilization, cutting off an auxiliary cell at the upper side and the carpogonium cutting off a small cell that bridges the gap between it and the auxiliary cell. The auxiliary cell dividing transversely and the gonimoblast filaments growing from the upper (and larger) daughter cell. The gonimoblast filaments with most of the cells developing into carposporangia. Mature cystocarps borne at tips of branchlets, globose, surrounded by an involucre of incurved rays.

Tetrasporophytes with the tetrasporangia developing from superficial cells of branchlets and borne more or less freely exposed. The tetrasporangia tetrahedrally divided.

STRUCTURE AND REPRODUCTION. Davis, 1896. Kylin, 1923, pp. 58–61; figs. 39–40. Phillips, 1897, pp. 361–366; pl. 18, figs. 16, 18.

KEY TO THE SPECIES IN THE LOCAL FLORA

1. Margins of ultimate branchlets smooth.......................... 2
1. One or both margins of ultimate branchlets serrate............... 3

   2. Branchlets curving toward branch apex; length
      about ten times the breadth......................*P. californica*
   2. Branchlets not curving toward branch apex; length
      about five times maximum breadth................*P. hypnoides*
3. Serrate on both margins ....*P. filicina*
3. Serrate only on abaxial margin...........................*P. densa*

Ptilota hypnoides Harvey   Pl. 85, figs. 3–4

   *Harvey, 1833, p. 164. *Harvey, 1853, p. 220; pl. 32, fig. *A*. *Anderson, 1891, p. 222. *Howe, 1893, p. 67. *Kylin, 1941, p. 28. *Phyc. Bor.-Amer. No. 599.

Thalli, as found on the Monterey Peninsula, up to 25 cm. tall; blackish-red in color. Frequently with several erect shoots from a common irregularly hemispherical base. Erect shoots with a leaflet opposite each branch and successive pairs regularly alternate. The branch opposite each leaflet usually very short but here and there becoming long and with 3–4 orders of branching. The leaflets lanceolate, with smooth margins, and with a length not over six times the breadth. The leaflets with the upper half gradually attenuated to a point and with the abaxial margin of the lower half more strongly curved than the adaxial margin.

   LOCAL DISTRIBUTION. Isolated stunted thalli 6–8 cm. tall have been found on articulated corallines at Point Pinos; Point Joe; Midway Point; and the north end of Carmel Beach. Well-developed thalli 15 cm. or more tall are frequently cast ashore in abundance at the Middle Reef of Moss Beach.
   TYPE LOCALITY. Monterey, California.
   PACIFIC COAST DISTRIBUTION. Alaska (Sitka) to central California (San Luis Obispo County).

Ptilota californica Ruprecht   Pl. 85, figs. 1–2

   Ruprecht ex Harvey, 1853, p. 222.

Thalli, as found on the Monterey Peninsula, up to 25 cm. tall; deep rose-red in color. Frequently with several erect shoots from a common disc-shaped base. Erect shoots with a leaflet opposite each branch and successive pairs regularly alternate. The branch opposite most leaflets elongating considerably and with 2–4 orders of branching. The final orders of branches with regularly alternating pairs of leaflets and branch primordia. The leaflets linear-lanceolate, with a length 5–10 times the breadth and with smooth margins; the lower half bending rather abruptly toward the branch apex, the upper half gradually narrowing to a rounded tip.

   LOCAL DISTRIBUTION. Growing in the lower littoral. Pacific Grove; Point Joe. Cast ashore Middle Reef of Moss Beach.

Type Locality. "Northern California" (probably Bodega or Fort Ross).

Pacific Coast Distribution. Southern Oregon (Cape Arago) to southern California (San Diego).

Ptilota filicina (Farlow) J. G. Agardh   Pl. 85, figs. 5–6

J. G. Agardh, 1876, p. 76. *Anderson, 1891, p. 222. Phyc. Bor.-Amer. No. 643.
Ptilota plumosa var. *filicina* Farlow, 1875, p. 374. *Howe, 1893, p. 68.
*Davis, 1896, p. 366.
Ptilota californica var. *concinna* Harvey, 1853, p. 222.

Thalli, as found on the Monterey Peninsula, usually 10–35 cm. tall but at times up to 45 cm.; deep bright red in color. With several long branches and these with 2–4 orders of branching. The branches with leaflets and unbranched branches in opposite pairs and regularly alternate. The leaflets slightly falcate, with both margins serrate, tips of leaflets acute; branches opposite the leaflets frequently 2–5 cm. long and with well-developed leaflets.

Local Distribution. Isolated thalli have been collected between the mean low-tide and −1.5-foot tide levels at the Middle Reef of Moss Beach and at Cypress Point. Frequently cast ashore in abundance at Moss Beach.

Type Locality. Pacific Grove, California.

Pacific Coast Distribution. Alaska (Pribilof Islands) to central California (Carmel Bay).

Ptilota densa C. A. Agardh   Pl. 85, figs. 7–8

C. A. Agardh, 1822, p. 387. Harvey, 1853, p. 219; pl. 32, fig. B. *Howe, 1893, p. 68. *Kylin, 1941, p. 28. Phyc. Bor.-Amer. No. 1345.
Ptilota pectinata *Harvey, 1833, p. 165.

Thalli, as found on the Monterey Peninsula, 10–25 cm. tall; dull brownish-red in color. With an obscure central axis and with certain of the lower branches equaling it in length. Sides of axis and major branches densely fringed with leaflets and very short branches bearing leaflets. Leaflets and short branchlets in opposite pairs and regularly alternate. The leaflets falcate, with the adaxial margin smooth and concave, the abaxial margin strongly serrate and convex.

Local Distribution. Isolated thalli have been found on articulated corallines growing between the 0.5- and −1.5-foot tide levels. Middle Reef of Moss Beach; Cypress Point; Pescadero Point. Frequently cast ashore in abundance at Point Pinos; Moss Beach; Fanshell Beach; and Carmel Beach.

Type Locality. Monterey, California (erroneously given as Cape of Good Hope, Africa, in the original description).

Pacific Coast Distribution. Central California (Tomales Bay) to southern California (San Pedro).

Family DELESSERIACEAE

Thalli foliaceous or markedly compressed and divided into many segments. The thalli frequently with a midrib or veins, or both. The blade or each segment of a blade with an axial filament each of whose cells bears an opposed pair of filaments. Successive lateral filaments adjoining one another and compacted into a parenchymatous sheet one or more than one cell in thickness.

Heterothallic. The spermatangia in sori and these usually irregularly scattered over blade. Carpogonial filaments 4-celled; restricted to axial filament of blade or scattered over blade. Supporting cell of carpogonial filament usually with two sterile filaments. The auxiliary cell formed after fertilization and cut off directly from supporting cell of carpogonial filament. The auxiliary cell, supporting cell and sterile filaments from the latter usually fusing to form an irregularly shaped placental cell from which gonimoblast filaments grow toward the thallus surface. Gonimoblast filaments with all cells or with only the terminal cells developing into carposporangia. ·The mature cystocarp projecting beyond surface of thallus and surrounded by a pericarp.

Tetrasporophytes with the tetrasporangia in sori. The sori definitely arranged or indiscriminately scattered on surface of blade. The tetrasporangia tetrahedrally divided.

KEY TO THE GENERA IN THE LOCAL FLORA

1. Carpogonial filaments and cystocarps restricted to midrib of thallus.. 2
1. Carpogonial filaments and cystocarps scattered over entire blade.... 4
   2. New blades developing from margin of old blades.............. 3
   2. New blades developing from midrib of old blades.*Delesseria* (p. 338)
3. Primary and secondary filaments from axial filament
     extending to thallus margin.............*Branchioglossum* (p. 335)
3. Only the primary filaments from axial filament
     extending to thallus margin..............*Membranoptera* (p. 336)
   4. Gonimoblast filaments with carposporangia in chains............ 5
   4. Gonimoblast filaments with terminal carposporangia........... 11
5. Thalli free-living 6
5. Thalli parasitic ....*Polycoryne* (p. 347)
   6. Tetrasporangial sori scattered over entire blade................ 7
   6. Tetrasporangial sori not scattered over entire blade............. 9
7. Thallus with a percurrent midrib.................*Phycodrys* (p. 342)
7. Thallus lacking a percurrent midrib........................... 8
   8. Blade with a network of coarse veins...........*Polyneura* (p. 340)
   8. Blade with inconspicuous veins...........*Myriogramme* (p. 345)

Branchioglossum Kylin, 1924

Thalli erect, ribbon-like, suboppositely branched, and with 3–4 orders of branching. New branches developing at margins of old branches. The branches with a percurrent midrib more than one cell in thickness and with the portions lateral to the midrib monostromatic. Each branch with every cell of axial filament bearing an opposite pair of filaments and these bearing secondary filaments on the abaxial side only. The primary and secondary filaments compacted into a parenchymatous monostromatic sheet and all filaments extending to margin of blade. The terminal cell of each primary lateral filament potentially capable of producing a new lateral branch.

Heterothallic. The spermatangia in sori covering most of monostromatic portion of branch tips. Carpogonial filaments and development of cystocarps unknown. The mature cystocarps borne along the midrib, bulging toward one side of the thallus and with a single ostiole in the overlying vegetative tissue.

Tetrasporophytes with tetrasporangia in sori borne on monostromatic portion of branches or in small proliferous blades growing from midrib. The sori rounded or linear and lying a short distance in from margin of blade. The tetrasporangia tetrahedrally divided.

STRUCTURE AND REPRODUCTION. Kylin, 1924, p. 8; fig. 2.

Branchioglossum Woodii (J. G. Agardh) Kylin

Pl. 86, figs. 5–8

Kylin, 1924, p. 8; fig. 2 *A*. Kylin, 1941, p. 30; pl. 10, figs. 25–26.
Delesseria Woodii J. G. Agardh, 1872, p. 54.

Thalli, as found on the Monterey Peninsula, usually 1–2.5 cm.

tall but occasionally up to 7 cm.; deep pink in color. With a percurrent axis that is profusely and suboppositely branched. The branches similar to the axis and with one or with two orders of branching. The axis and branches linear, 2.5–3 mm. broad, abruptly attenuated at upper end and terminating in an acute tip. Midrib of axis and major branches flattened and up to 1 mm. broad. Monostromatic portion of branches with cells near branch tips arranged in diagrammatic regularity. The tetrasporangia in interrupted linear sori on either side of midrib of branches.

LOCAL DISTRIBUTION. Isolated specimens have been found on rocks between the −0.5- and −1.5-foot tide levels at Asilomar Point; Pescadero Point; Pescadero Rocks; and Mission Point. Specimens have also been dredged from a depth of 30–35 feet a quarter-mile from Municipal Wharf, Monterey, and near Point Pinos.

TYPE LOCALITY. Vancouver Island, British Columbia.

PACIFIC COAST DISTRIBUTION. Known only from the type locality; the Monterey Peninsula; and Santa Barbara, California.

Membranoptera Stackhouse, 1809

Thalli growing erect from a small conical holdfast; alternately or subdichotomously divided into broad to narrow linear blades. The blades with a percurrent midrib more than one cell in thickness; portions lateral to midrib monostromatic and with or without delicate diagonal parallel veins. Occasionally with small proliferous blades from midrib. The blade with each cell of the axial filament bearing an opposite pair of filaments and these bearing secondary filaments on the abaxial side only. The primary and secondary filaments compacted into a monostromatic parenchymatous sheet in which the secondary filaments do not extend to the blade margin.

Heterothallic. The spermatangia in sori borne at tips of blades or borne along either side of midrib through upper half of blade. Carpogonial filaments 4-celled, the supporting cell always a pericentral cell cut off from the axial filament of a blade. The supporting cell also cutting off two sterile cells, one of which develops into a 2- or a 3-celled sterile filament. The auxiliary cell cut off from supporting cell after fertilization; producing gonimoblast filaments on side toward thallus surface and with carposporangia formed in chains at outer end of gonimoblast filaments. The mature cystocarps borne along the midrib, lying some distance back from blade apex, surrounded by a hemispherical ostiolate pericarp.

Tetrasporophytes with the tetrasporangia in sori at tips of blades or borne along either side of the midrib. The tetrasporangia tetrahedrally divided.

STRUCTURE AND REPRODUCTION. Kylin, 1923, pp. 108–113; figs. 69–71. Kylin, 1924, pp. 15–17; figs. 7–9. Phillips, 1898, pp. 183–186; pl. 16, figs. 17–19.

KEY TO THE SPECIES IN THE LOCAL FLORA

1. Blades with conspicuous parallel veins..............*M. multiramosa*
1. Blades without or with inconspicuous veins............*M. Weeksiae*

Membranoptera multiramosa Gardner   Pl. 86, figs. 3–4

Gardner, 1926, p. 209; pl. 19, fig. 1.
Membranoptera edentata *Kylin, 1941, p. 30; pl. 10, fig. 27.

Thalli, as found on the Monterey Peninsula, 3–5 cm. tall; bright rose-red in color. Regularly branched in an alternate fashion from margins of blades and with 3–5 orders of branching. Occasionally with small proliferous blades from midrib. The blades with conspicuous diagonally parallel veins. Margins of blades smooth or dentate, at times much crisped. The blades (except at region of branching) 2–2.5 mm. broad. Cystocarps with a fimbriate ostiole. The tetrasporangial sori in narrow bands along either side of midrib; usually in upper part of blade but sometimes extending down to lower third of blade.

LOCAL DISTRIBUTION. Growing between the −0.5- and −1.5-foot tide levels on the vertical face of sheltered rocks. Fairly common at Pescadero Point. Also found repeatedly at 1.0-foot tide level in a tide pool in a cave at Mission Point.

TYPE LOCALITY. Moss Beach, San Mateo County, California.

PACIFIC COAST DISTRIBUTION. As above.

Membranoptera Weeksiae Setchell and Gardner   Pl. 87, fig. 1

Setchell and Gardner apud Gardner, 1926, p. 209; pl. 19, fig. 2.
Delesseria alata Anderson [not of (Hudson) Stackhouse]. *Anderson, 1891, p. 224. *Howe, 1893, p. 68.

Thalli, as found on the Monterey Peninsula, usually 3–5 cm. tall but at times up to 9 cm.; bright rose-red in color. Profusely branched and with 4–6 orders of branching. The branching usually alternate but at times subopposite or unilateral. The branches 0.5–1.5 mm. broad, with a conspicuous percurrent midrib but without evident veins in the monostromatic portion lateral to midrib. Margins of branches smooth and flat.

LOCAL DISTRIBUTION, Growing between the mean low-tide and −1.5-foot tide levels. Epiphytic or saxicolous. Pacific Grove; Moss Beach; Pescadero Point; Pebble Beach. Epiphytic on *Pterygophora californica* and *Desmarestia latifrons* cast ashore on Carmel Beach.

TYPE LOCALITY. Pacific Grove, California.

PACIFIC COAST DISTRIBUTION. Central California (San Francisco to Carmel Bay).

Delesseria Lamouroux, 1813

Thalli erect, attached by a disc-shaped holdfast or by short haptera. With a linear percurrent axis. The axis with a percurrent midrib several cells in thickness and the portions lateral to the midrib monostromatic. The axis freely branched and with the branches borne alternately along the midrib. The branches similar to axis in shape and structure, and similarly branched to the third or fourth order. Branch apices with an evident apical cell. Monostromatic portion of branches with only the primary filaments from axial filament extending to branch margins.

Heterothallic. The spermatangia in minute sori irregularly distributed over monostromatic portion of ultimate branchlets. Carpogonial filaments 4-celled, borne only along the midrib. Supporting cell of carpogonial filament also bearing two groups of sterile cells. The auxiliary cell cut off at upper end of supporting cell after fertilization. The gonimoblast filaments growing toward thallus surface and with the carposporangia borne in chains. The mature cystocarps borne along the midrib, restricted to the final orders of branching, surrounded by a hemispherical ostiolate pericarp.

Tetrasporophytes with the tetrasporangia in linear sori lateral to the midrib and restricted to the last and next to last orders of branching. The tetrasporangia tetrahedrally divided.

STRUCTURE AND REPRODUCTION. Kylin, 1923, pp. 92–108; figs. 61–68. Kylin, 1924, pp. 24–26; figs. 15–16. Svedelius, 1914.

With one species in the local flora.

Delesseria decipiens J. G. Agardh   Pl. 87, figs. 3–4

J. G. Agardh, 1872, p. 58. *Anderson, 1891, p. 224.
Apoglossum decipiens J. G. Agardh, 1898, p. 194. *Phyc. Bor.-Amer. No. 1141.

Thalli, as found on the Monterey Peninsula, usually 15–25 cm.

tall but at times up to 50 cm.; bright pink to deep purplish-red in color. Branching to four or five orders; frequently with lower portion of axis stipe-like because of abrasion of mono-stromatic portions. The axis 8–12 mm. broad and the midrib 0.5–1.0 mm. broad. The branches regularly alternate, distichous, at first lanceolate, later linear. Monostromatic portions of axis and branches with minute parallel veins lying diagonal to the midrib.

LOCAL DISTRIBUTION. Growing on rocks between the 0.5- and −1.5-foot tide levels. Point Pinos; Asilomar Point; Pescadero Point; Pebble Beach; Mission Point.

TYPE LOCALITY. Vancouver Island, British Columbia.

PACIFIC COAST DISTRIBUTION. Alaska (Prince William Sound) to central California (Carmel Bay).

Erythroglossum J. G. Agardh, 1898

Thalli wholly erect or with a branched prostrate base and certain of its branches erect. The blades irregularly branched and with new branches developing at margins of old blades. The blades with a percurrent midrib more than one cell in thickness; portions of blade lateral to midrib monostromatic and without microscopic or macroscopic veins. Thallus apex with a conspicuous apical cell and an evident axial filament, cells lateral to the axial filament not regularly arranged.

Spermatangia unknown. Carpogonial filaments and development of the cystocarp unknown. The mature cystocarps scattered over monostromatic portion of blade; surrounded by an ostiolate pericarp.

Tetrasporophytes with the tetrasporangia in linear sori lying just within and parallel to the blade margins. The tetrasporangia tetrahedrally divided.

STRUCTURE AND REPRODUCTION. Kylin, 1924, pp. 30–33; figs. 22–23.

KEY TO THE SPECIES IN THE LOCAL FLORA

1. Margins of blade smooth.........................*E. divaricatum*
1. Margins of blade dentate.......................*E. californicum*

Erythroglossum californicum J. G. Agardh   Pl. 87, figs. 5–6

J. G. Agardh, 1898, p. 176. Kylin, 1924, p. 32; fig. 22 *F.* Kylin, 1941, p. 31; pl. 10, fig. 28.

Delesseria californica J. G. Agardh, 1884, p. 69.

Thalli, as found on the Monterey Peninsula, 3 cm. tall; bright rose-red in color. The thallus with a ribbon-like, branched base and with the ends of certain branches bending upward and becoming erect blades. The erect blades linear, stipitate at base; with a percurrent midrib. Margins of blades dentate but the blade without a vein between each dentation and the midrib. Tetrasporangial sori vertically linear and just within the blade margins.

LOCAL DISTRIBUTION. Growing on a sponge at —1.0-foot tide level at Asilomar Point.

TYPE LOCALITY. "California."

PACIFIC COAST DISTRIBUTION. Known definitely only from the Monterey Peninsula and from Santa Barbara, California.

The occurrence of this species in the local flora may be open to question because all specimens in the single collection were sterile. The determination of these specimens as *E. californicum* has been confirmed by Professor Kylin, who has compared them with the type in Agardh's herbarium.

Erythroglossum divaricatum Setchell and Gardner

Pl. 87, fig. 7

Setchell and Gardner apud Gardner, 1926, p. 207; pl. 17, fig. 2.

Thalli growing in dense tufts 1.5–2.5 cm. tall and up to 6 cm. broad; deep rose-pink in color. The thalli profusely and irregularly branched, the branches diverging widely and at times appearing to be dichotomously divided. The branches narrowly linear, up to 0.5 mm. broad, of approximately the same width throughout; with an indistinct midrib and the monostromatic portion lateral to the midrib with a smooth margin. Tips of branches acuminate.

LOCAL DISTRIBUTION. Growing on the vertical face of rocks between the mean low-tide and —1.5-foot tide levels. Pacific Grove; Arch Rock; Asilomar Point; Middle Reef of Moss Beach.

TYPE LOCALITY. Pacific Grove, California.

PACIFIC COAST DISTRIBUTION. As above.

Polyneura Kylin, 1924

Thalli with one or more erect blades attached either by a disc-shaped holdfast or by flattened, irregularly divided, ribbon-like branches. The erect blades stipitate, ovate to broadly obcuneate, entire but more or less deeply incised; without a midrib but with conspicuous anastamosing veins. Younger portions of blade monostromatic, older portions more than one cell in thickness. The blades occasionally with small proliferous blades from the margin.

Heterothallic. The spermatangia in sori scattered over the entire blade. The carpogonial filaments 4-celled, borne in pairs on a supporting cell, which also bears a single group of sterile cells. The gonimoblast filaments radiately branched and all directed toward surface of thallus. The carposporangia developed in chains at the free ends of gonimoblast filaments. The mature cystocarps scattered over entire surface of blade, surrounded by an ostiolate pericarp.

Tetrasporophytes with the tetrasporangia in rounded to sublinear sori. The sori usually scattered over entire blade but sometimes restricted to blade margins. The tetrasporangia tetrahedrally divided.

STRUCTURE AND REPRODUCTION. Kylin, 1924, pp. 33–43; figs. 24–34.

With one species in the local flora.

Polyneura latissima (Harvey) Kylin   Pl. 87, fig. 8

*Kylin, 1924, p. 37; figs. 27–28. *Kylin, 1941, p. 31.
Hymenena latissima Harvey, 1862, p. 170.
Nitophyllum latissimum (Harvey) J. G. Agardh, 1871, p. 49. *Anderson 1891, p. 224. *Howe, 1893, p. 68. *Nott, 1900, p. 16; pl. 1; pl. 2, fig. 4; pl. 9, fig. 44. Phyc. Bor.-Amer. No. 335.

Thalli, as found on the Monterey Peninsula, usually 10–15 cm. tall but at times up to 30 cm.; deep pink to lake red in color. Young thalli with oblanceolate blades, older thalli with more or less deeply incised obcuneate blades. Blades of any age usually more or less lacerated. The veins conspicuous, anastamosing to form an areolate reticulum covering all but the blade margins. Tetrasporangial sori minute, scattered over both surfaces of blade, several in each inter-reticular area between veins.

LOCAL DISTRIBUTION. Growing between the mean low-tide and −1.5-foot tide levels on vertical face of rocks somewhat sheltered from full force of surf. Abundant in favorable habitats. Mussel Point; Point Pinos; Middle Reef of Moss Beach; Point Joe; Fanshell Beach; Cypress Point; Pescadero Point; Arrowhead Point; Mission Point. Also dredged from a depth of 30–35 feet a quarter-mile from Municipal Wharf, Monterey, and near Mussel Point; and from 12 to 15 feet near Point Aulon.

TYPE LOCALITY. Esquimalt, British Columbia.

PACIFIC COAST DISTRIBUTION. British Columbia (Vancouver Island) to Baja California (20 miles south of Tia Juana).

Phycodrys Kützing, 1843

Thalli, at least at first, with a disc-shaped holdfast and an erect blade. The blades more or less elliptical, with a percurrent midrib and opposite veins, monostromatic except for midrib and veins, margins of blades smooth to strongly dentate. The blades eventually becoming pinnately and oppositely branched through a formation of new blades at the margin. Older blades often with all of the lower portion but the midrib eroded away, the blades then appearing as if borne on an oppositely branched axis.

Heterothallic. The spermatangia in a continuous belt just within the blade margin or in small rounded sori· scattered over entire monostromatic portion of blade. Carpogonial filaments developed over entire blade, 4-celled and with the supporting cell also bearing two groups of sterile cells. The auxiliary cell cut off from supporting cell after fertilization. The supporting cell, the sterile· cell it bears, and the auxiliary cell uniting to form an irregularly shaped placental cell with radiately branched gonimoblast filaments toward the thallus surface. The carposporangia developed in chains at free ends of the gonimoblast filaments. The mature cystocarp with an ostiolate pericarp.

Tetrasporophytes with the tetrasporangia in rounded sori. The sori usually scattered over entire blade but sometimes restricted to margin of blade or to proliferous outgrowths from it. The tetrasporangia tetrahedrally divided.

STRUCTURE AND REPRODUCTION. Kylin, 1923, pp. 64–80; figs. 43–51.

With one species in the local flora.

Phycodrys Setchellii Skottsberg   Pl. 87, fig. 2; pl. 88, fig. 7

SKOTTSBERG, 1922, p. 433; pl. 50.
Delesseria quercifolia Farlow [not of Bory]. Farlow, 1875, p. 364. *Anderson, 1891, p. 224. Phyc. Bor.-Amer. No. 434.

Thalli, as found on the Monterey Peninsula, up to 15 cm. tall; pinkish-red in color. The secondary blades elliptical to obovate, with conspicuous midrib and veins, and with basal portion of the midrib distinctly stipe-like. Margins of blade dentate external to veins. The spermatangia and tetrasporangia in small sori scattered over entire monostromatic portion of blade.

LOCAL DISTRIBUTION. Isolated thalli have been collected between the mean low-tide and −1.5-foot tide levels at Municipal Wharf, Monterey; Point Pinos; Asilomar Point; Middle Reef of Pebble Beach. Also dredged from a depth of 30–35 feet a quarter-mile from Municipal Wharf, Monterey, and from 20 to 30 feet near Arrowhead Point.

TYPE LOCALITY. Fort Point, San Francisco, California.

PACIFIC COAST DISTRIBUTION. Central California (Bolinas) to Baja California (5 miles south of international border).

Anisocladella Skottsberg, 1923

Thalli with a very narrow, flattened, branched, ribbon-like base and with the ends of certain branches bending upward and developing into erect blades. The blades more or less ligulate, undivided but occasionally with proliferous bladelets at the margins. The blades with a percurrent midrib and with or without unbranched parallel veins slightly diagonal to the midrib. Margins of blades smooth to strongly dentate. Apex of blade with each cell of the axial filament bearing two opposite lateral filaments, one more strongly developed than the other. Successive pairs of filaments with the long and short filaments alternating. The blades monostromatic except for midrib and veins.

Spermatangia unknown. Carpogonial filaments and development of cystocarp unknown. Mature cystocarps with a hemispherical pericarp and borne a short distance out from midribs of blades.

The tetrasporophytes with tetrasporangia in sori. Each blade with two sori, one on either side of the midrib, and extending halfway from apex to base of blade. The tetrasporangia tetrahedrally divided.

STRUCTURE AND REPRODUCTION. Kylin, 1924, p. 45.

With one species in the local flora.

Anisocladella pacifica Kylin   Pl. 88, figs. 5–6

*Kylin, 1941, p. 31; pl. 11, fig. 29.

Thalli, as found on the Monterey Peninsula, with erect blades usually 1.5–3.0 cm. tall but occasionally up to 5 cm.; deep rose-pink in color. Mature blades linear, 2.5–5.0 mm. broad, with an obtusely pointed apex and with the base narrowed to a short stipe. Each blade with opposite to subopposite pairs of diagonal unbranched veins extending to or projecting beyond the blade margin. Prostrate portion of thallus freely branched and frequently with the branches reduced to a midrib. Branching of prostrate portion opposite but appearing to be alternate or irregular because most of the branches are reduced to spines. Tetrasporangial sori in upper part of erect blades and extending halfway from midrib to blade margin.

LOCAL DISTRIBUTION. Growing on the vertical face of rocks between the mean low-tide and −1.0-foot tide levels. Fairly common at Mussel Point; Asilomar Point; Middle Reef of Moss Beach; Cypress Point; Pescadero Point; Pebble Beach.

TYPE LOCALITY. Asilomar Point, Pacific Grove, California.

PACIFIC COAST DISTRIBUTION. As above.

Although growing on the vertical face of rocks, the thalli are so deeply buried in sand that one sees only the upper part of the erect blades. Thus the collector is apt to overlook this small alga even though it is relatively common locally. When present it usually grows in patches up to a meter or more broad.

Nienburgia Kylin, 1935

Thalli differentiated into prostrate and erect branches. The prostrate system of branches irregularly branched, the branches thickened but the axial portion without a midrib; margins of prostrate branches with spine-like teeth. The erect branches alternately to subdichotomously divided into linear segments with a percurrent midrib but without veins; all segments the same breadth or segments of the final orders of branching much narrower than others. Margins of segments regularly or irregularly serrate. The segments several cells in thickness; the medulla about five cells in thickness and composed of large cells, the cortex composed of vertical rows of small cubical cells.

Heterothallic. The spermatangia in small elliptical to linear sori on tips of segments or on small proliferous outgrowths. Carpogonial filaments four-celled, borne on a supporting cell cut off parallel to surface of blade; the supporting cell also with two sterile filaments. The auxiliary cell formed after fertilization and producing gonimoblast filaments branching toward thallus surface and with carposporangia developing in rows at the distal end. The mature cystocarps scattered over both surfaces of blade, projecting beyond surface of blade and surrounded by a hemispherical ostiolate pericarp.

Tetrasporophytes with the tetrasporangia in rounded sori borne at the tips of blade segments or in small proliferous segments. The tetrasporangia tetrahedrally divided.

STRUCTURE AND REPRODUCTION. Kylin, 1924, pp. 46–50; figs. 36–40 (as *Heteronema*).

Nienburgia Andersoniana (J. G. Agardh) Kylin

Pl. 90, figs. 1–2

Kylin, 1935*B*, p. 1. *Kylin, 1941, p. 32.
Neuroglossum Andersonianum J. G. Agardh, 1876, p. 474.
Nitophyllum Andersonianum (J. G. Agardh) Farlow, 1875, p. 365 (name only). *Anderson, 1891, p. 224. *Howe, 1893, p. 68. *Nott, 1900, p. 32; pl. 4, fig. 17; pl. 5; pl. 9, fig. 45.
Heteronema Andersoniana (J. G. Agardh) *Kylin, 1924, p. 46; figs. 36–39.

Thalli, as found on the Monterey Peninsula, up to 30 cm. tall; bright rose-red to dull carmine in color. Erect branches usually alternately branched; with all segments the same breadth or with certain segments much narrower than others. The segments with a flattened percurrent midrib. Serration of margins of segments usually irregular in lower portion of erect branches and regularly alternate in upper portion. Bases of erect branches often stem-like because of abrasion of portions lateral to the midrib.

LOCAL DISTRIBUTION. Growing on rocks between the mean low-tide and −1.5-foot tide levels. Isolated thalli found at Mussel Point; Asilomar Point; Middle Reef of Moss Beach; Cypress Point; Pebble Beach. Also dredged from a depth of 20–25 feet near Point Aulon and at Stillwater Cove.

TYPE LOCALITY. Santa Cruz, California.

PACIFIC COAST DISTRIBUTION. Central California (Santa Cruz) to Baja California (Ensenada).

Myriogramme Kylin, 1924

Thalli erect, with a disc-shaped holdfast or a prostrate system of flattened branches. With erect blades, the blades more or less rounded but often deeply and irregularly sinuate or lobed. The blades without a midrib or veins; monostromatic in upper portion, more than one cell in thickness in lower portion. Apex of blade without an evident apical cell and with cells of apical region irregularly arranged because of intercalary cell divisions in cell rows posterior to apical cell.

Heterothallic. The spermatangia in small rounded sori either restricted to upper portion of or scattered over entire blade. Carpogonial filaments four-celled, borne on a supporting cell cut off parallel to blade surface, the supporting cell also with two two-celled sterile filaments. The auxiliary cell formed after fertilization and producing an outwardly branched system of gonimoblast filaments in which the carposporangia develop in rows at the distal end. Mature cystocarps scattered over both surfaces of blade, each cystocarp with an ostiolate pericarp projecting beyond the blade surface.

Tetrasporophytes with the tetrasporangia in small irregularly shaped or elliptical sori scattered over both surfaces of blade. The tetrasporangia tetrahedrally divided.

STRUCTURE AND REPRODUCTION. Kylin, 1924, pp. 55–61; figs. 43–46.

KEY TO THE SPECIES IN THE LOCAL FLORA

1. Blades more than 10 cm. tall..........................*M. spectabilis*
1. Blades less than 5 cm. tall.......................*M. Hollenbergii*

Myriogramme spectabilis (Eaton) Kylin   Pl. 88, fig. 1

Kylin, 1924, p. 58.
Nitophyllum spectabile Eaton, 1877, p. 245. *Anderson, 1891, p. 224. *Nott, 1900, p. 21; pl. 2, fig. 5.

Thalli, as found on the Monterey Peninsula, 10–25 cm. tall; bright rose-red in color. With a prostrate system of branches bearing erect blades. The erect blades irregularly ligulate, pinnately or palmately incised and the incisions narrow or ·broad. The blades without a midrib or veins; rarely with proliferous outgrowths at margin. The spermatangia in areolate patches. The cystocarps numerous, irregularly distributed over both surfaces of blade. Tetrasporangial sori elliptical, rather evenly spaced over both surfaces of blade.

LOCAL DISTRIBUTION. Dredged from a depth of 20 feet near Mussel Point and from a depth of 70–90 feet near Point Aulon. Also found cast ashore at Moss Beach; Pebble Beach; and Carmel Beach.

TYPE LOCALITY. Santa Cruz, California.

PACIFIC COAST DISTRIBUTION. Central California (Santa Cruz) to southern California (Redondo).

Myriogramme Hollenbergii Kylin   Pl. 88, figs. 2–4

*Kylin, 1941,.p. 32; pl. 11, fig. 30.

Thalli 1–2 cm. tall; bright red in color. With a disc-shaped base and above this a short stipe. The stipe terminating in a blade; the stipe at times also bearing lateral blades. The blades 5–10 mm. tall, 2–3 (–5) mm. broad, narrowly to broadly ovate, at times with one or two incisions at apex. The blades monostromatic throughout, without veins. The spermatangial sori lunate and on upper part of blade. Cystocarps usually but two or three on a blade. Tetrasporangial sori minute, irregularly shaped, irregularly scattered over entire blade.

LOCAL DISTRIBUTION. Growing between the mean low-tide and −1.0-foot tide levels. On piling of Municipal Wharf, Monterey. On rocks at Pebble Beach and at Pescadero Point. Three feet below water line on unloading hopper of a sardine cannery near Mussel Point.

TYPE LOCALITY. Municipal Wharf, Monterey, California.

PACIFIC COAST DISTRIBUTION. As above.

Polycoryne Skottsberg, 1919

Thalli small, solitary, growing parasitically on Delesseriaceae. Major portion of thallus lying external to host, tuberculate and covered with a number of small needle-like leaflets. Young leaflets with an apical cell but this becoming obscure as the leaflet continues development.

Heterothallic. The spermatangia scattered over surface of leaflets. Carpogonial filament four-celled, its supporting cell also bearing two sterile cells. The gonimoblast filaments with carposporangia developing in series at the distal end. Each leaflet with a single cystocarp borne either at the base or near the apex.

Tetrasporophytes with the tetrasporangia scattered over and embedded beneath surface of leaflets. The tetrasporangia tetrahedrally divided.

STRUCTURE AND REPRODUCTION. Kylin and Skottsberg, 1919, pp. 36–37; text figs. 17 E, 18; pl. 1, fig. 4. Kylin, 1924, pp. 62–64; fig. 48.

With one species in the local flora.

Polycoryne Gardneri Setchell

Setchell, 1923, p. 395.

Thalli 2–3 mm. in diameter; whitish in color. With needle-like leaflets radiating from a common center. Cystocarpic thalli with leaflets 1 mm. long and a single cystocarp at the base of a leaflet. Tetrasporophytes with leaflets about 3 mm. long and either the apical or median portion of fertile leaflets inflated.

LOCAL DISTRIBUTION. Parasitic on *Nienburgia Andersoniana* at Pebble Beach.

TYPE LOCALITY. Point Cavallo, Marin County, California.

PACIFIC COAST DISTRIBUTION. As above.

Hymenena Greville, 1830

Thalli differentiated into a prostrate, ribbon-like portion and erect, much-divided blades. The blades palmately or flabellately divided; the segments with or without microscopic veins, segments in lower portion of blade with a midrib. The blade segments more than one cell in thickness at the margins, the midrib several cells in thickness and without internal rhizoids.

Heterothallic. The spermatangia in areolate sori scattered over surface of blade. Carpogonial filament four-celled, its supporting cell also bearing two groups of sterile cells. The supporting cell, the sterile cells it bears, and the auxiliary cell uniting to form a large, irregularly shaped, placental cell bearing radiately branched gonimoblast filaments all directed toward one side of the thallus. Only the terminal cells of gonimoblast filaments developing into carposporangia. Mature cystocarps scattered over the entire blade, bulging conspicuously toward one side of the thallus, surrounded by an ostiolate pericarp.

Tetrasporophytes with the tetrasporangia in sori. The sori linear to elliptical, scattered over the entire blade. The tetrasporangia tetrahedrally divided.

STRUCTURE AND REPRODUCTION. Kylin, 1924, pp. 84–86; fig. 70.

KEY TO THE SPECIES IN THE LOCAL FLORA

1. Tetrasporophytes with linear sori................................ 2
1. Tetrasporophytes with oval sori................................. 4
  2. Sori transverse on blades..........................*H. multiloba*
  2. Sori in longitudinal flabellate rows......................... 3
3. Thalli robust, usually more than 15 cm. tall............*H. flabelligera*
3. Thalli delicate, usually less than 10 cm. tall................*H. Kylinii*
  4. Length of blade only slightly greater than breadth.....*H. Setchellii*
  4. Length of blade about three times the breadth ....*H. Smithii*

Hymenena flabelligera (J. G. Agardh) Kylin   Pl. 89, fig. 3

Kylin, 1924, p. 83; fig. 68.
Nitophyllum flabelligerum J. G. Agardh, 1876, p. 699.
Nitophyllum Harveyanum Nott [not of J. G. Agardh]. Nott, 1900, p. 29; pl. 4, figs. 13–14 (in part).

Thalli, as found on the Monterey Peninsula, 15–30 cm. tall; deep salmon-pink to dull carmine in color. The erect blades subdichotomously or palmately divided into many segments; the segments linear, usually with an entire margin. The segments with a distinct midrib in the lower portion, above this with a flabellate system of minute veins. The tetrasporangia in narrow linear sori running lengthwise on surface of blade segments and arranged in a flabellate manner. The sori covering upper half of a blade.

LOCAL DISTRIBUTION. Growing between the 1.0- and −1.0-foot tide levels on the vertical face of rocks exposed to considerable surf. Point Pinos; Asilomar Point; Point Joe; Cypress Point; Pescadero Point; Arrowhead Point; mouth of Carmel River.

TYPE LOCALITY. Golden Gate, San Francisco, California.

PACIFIC COAST DISTRIBUTION. Puget Sound to central California (Carmel Bay).

Tetrasporic individuals of this species are easily recognizable. Sterile thalli may be mistaken for *Botryoglossum Farlowianum* because of the size, and because of the stem-like base due to abrasion of all but the midrib in lower portions of the erect blades. *H. flabelligerum* differs from *B. Farlowianum* in that there are rarely any marginal proliferations from blade segments and in that the blades are thinner.

Hymenena Kylinii Gardner

Gardner, 1927, p. 242; pl. 32. *Kylin, 1941, p. 32.
Nitophyllum Harveyanum Nott [not of J. G. Agardh]. Nott, 1900, p. 29; pl. 4, figs. 13–14 (in part). Phyc. Bor.-Amer. No. 693.

Thalli, as found on the Monterey Peninsula, 8–10 cm. tall; deep rose-red in color. The erect blades dichotomously to sub-dichotomously divided into a few segments 5–8 mm. broad. The segments with blunt apices and smooth margins. Lower portion of blade with a midrib that gradually merges into a reticulum of minute veins. The tetrasporangia in narrow linear sori running lengthwise on surface of blade segments and arranged in a flabellate manner. The sori covering the upper third of a blade.

LOCAL DISTRIBUTION. Growing at mean low-tide level on rocks midway between Point Joe and Seal Rocks.

TYPE LOCALITY. San Francisco, California.

PACIFIC COAST DISTRIBUTION. Central California (San Francisco to Monterey Peninsula).

Closely resembling *H. flabelligera,* from which it differs in smaller size, less complex branching, and more delicate habit throughout.

Hymenena multiloba (J. G. Agardh) Kylin   Pl. 89, fig. 2

Kylin, 1935B, p. 3.
Nitophyllum multilobum J. G. Agardh, 1876, p. 698. *Anderson, 1891, p. 224. *Nott, 1900, p. 27; pl. 3, fig. 11; pl. 9, fig. 46. Phyc. Bor.-Amer. No. 336.
Nitophyllum Fryeanum Harvey, 1858, p. 128.
Hymenena Fryeanum (Harvey) Gardner, 1927, p. 244.
Myriogramme multiloba (J. G. Agardh) Kylin, 1924, p. 58.

Thalli, as found on the Monterey Peninsula, 4–6 cm. tall; dark red to dull carmine in color. The erect blades subdichotomously to palmately divided; the segments narrow, twisted and convoluted, with entire or toothed margins. The segments with a distinct midrib in lower portion; above this without minute veins. Tetrasporangial sori broadly linear, extending transversely across upper segments of blade.

LOCAL DISTRIBUTION. Growing on rocks and on crustose corallines between the mean low-tide and −1.0-foot tide levels. Pacific Grove; Pescadero Point; Mission Point.

TYPE LOCALITY. Golden Gate, San Francisco, California.

PACIFIC COAST DISTRIBUTION. Northern California (Cape Mendocino) to central California (Carmel Bay).

Hymenena Setchellii Gardner   Pl. 89, fig. 4

*Gardner, 1927, p. 245; pls. 28–31.
Nitophyllum Fryeanum Farlow [not of Harvey]. Farlow in Algae Exsicc. Amer. Bor. No. 69. *Anderson, 1891, p. 224. *Howe, 1893, p. 68. *Nott, 1900, p. 22; pl. 3, figs. 6–9; pl. 4, fig. 16. Phyc. Bor.-Amer. No. 1742.
Hymenena Fryeanum (Farlow) Kylin, 1924, p. 81.

Thalli, as found on the Monterey Peninsula, 6–15 cm. tall; bright rose-red in color. The erect blades palmately or irregularly divided, the segments relatively broad and with broadly rounded to somewhat tapering tips. Margins of segments entire or toothed, sometimes with minute proliferous outgrowths. Lower portion of segments with a midrib; above this with minute branching and anastamosing veins. Tetrasporangia in small elliptical sori with a tendency to lie in flabellate linear series. Sori covering entire surface of blade.

LOCAL DISTRIBUTION. Growing on rocks at mean low-tide level. Point Pinos. Also found cast ashore at Moss Beach; Pebble Beach; and Carmel Beach.

TYPE LOCALITY. Santa Cruz, California.

PACIFIC COAST DISTRIBUTION. Puget Sound to central California (Carmel Bay).

Hymenena Smithii Kylin   Pl. 89, fig. 1
   *Kylin, 1941, p. 33; pl. 11, fig. 31.

Thalli 3–7 cm. tall; bright rose-red in color. The erect blades one to three times divided and with a length about three times the breadth. The blades monostromatic except at extreme base; with a midrib in lower portion and with minute anastamosing veins above this. Tetrasporangia in small elliptical sori scattered over entire monostromatic portion of blade. Cystocarps hemispherical, scattered over entire blade.

   LOCAL DISTRIBUTION. On stipe of *Pterygophora californica* cast ashore at south end of Carmel Beach.
   TYPE LOCALITY. As above.
   PACIFIC COAST DISTRIBUTION. As above.

Cryptopleura Kützing, 1843

Thallus with a narrow, branched, ribbon-like base and with the ends of certain branches bending upward and growing erect. The erect branches broader than prostrate branches; flabellately, subalternately, or subdichotomously divided into narrow, ribbon-like segments. Basal portion of erect branch and its primary segments with a midrib; above this the midrib gradually giving way to a network of progressively narrower veins. Segments of erect branches more than one cell in thickness at margin; with or without proliferous marginal outgrowths.

Heterothallic. The spermatangia in linear or rounded sori. The sori borne along margins of blade segments or in proliferous outgrowths from margins of segments. Carpogonial filament four-celled, its supporting cell also bearing two groups of sterile cells. The supporting cell, the sterile cells borne on it, and the auxiliary cell uniting to form a large, irregularly shaped, placental cell bearing radiately branched gonimoblast filaments all directed toward one side of the thallus. Only the terminal cells of gonimoblast filaments developing into carposporangia. Mature cystocarps scattered over surface of blade segments, surrounded by an ostiolate pericarp.

Tetrasporophytes with the tetrasporangia in sori borne only along margins of branch segments or in proliferous outgrowths from margins of segments. The tetrasporangia developed either from innermost cortical cells or from cells of axial filament of a branch segment. The tetrasporangia tetrahedrally divided.

   STRUCTURE AND REPRODUCTION. Kylin, 1924, pp. 86–93; figs. 71–78.

KEY TO THE SPECIES IN THE LOCAL FLORA

1. Tetrasporangial sori lunate to elliptical..................*C. lobulifera*
1. Tetrasporangial sori more or less linear..................*C. violacea*

Cryptopleura lobulifera (J. G. Agardh) Kylin
Pl. 90, fig. 4; pl. 92, fig. 1

*Kylin, 1924, p. 90; figs. 75–76. *Kylin, 1941, p. 33.
Neuroglossum lobuliferum *J. G. Agardh, 1898, p. 121.
Cryptopleura brevis Gardner, 1927, p. 241; pl. 25, fig. 2; pl. 26.

Thalli, as found on the Monterey Peninsula, 7–15 cm. tall; purplish-olive in color. The erect branches subdichotomously divided and the segments diverging rather widely. The segments 8–15 mm. broad, usually with margins variously crisped and ruffled, at times with small proliferous outgrowths from the margins. Primary segments with a conspicuous midrib in basal portion and rather large veins above this; the ultimate segments with minute veins. Tetrasporangial sori lunate to elliptical, restricted to upper portion of segments, lying either just within margins of segments or in small flat proliferous outgrowths from segment margins.

LOCAL DISTRIBUTION. Growing on rocks between the 0.5- and −1.5-foot tide levels. Mussel Point; Point Aulon; Point Pinos; Middle Reef of Moss Beach; Point Joe; Fanshell Beach; Cypress Point; Pescadero Point; Pebble Beach; Mission Point; mouth of Carmel River.

TYPE LOCALITY. Pacific Grove, California.

PACIFIC COAST DISTRIBUTION. Central California (Tomales Bay to Morro Bay).

Cryptopleura violacea (J. G. Agardh) Kylin   Pl. 90, fig. 3

Kylin, 1924, p. 89. *Kylin, 1941, p. 33.
Nitophyllum violaceum J. G. Agardh, 1876, p. 700. *Anderson, 1891, p. 224. *Howe, 1893, p. 68. *Nott, 1900, p. 39; pl. 8; pl. 9, figs. 41–43. *Phyc. Bor.-Amer. No. 389.
Nitophyllum violaceum forma *crispulum* *Setchell in Phyc. Bor.-Amer. No. 694.

Thalli, as found on the Monterey Peninsula, 15–25 cm. tall; purplish-olive to purplish-red in color. The erect branches subdichotomously to irregularly divided. Midrib in lower portion of branches relatively inconspicuous; the anastamosing veins above the midrib also minute and inconspicuous but extending nearly to apices of segments. The segments linear, 5–20 mm. broad, with broadly rounded apices. Margins of segments usually not markedly ruffled and usually without proliferous outgrowths. The tetrasporangial sori usually linear and borne just within lateral margins of upper segments but at times rounded and borne on small proliferous bladelets from margins of segments.

LOCAL DISTRIBUTION. Growing on rocks between the 0.5- and −1.5-foot tide levels. Found on every rocky headland of the Monterey Peninsula but especially abundant between Point Pinos and Cypress Point. Also dredged from a depth of 30–35 feet a quarter-mile from the Municipal Wharf, Monterey; from 20 to 25 feet near Point Aulon; and from 15 to 20 feet at Stillwater Cove.

TYPE LOCALITY. Golden Gate, San Francisco, California.

PACIFIC COAST DISTRIBUTION. British Columbia (Vancouver Island) to southern California (Venice).

The chief distinction between *C. violaceum* and *C. lobuliferum* is in the shape of tetrasporangial sori, but this is not clear-cut because *C. violaceum* may have rounded sori if they are borne on proliferations from segments of a blade.

Botryoglossum Kützing, 1843

Thallus with a narrow, branched, ribbon-like base and with the ends of certain branches growing erect. The erect branches broader than prostrate branches, palmately to subdichotomously divided into ribbon-like segments. Basal portion of erect branches with a conspicuous midrib; often becoming stem-like through a thickening of the midrib and an abrasion of portions lateral to the midrib; upper portions of segments with progressively smaller, forked, longitudinal veins extending nearly to apices of segments. The segments more than one cell in thickness at the margin and almost always with numerous semicircular proliferations along the margins.

Heterothallic. The spermatangia in small sori borne on proliferous outgrowths from margins of segments. Carpogonial filament and development of cystocarp unknown; presumably as in *Cryptopleura*. Mature cystocarps irregularly distributed over both flattened faces of segments, rarely on proliferous outgrowths. The mature cystocarp bulging conspicuously toward one side of thallus, surrounded by an ostiolate pericarp.

Tetrasporophytes with the tetrasporangia in sori borne on proliferous outgrowths from margins of segments. The tetrasporangia developing exclusively from inner cortical cells. The tetrasporangia tetrahedrally divided.

STRUCTURE AND REPRODUCTION. Kylin, 1924, pp. 93–95; fig. 79.

With one species in the local flora.

Botryoglossum Farlowianum (J. G. Agardh) DeToni
Pl. 91, figs. 1–2

DeToni, 1900, p. 676. *Kylin, 1924, p. 93; fig. 79. *Kylin, 1941, p. 34.
Nitophyllum Farlowianum J. G. Agardh, 1898, p. 95.
Delesseria platycarpa Harvey [not of (Turner) C. A. Agardh]. *Harvey, 1833, p. 163. *Harvey, 1841, p. 407.
Botryoglossum platycarpum Harvey [not of (Turner) Kützing]. *Harvey, 1853, p. 100; pl. 21, fig. A.
Hymenena fissa Harvey [not of Greville]. *Harvey, 1853, p. 101.
Nitophyllum Ruprechtianum Anderson [not of J. G. Agardh]. *Anderson, 1891, p. 224. *Howe, 1893, p. 68. *Nott, 1900, p. 34; pl. 4, fig. 15; pls. 6–7; pl. 9, figs. 38–40.

Thalli, as found on the Monterey Peninsula, 10–35 cm. tall; bright red to deep purplish-red in color. Basal portion of mature erect branches stem-like and suboppositely to subdichotomously branched. Upper segments of erect branches usually densely fringed with more or less overlapping semicircular marginal proliferous outgrowths. The upper segments up to 2 cm. broad, with broadly rounded apices, and of a firm leathery texture.

LOCAL DISTRIBUTION. Growing in dense stands between the mean low-tide and −1.5-foot tide levels on rocks wherever there is considerable surf. Also dredged from a depth of 30–35 feet a quarter-mile from Municipal Wharf, Monterey; from 20 to 25 feet near Point Aulon; and from 15 to 20 feet at Stillwater Cove.

TYPE LOCALITY. "California."

PACIFIC COAST DISTRIBUTION. Puget Sound to central California (Carmel Bay).

Gonimophyllum Batters, 1892

Thalli small, solitary, growing parasitically on various Delesseriaceae. The thallus with rhizoidal filaments penetrating the host. Major portion of thallus lying external to host and consisting of a circular, entire to much-lobed, blade, which lies flattened against the host. Vegetative portion of blade three cells in thickness, with cells of the median layer much larger than others.

Heterothallic. The spermatangia scattered over surface of blade. Carpogonial filament four-celled, its supporting cell also bearing a two-celled and a one-celled filament. The gonimoblast filaments growing from an irregularly shaped placental cell, freely branched and with all branches toward one side of thallus. Only the terminal cells of gonimoblast filaments developing into carposporangia. The mature cystocarp bulging toward one side of thallus, surrounded by an ostiolate pericarp.

Tetrasporophytes with the sporangia in very minute sori on surface of blade. The sporangia either polysporangia or crucially (?) divided tetrasporangia.

STRUCTURE AND REPRODUCTION. Batters, 1892. Kylin, 1924, pp. 95–96; fig. 80.

With one species in the local flora.

Gonimophyllum Skottsbergii Setchell   Pl. 92, fig. 3

Setchell, 1923, p. 394. *Kylin, 1924, p. 96; fig. 80. *Kylin, 1941, p. 34.
Gonimophyllum Buffhami Nott [not of Batters]. *Nott, 1897, p. 82.

Thalli, as found on the Monterey Peninsula, up to 8 mm. in diameter; usually pinkish but always lighter in color than host. Borne on lower half of erect branches of host and frequently on the stipe-like portion. The blade circular, almost always irregularly lobed and laciniate. The cystocarps bulging prominently toward one side of blade. The tetrasporophytes with polysporangia containing 30–50 polyspores radiately disposed about a small central mass of cytoplasm.

LOCAL DISTRIBUTION. Parasitic on *Botryoglossum Farlowianum* at Mussel Point; Point Pinos; Middle Reef of Moss Beach; Cypress Point; and Pebble Beach. Parasitic on *Cryptopleura violacea* at Fanshell Beach; on *Hymenena multiloba* at Mission Point.

TYPE LOCALITY. Land's End, San Francisco, California.

PACIFIC COAST DISTRIBUTION. Known only from Friday Harbor, Washington; the type locality; and the Monterey Peninsula.

Family DASYACEAE

Thalli polysiphonous, erect, freely branched. The branching either radial or alternate and distichous but in either case growth of the branches sympodial and the branches with branched filaments (trichoblasts) from base to apex as a result of the sympodial mode of growth. The branches corticated or uncorticated.

Carpogonial filaments four-celled, its supporting cell also with two sterile filaments. The auxiliary cell cut off after fertilization and either fusing or not fusing with other cells to form a large placental cell. The gonimoblast filaments radiately branched and with carposporangia formed in chains of three to five at the distal end. The mature cystocarp surrounded by a pericarp.

Tetrasporophytes with the tetrasporangia developed in stichidia on branched trichoblasts. The tetrasporangia tetrahedrally divided.

With one genus, *Dasyopsis,* in the local flora.[7]

Dasyopsis Zanardini, 1843

Thalli erect, freely branched, with a percurrent axis and the axis radially or alternately branched. The axis and major branches cylindrical or somewhat flattened, densely fringed with branched filaments. Elongating ends of axis and branches a sympodium in which each successively formed filament functions briefly as the terminal filament. The region immediately posterior to the growing tip polysiphonous and the region posterior to this soon becoming corticated.

Spermatangia unknown. Carpogonial filament four-celled, its supporting cell a pericentral cell just back of the branch apex. The supporting cell also producing two groups of sterile cells. The auxiliary cell cut off at upper end of supporting cell and producing gonimoblast filaments that grow upward from it. Cells at the free ends of gonimoblast filaments forming carposporangia in basipetalous succession. The mature cystocarp surrounded by an ostiolate urn-shaped pericarp developed from pericentral cells adjoining supporting cell of carpogonial filament.

Tetrasporophytes with the tetrasporangia in stichidia borne on the lateral filaments fringing the axis and branches. The stichidia with tetrasporangia in transverse tiers. The tetrasporangia tetrahedrally divided.

STRUCTURE AND REPRODUCTION. Rosenberg, 1933, pp. 51–61; figs. 16–19.

With one species in the local flora.

Dasyopsis densa G. M. Smith   Pl. 92, fig. 2

G. M. Smith apud Smith and Hollenberg, 1943, p. 217; fig. 22.
Dasya plumosa Anderson [not of Harvey and Bailey]. Anderson in Algae Exsicc. Bor. Amer. No. 4. *Anderson, 1891, p. 225.

Thalli, as found on the Monterey Peninsula, up to 30 cm. tall,

---

[7] Possibly *Heterosiphonia* should be included in the local flora because Anderson (1894, p. 361) states that *Dasya coccinea* (Hudson) C. A. Agardh [*Heterosiphonia coccinea* (Hudson) Falkenberg] has been collected in Monterey Bay and Carmel Bay. Unfortunately, specimens of *Heterosiphonia* from these localities are not to be found in Anderson's herbarium. Thus one cannot tell whether the presumed *Heterosiphonia* of the local flora is the European *H. coccinea* or is one of the species known only from the Pacific Coast of North America.

bright red in color. The main axis percurrent, flattened, up to 2.5 mm. broad. The branching distichous, of two or three orders, and with the primary branches much shorter than the axis. Margins of branches and upper portion of axis with a continuous fringe of branched filaments whose branches are not widely divergent. The filaments up to 1 mm. long.

LOCAL DISTRIBUTION. Juvenile thalli dredged from a depth of 30–35 feet a quarter-mile from Municipal Wharf, Monterey. Adult thalli found cast ashore at Pacific Grove, Pebble Beach, and south end of Carmel Beach.

TYPE LOCALITY. Carmel, California.

PACIFIC COAST DISTRIBUTION. Central California (Santa Cruz to Carmel Bay).

Family RHODOMELACEAE

Thalli polysiphonous; usually erect but at times wholly prostrate. Freely branched, the branches almost always free from one another but in exceptional cases laterally compacted to form an expanded sheet. When not laterally united the branches either cylindrical or compressed; and either uncorticated, with only the major branches corticated, or with all branches corticated. Tips of branches usually with branched filaments (trichoblasts).

Heterothallic. The spermatangia borne on trichoblasts that may be free from one another or united in a flat sheet. Carpogonial filament four-celled, its supporting cell also bearing sterile filaments. The auxiliary cell cut off from supporting cell after fertilization and uniting with it and the sterile filaments to form a large placental cell. The gonimoblast filaments usually short and with only the terminal cells developing into carposporangia. The mature cystocarp surrounded by a pericarp.

Tetrasporophytes with the tetrasporangia formed internal to the pericentral cells or formed from corticating cells. The tetrasporangia produced by any branch of thallus or restricted to special branchlets (stichidia). The tetrasporangia tetrahedrally divided.

KEY TO THE GENERA IN THE LOCAL FLORA

1. Thalli free-living 2
1. Thalli parasitic 12
   2. Thallus branches not compacted in a flat sheet 3
   2. Thallus branches laterally compacted into
      a flat sheet . . . . *Amplisiphonia* (p. 372)

Polysiphonia Greville, 1824

Thallus freely branched and polysiphonous, wholly erect or partly erect and partly prostrate. Prostrate branches cylindrical, with one- or very rarely with two-celled rhizoids on ventral face and with erect branches on dorsal face. The erect branches radially branched, cylindrical, unlimited in growth, polysiphonous and with 4–24 pericentral cells in each segment. Older portions of branches regularly becoming corticated in certain species. Tips of branches usually with trichoblasts. The trichoblasts branched or unbranched, never more than one on a segment. The trichoblasts persisting for some time or shed soon after they are formed. The basal cell of a trichoblast (the scar cell) persisting long after the trichoblast is shed.

Heterothallic. The spermatangia borne on trichoblasts, usually developing on only one branch of a trichoblast: produced in abundance on several successive cells and lying in an ovoid to subcylindrical mass. Carpogonial filament four-celled, borne on a supporting cell cut off adaxially from the next to lowermost cell of a trichoblast. The supporting cell also bearing two sterile filaments. The auxiliary cell cut off at upper end of supporting cell after fertilization. The supporting cell, the sterile filaments on it, and the auxiliary cell uniting to form a placental cell from which short gonimoblast filaments grow outwards. Only the terminal cells of gonimoblast filaments developing into carposporangia. The mature cystocarp surrounded by an ostiolate pericarp developed from pericentral cells cut off from the three lowermost cells of the trichoblast bearing the cystocarp.

Tetrasporophytes with the tetrasporangia borne singly in several successive segments toward the upper end of a branch. Each tetrasporangium formed by division of a pericentral cell and lying beneath two sterile cover cells. The tetrasporangia tetrahedrally divided.

STRUCTURE AND REPRODUCTION. Kylin, 1923, pp. 116–123; figs. 73–77. Kylin, 1934, pp. 2–3. Rosenberg, 1933, pp. 10–22; figs. 1–6.

KEY TO THE SPECIES IN THE LOCAL FLORA

1. Segments with four pericentral cells.............................. 2
1. Segments with more than four pericentral cells................... 4
  2. Trichoblasts and scar cells lacking or very rare........*P. pacifica*
  2. A trichoblast or scar cell on every segment.................... 3
3. Each branch replacing a trichoblast or scar cell........*P. acuminata*
3. Each branch axillary to a trichoblast or
    scar cell...........................*P. flaccidissima* var. *Smithii*
  4. Major branches completely corticated................*P. Brodiaei*
  4. All branches uncorticated................................... 5
5. A trichoblast or scar cell on every segment and
    each a quarter of a turn to the right of the one below....*P. californica*
5. Trichoblasts and scar cell not so regularly arranged.............. 6
  6. Erect branches without an evident main axis...........*P. Hendryi*
  6. Erect branches with an evident main axis.............*P. Collinsii*

Polysiphonia pacifica Hollenberg Pl. 94, fig. 3

Hollenberg, 1942*A*, p. 777; figs. 2–3, 12–13.
Polysiphonia urceolata var. *patens* Harvey [not of (Dillwyn) Greville]. *Harvey, 1853, p. 32. *Anderson, 1891, p. 225.
Polysiphonia senticulosa Howe [not of Harvey]. *Howe, 1893, p. 68.

Thalli, as found on the Monterey Peninsula, up to 15 cm. tall; reddish-brown to blackish in color. With a feebly developed system of prostrate branches; the rhizoids on prostrate branches one per segment, not separated from the pericentral cell by a cross wall. The erect shoots with an obscure to distinct axis 100–200 μ in diameter; the branching profuse, alternate, at times tending to be distichous. Segments with 4 pericentral cells; those at base of axis with a length 6–10 times the breadth. Trichoblasts and scar cells exceedingly rare on vegetative branches. Spermatangial trichoblasts simple; 40–50 μ broad and 250–350 μ long when spermatangia are mature, markedly curved toward branch tip, at times with one or more sterile cells at apex. Cystocarps more or less urceolate, 200–300 μ broad, pedicellate but with a relatively short pedicel. Tetraspores 60–70 μ in diameter; in series of a dozen or more.

LOCAL DISTRIBUTION. Growing on rocks between the 2.0- and −1.0-foot tide levels. Asilomar Point; Middle Reef of Moss Beach; Pescadero Point; Mission Point.

TYPE LOCALITY. Santa Cruz, California.

PACIFIC COAST DISTRIBUTION. Alaska (Sitka) to central California (Carmel Bay).

The variety *delicatula* (Hollenberg, 1942A, p. 778) has thalli but 0.5–2.0 cm. tall. It has been found on piling of the Municipal Wharf at Monterey and has been dredged from a depth of 30–35 feet a quarter-mile from this wharf and from a depth of 25–30 feet near Point Aulon.

The variety *determinata* (*Hollenberg, 1942A, p. 778) has thalli 5–15 cm. tall. The extent to which the ultimate branchlets elongate is more or less limited (determinate) and the terminal branchlets are in distinctly penicillate tufts. The ultimate branchlets of this variety are often markedly curved. This variety has been found growing on rocks between the 2.5- and 1.0-foot tide levels at Asilomar Point, the Middle Reef of Moss Beach, and Arrowhead Point.

The variety *distans* (*Hollenberg 1942A, p. 779; fig. 16) has thalli 10–18 cm. tall. It differs from the type and other varieties in the much sparser branching and the greater distance between successive branches on erect shoots. Known locally only from specimens cast ashore at the south end of Carmel Beach.

Polysiphonia acuminata Gardner

Gardner, 1927D, p. 100. *Hollenberg, 1942A, p. 782.
Streblocladia camptoclada Gardner [not of (Montagne) Falkenberg].
Gardner in Phyc. Bor.-Amer. No. 1599.

Thalli 2–6 cm. tall; reddish-brown in color. Wholly erect or with a limited development of prostrate branches. Attached by rhizoids from base of erect shoots or from prostrate branches; the rhizoids unicellular, separated from pericentral cells by a cross wall. Erect shoots with a percurrent axis 300–500 μ in diameter.

Segments at base of shoot longer than broad, each with 4 pericentral cells. All branches uncorticated. Erect shoots with one trichoblast or scar cell at each segment and lying in a spiral with a ¼ divergence. The trichoblasts 2–4 times forked. Each lateral branch of an erect shoot entirely replacing a trichoblast or scar cell. Spermatangial trichoblasts with one fork fertile; the fertile fork 30–50 µ broad, 100–150 µ long, at times with one or two sterile cells at apex. Cystocarps subsessile, subspherical, 250–300 µ in diameter. Tetrasporangia 50–70 µ in diameter.

LOCAL DISTRIBUTION. Cast ashore near Monterey.
TYPE LOCALITY. White's Point, San Pedro, California.
PACIFIC COAST DISTRIBUTION. Central California (Monterey) to southern California (La Jolla).

Polysiphonia flaccidissima var. Smithii Hollenberg

Pl. 94, fig. 2

*Hollenberg, 1942A, p. 784.

Thalli, as found on the Monterey Peninsula, 2–3 cm. tall; brownish-red in color. With a prostrate system of branches attached to substratum by unicellular rhizoids. The erect shoots with an obscure axis 100–120 µ in diameter, the branching of 3–4 orders and sparse. Segments at base of axis with a length 2–4 times the breadth, each with 4 pericentral cells. All branches uncorticated. Branches with one trichoblast or scar cell at each segment and lying in a spiral with a ¼ divergence. The trichoblasts simple or bifurcate, not markedly narrowed toward the apex. Each lateral branch axillary to a trichoblast or scar cell. Spermatangia, cystocarps, and tetrasporangia unknown.

LOCAL DISTRIBUTION. Dredged from a depth of 35–40 feet near Monterey Street, Pacific Grove.
TYPE LOCALITY. Newport Bay, Orange County, California.
PACIFIC COAST DISTRIBUTION. Central California (Pacific Grove) to southern California (La Jolla).

Polysiphonia Brodiaei (Dillwyn) Greville   Pl. 93, fig. 2

Greville ex Harvey, 1833A, p. 328. Rosenvinge, 1909–1931 (1923), p. 430; figs. 376–384.
Conferva Brodiaei Dillwyn, 1809, pl. 109.

Thalli, as found on the Monterey Peninsula, 10–15 cm. tall; reddish-brown in color. With a prostrate system of branches bearing one-celled rhizoids on the under side. Erect shoots with several long branches from basal portion of shoot; each branch up to 400–500 µ in diameter and with a percurrent axis. Segments of branches with a length 1–2 times the breadth, with 7 pericentral cells. All major branches completely corticated. Branches with one trichoblast or scar cell at each segment and lying in a spiral with a ⅐ divergence. The trichoblasts persisting for a relatively long time, usually bifurcate, gradually tapering to a blunt tip. Lateral branches of erect shoots axillary to a trichoblast or scar cell. Spermatangial trichoblasts with the adaxial fork fertile and without a sterile tip; 40–50 µ broad, 160–200 µ long. Cystocarps urceolate, pedicellate, 400–430 µ broad. Tetrasporangia in linear series of 8–15; 70–80 µ in diameter.

LOCAL DISTRIBUTION. Growing between the mean low-tide and −1.5-foot tide levels on piling of Municipal Wharf and Fisherman's Wharf, Monterey. At −2.0-foot tide level on receiving hopper of a sardine cannery near Mussel Point.

TYPE LOCALITY. Forres, England.

PACIFIC COAST DISTRIBUTION. Central California (Sausalito) to southern California (Santa Monica).

Polysiphonia californica Harvey   Pl. 93; fig. 1

Harvey, 1853, p. 48. *Anderson, 1891, p. 224. *Kylin, 1941, p. 36. Phyc. Bor.-Amer. No. 1142.

Polysiphonia senticulosa Anderson [not of Harvey]. *Anderson, 1891, p. 224.

Thalli, as found on the Monterey Peninsula, 5–12 (−20) cm. tall; brownish-red in color. With a prostrate system of densely matted branches bearing one-celled rhizoids in groups of 2–3 on the under side. Erect shoots with an obscure axis, 220–275 µ in diameter, freely branched, the branching predominately opposite and the branches usually two segments apart. All branches uncorticated. Segments at base of axis with a length 1.5–2 times the breadth, usually with 12 pericentral cells and often with the pericentral cells spirally twisted. Branches with one trichoblast or scar cell at each segment and lying in a spiral with a ¼ divergence, namely, three pericentral cells to the left of the one below. The trichoblasts bi- to quadrifurcate, gradually tapering to a blunt tip. Each branch with a trichoblast or scar cell at one side of base. Cystocarps urceolate, pedicellate, 300–350 µ broad. Tetrasporangia 90–110 µ in diameter, in a linear series of 10–18; segments with tetrasporangia conspicuously inflated.

LOCAL DISTRIBUTION. Growing on rocks between the 1.0- and −1.5-foot tide levels. Mussel Point; Point Pinos; Asilomar Point; Middle Reef of Moss Beach; Pescadero Point. Also dredged from a depth of 20–25 feet near Pescadero Rock.

TYPE LOCALITY. Golden Gate, San Francisco, California.

PACIFIC COAST DISTRIBUTION. British Columbia (Port Holmes) to Baja California.

Polysiphonia Hendryi Gardner   Pl. 93, figs. 3–4

Gardner, 1927D, p. 101; pls. 24–25.

Thalli, as found on the Monterey Peninsula, 2–4 cm. tall; reddish-black in color. With an extensive system of prostrate branches. Attached by unicellular rhizoids from base of erect shoots or from the prostrate branches. Erect shoots with an indistinct axis 120–150 µ in diameter, the branching appearing as if dichotomous and with the branch tips outwardly curved. All branches uncorticated. Segments at base of axis with a length 0.5–2.0 times the breadth; each with 12–14 pericentral cells. A trichoblast or scar cell not regularly present on every segment. The trichoblasts usually bifurcate, not markedly attenuated toward the tips. Spermatangial trichoblasts with fertile branch abaxial; 32–36 µ broad, 100–130 µ long. Cystocarps subsessile, ovoid, 350–400 µ broad. Tetrasporangia 55–65 µ in diameter, in series of 4–8.

LOCAL DISTRIBUTION. Epiphytic on various algae growing between the 3.5- and 1.5-foot tide levels. East of Fanshell Beach; Pescadero Point; rocks north of Carmel Beach.

TYPE LOCALITY. Santo Domingo, Baja California, Mexico.

PACIFIC COAST DISTRIBUTION. Central California (Carmel Bay) to Baja California (Santo Domingo).

Polysiphonia Collinsii Hollenberg mss.

Polysiphonia Sancti-Petri Collins in Phyc. Bor.-Amer. No. 2247 (name only).

Thalli 2–4 cm. tall, reddish-brown to nearly black in color. With an extensive system of prostrate branches and attached by unicellular rhizoids from prostrate branches. Erect shoots with a conspicuous main axis, 150–180 µ in diameter, the branching frequently appearing as if unilateral. All branches uncorticated. Segments at base of axis with a length 2–4 times the breadth; each with 12–14 pericentral cells. Trichoblasts and scar cells 2–3 segments apart; lying in a spiral and usually in a ¼ divergence. The trichoblasts once- or twice-forked, not markedly attenuated at apices. Cystocarps subsessile, ovoid, 200–280 μ broad. Tetra-sporangia 40–70 μ in diameter, in series of a dozen or more.

LOCAL DISTRIBUTION. Growing on rocks or on coralline algae in the mid-littoral zone. Fanshell Beach; Pescadero Point.

TYPE LOCALITY. As above.

PACIFIC COAST DISTRIBUTION. British Columbia (Vancouver Island) to southern California (La Jolla).

Closely resembling *P. Hendryi* but differing in the more distinct axis of erect branches. *P. Collinsii* is saxicolous, *P. Hendryi* is epiphytic.

Lophosiphonia Falkenberg, 1897

Thalli freely branched and evidently polysiphonous; with prostrate rhizome-like branches bearing erect branches. The prostrate branches cylindrical, freely branched, and capable of indefinite growth, bearing unicellular rhizoids on ventral face (often one on each segment) and erect polysiphonous branches on dorsal face. Tips of the prostrate branches without trichoblasts. The erect branches polysiphonous, simple or sparingly branched, not growing indefinitely. The erect branches arising endogenously some distance back from apex of a horizontal branch. Tips of erect branches with or without trichoblasts.

Heterothallic. The spermatangia borne in dense clusters on trichoblasts at apices of erect branches. Carpogonial filament four-celled, borne on the next to lowermost cell of a trichoblast at apex of an erect filament. Development of cystocarp unknown but presumably as in *Polysiphonia*. The mature cystocarp surrounded by an urn-shaped pericarp developed from lower cells of a fertile trichoblast.

Tetrasporophytes with the tetrasporangia restricted to upper portions of erect branches; the tetrasporangia produced singly in several successive segments and lying in a straight or a spiral row. The tetrasporangia tetrahedrally divided.

STRUCTURE AND REPRODUCTION. Falkenberg, 1901, pp. 495–503; pl. 9, figs. 7–10, 21–24. Börgesen, 1915, pp. 294–299, 475–476; figs. 292–298, 432.

With one species in the local flora.

Lophosiphonia villum (J. G. Agardh) Setchell and Gardner
Pl. 94, fig. 1

Setchell and Gardner, 1903, p. 329. *Kylin, 1941, p. 40.
Polysiphonia villum J. G. Agardh, 1863, p. 941.

Thalli, as found on the Monterey Peninsula, forming a velvety layer up to a meter or more broad, reddish-brown in color. The branches uncorticated, with four pericentral cells, 50–60 μ in diameter and segments in mature portion 100–120 μ long. Erect branches up to 1 cm. tall, very sparingly branched, with slightly curved apices. Trichoblasts of erect branches long, once- or twice-forked, 15–20 μ broad at base. Tetrasporangia about 50 μ in diameter, in rows of a dozen or more.

LOCAL DISTRIBUTION. Growing between the 5.0- and 3.0-foot tide levels on cliffs or on vertical face of rocks more or less sheltered from direct sunlight. Mussel Point; Point Pinos; Point Joe; Fanshell Beach; Cypress Point; Pescadero Point; Pebble Beach.

TYPE LOCALITY. "Tropical America."

PACIFIC COAST DISTRIBUTION. Central California (Pacific Grove) to Mexico (Gulf of California).

Pterosiphonia Falkenberg, 1897

Thalli freely branched and polysiphonous; usually wholly erect but at times partly prostrate. Erect branches distichously branched into several orders of branching and with the branching of all orders regularly alternate and all branches lying in one plane. The branches cylindrical or markedly compressed, with 4–20 pericentral cells in each segment. Older portions of branches regularly corticated in certain species, uncorticated in others. Tips of vegetative branches without trichoblasts.

Heterothallic. The spermatangia borne upon trichoblasts produced in clusters at tips of branches. Carpogonial filaments four-celled; development of carpogonial filament and cystocarp as in *Polysiphonia*. The mature cystocarps surrounded by an ostiolate pericarp.

Tetrasporophytes with the tetrasporangia borne singly in several successive segments toward upper ends of branches. The tetrasporangia tetrahedrally divided.

STRUCTURE AND REPRODUCTION. Suneson, 1940.

KEY TO THE SPECIES IN THE LOCAL FLORA

1. Older branches completely corticated......................*P. Baileyi*
1. All branches uncorticated...................................... 2
  2. Branches cylindrical..............................*P. bipinnata*
  2. Branches markedly compressed....................*P. dendroidea*

Pterosiphonia dendroidea (Montagne) Falkenberg

Pl. 95, fig. 3

Falkenberg, 1901, p. 268. *Kylin, 1941, p. 39.
Polysiphonia dendroidea Montagne, 1837, p. 353.
Polysiphonia parasitica var. *dendroidea* (Montagne) J. G. Agardh, 1863,
p. 931. *Anderson, 1891, p. 224. *Howe, 1893, p. 68. Phyc. Bor.-Amer. No. 642.

Thalli, as found on the Monterey Peninsula, 2–8 cm. tall;
rose-red in color. With a prostrate rhizome-like portion bearing
many erect branches. The erect branches with a conspicuous
percurrent axis distichously and pinnately branched from base
to axis; all lateral branches of axis approximately the same length.
The axis and branches markedly compressed and uncorticated.
The segments with 8–12 pericentral cells. The axis and branches
regularly with 2 segments between successive branches and with
the segments broader than tall.

LOCAL DISTRIBUTION. Growing on rocks between the mean low-tide
and −1.5-foot tide levels. Especially abundant in crevices and on sheltered
parts of rocks. Mussel Point; Point Pinos; Asilomar Point; Middle Reef
of Moss Beach; Point Joe; Fanshell Beach; Cypress Point; Pescadero
Point; Pebble Beach; Arrowhead Point; Mission Point. Also dredged
from a depth of 20–25 feet near Point Aulon and near Pescadero Rock.

TYPE LOCALITY. Callao, Peru.

PACIFIC COAST DISTRIBUTION. British Columbia (Vancouver Island)
to southern California (San Diego).

Pterosiphonia bipinnata (Postels and Ruprecht) Falkenberg

Falkenberg, 1901, p. 273. *Kylin, 1941, p. 39. Phyc. Bor.-Amer. Nos. 1145, 1698.
Polysiphonia bipinnata Postels and Ruprecht, 1840, p. 22. *Howe, 1893,
p. 68. *Phyc. Bor.-Amer. No. 144.

Thalli, as found on the Monterey Peninsula, 6–12 cm. tall;
brownish-red to bright red in color. The erect branches cylindrical, uncorticated, laxly branched. The final orders of branching
with the distichous arrangement characteristic of the genus, the
primary orders frequently with this obscured through torsion.
The segments with 11–13 pericentral cells. Major branches with
3 segments between successive lateral branches and the segments
with a length 3–8 times the breadth; smaller branches with 2 segments between successive lateral branches and the segments with
a length 2–3 times the breadth.

LOCAL DISTRIBUTION. Growing on rocks at mean low-tide level. Monterey; Point Pinos; Middle Reef of Moss Beach; Pebble Beach.

TYPE LOCALITY. Kamchatka Peninsula, U.S.S.R.

PACIFIC COAST DISTRIBUTION. Alaska (Shumagin Islands) to southern California (San Pedro).

Pterosiphonia Baileyi (Harvey) Falkenberg Pl. 95, fig. 4

Falkenberg, 1901, p. 270. *Kylin, 1941, p. 38.
Rytiphlaea (?) *Baileyi* *Harvey, 1853, p. 29.
Polysiphonia Baileyi (Harvey) J. G. Agardh, 1863, p. 937. *Anderson, 1891, p. 225. *Howe, 1893, p. 68. *Phyc. Bor.-Amer. No. 339.

Thalli, as found on the Monterey Peninsula, 8–25 cm. tall; reddish-black in color. Usually with several erect shoots from a common base. Each shoot with a more or less percurrent, cylindrical, completely corticated axis; the axis unbranched below and much-branched above. Branching of axis distichously pinnate, the primary lateral branches of axis corticated and the lower ones rebranched in same manner as axis. All branches usually lying in the same plane; the ultimate branches uncorticated and the segments with 12–14 pericentral cells.

LOCAL DISTRIBUTION. Growing on the vertical face of rocks between the 0.5- and −1.0-foot tide levels. Never present in abundance. Mussel Point; Point Aulon; Point Pinos; Middle Reef of Moss Beach; Point Joe; Fanshell Beach; Cypress Point; Pescadero Point; Pebble Beach; Arrowhead Point; Mission Point. Also dredged from a depth of 20–25 feet near Mussel Point and Point Aulon.

TYPE LOCALITY. Monterey, California.

PACIFIC COAST DISTRIBUTION. Northern California (Crescent City) to southern California (La Jolla).

Pterochondria Hollenberg, 1942

Thalli freely branched and polysiphonous; wholly erect and attached by rhizoids. Erect branches alternately branched into several orders of branching and with all branches lying in one plane. The branches compressed, uncorticated, and each segment with several pericentral cells. Tips of branches without trichoblasts.

Heterothallic. The spermatangia borne upon the flattened faces of disc-shaped plates produced at the tips of branches. Carpogonial filament and development of cystocarp unknown but presumably as in *Pterosiphonia*. The mature cystocarps borne terminally on branches and surrounded by an ostiolate pericarp.

Tetrasporophytes with the tetrasporangia borne singly within several successive segments toward upper ends of branches and on the adaxial side of a branch. The tetrasporangia tetrahedrally divided.

STRUCTURE AND REPRODUCTION. Hollenberg, 1942, pp. 533–544.

Pterochondria Woodii (Harvey) Hollenberg Pl. 95, figs. 1–2

*Hollenberg, 1942, p. 533.
Polysiphonia Woodii Harvey, 1853, p. 52. *Anderson, 1891, p. 225. *Howe, 1893, p. 68. *Phyc. Bor.-Amer. No. 46.
Pterosiphonia Woodii (Harvey) Falkenberg, 1901, p. 274. Collins, 1913, p. 121. *Kylin, 1941, p. 38. *Phyc. Bor.-Amer. No. 1545.

Thalli, as found on the Monterey Peninsula, usually 8–15 cm. tall but occasionally up to 25 cm.; the lower portion greenish-yellow and the upper portion deep red in color. The thalli erect, laxly branched, and without a percurrent axis. The branching distichous, regularly alternate; the branches widely divergent and successive branches progressively smaller toward thallus apex. The branches markedly compressed and uncorticated. The segments with 16–25 pericentral cells. Major branches with 4–6 segments between successive branches and the segments broader than tall; smaller branches with 2–4 segments between successive branches and the segments about as broad as tall.

LOCAL DISTRIBUTION. Regularly epiphytic on *Cystoseira osmundacea;* occasionally developing on Laminariales or on foliose Florideae. Found locally wherever *Cystoseira* grows but present in abundance only during the summer and early autumn.

TYPE LOCALITY. Between Tomales Point and Point Reyes, California.

PACIFIC COAST DISTRIBUTION. British Columbia (Vancouver Island) to southern California (San Pedro).

Herposiphonia Nägeli, 1846

Thalli evidently polysiphonous, branched; wholly prostrate, partly prostrate and partly erect, or almost wholly erect. With a percurrent axis in which each segment bears one of two types of branch, either a simple branch or a compound branch similar to the axis. The simple and compound branches borne in a regular sequence and always with three simple branches intervening between successive compound branches. The branches distichously arranged but this at times obscured through torsion of branches. The simple branches of limited growth, 12–20 segments in length, with or without trichoblasts at the apex. The compound branches with an indefinite number of segments and with 8–20 pericentral cells in each segment. All branches of thallus uncorticated.

Heterothallic. The spermatangia borne in dense masses on unbranched trichoblasts at tips of simple branches. The carpogonial filament four-celled. Development of cystocarp unknown but presumably as in *Polysiphonia*. Mature cystocarp either at apex or base of a simple branch and surrounded by an urn-shaped pericarp.

Tetrasporophytes with the tetrasporangia restricted to simple branches and produced singly within 3–8 successive segments. The tetrasporangia tetrahedrally divided.

STRUCTURE AND REPRODUCTION. Börgesen, 1915, pp. 286–292, 469–475; figs. 287–289, 428–431. Falkenberg, 1901, pp. 302–318; pl. 3, figs. 8–17, 19–20.

KEY TO THE SPECIES IN THE LOCAL FLORA

1. All compound branches approximately the same length..*H. verticillata*
1. Lower compound branches much longer than upper ones........... 2
  2. Thalli erect, standing free from substratum..............*H. rigida*
  2. Thalli almost wholly prostrate.....................*H. pygmaea*

Herposiphonia rigida Gardner   Pl. 95, fig. 5; pl. 96, fig. 3

Gardner, 1927D, p. 100; pl. 23.

Thalli, as found on the Monterey Peninsula, up to 3 cm. tall; bright red in color. The erect branches rigid, distichously branched, with all branches lying in the same plane. The lower compound branches much longer than the upper ones, up to 2 cm. long, repeating the branching of the axis. Simple branches straight or slightly arcuate, about 1 mm. long. The simple and compound branches not overlapping one another and showing very clearly the three simple branches between successive compound branches. Segments of axis and compound branches with a breadth 1.5 times the length and each segment with 9–12 pericentral cells. Simple branches with 10–12 segments and each segment with 8–10 pericentral cells.

LOCAL DISTRIBUTION. Growing on rocks between the mean low-tide and −1.0-foot tide levels. Isolated thalli have been found at Mussel Point; Asilomar Point; Middle Reef of Moss Beach; Cypress Point; and Pescadero Rock. Also dredged from a depth of 30–35 feet a quarter-mile from Municipal Wharf, Monterey.

TYPE LOCALITY. Friday Harbor, Washington.

PACIFIC COAST DISTRIBUTION. Puget Sound to southern California (Santa Monica).

Herposiphonia pygmaea Hollenberg mss.   Pl. 96, fig. 2

Thalli, as found on the Monterey Peninsula, up to 3 cm. long; reddish-black in color. The entire thallus closely adherent to the substratum, with a percurrent axis. Lower compound branches of axis much longer than upper ones and up to 5 mm. long. Simple branches straight or slightly curved; about .5 mm. long. The compound and simple branches not overlapping one another and showing very clearly the three simple branches between successive compound branches. Segments of axis and compound branches about as broad as long and each with 10–12 pericentral cells. Simple branches with 13–18 segments and each segment with 8 pericentral cells.

LOCAL DISTRIBUTION. On *Calliarthron* and *Bossea* spp. dredged from a depth of 20–25 feet near Point Aulon and from 35–40 feet near Point Pinos.

Herposiphonia verticillata (Harvey) Kylin   Pl. 96, fig. 1

Kylin, 1925, p. 74.
Polysiphonia verticillata Harvey, 1833, p. 165. Harvey, 1853, p. 53. *Anderson, 1891, p. 225. Phyc. Bor.-Amer. No. 640.

Thalli, as found on the Monterey Peninsula, densely matted but with certain compound branches standing free from the mat; brownish-olive to reddish-brown in color. The compound branches distichously branched but with the branches more or less curved and standing at various angles to the axis; the lower compound branches not much longer than the upper ones. The compound and simple branches so overlapping one another that the characteristic succession of simple and compound branches is evident only in occasional branches. Segments of compound branches with a breadth about double the length and each segment with 14–16 pericentral cells. Simple branches with 14–16 segments and 12 pericentral cells in each segment.

LOCAL DISTRIBUTION. Usually found on articulated corallines (especially *Corallina*) growing between the 0.5- and −1.5-foot tide levels. Mussel Point; Point Pinos; Asilomar Point; Middle Reef of Moss Beach; Point Joe; Pescadero Point; Pebble Beach; Mission Point.

TYPE LOCALITY. "California." Undoubtedly either San Francisco or Monterey.

PACIFIC COAST DISTRIBUTION. Central California (San Francisco) to Baja California (Ensenada).

Taenioma J. G. Agardh, 1863

Thallus with a prostrate axis bearing erect, freely branched shoots at frequent intervals. Both the prostrate and erect portions flattened, polysiphonous, and with four pericentral cells in each segment. The prostrate axis with one- or with two-celled rhizoids

and, according to the species, with or without two opposed pericentral cells in every segment cutting off two short corticating
cells. The erect shoots always with two opposed pericentral cells
in every segment cutting off a pair of short corticating cells. Tips
of branches of certain species regularly terminating in a pair of
unbranched filaments. Branches of erect shoots apparently arising
endogenously from the axial cell of a segment a short distance
back from the growing apex.

Heterothallic. The spermatangia borne on short, flattened
branchlets near apex of erect shoot and covering flattened faces
of branchlet. Carpogonial filament and development of cystocarp
unknown. The mature cystocarp surrounded by a pericarp and
borne on flattened face of a branch of erect shoot.

Tetrasporophytes with the tetrasporangia borne on short,
stichidium-like branchlets of erect shoots, and with several successive segments each producing an opposed pair of tetrasporangia.
The tetrasporangia cruciately (?) divided.

STRUCTURE AND REPRODUCTION. Börgesen, 1915–20, pp. 338–341; fig.
337. Falkenberg, 1901, pp. 709–711; pl. 15, figs. 21–29. Thompson, 1910.

With one species in the local flora.

Taenioma Clevelandii Farlow   Pl. 96, figs. 4–5

Farlow, 1877, p. 236. *Hollenberg, 1942, p. 534.

Thalli, as found on the Monterey Peninsula, 5–8 cm. tall;
deep pinkish-red in color. Prostrate portion of thallus with two
opposed cells of every segment cutting off two short corticating
cells. Rhizoids of prostrate portion two-celled and growing out
from the corticating cells. Erect shoots freely branched but with
six or more segments between successive branches. The branches
linear, 150–200 μ broad, with a rounded base and with the apex
gradually attenuated. Apices of branches not terminating in a
pair of unbranched filaments.

LOCAL DISTRIBUTION. Cast ashore at Moss Beach. On holdfast of
Nereocystis Luetkeana cast ashore at Carmel Beach.

TYPE LOCALITY. San Diego, California.

PACIFIC COAST DISTRIBUTION. Known only from the Monterey Peninsula; San Pedro, California; and the type locality.

There are no gross morphological characters to especially
attract the attention of the collector and the unusual features of
the alga do not become evident until it is examined under the
microscope.

Amplisiphonia Hollenberg, 1939

Thallus a prostrate, indefinitely expanded, rosette-like, crustose sheet with semicircular lobes overlapping one another. Attached to substratum by numerous unicellular rhizoids from lower surface. Growth marginal and due to a continuous marginal row of apical cells. Margin of thallus one cell in thickness and with the cells regularly arranged in parallel rows. The portion some distance in from margin becoming polysiphonous by each cell cutting off three pericentral cells on the dorsal face and two pericentral cells on the ventral face. Older portions of thallus remaining three cells in thickness.

Spermatangia and cystocarps unknown.

Tetrasporophytes with the tetrasporangia borne in erect ruffled lobes at the margin of thallus. The tetrasporangia in parallel radiating rows, embedded within thallus, and formed by division of pericentral cells. The tetrasporangia cruciately divided.

STRUCTURE AND REPRODUCTION. Hollenberg, 1939.

Amplisiphonia pacifica Hollenberg   Pl. 96, figs. 7–9

*Hollenberg, 1939, p. 382; figs. 1–13.

Thalli, as found on the Monterey Peninsula, usually 10–15 cm. in diameter but occasionally up to 30 cm.; dull red in color. Deeply and irregularly lobed, about 140 µ in thickness. Fruiting lobes of tetrasporophytes marginal, obovate-cuneate; prostrate when young, erect when mature.

LOCAL DISTRIBUTION. Growing on rocks and on crustose corallines between the 1.0- and −1.0-foot tide levels. Isolated thalli have been collected at the foot of Fifth Street, Pacific Grove; Pescadero Point; and Mission Point.

TYPE LOCALITY. Corona del Mar, California.

PACIFIC COAST DISTRIBUTION. Central California (Moss Beach, San Mateo County) to southern California (Corona del Mar).

Chondria C. A. Agardh, 1817

Thalli erect, bushy, polysiphonous, but this completely obscured by corticating cells. With several erect shoots from a common base. The erect shoots cylindrical, alternately to irregularly branched into successive orders of progressively smaller branches. Branches of the ultimate order constricted at base and spindle- or club-shaped. Tips of growing branches with branched trichoblasts.

Heterothallic. The spermatangia borne upon trichoblasts whose branches are usually laterally adjoined to form a small plate. The spermatangial plates colorless, flat or curved, usually produced in dense clusters at the tips of branches. Carpogonial filament four-celled, its supporting cell cut off from the median cell of a three-celled fertile trichoblast. The supporting cells also bearing two sterile filaments. The auxiliary cell cut off at upper end of supporting cell after fertilization; fusing with the supporting cell and its sterile filaments to form a placental cell of relatively small size. The gonimoblast filaments branched and with only the terminal cells developing into carposporangia. The mature cystocarp surrounded by a sessile ostiolate pericarp that usually has a short horn-like basal projection. The pericarp more than one cell in thickness throughout.

Tetrasporophytes with the tetrasporangia restricted to the ultimate branchlets. The tetrasporangia irregularly distributed and embedded just beneath surface of branch. The tetrasporangia tetrahedrally divided.

STRUCTURE AND REPRODUCTION. Falkenberg, 1901, pp. 190–210; pl. 22, figs. 4–23. Kylin, 1928, pp. 79–91; figs. 51–56.

With one species in the local flora.

Chondria decipiens Kylin   Pl. 96, fig. 6

*Kylin, 1941, p. 41; pl. 12, fig. 36.
Chondria atropurpurea var. *tenuior* Farlow in Algae Exsicc. Amer. Bor. No. 57.
Chondriopsis atropurpurea Anderson [not of (Harvey) J. G. Agardh]. *Anderson, 1891, p. 225.

Thalli, as found on the Monterey Peninsula, 10–15 cm. tall; dark brown in color. With several shoots arising from a common base. Each shoot with a few long branches and numerous branchlets. The branchlets slender and spindle-shaped, rarely over 4 mm. in length. Cystocarps borne in groups near the tips of branchlets; the pericarp spherical to oval, 0.5–0.9 mm. in diameter, with a short prong at base and on the abaxial side. The tetrasporophytes with tetrasporangia restricted to upper half of fertile branchlets.

LOCAL DISTRIBUTION. Growing at mean low-tide level on piling of Municipal Wharf, Monterey. On rocks between the 1.0- and 0.5-foot tide levels, east of Mussel Point.

TYPE LOCALITY. Municipal Wharf, Monterey.

PACIFIC COAST DISTRIBUTION. Definitely known only from Santa Cruz, California, and from Monterey.

Rhodomela C. A. Agardh, 1822

Thalli erect, usually with several erect shoots growing from a common base. The erect shoots cylindrical or slightly compressed, with several long branches or divided into progessively smaller branches; in either case the branches of all orders usually clothed from base to apex with short branchlets all of approximately the same length. Tips of developing branches with branched trichoblasts. All branches polysiphonous but the polysiphonous organization soon obliterated by division and redivision of the pericentral cells.

Heterothallic. The spermatangia borne either on trichoblasts or upon the surface of young branches. The fertile branches usually in corymbose clusters and completely covered with spermatangia. The carpogonial filament four-celled, borne on an adaxial supporting cell cut off from the next to lowermost cell of a fertile trichoblast. The supporting cell also bearing two sterile filaments. The auxiliary cell cut off at upper end of supporting cell after fertilization; soon fusing with supporting cell and its sterile filaments to form a large, irregularly shaped, placental cell producing short gonimoblast filaments at the upper end. Only the terminal cells of gonimoblast filaments developing into carposporangia. The mature cystocarp surrounded by an ostiolate pericarp.

The tetrasporophytes with the tetrasporangia borne in two vertical rows in inflated, stichidium-like branchlets. Two opposite pericentral cells in several successive segments of a fertile branchlet producing tetrasporangia. The tetrasporangia tetrahedrally divided.

STRUCTURE AND REPRODUCTION. Kylin, 1914. Kylin, 1923, pp. 114–115; fig. 62. Kylin, 1934B, pp. 12–14; fig. 3. Rosenberg, 1933, pp. 28–31; fig. 9.

With one species in the local flora.

Rhodomela larix (Turner) C. A. Agardh   Pl. 97, fig. 1

C. A. Agardh, 1822, p. 376. *Harvey, 1853, p. 24. *Anderson, 1891, p. 224. *Howe, 1893, p. 68. Phyc. Bor.-Amer. Nos. 241, 1699.
Fucus larix Turner, 1819, p. 23; pl. 207.

Thalli, as found on the Monterey Peninsula, 10–20 cm. tall; brownish-black to black in color. Erect shoots without or with a few long branches; the major branches closely beset with spirally arranged, cylindrical branchlets 5–10 mm. long. The branches and branchlets wiry in texture.

LOCAL DISTRIBUTION. Growing on rocks between the 2.0- and 0.5-foot tide levels. Abundant at Asilomar Point; Middle Reef of Moss Beach; Fanshell Beach; and Cypress Point.

TYPE LOCALITY. Nootka Sound, Vancouver Island, British Columbia.

PACIFIC COAST DISTRIBUTION. Alaska (Port Clarence) to central California (San Luis Obispo County).

Odonthalia Lyngbye, 1819

Thalli erect, freely branched, and with several long branches. The long branches cylindrical to markedly flattened, with or without a midrib if flattened. All long branches bearing distichously and alternately arranged short branchlets from base to apex. The branchlets usually flattened. The branches with each cell of the axial filament surrounded by four pericentral cells and these cells soon becoming corticated.

Heterothallic. The spermatangia covering the surface of short simple branchlets. The carpogonial filament four-celled, its supporting cell a pericentral cell of an axial filament of a simple branchlet. The supporting cell also bearing two sterile filaments. The auxiliary cell cut off at the upper end of the supporting cell and the gonimoblast filaments growing upward from it. The mature cystocarp surrounded by a conspicuous ostiolate pericarp.

Tetrasporophytes with the tetrasporangia produced in stichidium-like simple branchlets that are often borne in clusters. Two opposite pericentral cells of several successive axial cells each producing a tetrasporangium that lies beneath two cover cells. The tetrasporangia tetrahedrally divided.

STRUCTURE AND REPRODUCTION. Kylin, 1934B, pp. 5–12; figs. 1–2.

With one species in the local flora.

Odonthalia floccosa (Esper) Falkenberg   Pl. 97, fig. 2

Falkenberg, 1901, p. 607.
Fucus floccosa Esper, 1797–1802, p. 115; pl. 130.
Rhodomela floccosa (Esper) C. A. Agardh, 1822, p. 376. *Harvey, 1853, p. 24. *Anderson, 1891, p. 224. *Howe, 1893, p. 68.
Odonthalia aelutica Butler and Polley [not of (C. A. Agardh) J. G. Agardh]. Butler and Polley in Phyc. Bor.-Amer. No. 1147.

Thalli, as found on the Monterey Peninsula, up to 40 cm. tall; blackish-brown in color. Major branches cylindrical to slightly compressed, about 1 mm. in diameter. The major branches alternately and distichously branched with short branchlets. The ultimate branchlets flattened and very gradually attenuated to an acute tip. Fertile branchlets, especially those of cystocarpic plants, in dense head-like clusters.

LOCAL DISTRIBUTION. Monterey; Pacific Grove.
TYPE LOCALITY. Trinidad, California.
PACIFIC COAST DISTRIBUTION. Puget Sound to southern California (Santa Barbara).

Known locally from several herbarium specimens labeled "Monterey" or "Pacific Grove." The latest known dated specimens from Monterey are those of Miss Agnes E. Howe collected on July 3, 1893, and of Professor Setchell collected on May 16, 1897. There is a possibility that these and other specimens collected in years past were found between Fisherman's Wharf and Point Alones, a stretch of shore line now covered by sardine canneries.

Laurencia Lamouroux, 1813

Thalli erect, solitary or in gregarious tufts from a common disc-shaped base. The erect shoots cylindrical or markedly flattened, the branching pinnate or radial. The branch tips blunt and terminating in a small depression containing a single apical cell, the tips with evanescent trichoblasts. Thalli of a firm cartilaginous texture, solidly parenchymatous; the medulla with large, colorless, vertically elongated cells; the cortex with small isodiametric or palisade-like cells.

Heterothallic. The spermatangia borne on trichoblasts that lie closely packed within cup-shaped depressions near branch tips. Carpogonial filament four-celled, borne upon a trichoblast but this evident only very early in development of carpogonial filament. Supporting cell of carpogonial filament also bearing sterile filaments. The auxiliary cell cut off from supporting cell after fertilization and fusing with it and its sterile filaments to form a large irregularly shaped placental cell. The gonimoblast filaments growing upward from placental cell and with only the terminal cells developing into carposporangia. The mature cystocarp surrounded by a pericarp partially united with adjoining vegetative tissues of the thallus.

Tetrasporophytes with the tetrasporangia separated from one

another and embedded just beneath the surface of branches. The tetrasporangia tetrahedrally divided.

STRUCTURE AND REPRODUCTION. Falkenberg, 1901, pp. 237–246; pl. 23, figs. 3–36. Kylin, 1923, pp. 123–130; figs. 78–82. Kylin, 1928, pp. 91–94; figs. 57–58.

KEY TO THE SPECIES IN THE LOCAL FLORA

1. Thalli with the erect branches laterally adjoined in
   a cushion-like mass ....*L. crispa*
1. Thalli with the erect branches free from one another.............. 2
   2. Branches markedly compressed.............................. 3
   2. Branches approximately cylindrical 4
3. Lower portion of axis naked........................*L. spectabilis*
3. Lower portion of axis with many branches..............*L. splendens*
   4. Thalli reddish purple, axis up to 2.5 mm. in diameter.....*L. pacifica*
   4. Thalli deep red, axis less than 1.5 mm. in diameter......*L. Gardneri*

Laurencia spectabilis Postels and Ruprecht   Pl. 97, figs. 4–5

Postels and Ruprecht, 1840, p. 16. Yamada, 1931, p. 246. *Kylin, 1941, p. 43.
Laurencia pinnatifida Harvey [not of (Gmelin) Lamouroux]. *Harvey, 1833, p. 164. *Harvey, 1841, p. 408. *Harvey, 1853, p. 70. *Anderson, 1891, p. 225. *Howe, 1893, p. 68. Phyc. Bor.-Amer. No. 543.
Laurencia pinnatifida var. *spectabilis* (Postels and Ruprecht) Anderson. *Howe, 1893, p. 68.

Thalli, as found on the Monterey Peninsula, usually 15–20 cm. tall but occasionally up to 30 cm.; deep dull purplish-red in color. Erect shoots free from one another, markedly compressed, undivided in lower third, above this pinnately divided and with the branching alternate to subopposite, the branches without a midrib. The lower branches long and pinnately divided, the upper branches short and simple. The ultimate branchlets oblong to obovate, with a slight indentation at the apex.

LOCAL DISTRIBUTION. Growing on rocks between the 1.0- and −1.5-foot tide levels. Widely distributed over the entire Peninsula but especially abundant at Pebble Beach. Also dredged from a depth of 30–35 feet a quarter-mile from Municipal Wharf, Monterey; and from 15 to 20 feet at Stillwater Cove.

TYPE LOCALITY. Norfolk Sound near Sitka, Alaska.

PACIFIC COAST DISTRIBUTION. Alaska (Sitka) to southern California (San Diego).

Laurencia splendens Hollenberg   Pl. 97, fig. 3

Hollenberg apud Smith and Hollenberg, 1943, p. 219; fig. 24.
Laurencia pinnatifida var. *spectabilis* Anderson in Algae Exsicc. Amer. Bor. No. 59.

Thalli, as found on the Monterey Peninsula, 8–10 cm. tall;

reddish-brown in color. Erect shoots free from one another, markedly compressed, bi- or tripinnate and with all branches in one plane. The primary axis percurrent, 2–3 mm. broad, bearing lateral branches from base to apex. Surface cells of axis approximately isodiametric and the free face not bulging outward.

LOCAL DISTRIBUTION. Growing between the 1.0- and −0.5-foot tide levels on rocks at Asilomar Point and at the east side of the Middle Reef of Moss Beach.

TYPE LOCALITY. Middle Reef of Moss Beach.

PACIFIC COAST DISTRIBUTION. Known only from Santa Cruz, California, and from the type locality.

This species resembles *L. spectabilis* but is smaller in all proportions. In *L. spectabilis* the lower third of a shoot is usually naked, in *L. splendens* this portion of a shoot bears many branches.

Laurencia crispa Hollenberg   Pl. 98, fig. 3

Hollenberg apud Smith and Hollenberg, 1943, p. 219; figs. 25–27.

Thalli 8–10 cm. tall; greenish-brown in color. With many erect branches laterally compacted in a cushion-like mass and the cushions up to 15 cm. in diameter. The axis of erect shoots up to 2 mm. in diameter, cylindrical to somewhat angular or flattened, with 3–4 orders of lateral branches and the branchlets reduced to short blunt projections. The thallus of a crisp, but tender, texture and breaking readily when bent. Surface cells of thallus 15–25 μ in diameter, isodiametric, not forming a palisade-like layer; medullary cells large, colorless, the cell walls without lenticular thickenings.

LOCAL DISTRIBUTION. Growing on rocks between the 1.5- and 0.5-foot tide levels, Mussel Point. Also found cast ashore between Mussel Point and Point Aulon.

TYPE LOCALITY. Sandy beach at foot of Seventh Street, Pacific Grove, California.

PACIFIC COAST DISTRIBUTION. As above.

Living thalli are easily recognized by their cushion-like mode of growth and by the crisp texture of the branches.

Laurencia pacifica Kylin   Pl. 98, fig. 4

*Kylin, 1941, p. 42; pl. 13, fig. 8.

Laurencia virgata Harvey [not of J. G. Agardh]. *Harvey, 1853, p. 71. *Anderson, 1891, p. 225. *Howe, 1893, p. 68.

Laurencia paniculata Collins [not of (C. A. Agardh) J. G. Agardh]. Collins in Phyc. Bor.-Amer. No. 1093.

Thalli, as found on the Monterey Peninsula, usually 10–15 cm.

tall but occasionally up to 25 cm.; usually deep reddish-purple in color. Erect shoots free from one another, conical, profusely branched and with the branching radial to an obscure central axis. The branches subcylindrical, 1–1.5 mm. in diameter; repeatedly branched and with the ultimate branchlets in whorls of three or four. Apices of ultimate branchlets broadly rounded, slightly inflated, with a pit at the tip.

LOCAL DISTRIBUTION. Growing on rocks between the 1.5- and −1.5-foot tide levels. Very abundant at Pebble Beach. Also known from Mussel Point; Point Pinos; Cypress Point; and Pescadero Point.

TYPE LOCALITY. La Jolla, California.

PACIFIC COAST DISTRIBUTION. Central California (Pacific Grove) to southern California (La Jolla).

Laurencia Gardneri Hollenberg   Pl. 98, fig. 5

Hollenberg apud Smith and Hollenberg, 1943, p. 218; fig. 23.
Laurencia subopposita Collins [not of (J. G. Agardh) Setchell]. *Collins in Phyc. Bor.-Amer. No. 2145.

Thalli 6–10 cm. tall, rich red in color. The erect shoots densely tufted, repeatedly branched, and with the branching radial to an obscure central axis. The branches cylindrical, cartilaginous in texture, about 1 mm. in diameter, frequently more or less arcuate. The surface cells 25–40 μ broad, usually vertically elongated to thallus surface but not forming a palisade-like layer. The cell walls rarely with lenticular thickenings.

LOCAL DISTRIBUTION. Frequently cast ashore in abundance between Mussel Point and Point Aulon and in sandy coves near Asilomar Point. Also dredged from a depth of 30 feet near Mussel Point; from 35 to 40 feet near Point Aulon; from 30 to 35 feet near Point Pinos; from 20 to 25 feet near Pescadero Rock and near Arrowhead Point.

TYPE LOCALITY. Sandy beach at foot of Seventh Street, Pacific Grove, California.

PACIFIC COAST DISTRIBUTION. As above.

Resembling *L. pacifica* but smaller in all dimensions. *L. Gardneri* may also be distinguished by the curvature of the branches.

Ricardia Derbès and Solier, 1856

Thalli obpyriform to ellipsoidal, growing parasitically on branch tips of *Laurencia* and paler in color than the host. With a single large cylindrical rhizoidal cell penetrating deep into tissue of host. Very young germlings polysiphonous, slightly older germlings with the pericentral cells corticated and the cortication completely obscuring the polysiphonous organization. Older thalli solidly parenchymatous and with progressively smaller cells to thallus surface, at times becoming hollow at the center. Apices of thalli with branched or unbranched trichoblasts.

Heterothallic. The spermatangia developed on trichoblasts growing from superficial (corticating) cells of thallus; the trichoblasts grouped in sori scattered over surface of thallus. Carpogonial filament four-celled, borne on a supporting cell cut off from the next to lowermost cell of a trichoblast. The supporting cell also bearing two sterile filaments. The auxiliary cell cut off from supporting cell after fertilization; uniting with it and its sterile filaments to form a large, irregularly shaped, placental cell. The gonimoblast filaments growing upward from the placental cell and with only the terminal cells developing into carposporangia. The mature cystocarp surrounded by a pericarp immersed in and laterally united with thallus.

Tetrasporophytes with the tetrasporangia remote from one another and embedded just beneath the thallus surface. The tetrasporangia tetrahedrally divided.

STRUCTURE AND REPRODUCTION. Börgesen, 1930, pp. 74–80; figs. 29–31. Kylin, 1928, pp. 94–102; figs. 59–64.

With one species in the local flora.

Ricardia saccata (J. G. Agardh) Kylin   Pl. 98, fig. 2

Kylin, 1928, p. 94; figs. 59–64.
   Chylocladia (?) *saccata* *J. G. Agardh, 1849, p. 89. *Harvey, 1853, p. 79.
   Ricardia Montagnei Farlow [not of Derbès and Solier]. Farlow, 1877, p. 237. *Anderson, 1891, p. 223. Phyc. Bor.-Amer. No. 338.
   Ricardia Montagnei var. *gigantea* Farlow in Algae Exsicc. Amer. Bor. No. 58. Farlow, 1889, p. 2. *Setchell, 1905, p. 60.

Thalli, as found on the Monterey Peninsula, up to 3.5 cm. long; pink to light purplish-red when young, later becoming yellowish in color. Young thalli obovoid and with a smooth surface. Older thalli ellipsoidal and the surface with rounded, wart-like elevations. The trichoblasts branched and usually restricted to upper part of thallus.

LOCAL DISTRIBUTION. Parasitic on *Laurencia pacifica*. Appearing in the spring and disappearing in the autumn. Very abundant at Pebble Beach. Also known from Mussel Point and the Middle Reef of Moss Beach.

TYPE LOCALITY. "California" (probably the vicinity of Monterey).

PACIFIC COAST DISTRIBUTION. Central California (Pacific Grove) to southern California (La Jolla).

Janczewskia Solms-Laubach, 1877

Thalli small yellowish to pinkish warty cushions growing parasitically on various Rhodomelaceae, especially certain species of *Laurencia* and *Chondria*. The thalli with rhizoidal filaments or strands of rhizoidal filaments penetrating the host. Major portion of thallus lying external to host and composed of a solidly parenchymatous tissue. The reproductive organs borne in tuberculate outgrowths from thallus surface.

Heterothallic. The spermatangia produced within ellipsoidal conceptacles deeply embedded within the tuberculate outgrowths. The spermatangia developing in plumose clusters completely or incompletely lining the conceptacle. Structure of carpogonial filament and development of the cystocarp unknown. The mature cystocarp surrounded by an urn-shaped pericarp produced by an upgrowth of tissues adjoining the pericarp.

Tetrasporophytes with the tetrasporangia lying at the base of oval or irregularly shaped conceptacles. The tetrasporangia intermingled with paraphyses (trichoblasts?). The tetrasporangia tetrahedrally divided.

STRUCTURE AND REPRODUCTION. Börgesen, 1930, pp. 71–74; figs. 27–28. Falkenberg, 1901, pp. 255–261; pl. 24, figs. 16–19. Setchell, 1914*A*.

With one species in the local flora.

Janczewskia Gardneri Setchell and Guernsey   Pl. 98, fig. 1

Setchell and Guernsey apud *Setchell, 1914*A*, p. 12; pl. 1, figs. 4–6; pl. 3, figs. 15–16; pl. 5, fig. 25. *Kylin, 1941, p. 43.
Janczewskia verrucaeformis Nott [not of Solms-Laubach]. *Nott, 1897, p. 83. Phyc. Bor.-Amer. No. 887.

Thalli, as found on the Monterey Peninsula, 4–10 mm. in diameter; light pink in color. The thallus an irregularly shaped cushion densely covered with cylindrical tuberculate outgrowths. The parasites usually remote from one another and on flattened faces of older portions of host.

LOCAL DISTRIBUTION. Parasitic on *Laurencia spectabilis*. Common at Pebble Beach but occasionally found wherever the host is present.

TYPE LOCALITY. Duxbury Reef, Marin County, California.

PACIFIC COAST DISTRIBUTION. British Columbia (Vancouver Island) to central California (Carmel Bay).

BIBLIOGRAPHY

ABE, K. **1935**. Zur Kenntnis der Entwicklungsgeschichte von Heterochordaria, Scytosiphon, und Sorocarpus. *Sci. Repts. Tôhoku Imp. Univ.*, 4th ser., Biol. **9**: 329–337. 6 figs., 1 pl.

——. **1935A**. Kopulation der Schwärmer aus Unilokularem Sporangium von Heterochordaria Abietina. *Ibid.*, **10**: 287–290. 2 figs.

——. **1936**. Kernphasenwechsel von Heterochordaria Abietina. *Ibid.*, **11**: 239–241. 2 pls.

——. **1938**. Entwicklung der Fortpflanzungsorgane und Keimungsgeschichte von Desmarestia viridis (Müll.) Lamour. *Ibid.*, **12**: 475–482. 6 figs., 1 pl.

AGARDH, C. A. **1820**. *Species algarum.* Stockholm. Vol. 1, Pt. 1, 168 pages.

——. **1821**. *Icones algarum ineditae.* Stockholm. Fasc. 2. 2 pages. pls. 11–20.

——. **1822**. *Species algarum.* Stockholm. Vol. 1, Pt. 2, pp. 169–531.

——. **1824**. *Systema algarum.* Lund. 312 pages.

——. **1828**. *Species algarum.* Stockholm. Vol. 2, Pt. 1, 189 pages.

——. **1846**. *Icones algarum ineditae.* Ed. nova. Lund. 4 pages, 20 pls.

AGARDH, J. G. **1841**. In historiam algarum symbolae. *Linnaea*, **15**: 1–50.

——. **1847**. Nya alger från Mexico. *Öfvers. Kgl. Svensk. Vetensk. Ak. Förh.*, 1847 (No. 1): 5–17.

——. **1848**. *Species genera et ordines algarum.* Lund. Vol. 1. 363 pages.

——. **1849**. Algologiska Bidrag. *Öfvers. Kgl. Svensk. Vetensk. Ak. Förh.*, **6**: 79–89.

——. **1851**. *Species genera et ordines algarum.* Lund. Vol. 2, Pt. 1. 351 pages.

——. **1852**. *Ibid.* Vol. 2, Pt. 2, pp. 337–720.

——. **1863**. *Ibid.* Vol. 2, Pt. 3, pp. 710–1291.

——. **1872**. Bidrag till Florideernes Systematik. *Lunds Univ. Årsskr.*, **8** (No. 6): 1–60.

——. **1876**. *Species genera et ordines algarum.* Lund. Vol. 3, Pt. 1. *Epicrisis systematis floridearum.* 724 pages.

——. **1883**. Till Algernas Systematik. Nya Bidrag. Tredje Afdelningen. *Lunds Univ. Årsskr.*, **19**: 1–177. 4 pls.

——. **1885**. Till Algernas Systematik. Nya Bidrag. Fjerde Afdelningen. *Ibid.*, **21** (No. 3): 1–117. 1 pl.

——. **1887**. Till Algernas Systematik. Nya Bidrag. Femte Afdelningen. *Ibid.*, **23**: 1–174. 5 pls.

——. **1892**. *Analecta algologica.* Lund. 182 pages, 3 pls.

——. **1894**. *Analecta algologica. Continuatio II.* Lund. 98 pages, 1 pl.

——. **1898**. *Species genera et ordines algarum.* Lund. Vol. 3, Pt. 3. *De dispositione Delesseriearum mantissa algologica.* 239 pages.

ANDERSON, C. L. **1891**. List of California marine algae, with notes. *Zoe*, **2**: 217–225.

——. **1894**. Some new and some old algae but recently recognized on the California coast. *Ibid.*, **4**: 358–362. 2 figs.

ANGST, LAURA. **1926**. The gametophyte of Soranthera ulvoidea. *Publ. Puget Sound Biol. Sta.*, **5**: 159–163. 1 pl.

——. **1927**. The holdfast of Soranthera ulvoidea. *Ibid.*, **5**: 265–275. 2 pls.

ANGST, LAURA. 1927*A*. Gametophytes of Costaria costata. *Publ. Puget Sound Biol. Sta.,* 5: 293–307. 4 pls.

ANNAND, P. L. 1937. A taxonomic study of the algae of the British chalk-cliffs. *Jour. Bot.,* 75 (Supplement 2): 1–51. 15 figs.

ARDISSONNE, F. 1886. *Phycologia mediterranea.* Varese. Vol. 2. 325 pages.

ARESCHOUG, J. E. 1846. Enumeratio phycearum in maribus Scandinaviae crescentium. Sectio prior, Fucaceas continens. *Nova Acta Reg. Soc. Sci. Upsaliensis,* 13: 223–382. 9 pls.

——. 1850. Enumeratio phycearum in maribus Scandinaviae crescentium. Sectio posterior, Ulvaceas continens. *Ibid.,* 14: 385–454. 3 pls.

——. 1866. *Observationes phycologicae.* Pt. 1. *De confervaceis nonnullis.* Upsala. 26 pages, 4 pls.

——. 1876. De tribus Laminarieis et de Stephanocystide osmundaceae (Turn.) Trev. observationes praecursoriae. *Bot. Notiscr,* 1876: 65–73.

ARTARI, A. 1913. Zur Physiologie der Chlamydomonaden. *Jahrb. Wiss. Bot.,* 52: 410–466. 3 figs. 1 pl.

BATTERS, E. A. 1892. Gonimophyllum Buffhami: a new marine alga. *Jour. Bot.,* 30: 65–67. 1 pl.

——. 1895. On some new British marine algae. *Ann. Bot.,* 9: 307–321. 1 pl.

——. 1902. A catalogue of the British marine algae. *Jour. Bot.,* 40 (Supplement 1): 1–107.

BERTHOLD, G. 1882. Die Bangiaceen des Golfes von Neapel und der angrenzenden Meeres-Abschnitte. *Fauna und Flora des Golfes von Neapel und der angrenzenden Meeres-Abschnitte.* Monographie 8: 1–28. 1 pl.

——. 1884. Die Cryptonemiaceen des Golfes von Neapel und der angrenzenden Meeres-Abschnitte. *Ibid.,* Monographie 12: 1–27. 8 pl.

BLANKINSHIP, J. W., AND C. A. KEELER. 1892. On the natural history of the Farallon Islands. *Zoe,* 3: 144–165.

BLIDING, C. 1928. Studien über die Florideenordnung Rhodymeniales. *Lunds Univ. Årsskr.,* N.F., 24 (No. 3): 1–74. 52 figs.

BÖRGESEN, F. 1914. The marine algae of the Danish West Indies. Part 2. Phaeophyceae. *Dansk. Bot. Ark.,* 2 (No. 2): 1–66. 44 figs.

——. 1915–1920. The marine algae of the Danish West Indies. Part 3. Rhodophyceae. *Ibid.,* 3 (No. 1): 1–498. 435 figs.

——. 1930. Marine algae from the Canary Islands. Part 3, Rhodophyceae. *Biol. Meddel. Kgl. Dansk Vidensk Selsk.,* 19 (No. 1): 1–158. 66 figs.

BORNET, E., AND C. FLAHAULT. 1888. Note sur deux nouveaux genres d'algues perforantes. *Jour. de Bot.,* 2: 161–165.

——. 1889. Sur quelques plantes vivant dans le test calcaire des mollusques. *Bull. Soc. Bot. France,* 36: cxlvii–clxxii. 7 pls.

BORY DE SAINT VINCENT, J. B. 1826. Macrocyste. *Dict. Classique d'Hist. Nat.,* 10: 8–10.

BORZI, A. 1895. *Studi algologici.* Palermo. Fasc. 2, pp. 121–378. pls. 10–31.

BUFFHAM, T. H. 1896. On Bonnemaisonia hamifera Hariot. *Jour. Queckett Micr. Club,* 2d ser., 6: 177–182. 1 pl.

CAPT, L. 1930. The morphology and life history of Antithamnion. *Publ. Puget Sound Biol. Sta.,* 7: 369–389. 5 pls.

CARTER, NELLIE. 1919. The cytology of the Cladophoraceae. *Ann. Bot.,* 33: 467–478. 2 figs. 1 pl.

——. 1926. An investigation into the cytology and biology of the Ulvaceae. *Ibid.,* 40: 665–689. 2 pls.

CHAUVIN, J. F. 1842. *Recherches sur l'organisation, la fructification et la classification de plusieurs genres d'algues, avec la description de quelques espèces inedètes ou peu connues.* Caen. 132 pages.

CHEMIN, E. **1929**. Développement des spores issues du cystocarpe de Gymnogongrus norvegicus J. Ag. *Bull. Soc. Bot. France,* 76: 305–308. 2 figs.

——. **1930**. Ahnfeltia plicata Fries et son mode de reproduction. *Ibid.,* 77: 342–354. 7 figs.

——. **1933**. Sur le mode de reproduction de Gymnogongrus Griffithsiae Mart. et de quelques espèces du même genre. *Ibid.,* 80: 755–770. 8 figs. 2 pls.

CLAUSSEN, H. **1929**. Zur Entwicklungsgeschichte von Phyllophora Brodiaei. *Ber. Deutsch. Bot. Ges.,* 47: 544–547. 1 fig.

CLELAND, R. E. **1919**. The cytology and life history of Nemalion multifidum. *Ann. Bot.,* 33: 323–351. 3 figs. 3 pls.

CLINT, HILDA B. **1927**. The life history and cytology of *Sphacelaria bipinnata* Sauv. *Univ. Liverpool Publ. Hartley Bot. Lab.,* 3: 5–25. 5 figs.

COHN, F. **1872**. Ueber parasitische Algen. *Beitr. Biol. Pflanzen,* 1 (Abt. 2): 87–106. 2 pls.

COLLINS, F. S. **1903**. The Ulvaceae of North America. *Rhodora,* 5: 1–31. 3 pls.

——. **1906**. New species, etc., issued in the Phycotheca Boreali-Americana. *Ibid.,* 8: 104–113.

——. **1909**. The green algae of North America. *Tufts College Studies. Scientific Series,* 2: 79–480. 18 pls.

——. **1909A**. New species of Cladophora. *Rhodora,* 11: 17–20. 1 pl.

——. **1913**. The marine algae of Vancouver Island. *Bull. Victoria Memorial Museum,* 1: 99–137.

——. **1918**. The green algae of North America. Second supplementary paper. *Tufts College Studies. Scientific Series,* 4 (No. 7): 1–106. 3 pls.

COVILLE, F. V. **1895**. The botanical explorations of Thomas Coulter in Mexico and California. *Bot. Gaz.,* 20: 519–531.

DAMMAN, HILDEGARD. **1930**. Entwicklungsgeschichtliche und zytologische Untersuchungen an Helgoländer Meeresalgen. *Wiss. Meeresunters. Abt. Helgoland,* N.F., 18 (Abhandl. 4) : 1–36. 22 figs. 1 pl.

DANGEARD, P. **1927**. Recherches sur les Bangia et les Porphyra. *Botaniste,* 18: 183–244. 11 figs. 5 pls.

——. **1931**. L'Ulvella lens de Crouan et l'Ulvella Setchellii sp. nov. *Bull. Soc. Bot. France,* 78: 312–318. 1 fig. 1 pl.

DANGEARD, P. A. **1910**. Sur une algue marine du Laboratoire de Concarneau. *Compt. Rend. Acad. Sci. Paris,* 151: 991–993.

——. **1912**. Recherches sur quelques algues nouvelles ou peu connues. *Botaniste,* 12: i–xix. 2 pls.

DARBISHIRE, O. V. **1898**. Ueber Bangia pumila Aresch., eine endemische Alge der östlichen Ostsee. *Wiss. Meeresunters. Abt. Kiel,* N.F., 3: 25–31. 10 figs.

DAVIS, B. M. **1894**. Euglenopsis, a new alga-like organism. *Ann. Bot.,* 8: 377–390. 1 pl.

——. **1896**. Development of the procarp and cystocarp in the genus Ptilota. *Bot. Gaz.,* 22: 353–378. 2 pls.

——. **1908**. Spore formation in Derbesia. *Ann. Bot.,* 22: 1–20. 2 pls.

DAWSON, E. Y. **1941**. A review of the genus Rhodymenia with descriptions of new species. *Allan Hancock Pacific Expeditions,* 3: 123–180. 13 pls.

DECAISNE, J. **1842**. *Essai sur une classification des algues et polypiers calcifères.* Paris. 120 pages. 4 pls.

——. **1864**. *Botanique, in Voyage autour du monde sur la frégate la Vénus commandée par Abel Du Petit-Thouars.* Paris. 54 pages. (Atlas of 28 pls. published in 1846.)

DELF, E. MARION. 1912. The attaching discs of the Ulvaceae. *Ann. Bot.*, 26: 403–408. 3 figs. 1 pl.

DERBÈS, A., AND A. J. J. SOLIER. 1856. Mémoire sur quelques points de la physiologie des algues. *Suppl. aux Compt. Rend. Acad. Sci. Paris*, 1: 1–120. 23 pls.

DeTONI, J. B. 1895. *Sylloge Algarum*. Patavia. Vol. 3. 638 pages.

——. 1903. *Ibid.*, 4 (Sec. 3): 775–1521.

DILLWYN, L. W. 1809. *British Confervae*. London. 87 pages. 115 pls.

DODEL, A. 1876. Ulothrix zonata. *Jahrb. Wiss. Bot.*, 10: 417–550. 8 pls.

DREW, KATHLEEN. 1928. A revision of the genera Chantransia, Rhodochorton, and Acrochaetium. *Univ. Calif. Publ. Bot.*, 14: 139–224. 12 pls.

——. 1934. Contributions to the cytology of Spermothamnion Turneri (Mert.) Aresch. *Ann. Bot.*, 48: 549–573. 2 figs. 2 pls.

——. 1935. The life-history of Rhodochorton violaceum (Kütz.) comb. nov. (Chantransia violacea Kütz.). *Ibid.*, 49: 439–450. 18 figs.

——. 1937. Spermothamnion Snyderae Farlow, a floridean alga bearing polysporangia. *Ibid.*, N.S., 1: 463–476. 12 figs. 1 pl.

DUBY, J. E. 1830. *Botanicon Gallicum seu synopsis plantarum in Flora Gallica descriptarum*. Editio secunda. Paris Part 2. *Plantas cellulares continens*, pp. 546–1068.

DUNAL, F. 1838. Extrait d'un mémoire sur les algues qui colorent en rouge certains eaux des marais salants meditérranéens. *Ann. Sci. Nat. Bot.*, 2ᵉ ser., 9: 172–175.

DURIEU DE MAISONNEUVE, M. C. 1846. Exploration scientifique de Algerie. Paris. Sciences naturelles. *Botanique*, Vol. 1. *Cryptogamie*. 631 pages.

EATON, D. C. 1877. Description of a new alga of California. *Proc. Amer. Acad. Arts & Sci.*, N.S., 4: 245.

ESPER, E. J. C. 1797–1802. *Icones fucorum*. Nürnberg. 133 pages. 177 pls.

FALKENBERG, P. 1901. Die Rhodomelaceen des Golfes von Neapel und der angrenzenden Meeres-Abschnitte. *Fauna und Flora des Golfes von Neapel und der angrenzenden Meeres-Abschnitte*. Monographie 26: 1–753. 10 figs. 24 pls.

FARLOW, W. G. 1875. List of the marine algae of the United States, with notes on new and imperfectly known species. *Proc. Amer. Acad. Arts & Sci.*, N.S., 2: 351–380.

——. 1876. List of the marine algae of the United States. *U.S. Commission of Fish and Fisheries. Report of Commissioner for 1873–74 and 1874–75*, pp. 691–718.

——. 1877. On some algae new to the United States. *Proc. Amer. Acad. Arts & Sci.*, N.S., 4: 235–245.

——. 1889. On some new or imperfectly known algae of the United States. I. *Bull. Torrey Bot. Club*, 16: 1–12. 2 pls.

——. 1899. Three undescribed Californian algae. *Erythea*, 7: 73–76.

FARMER, J. B., AND J. L. WILLIAMS. 1898. Contributions to our knowledge of the Fucaceae: their life-history and cytology. *Phil. Trans. Roy. Soc. London*, Ser. B, 190: 623–645. 6 pls.

FELDMANN, J. 1937. Les algues marines de côte des Albères. *Rev. Algologique*, 9: 141–335. 67 figs. 10 pls.

FELDMANN, J., AND G. HAMEL. 1936. Floridées de France. *Ibid.*, 9: 85–140. 36 figs. 6 pls.

FOSLIE, M. H. 1897. On some Lithothamnia. *Kgl. Norske Vidensk. Selsk. Skr.*, 1897 (No. 1): 1–20.

——. 1900. Five new calcareous algae. *Ibid.*, 1900 (No. 3): 1–6.

——. 1901. New Melobesieae. *Ibid.*, 1900 (No. 6): 1–24.

FOSLIE, M. H. 1902. New species or forms of Melobesieae. *Kgl. Norske Vidensk. Selsk. Skr.*, 1902 (No. 2): 1–11.

——. 1903. Two new Lithothamnia. *Ibid.*, 1903 (No. 2): 1–4.

——. 1905. Remarks on northern Lithothamnia. *Ibid.*, 1905 (No. 3): 1–138.

——. 1906. Algologiske Notiser II. *Ibid.*, 1906 (No. 2): 1–28.

——. 1907. Algologiske Notiser III. *Ibid.*, 1906 (No. 8): 1–34.

——. 1907*A*. Algologiske Notiser IV. *Ibid.*, 1907 (No. 6): 1–30.

——. 1909. Algologiske Notiser VI. *Ibid.*, 1909 (No. 2): 1–63.

——. 1929. *Contributions to a monograph of the Lithothamnia.* Trondhjem. 60 pages. 75 pls.

FØYN, B. 1934. Lebenszyklus, Cytologie und Sexualität der Chlorophycee Cladophora Suhriana Kützing. *Arch. Protistenk.*, 83: 1–56. 18 figs. 5 pls.

——. 1934*A*. Lebenszyklus und Sexualität der Chlorophycee Ulva Lactuca L. *Ibid.*, 83: 154–177. 18 figs.

FREEMAN, E. M. 1899. Observations on Constantinea. *Minnesota Bot. Studies*, 2: 175–190. 2 pls.

FRIES, E. 1835. *Corpus florarum provincalium Sueciae.* Upsala. I. *Floram Scanicum.* 394 pages.

FRYE, T. C. 1918. The age of Pterygophora californica. *Publ. Puget Sound Biol. Sta.*, 2: 65–71. 1 pl.

FRYE, T. C., G. B. RIGG, AND W. C. CRANDALL. 1915. The size of kelps on the Pacific Coast of North America. *Bot. Gaz.*, 60: 473–482. 2 figs.

GAIL, F. W. 1918. Some experiments with Fucus to determine the factors controlling its vertical distribution. *Publ. Puget Sound Biol. Sta.*, 2: 139–151.

——. 1919. Hydrogen ion concentration and other factors affecting the distribution of Fucus. *Ibid.*, 2: 287–306. 2 pls.

GARDNER, N. L. 1909. New Chlorophyceae from California. *Univ. Calif. Publ. Bot.*, 3: 371–375. 1 pl.

——. 1910. Variations in nuclear extrusion among the Fucaceae. *Ibid.*, 4: 121–136. 2 pls.

——. 1913. New Fucaceae. *Ibid.*, 4: 317–374. 18 pls.

——. 1917. New Pacific Coast marine algae. I. *Ibid.*, 6: 377–416. 5 pls.

——. 1919. New Pacific Coast marine algae. IV. *Ibid.*, 6: 487–496. 1 pl.

——. 1922. The genus Fucus on the Pacific Coast of North America. *Ibid.*, 10: 1–180. 60 pls.

——. 1926. New Rhodophyceae from the Pacific Coast of North America. I. *Ibid.*, 13: 205–226. 7 pls.

——. 1927. New Rhodophyceae from the Pacific Coast of North America. II. *Ibid.*, 13: 235–272. 12 pls.

——. 1927*A*. New Rhodophyceae from the Pacific Coast of North America. III. *Ibid.*, 13: 333–368. 13 pls.

——. 1927*B*. New Rhodophyceae from the Pacific Coast of North America. IV. *Ibid.*, 13: 373–402. 11 pls.

——. 1927*C*. New Rhodophyceae from the Pacific Coast of North America. V. *Ibid.*, 13: 403–434. 10 pls.

——. 1927*D*. New Rhodophyceae from the Pacific Coast of North America. VI. *Ibid.*, 14: 99–138. 17 pls.

——. 1927*E*. New species of Gelidium on the Pacific Coast of North America. *Ibid.*, 13: 273–318. 19 pls.

GMELIN, S. G. 1768. *Historia fucorum.* Petropoli. 239 pages. 33 pls.

GRAY, J. E. 1867. Lithothrix, a new genus of Corallinae. *Jour. Bot.*, 5: 33. 2 figs.

GRAY, S. F. 1821. *A natural arrangement of British plants.* London. Vol 1. 824 pages. 21 pls.

GREGORY, BERYL D. 1934. On the life history of Gymnogongrus Griffithsiae and Ahnfeltia plicata. *Jour. Linn. Soc. Bot.,* 49: 531–551. 26 figs.

GREVILLE, R. K. 1827. *Scottish cryptogamic flora.* Edinburgh. Vol. 5. pls. 241–300.

——. 1830. *Algae Britannicae.* Edinburgh. 218 pages. 19 pls.

GRIGGS, R. F. 1906. Renfrewia parvula, a new kelp from Vancouver Island. *Postelsia,* 2: 247–274. 4 pls.

——. 1909. The sporophylls of Lessonia. *Ohio Nat.,* 9: 437–439. 1 fig.

GROSSE, ILSE. 1931. Entwicklungsgeschichte, Phasenwechsel und Sexualität bei der Gattung Ulothrix. *Arch. Protistenk.,* 73: 206–234. 20 figs.

HAMEL, A. AND G. 1929. Sur l'hétérogamie d'une Cladophoracée, Lola (nov. gen.) lubrica (Setch. et Gardn.). *Compt. Rend. A'cad. Sci. Paris,* 189: 1094–1096.

HAMEL, G. 1924. Floridées de France. I. *Rev. Algologique,* 1: 278–292. 2 figs.

HARIOT, P. 1889. *Algues,* in *Mission scientifique du Cap Horn, 1882–1883.* Paris. Vol. 5. *Botanique,* pp. 1–109. 9 pls.

HARTGE, L. A. 1928. Nereocystis. *Publ. Puget Sound Biol. Sta.,* 6: 207–237. 7 pls.

HARTMANN, M. 1929. Ueber die Sexualität und den Generationswechsel von Chaetomorpha und Enteromorpha. *Ber. Deutsch. Bot. Ges.,* 47: 485–494. 1 fig.

HARVEY, W. H. 1833. *Algae,* in Hooker and Arnott's *Botany of Captain Beechey's voyage.* London. pp. 163–165.

——. 1833*A. Algae Confervoideae,* in W. J. Hooker, *British Flora,* Vol. 2 (Part 1): pp. 322–385.

——. 1841. *Algae,* in Hooker and Arnott's *Botany of Captain Beechey's voyage.* London. pp. 406–409.

——. 1847. *Nereis Australis.* London. 124 pages. 50 pls.

——. 1849. *Phycologica Britannica.* London. Vol. 2. pls. 121–240.

——. 1851. *Ibid.,* Vol. 3. pls. 241–360.

——. 1852. Nereis Boreali-Americana. Part I. Melanospermeae. *Smithsonian Contr. to Knowledge,* 3 (Article 4): 1–150. 12 pls.

——. 1853. Nereis Boreali-Americana. Part II. Rhodospermeae. *Ibid.,* 4 (Article 5): 1–258. 24 pls.

——. 1858. Nereis Boreali-Americana. Part III. Chlorospermeae. *Ibid.,* 10 (Article 2): 1–140. 14 pls.

——. 1862. Notice of a collection of algae made on the northwest coast of North America, chiefly at Vancouver's Island, by David Lyall, Esq., M.D., R.N., in the years 1859–1861. *Jour. Linn. Soc. Bot.,* 6: 157–177.

HARVEY, W. H., AND J. W. BAILEY. 1851. Descriptions of seventeen new species of algae, collected by the United States Exploring Expedition. *Proc. Boston Soc. Nat. Hist.,* 3: 370–373.

HAZEN, T. E. 1902. The Ulotrichaceae and Chaetophoraceae of the United States. *Mem. Torrey Bot. Club,* 11: 135–250. 23 pls.

HERVEY, A. B. 1881. *Sea mosses.* Boston. 281 pages. 20 pls.

HOFFMANN, EDNA J. 1911. Fructification of Macrocystis. *Univ. Calif. Publ. Bot.,* 4: 151–158. 1 pl.

HOLLENBERG, G. J. 1935. A study of Halicystis ovalis. I. Morphology and reproduction. *Amer. Jour. Bot.,* 22: 783–812. 5 figs. 4 pls.

——. 1936. A study of Halicystis ovalis. II. Periodicity in the formation of gametes. *Ibid.,* 23: 1–3. 1 fig.

HOLLENBERG, G. J. 1939. A morphological study of Amplisiphonia a new member of the Rhodomelaceae. *Bot. Gaz.*, 101: 380–390. 13 figs.

———. 1940. New marine algae from southern California. I. *Amer. Jour. Bot.*, 27: 868–877. 17 figs.

———. 1941. Observations on Ralfsiaceae (Abstract). *Ibid.*, 28: 728.

———. 1942. Phycological notes—I. *Bull. Torrey Bot. Club*, 69: 528–538. 15 figs.

———. 1942A. An account of the species of Polysiphonia on the Pacific Coast of North America. I. Oligosiphonia. *Amer. Jour. Bot.*, 29: 772–785. 21 figs.

HOLTZ, F. H. 1903. Observations on Pelvetia. *Minnesota Bot. Studies*, 3: 23–45. 6 pls.

HOOKER, J. D. 1847. *The botany of the Antarctic voyage of H. M. discovery ships "Erebus" and "Terror,"* etc. London. Vol. 1, Part 2. *Flora Antarctica*, pp. 209–574. 108 pls.

HOOKER, W. J. 1836. A brief memoir of the life of David Douglas, with extracts from his letters. *Companion to Bot. Magazine*, 2: 79–182.

HOWE, M. A. 1893. A month on the shores of Monterey Bay. *Erythea*, 1: 63–68.

———. 1914. The marine algae of Peru. *Mem. Torrey Bot. Club*, 15: 1–185. 44 figs. 66 pls.

HOWE, M. A., AND W. D. HOYT. 1916. Notes on some marine algae from the vicinity of Beaufort, North Carolina. *Mem. New York Bot. Gard.*, 6: 105–123. 5 pls.

HUBER, J. 1892. Contributions á la connaissance des Chaetophorées épiphytes et endophytes et de leur affinités. *Ann. Sci. Nat. Bot.*, 7ᵉ sér., 16: 265–359. 11 pls.

HUDSON, G. 1763. *Flora anglica.* London. Ed. 1. 506 pages.

HUS, H. T. A. 1900. Preliminary notes on west-coast Porphyras. *Zoe*, 5: 61–70.

———. 1902. An account of the species of Porphyra found on the Pacific Coast of North America. *Proc. Calif. Acad. Sci.*, 3d ser., Botany, 2: 173–240. 3 pls.

JOHNSON, T. 1891. Observations of Phaeozoosporeae. *Ann. Bot.*, 5: 135–144. 1 pl.

———. 1892. Stenogramme interrupta (C. Ag.) Mont. *Ibid.*, 6: 361–367. 1 pl.

JORDE, INGERID. 1933. Untersuchungen über den Lebenszyklus von Urospora Aresch. und Codiolum A. Braun. *Nyt Mag. Naturvidensk.*, 73: 1–19. 5 figs. 1 pl.

KANDA, T. 1936. On the gametophytes of some Japanese species of Laminariales. *Sci. Papers Inst. Algological Research, Hokkaido Imp. Univ.*, 1: 221–260. 27 figs. 3 pls.

———. 1938. On the gametophytes of some Japanese species of Laminariales. II. *Ibid.*, 2: 87–111. 24 figs. 2 pls.

KJELLMAN, F. R. 1872. *Bidrag till Kännedomen om Skandinaviens Ectocarpeer och Tilopterider.* Stockholm. 112 pages. 2 pls.

———. 1883. The algae of the Arctic Sea. *Kgl. Svensk. Vetensk. Ak. Handl.*, 20 (No. 5): 1–350. 31 pls.

———. 1889. Om Beringshafvets Algflora. *Ibid.*, 23 (No. 8): 1–58. 7 pls.

———. 1889A. Undersökning af några till slägtet Adenocystis Hook. fil. et Harv. Hanförda Alger. *Bihang Kgl. Svensk. Vetensk. Ak. Handl.*, 15 (Afd. 3, No. 1): 1–20. 1 pl.

KJELLMAN, F. R. **1890.** *Handbok i Skandinaviens Hafsalgflora.* Stockholm. I. Fucoideae. 103 pages.

KLEBS, G. **1881.** Beiträge zur Kenntniss niederer Algenformen. *Bot. Zeitg.,* **39**: 249–257, 265–272, 281–290, 297–308, 313–319, 329–336. 2 pls.

KNIGHT, MARGERY. **1923.** The life-history and cytology of Pylaiella littoralis Kjellm. *Trans. Roy. Soc. Edinburgh,* **53**: 343–360. 6 pls.

――. **1929.** The life-history and cytology of Ectocarpus siliculosus Dillw. *Ibid.,* **56**: 307–332. 3 figs. 6 pls.

KORNMANN, P. **1938.** Zur Entwicklungsgeschichte von Derbesia und Halicystis. *Planta,* **28**: 464–470. 4 figs.

KUCKUCK, P. **1894.** Bemerkungen zur marinen Algenvegetation von Helgoland. *Wiss. Meeresunters.,* N.F., **1** (Heft 1): 225–263. 29 figs.

――. **1896.** Bemerkungen zur marinen Algenvegetation von Helgoland. *Ibid.,* **2** (Heft 1): 373–400. 21 figs.

――. **1896A.** Beiträge zur Kenntnis der Meeresalgen. 1. Über Rhododermis parasitica Batters. *Ibid.,* **2** (Heft 1): 329–336. 2 pls.

――. **1899.** Beiträge zur Kenntnis der Meeresalgen. 8. Compsonema, ein neues Genus der Phaeosporeen. *Ibid.,* Abt. Helgoland, **3**: 90–92. 4 figs. 1 pl.

――. **1907.** Über den Bau und die Fortpflanzung von Halicystis Areschoug und Valonia Ginnani. *Bot. Zeitg.,* **65**: 139–185. 25 figs. 2 pls.

――. **1912.** Die Fortpflanzung der Phaeosporeen. *Wiss. Meeresunters.,* N.F., Abt. Helgoland, **5**: 153–186. 4 figs. 2 pls.

――. **1912A.** Untersuchungen über Chrysymenia. *Ibid.,* **5**: 209–226. 7 figs. 2 pls.

――. **1929.** Fragmente einer Monographie der Phaeosporeen. *Ibid.,* **17** (Abhandl. 4): 1–93. 155 figs.

KUNIEDA, H., AND S. SUTO. **1938.** The life-history of Colpomenia sinuosa (Scytosiphonaceae), with special reference to the conjugation of anisogametes. *Bot. Mag. Tokyo,* **52**: 539–546. 2 figs.

KUNTH, K. S. **1822.** *Synopsis plantarum quas in itinere ad plagem aequinoctialem orbis novi, collegerunt Al. de Humboldt et Am. Bonpland.* Paris. Vol. 1, 491 pages.

KURSSANOW, L. J., AND N. M. SCHEMAKHANOVA. **1927.** Le cycle de développement du Chlorochytrium Lemnae Cohn. *Arch. Russ. Protistol.,* **6**: 131–146. 2 figs. 2 pl.

KÜTZING, F. T. **1843.** *Phycologia generalis.* Leipzig. 458 pages. 80 pls.

――. **1845.** *Phycologia germanica.* Nordhausen. 340 pages.

――. **1847.** Diagnosen und Bemerkungen zu neuen oder kritischen Algen. *Bot. Zeitg.,* **5**: 1–5, 22–25, 33–38, 52–55.

――. **1849.** *Species algarum.* Leipzig. 922 pages.

――. **1853.** *Tabulae phycologicae.* Nordhausen. Vol. 3. 27 pages. 100 pls.

――. **1854.** *Ibid.,* Vol. 4. 23 pages. 100 pls.

――. **1856.** *Ibid.,* Vol. 6. 30 pages. 100 pls.

――. **1859.** *Ibid.,* Vol. 9. 42 pages. 100 pls.

KYLIN, H. **1914.** Studien über die Entwicklungsgeschichte von Rhodomela virgata Kjellm. *Svensk. Bot. Tidsskr.,* **8**: 33–69. 13 figs. 2 pls.

――. **1916.** Die Entwicklungsgeschichte von Griffithsia corallina (Lightf.) Ag. *Zeitschr. Bot.,* **8**: 99–123. 11 figs. 1 pl.

――. **1916A.** Die Entwicklungsgeschichte und die systematische Stellung von Bonnemaisonia asparagoides (Woodw.) Ag., nebst einigen Worten über den Generationswechsel der Algen. *Ibid.,* **8**: 545–586. 11 figs.

――. **1916B.** Ueber die Befruchtung und Reduktionsteilung bei Nemalion multifidum. *Ber. Deutsch. Bot. Ges.,* **34**: 257–271. 7 figs.

BIBLIOGRAPHY 391

KYLIN, H. 1921. Über die Entwicklungsgeschichte der Bangiaceen. *Ark. för Bot.*, 17 (No. 5): 1–12. 7 figs.
——. 1923. Studien über die Entwicklungsgeschichte der Florideen. *Kgl. Svensk. Vetensk. Ak. Handl.*, 63 (No. 11): 1–139. 82 figs.
——. 1924. Studien über die Delesseriaceen. *Lunds Univ. Årsskr.*, N.F., 20 (No. 6): 1–111. 80 figs.
——. 1925. The marine red algae in the vicinity of the biological station at Friday Harbor, Wash. *Ibid.*, 21 (No. 9): 1–87. 47 figs.
——. 1928. Entwicklungsgeschichtliche Florideenstudien. *Ibid.*, 24 (No. 4): 1–127. 64 figs.
——. 1930. Über die Entwicklungsgeschichte der Florideen. *Ibid.*, 26 (No. 6): 1–103. 56 figs.
——. 1930*A*. Über Heterogamie bei Enteromorpha intestinalis. *Ber. Deutsch. Bot. Ges.*, 48: 458–464. 1 fig.
——. 1931. Die Florideenordnung Rhodymeniales. *Lunds Univ. Årsskr.*, N.F., 27 (No. 11): 1–48. 8 figs. 20 pls.
——. 1932. Die Florideenordnung Gigartinales. *Ibid.*, 28 (No. 8): 1–88. 22 figs. 28 pls.
——. 1933. Über die Entwicklungsgeschichte der Phaeophyceen. *Ibid.*, 29 (No. 7): 1–102. 35 figs. 2 pls.
——. 1934. Zur Kenntnis der Entwicklungsgeschichte einiger Phaeophyceen. *Ibid.*, 30 (No. 9): 1–18. 10 figs.
——. 1934*A*. Über die systematische Stellung der Gattung Opuntiella und Turnerella. *Förhandl. Kgl. Fysiografiska Sallsk. i Lund*, 4 (No. 8): 1–6. 2 figs.
——. 1934*B*. Über den Aufbau der Prokarpien bei den Rhodomelaceen nebst einigen Worten über Odonthalia dentata. *Ibid.*, 4 (No. 9): 1–22. 5 figs.
——. 1935. Über einige kalkbohrende Chlorophyceen. *Ibid.*, 5 (No. 19): 1–19. 7 figs.
——. 1935*A*. Über Rhodomonas, Platymonas, und Prasinocladus. *Ibid.*, 5 (No. 22): 1–13. 3 figs.
——. 1935*B*. Zur Nomenklatur einiger Delesseriaceen. *Ibid.*, 5 (No. 23): 1–5.
——. 1937. Bemerkungen über die Entwicklungsgeschichte einiger Phaeophyceen. *Lunds Univ. Årsskr.*, N.F., 33 (No. 1): 1–34. 5 figs.
——. 1940. Die Phaeophyceenordnung Chordariales. *Ibid.*, 36 (No. 9): 1–67. 30 figs. 8 pls.
——. 1941. Californische Rhodophyceen. *Ibid.*, 37 (No. 2): 1–51. 7 figs. 13 pls.
KYLIN, H., AND C. SKOTTSBERG. 1919. Zur Kenntnis der subantarktischen und antarktischen Meeresalgen. II. Rhodophyceen. *Wiss. Ergebn. d. Schwed. Südpolar-Exp. 1901–1903*, 4 (No. 15): 1–88. 38 figs. 1 pl.
LAGERHEIM, G. 1883. Bidrag till Sveriges algflora. *Öfvers. Kgl. Svensk. Vetensk.-Ak. Forh.*, 39 (No. 2): 37–78. 2 pls.
——. 1885. Codiolum polyrhizum n. sp. *Ibid.*, 42 (No. 8): 21–31. 1 pl.
LAMBERT, F. D. 1930. On the structure and development of Prasinocladus. *Zeitschr. Bot.*, 23: 227–244. 4 figs.
LAMOUROUX, J. V. 1809. Mémoire sur trois nouveaux genres de la famille des algues marines. *Jour. de Bot.*, 2: 129–135. 1 pl.
——. 1813. Essai sur les genres de la famille des thalassiophytes non articulées. *Ann. du Mus. d'Hist. Nat. Paris*, 20: 21–47, 115–139, 267–293. 7 pls.
LEAVITT, CLARA L. K. 1904. Observations on Callymenia phyllophora J. Ag. *Minnesota Bot. Studies*, 3: 291–296. 2 pls.
LEJOLIS, A. 1863. Liste des algues marines de Cherbourg. *Mém. Soc. Imp. Sci. Nat. de Cherbourg*, 10: 1–168. 6 pls.

LERCHE, WITTA. 1937. Untersuchungen über Entwicklung und Fortpflanzung in der Gattung Dunaliella. *Arch. Protistenk.*, **88**: 236–268. 5 figs. 3 pls.

LEVRING, T. 1935. Zur Kenntnis der Algenflora von Kullen an der schwedischen Westküste. *Lunds Univ. Årsskr.*, N.F., **31** (No. 4): 1–64. 11 figs.

——. 1937. Zur Kenntnis der Algenflora der norwegischen Westküste. *Ibid.*, **33** (No. 8): 1–147. 19 figs. 4 pls.

——. 1939. Über die Phaeophyceengattungen Myriogloia Kuck. und Haplogloia nov. gen. *Bot. Notiser, 1939*: 40–52. 2 figs.

LEVYNS, M. R. 1933. Sexual reproduction in Macrocystis pyrifera Ag. *Ann. Bot.*, **47**: 349–353. 9 figs.

LEWIS, I. F. 1909. The life history of Griffithsia Bornetiana. *Ibid.*, **23**: 639–690. 2 figs. 5 pls.

LEWIS, I. F., AND W. R. TAYLOR. 1921. Notes from the Woods Hole Laboratory, 1921. *Rhodora, 23*: 249–256. 2 figs. 1 pl.

LINK, H. F. 1820. *Epistola de algis aquaticis in genera disposendis,* in Nees, *Horae Physicae.* Berlin. pp. 1–8. 1 pl.

LINNAEUS, C. 1753. *Species plantarum.* Ed. 1. Stockholm. 1200 pages.

——. 1755. *Flora suecica.* Ed. 2. Stockholm. 464 pages.

——. 1771. *Mantissa plantarum.* Ed. 2. Stockholm. 587 pages.

LIST, HEDWIG. 1930. Die Entwicklungsgeschichte von Cladophora glomerata Kützing. *Arch. Protistenk.*, **72**: 453–481. 7 figs.

LYNGBYE, H. C. 1819. *Tentamen hydrophytologiae Danicae.* Copenhagen. 248 pages. 70 pls.

McKAY, HAZEL H. 1933. The life history of Pterygophora californica. *Univ. Calif. Publ. Bot.*, **17**: 111–148. 7 pls.

MACMILLAN, C. 1899. Observations on Nereocystis. *Bull. Torrey Bot. Club,* **26**: 273–296. 2 pls.

——. 1900. Observations on Lessonia. *Bot. Gaz.*, **30**: 318–334. 3 pls.

——. 1902. Observations on Pterygophora. *Minnesota Bot. Studies*, **2**: 723–741. 6 pls.

MANZA, A. V. 1937. The genera of the articulated corallines. *Proc. Natl. Acad. of Sci. of U.S.A.*, **23**: 44–48.

——. 1937*A*. Some North Pacific species of articulated corallines. *Ibid.*, **23**: 561–567.

——. 1940. A revision of the genera of articulated corallines. *Philippine Jour. Sci.*, **71**: 239–316. 20 pls.

MERTENS, H. 1829. Zwei botanisch-wissenschaftliche Berichte vom Dr. Heinrich Mertens . . . . Erst Bericht über verschiedene Fucus-Arten an der Vater, Prof. Mertens in Bremen. *Linnaea*, **4**: 43–58.

MOEWUS, F. 1938. Die Sexualität und der Generationswechsel der Ulvaceen und Untersuchungen über die Parthenogenese der Gameten. *Arch. Protistenk.*, **91**: 357–441. 25 figs.

——. 1940. Über Zoosporen-Kopulation bei Monostroma. *Biol. Zentralbl.*, **60**: 225–238. 18 figs.

MONTAGNE, C. 1837. Centurie des plantes cellulaires exotiques nouvelles. *Ann. Sci. Nat. Bot.*, 2ᵉ sér., **8**: 345–370.

——. 1850. Cryptogamia Guyanensis. *Ibid.*, 3ᵉ sér., **14**: 283–309.

MOORE, G. T. 1900. New or little-known unicellular algae. I. Chlorocystis Cohnii. *Bot. Gaz.*, **30**: 100–112. 1 pl.

MOORE, LAURA B. 1928. Pelvetia fastigiata. *Ibid.*, **86**: 419–434. 25 figs.

MUENSCHER, W. L. C. 1915. Ability of seaweeds to withstand desiccation. *Puget Sound Marine Station Publ.*, **1**: 19–23.

MÜLLER, O. F. 1782. *Flora Danica.* Copenhagen. Vol. 5, Fasc. 13. 8 pages. pls. 721–780.

MÜLLER, O. F. 1782A. *Flora Danica*. Copenhagen. Vol. 5, Fasc. 15. 6 pages. pls. 841–900.

MYERS, MARGRET E. 1925. Contributions towards a knowledge of the life-histories of the Melanophyceae. *Univ. Calif. Publ. Bot.*, 13: 109–124. 3 pls.

——. 1928. The life-history of the brown alga, Egregia Menziesii. *Ibid.*, 14: 225–246. 4 pls.

NÄGELI, C. 1862. Beiträge zur Morphologie und Systematik der Ceramiaceen. *Sitzungsber. Bayerisch. Akad. Wiss.*, 2: 297–415.

NARDO, G. D. 1834. De novo genere algarum cui nomen est Hildenbrandia. *Isis*, 1834: 675–676.

NEWTON, LILY. 1931. *A handbook of the British seaweeds*. London. 478 pages. 270 figs.

NICHOLS, M. B. 1908. Contributions to a knowledge of the California species of crustose corallines. I. *Univ. Calif. Publ. Bot.*, 3: 341–348. 1 pl.

——. 1909. Contributions to a knowledge of the California species of crustose corallines. II. *Ibid.*, 3: 349–370. 4 pls.

NIENBURG, W. 1913. Die Konzeptakelentwicklung bei den Fucaceen. *Zeitschr. Bot.*, 5: 1–27. 9 figs.

NOTT, C. P. 1897. Some parasitic Florideae of the Californian coast. *Erythea*, 5: 81–84.

——. 1900. Nitophylla of California. *Proc. Calif. Acad. Sci.*, 3d ser., Botany, 2: 1–62. 9 pls.

OKAMURA, K. 1907. *Icones of Japanese algae*. Tokyo. Vol. 1, No. 1, 20 pages. 5 pls.

OLTMANNS, F. 1889. Beiträge zur Kenntniss der Fucaceen. *Bibliotheca Botanica*, 3 (Heft 14): 1–94. 15 pls.

——. 1898. Zur Entwicklungsgeschichte der Florideen. *Bot. Zeitg.*, 56: 99–140. 4 pls.

——. 1922. *Morphologie und Biologie der Algen*. 2d ed. Jena. Vol. 1, 459 pages. 287 figs.

OSTERHOUT, W. J. V. 1896. On the life-history of Rhabdonia tenera. *Ann. Bot.*, 10: 403–427. 2 pls.

PAPENFUSS, G. F. 1934. Alternation of generations in Sphacelaria bipinnata Sauv. *Bot. Notiser*, 1934: 437–444. 9 figs.

——. 1935. Alternation of generations in Ectocarpus siliculosus. *Bot. Gaz.*, 96: 421–446. 13 figs. 2 pls.

——. 1942. Studies of South African Phaeophyceae. I. Ecklonia maxima, Laminaria pallida, Macrocystis pyrifera. *Amer. Jour. Bot.*, 29: 15–24. 59 figs.

PHILLIPS, R. W. 1897. On the development of the cystocarp in Rhodymeniales. *Ann. Bot.*, 11: 347–368. 2 pls.

——. 1898. The development of the cystocarp in Rhodymeniales: II, Delesseriaceae. *Ibid.*, 12: 173–202. 2 pls.

POSTELS, A., AND F. RUPRECHT. 1840. *Illustrationes algarum in itinere circa orbem . . . . exsecuto in Oceano Pacifico imprimis septentrionali ad littora Rossica Asiatico-Americana collectarum*. St. Petersburg. 22 pages. 40 pls.

PRINGSHEIM, N. 1871. Über die männlichen Pflanzen und die Schwärmsporen der Gattung Bryopsis. *Monatsber. Akad. Wiss. Berlin*, 1871: 240–255. 1 pl.

PRINTZ, H. 1922. Über den Generationswechsel bei den Alarien der norwegischen Westküste. *Kgl. Norske Vidensk. Sels. Skr. Trondhjem*, 1922 (No. 1): 1–27. 14 figs.

PRINTZ, H. 1927. *Chlorophyceae,* in A. Engler and K. Prantl, *Die natürlichen Pflanzenfamilien.* Leipzig. 2d ed. Vol. 3. 464 pages. 366 figs.

——. 1932. Observations on the structure and reproduction in Urospora Aresch. *Nyt Mag. Naturvidensk.,* **70:** 273–287. 2 pls.

RAMALEY, F. 1903. Observations on Egregia Menziesii. *Minnesota Bot. Studies,* **3:** 1–9. 4 pls.

RAMANTHAN, K. R. 1939. The morphology, cytology, and alternation of generations in Enteromorpha compressa (L.) Grev. var. ligulata (J. Ag.) Hauck. *Ann. Bot.,* N.S., **3:** 375–398. 74 figs.

REINBOLD, T. 1889. Die Chlorophyceen (Grüntange) der Kieler Föhrde. *Schr. Naturw. Ver. Schleswig-Holstein,* **8:** 109–185.

REINKE, J. 1879. Zwei parasitische Algen. *Bot. Zeitg.,* **37:** 473–478. 1 pl.

——. 1889. Algenflora der westlichen Ostsee deutschen Antheils. *Ber. d. Kommiss. z. wiss. Untersuch. d. deutsch. Meere,* **6:** 1–101. 8 figs.

——. 1892. *Atlas deutscher Meeresalgen.* Berlin. Pt. 2, pp. 35–70. pls. 26–50.

——. 1903. *Studien zur vergleichenden Entwicklungsgeschichte der Laminariaceen.* Kiel. 67 pages. 15 figs.

REINSCH, P. F. 1874–1875. *Contributiones ad Algologiam et Fungologiam.* Nuremberg. 103 pages. 131 pls.

RICHARDS, H. M. 1891. On the structure and development of Choreocolax Polysiphoniae, Reinsch. *Proc. Amer. Acad. Arts & Sci.,* **26:** 46–63. 1 pl.

ROSENBERG, T. 1933. *Studien über Rhodomelaceen und Dasyaceen.* Lund. 87 pages. 25 figs.

ROSENVINGE, L. K. 1893. Grønlands Havalger. *Meddelser om Grønland,* **3:** 765–981. 57 figs. 2 pls.

——. 1909–1931. The marine algae of Denmark. Rhodophyceae. *Kgl. Danske Vidensk. Selsk. Skr.,* 7 Raekke, Afd., **7:** 1–637. 618 figs. 8 pls.

——. 1929. Phyllophora Brodiaei and Actinococcus subcutaneus. *Kgl. Danske Vidensk. Selsk. Biol. Medd.,* **8** (No. 4): 1–40. 18 figs. 1 pl.

——. 1931. The reproduction of Ahnfeltia plicata. *Ibid.,* **10** (No. 2): 1–29. 18 figs.

——. 1935. On some Danish Phaeophyceae. *Kgl. Danske Vidensk. Selsk.,* 9th ser., *Naturv. og Math.,* **6** (No. 3): 1–40. 41 figs.

ROTH, A. G. 1806. *Catalecta botanica.* Leipzig. Fasc. 3. 350 pages. 12 pls.

RUPRECHT, F. J. 1851. *Tange des Ochotskischen Meeres,* in A. T. Middendorff, *Sibirische Reise.* St. Petersburg. Vol. 1, Pt. 2, pp. 193–435. pls. 9–18.

——. 1852. Neue oder unvollständig bekannte Pflanzen aus dem nördlichen Theile des Stille Oceans. *Mém. de l'Acad. St. Pétersb. Sci. Nat.,* **7:** 57–82. 8 pls.

SAUNDERS, DE A. 1895. A preliminary paper on Costaria with description of a new species. *Bot. Gaz.,* **20:** 54–57. 1 pl.

——. 1898. Phycological memoirs. *Proc. Calif. Acad. Sci.,* 3d ser., *Botany,* **1:** 147–168. 21 pls.

——. 1899. New or little-known brown algae of the Pacific coast. *Erythea,* **7:** 37–40. 1 pl.

——. 1899A. Four siphonaceous algae of the Pacific coast. *Bull. Torrey Bot. Club,* **26:** 1–4. 1 pl.

——. 1901. Papers from the Harriman Alaska Expedition. XXV. The algae. *Proc. Washington Acad. Sci.,* **3:** 391–486. 20 pls.

SAUVAGEAU, C. 1897. Sur quelques Myrionémacées. *Ann. Sci. Nat. Bot.,* 8ᵉ sér., **5:** 161–288. 29 figs.

SAUVAGEAU, C. 1916. Sur les gamétophytes de deux Laminaires (Laminaria flexicaulis et saccharina). *Compt. Rend. Acad. Sci. Paris,* 162: 601–604. 1 fig.

——. 1916*A*. Sur la sexualité hétérogamique d'une Laminaire (Alaria esculenta). *Ibid.,* 162: 840–842. 1 fig.

——. 1918. Recherches sur les Laminaires des côtes de France. *Mém. Acad. Sci. Paris,* 56: 1–240. 85 figs.

——. 1927. Sur le Colpomenia sinuosa Derb. et Sol. *Bull. Sta. Biol. Arachon,* 24: 309–353. 8 figs.

——. 1929. Sur le développement de quelques Phéosporées. *Ibid.,* 26: 253–420. 20 figs.

SCHMITZ, F. 1893. Die Gattung Actinococcus. *Flora,* 77: 367–418. 6 figs. 1 pl.

SCHMITZ, F., AND P. HAUPTFLEISCH. 1896–1897. *Rhodophyceae,* in A. Engler and K. Prantl, *Die natürlichen Pflanzenfamilien.* Leipzig. Teil 1, Abt. 2: 298–544. 97 figs.

SCHRADER, H. F. 1903. Observations on Alaria nana sp. nov. *Minnesota Bot. Studies,* 3: 157–165. 4 pls.

SCHREIBER, E. 1930. Untersuchungen über Parthenogenesis, Geschlechtsbestimmung und Bastardierungsvormögen bei Laminarien. *Planta,* 12: 331–353. 12 figs.

——. 1932. Über die Entwicklungsgeschichte und die systematische Stellung der Desmarestiaceen. *Zeitschr. Bot.,* 25: 561–582. 12 figs.

——. 1935. Über Kultur und Geschlechtsbestimmung von Dictyota dichotoma. *Planta,* 24: 266–275. 4 figs.

SETCHELL, W. A. 1903. On the classification and geographical distribution of the Laminariaceae. *Trans. Connecticut Acad.,* 9: 333–375.

——. 1896. Notes on kelps. *Erythea,* 4: 41–48. 1 pl.

——. 1896*A*. The elk-kelp. *Ibid.,* 4: 179–184. 1 pl.

——. 1901. Notes on algae. I. *Zoe,* 5: 121–129.

——. 1905. Parasitic Florideae of California. *Nuova Notarisia,* 16: 59–63.

——. 1905*A*. Regeneration in kelps. *Univ. Calif. Publ. Bot.,* 2: 139–168. 3 pls.

——. 1906. A revision of the genus Constantinea. *Nuova Notarisia,* 17: 162–173.

——. 1908. Critical notes on Laminariaceae. *Ibid.,* 19: 90–101.

——. 1908*A*. Nereocystis and Pelagophycus. *Bot. Gaz.,* 45: 125–134.

——. 1912. Algae novae et minus cognitae. *Univ. Calif. Publ. Bot.,* 4: 229–268. 7 pls.

——. 1914. Parasitic Florideae. I. *Ibid.,* 6: 1–34. 6 pls.

——. 1914*A*. The Scinaia assemblage. *Ibid.,* 6: 79–152. 7 pls.

——. 1915. The law of temperature connected with the distribution of the marine algae. *Ann. Missouri Bot. Gard.,* 2: 287–305.

——. 1920. The temperature interval in the geographical distribution of marine algae. *Science,* N.S., 52: 187–190.

——. 1920*A*. Stenothermy and zone-invasion. *Amer. Nat.,* 54: 385–397.

——. 1922. Cape Cod and its relation to the marine flora of New England. *Rhodora,* 24: 1–11. 1 pl.

——. 1923. Parasitic Florideae. II. *Univ. Calif. Publ. Bot.,* 10: 393–396.

——. 1923*A*. A revision of the west North American species of Callophyllis. *Ibid.,* 10: 397–401.

——. 1932. Macrocystis and its holdfasts. *Ibid.,* 16: 445–492. 16 pls.

SETCHELL, W. A., AND N. L. GARDNER. 1903. Algae of Northwestern America. *Ibid.,* 1: 165–418. 21 pls.

SETCHELL, W. A., AND N. L. GARDNER. 1919. The marine algae of the Pacific Coast of North America. Part 1, Myxophyceae. *Univ. Calif. Publ. Bot.,* **8**: 1–138. 8 pls.

———. 1920. The marine algae of the Pacific Coast of North America. Part 2, Chlorophyceae. *Ibid.,* **8**: 139–381. 25 pls.

———. 1920*A*. Phycological contributions. I. *Ibid.,* **7**: 279–303. 11 pls.

———. 1922. Phycological contributions. II. New species of Myrionema. *Ibid.,* **7**: 334–352. 3 pls.

———. 1922*A*. Phycological contributions. III. New species of Compsonema. *Ibid.,* **7**: 353–376. 5 pls.

———. 1922*B*. Phycological contributions. IV. New species of Hecatonema. *Ibid.,* **7**: 377–384. 2 pls.

———. 1922*C*. Phycological contributions. V. New species of Pylaiella and Streblonema. *Ibid.,* **7**: 385–402. 3 pls.

———. 1922*D*. Phycological contributions. VI. New species of Ectocarpus. *Ibid.,* **7**: 403–426. 5 pls.

———. 1924. Phycological contributions. VII. *Ibid.,* **13**: 1–13.

———. 1924*A*. Expedition of the California Academy of Sciences to the Gulf of California in 1921. The marine algae. *Proc. Calif. Acad. Sci.,* 4th ser., **12**: 695–949. 77 pls.

———. 1925. The marine algae of the Pacific Coast of North America. Part 3, Melanophyceae. *Univ. Calif. Publ. Bot.,* **8**: 383–898. 74 pls.

———. 1933. A preliminary survey of Gigartina, with special reference to its Pacific North American species. *Ibid.,* **17**: 255–340. 20 pls.

———. 1937. Iridophycus in the northern hemisphere. *Proc. Natl. Acad. of Sci. of U.S.A.,* **23**: 169–174.

SETCHELL, W. A., AND LUCILE R. MASON. 1943. New or little-known crustose corallines of Pacific North America. *Ibid.,* **29**: 92–97.

SJÖSTEDT, L. G. 1926. Floridean studies. *Lunds Univ. Arsskr.,* N.F., **22** (No. 4): 1–94. 42 figs.

SKOTTSBERG, C. 1907. Zur Kenntnis der subantarktischen und antarktischen Meeresalgen. I. Phaeophyceen. *Wiss. Ergebn. d. Schwed. Südpolar-Exp.,* **4** (No. 6): 1–172. 187 figs. 10 pls.

———. 1915. Notes on Pacific Coast algae. I. Pylaiella Postelsiae n. sp., a new type in the genus Pylaiella. *Univ. Calif. Publ. Bot.,* **6**: 153–164. 3 pls.

———. 1922. Notes on Pacific Coast algae. II. On the Californian Delesseria quercifolia. *Ibid.,* **7**: 427–436. 1 pl.

SMITH, G. M. 1930. Observations on some siphonaceous green algae from the Monterey Peninsula. *Contributions to marine biology, lectures and symposia given at the Hopkins Marine Station Dec. 20–21, 1929.* Stanford University. pp. 222–233. 3 figs.

———. 1933. *The fresh-water algae of the United States.* New York. 716 pages. 449 figs.

———. 1938. *Cryptogamic botany.* New York. Vol. 1. 545 pages. 299 figs.

———. 1942. Notes on some brown algae from the Monterey Peninsula, California. *Amer. Jour. Bot.,* **29**: 645–653. 13 figs.

SMITH, G. M., AND G. J. HOLLENBERG. 1943. On some Rhodophyceae from the Monterey Peninsula, California. *Amer. Jour. Bot.,* **30**: 211–222. 30 figs.

SMITH, J. E. 1812. *English Botany.* London. Vol. 23. 72 pages. 72 pls.

SOLIER, A. J. J. 1847. Mémoire sur deux algues zoosporées, devant former un genre distinct, le genre Derbesia. *Ann. Sci. Nat. Bot.,* 3ᵉ sér., **7**: 157–166. 1 pl.

STACKHOUSE, J. 1801. *Nereis Britannica.* Bath. 112 pages. 24 pls.

STURCH, H. H. Choreocolax Polysiphoniae, Reinsch. *Ann. Bot.*, **40**: 585–605. 15 figs.

SUNESON, S. 1937. Studien über die Entwicklungsgeschichte der Corallinaceen. *Lunds Univ. Årsskr. N.F.*, **33** (No. 2): 1–101. 42 figs. 4 pls.

——. 1940. Studies on the structure and the reproduction of Pterosiphonia parasitica. *Bot. Tidskr.*, **34**: 315–333. 11 figs.

SURINGAR, W. R. F. 1867. Algarum Japonicarum Musei Botanici Lugduno-Batavi, Index praecursorius. *Annales Bot. Musei Bot. L. B.* (citation from Setchell and Gardner, 1920, p. 322).

SVEDELIUS, N. 1914. Über die Zystokarpienbildung bei Delesseria sanguinea. *Svensk Bot. Tidskr.*, **8**: 1–31. 22 figs. 2 pls.

——. 1917. Die Monosporen bei Helminthora divaricata nebst Notiz über die Zweikernigkeit ihres Karpogons. *Ber. Deutsch. Bot. Ges.*, **35**: 212–224. 7 figs.

——. 1933. On the development of Asparagopsis armata Harv. and Bonnemaisonia asparagoides (Woodw.) Ag. *Nova Acta Reg. Soc. Sci. Upsaliensis*, 4th ser., **9** (No. 1): 1–61. 49 figs.

TAYLOR, W. R. 1937. Marine algae of the northeastern coast of North America. *Univ. Michigan Studies Sci. Series*, **13**: 1–427. 60 pls.

TEODORESCO, E. C. 1905. Organisation et développement du Dunaliella, nouveau genre de Volvocacée-Polyblepharidée. *Beih. Bot. Centralbl.*, **18**: 215–232. 5 figs. 2 pls.

——. 1906. Observations morphologiques et biologiques sur le genre Dunaliella. *Rev. Gen. Botanique*, **18**: 353–371, 409–427. 25 figs. 3 pls.

THOMPSON, ELIZABETH I. 1910. The morphology of Taenioma. *Bull. Torrey Bot. Club*, **37**: 97–106. 2 pls.

THURET, G. 1854. Recherches sur la fécondation des Fucacées, suivies d'observations sur les anthéridies des algues. *Ann. Sci. Nat. Bot.*, 4e sér., **3**: 197–214. 4 pls.

THURET, G., AND E. BORNET. 1878. *Études phycologiques.* Paris. 105 pages. 51 pls.

TURNER, D. 1808. *Historia fucorum.* London. Vol. 1. 164 pages. 71 pls.

——. 1809. *Ibid.*, Vol. 2. 162 pages. 63 pls.

——. 1819. *Ibid.*, Vol. 4. 153 pages. 60 pls.

TURTON, W. 1806. *A general system of nature by Sir Charles Linné. A translation with additions and biography.* London. Vol. 6 (citation from Drew, 1928, p. 200).

TWISS, W. C. 1911. Erythrophyllum delesserioides J. Ag. *Univ. Calif. Publ. Bot.*, **4**: 159–176. 4 pls.

VALIANTE, R. 1883. Le Cystoseirae del golfo di Napoli. *Fauna und Flora des Golfes von Neapel und der angrenzenden Meeres-Abschnitte.* Monographie **7**: 1–30. 15 pls.

WEST, G. S. 1916. Algological notes. 20. On a new marine genus of the Volvocaceae. *Jour. Bot.*, **54**: 2–4. 1 fig.

WESTBROOK, M. A. 1930. Callithamnion tetricum (Dillw.) Ag. *Ibid.*, **68**: 193–203. 13 figs.

——. 1934. Antithamnion spirographidis Schiffner. *Ibid.*, **72**: 65–68. 6 figs.

WILLE, N. 1901. Studien über Chlorophyceen. VII. Über einige Rhizoclonium-Arten. *Vidensk. Selsk. Skr. Christiana (Mat.-Nat. Kl.)*, 1900 (No. 6): 34–41. 1 pl.

——. 1903. Algologischen Notizen. IX. Über eine neue Art der Gattung Carteria Diesing. *Nyt Mag. Naturvidensk.*, **41**: 89–94. 3 figs.

WILLE, N. 1906. Über die Entwicklung von Prasiola furfuracea (Fl. Dan.) Me-
negh. *Vidensk. Selsk. Skr. Christiana (Mat.-Nat. Kl.)*, 1906 (No. 3):
4–16. 1 pl.

———. 1909. *Conjugatae und Chlorophyceae*, in A. Engler and K. Prantl, *Die
natürlichen Pflanzenfamilien*. Leipzig. Nachträge zum I Teil, Abt. 2:
1–134. 70 figs.

WILLIAMS, J. L. 1904. Studies in the Dictyotaceae. I, II. *Ann. Bot.*, 18: 141–
160, 181–204. 5 pls.

WILLIAMS, MAY M. 1925. The cytology of the gametangia of Codium tomentosum (Stack.). *Proc. Linn. Soc. New South Wales*, 50: 98–111. 42 figs.

WILSON, HARRIET L. 1910. Gracilariophila, a new parasite on Gracilaria confervoides. *Univ. Calif. Publ. Bot.*, 4: 75–84. 2 pls.

WOLF, J. J. 1904. Cytological studies on Nemalion. *Ann. Bot.*, 18: 607–630.
1 fig. 2 pls.

YABE, Y. 1932. On the sexual reproduction of Prasiola japonica Yatabe. *Rept.
Tokyo Bunrika Daigaku*, Sec. B, 1: 39–40. 1 pl.

YAMADA, Y. 1931. Notes on Laurencia, with special reference to the Japanese
species. *Univ. Calif. Publ. Bot.*, 16: 185–310. 20 figs. 30 pls.

YAMADA, Y., AND T. KANDA. 1941. On the culture experiment of Monostroma
zostericola and Enteromorpha nana var. minima, *Sci. Papers Inst. Algological Research, Hokkaido Imp. Univ.*, 2: 217–226. 8 figs. 4 pls.

YAMADA, Y., AND E. SAITO. 1938. On some culture experiments with the
swarmers of certain species belonging to the Ulvaceae. *Ibid.*, 2: 35–51.
12 figs. 1 pl.

YAMANOUCHI, S. 1906. The life history of Polysiphonia. *Bot. Gaz.*, 42: 401–
449. 3 figs. 10 pls.

YENDO, K. 1903. Three marine species of Ecballocystis. *Bot. Mag. Tokyo*,
17: 199–206. 1 pl.

———. 1919. The germination and development of some marine algae. II.
Ibid., 33: 171–184. 1 pl.

ZANARDINI, G. A. M. 1847. *Notizie intorno alle cellulari marine delle lagune
e de' litorali di Venezia*. Venice. 88 pages. 4 pls.

ZIMMERMANN, W. 1925. Helgoländer Meeresalgen. *Wiss. Meeresunters.*, Abt.
Helgoland, N.F., 16: 1–25. 1 pl.

ZINNECKER, EMMI. 1935. Reduktionsteilung, Kernphasenwechsel und Geschlechtsbestimmung bei Bryopsis plumosa (Huds.) Ag. *Oesterr. Bot.
Zeitschr.*, 84: 53–72. 6 figs.

KEYS TO THE GENERA

The descriptions of genera given on preceding pages show that generic distinctions are based in large part upon reproductive structures. However, any person attempting to identify an alga by means of a key based upon reproductive structures immediately runs into two difficulties: only vegetative material may be available for identification, or the reproductive structures are so complex that specially stained sections are needed to make out the necessary details. For these reasons the following keys for the genera of marine algae found on the Monterey Peninsula have utilized external form and internal vegetative structure as far as possible, and reproductive structures have been included only as a last resort. The keys are based upon the assumption that entire mature plants are available for determination—not fragments cast ashore on the beach or juvenile plants collected directly from the rocks. In the cases where species of a genus are of different shape, the genus appears more than once in the key. So, also, do certain genera as to which a person using the keys may have difficulty in deciding between two alternative entries.

Attention should be called to the fact that generic distinctions apply only to species of the local flora. Most of the generic distinctions are valid also for species found elsewhere along the Pacific Coast, but use of the keys to identify algae of other Pacific Coast localities may occasionally lead to difficulties.

The green algae (Chlorophyta), the brown algae (Phaeophyta), and the red algae (Rhodophyta) are each treated in a separate key. The Chlorophyta are easily differentiated from other algae by their grass-green color. Phaeophyta are typically an olive brown and Rhodophyta are typically a rose red to deep purplish red. However, one cannot always distinguish between Rhodophyta and Phaeophyta on the basis of color alone because many "red" algae growing in the upper half of the inter-tidal zone (as *Gigartina, Gracilaria,* and *Cumagloia*) have a brown color closely resembling that of Phaeophyta. Fruiting Rhodophyta of a brownish color almost always may be distinguished by the reddish color of their spores. If brownish-colored Rhodophyta are plunged in boiling water for a minute and then transferred to alcohol for a couple of minutes they become more or less reddish; Phaeophyta treated in the same manner do not become reddish.

CHLOROPHYTA

1. Thallus free-living or epiphytic on other organisms............... 2
1'. Thallus growing within other algae or within shells of molluscs....29

21. Filaments unbranched..22
21. Filaments branched..25
   22. Filaments entangled in mats that are
      frequently free-floating.................*Rhizoclonium* (p. 61)
   22. Filaments sessile, not bent and entangled
      with one another...23
23. Chloroplast a transverse band encircling
     cytoplasm of cell..........................*Ulothrix* (p. 33)
23. Chloroplast not a transverse band.............................24
   24. Basal cell several times longer than cells
      in upper part of filament...............*Chaetomorpha* (p. 55)
   24. Basal cell not more than double length of cells
      in upper part of filament...................*Urospora* (p. 63)
25. Filaments united in branching, rope-like strands
     by means of short, recurved branches....*Spongomorpha* (p. 64)
25. Filaments not in rope-like strands............................26
   26. Filaments repeatedly branched...............*Cladophora* (p. 56)
   26. Branching restricted to a few short
      lateral branches.......................*Rhizoclonium* (p. 61)
27. With four flagella............................*Platymonas* (p. 30)
27. With two flagella..28
   28. Surface of cell longitudinally ridged.......*Stephanoptera* (p. 27)
   28. Surface of cell not ridged....................*Dunaliella* (p. 28)
29. Growing within shells of molluscs.................*Gomontia* (p. 40)
29. Growing within other algae....................................30
   30. Thallus unicellular 31
   30. Thallus multicellular 32
31. The cell without a basal stipe................*Chlorochytrium* (p. 66)
31. The cell with a basal stipe.......................*Codiolum* (p. 68)
   32. Growing within cell walls of filamentous or
      siphonaceous algae ....*Entocladia* (p. 34)
   32. Growing within tissues of foliose algae....................33
33. Endophyte with tips of branches inflated when
     lying just beneath surface of host.........*Endophyton* (p. 36)
33. Endophyte deep-seated within host and
     without inflated branch tips.............*Pseudodictyon* (p. 36)

PHAEOPHYTA

1. Thallus not filamentous....................................... 2
1. Thallus filamentous (sometimes with major branches corticated)....50
   2. Thallus not crustose.. 3
   2. Thallus crustose 45
3. Thallus cylindrical throughout or slightly flattened................ 4
3. Thallus not cylindrical throughout.............................12
   4. Thallus unbranched, constricted at intervals..*Scytosiphon* (p. 128)
   4. Thallus branched... 5
5. Branch tips with a conspicuous apical cell; cells
     below it in regular transverse rows ....*Sphacelaria* (p. 99)
5. Branch tips without an evident apical cell.......................6

24. Blade with a percurrent midrib or percurrent ribs............25
24. Blade without midrib or ribs...............*Laminaria* (p. 134)
25. With a percurrent midrib........................*Alaria* (p. 146)
25. With five percurrent ribs......................*Costaria* (p. 137)
26. The rhizome flattened and with haptera
    restricted to lateral margins............................27
26. The rhizome cylindrical..................*Laminaria* (p. 134)
27. Blade without a midrib and the entire surface
    with a reticulum of ridges............*Dictyoneurum* (p. 139)
27. Blade with a thin smooth midrib, remainder
    of surface with a reticulum of ridges..*Dictyoneuropsis* (p. 140)
28. Blade with a stipe over 5 cm. long..........*Laminaria* (p. 134)
28. Blade, if stipitate, with stipe less than 1 cm. long............29
29. Blade a markedly flattened sac................................30
29. Blade solid 31
30. Length of blade more than 20 times breadth..*Scytosiphon* (p. 128)
30. Length of blade less than 8 times breadth....*Coilodesme* (p. 131)
31. Medullary cells 4–5 times larger than surface cells................32
31. Medullary cells approximately same size and
    shape as surface cells.....................*Punctaria* (p. 123)
32. Reproductive organs grouped in sori.........*Halorhipis* (p. 125)
32. Reproductive organs entirely covering surface
    of blade ....*Ilea* (p. 126)
33. With leaf- or ribbon-like blades borne laterally along an erect axis..34
33. Blades not borne laterally along an erect axis....................39
34. Blades borne radially about the axis.........*Cystoseira* (p. 156)
34. Blades not borne radially about the axis....................35
35. Blades borne unilaterally on branches of axis,
    each blade with a basal pneumatocyst.....*Macrocystis* (p. 143)
35. Blades in two vertical rows and on opposite sides of axis..........36
36. Axis terminating in a conspicuous blade....................37
36. Axis not terminating in a conspicuous blade.................38
37. Terminal blade with a midrib.....................*Alaria* (p. 146)
37. Terminal blade without a midrib............*Pterygophora* (p. 147)
38. Blades opposite or regularly alternate......*Desmarestia* (p. 118)
38. Blades densely crowded and some replaced
    by a pneumatocyst.........................*Egregia* (p. 149)
39. Thallus with undivided blades................................40
39. Thallus with divided blades..................................44
40. Apex of stipe with a large globose
    pneumatocyst, the stipe very long........*Nereocystis* (p. 141)
40. Apex of stipe lacking a pneumatocyst......................41
41. Stipe undivided and bearing many blades at apex...*Postelsia* (p. 142)
41. Stipe dichotomously divided and each final
    dichotomy with a single blade............................42
42. Surface of blades smooth...............*Lessoniopsis* (p. 145)
42. Surface of blades with a network of ridges..................43
43. The blades without a midrib................*Dictyoneurum* (p. 139)
43. The blades with a thin percurrent midrib...*Dictyoneuropsis* (p. 140)

RHODOPHYTA

10. Spores formed singly by diagonal division
     of a parent cell....................*Erythrotrichia* (p. 162)
10. Spores not formed singly and not by diagonal
     divisions of a parent cell..................*Bangia* (p. 167)
11. Mature thallus less than 1 cm. tall, the cells not touching
     one another 12
11. Mature thallus more than 1 cm. tall, the cells touching
     one another 13
    12. Cells with a single stellate chromatophore.*Goniotrichum* (p. 161)
    12. Cells with several disc-shaped
         chromatophores ....*Goniotrichopsis* (p. 161)
13. Lateral branches in transverse whorls........*Gloiosiphonia* (p. 208)
13. Lateral branches not in transverse whorls.....................14
    14. Branching dichotomous 15
    14. Branching not dichotomous.............................19
15. Ends of branches not enlarged..............................16
15. Ends of branches terminating in obovoid
     enlargements ....*Botryocladia* (p. 296)
    16. Branches with alternate dark and light bands..............17
    16. Branches without alternate dark and light bands............18
17. Superficial cells in vertical rows.............*Centroceros* (p. 327)
17. Superficial cells not in vertical rows...........*Ceramium* (p. 324)
    18. Branches of a wiry texture...............*Ahnfeltia* (p. 271)
    18. Branches of a soft gelatinous texture......*Gloiophloea* (p. 189)
19. Branches hollow and transversely septate.....................20
19. Branches solid and not transversely septate...................21
    20. Mature thallus over 15 cm. tall, major branches
         with many short branchlets.........*Gastroclonium* (p. 302)
    20. Thalli less than 3 cm. tall.................*Coeloseira* (p. 304)
21. Thallus with a few long branches, rarely with short branches.....22
21. Thallus with many branches.................................23
    22. Center of branches with parallel filaments....*Nemalion* (p. 186)
    22. Center of branches parenchymatous.........*Gracilaria* (p. 266)
23. Major branches with many short lateral branches, all approxi-
     mately the same length................................24
23. Major branches with progressively shorter branches.............32
    24. Short lateral branches distichous.........................25
    24. Short lateral branches not distichous......................29
25. Short branches filamentous....................*Dasyopsis* (p. 356)
25. Short branches not filamentous..............................26
    26. The two branches of a pair unlike........................27
    26. The two branches of a pair alike...............*Pikea* (p. 201)
27. Short branches flattened and resembling
     minute leaves ....*Ptilota* (p. 331)
27. Short branches not markedly flattened........................28
    28. Long and short branches regularly
         alternate ....*Bonnemaisonia* (p. 191)
    28. Long and short branches not regularly
         alternate ....*Baylesia* (p. 201)

29. Short branches irregularly arranged..........................30
29. Short branches spirally arranged.............................31
    30. Branches with alternate dark and light bands.*Ceramium* (p. 324)
    30. Branches without alternate dark and light
        bands ....*Cumagloia* (p. 188)
31. Apices of short branches blunt................*Rhodomela* (p. 374)
31. Apices of short branches acutely pointed.......*Odonthalia* (p. 375)
    32. Branching of smaller branches unilateral (pectinate)........33
    32. Branching of smaller branches not unilateral................34
33. Unilateral branches incurved toward apex of
      branch bearing them..................*Plocamium* (p. 263)
33. Unilateral branches curved away from apex of branch
      bearing them ....*Microcladia* (p. 329)
    34. Branches with alternate dark and light bands..:.............35
    34. Branches without alternate dark and light bands.............36
35. Superficial cells in vertical rows..............*Centroceros* (p. 327)
35. Superficial cells not in vertical rows..........*Ceramium* (p. 324)
    36. Branching distichous 37
    36. Branching not distichous.............................42
37. The two opposite branches of a pair unlike....................38
37. The two opposite branches of a pair alike....................40
    38. Short branches flattened and resembling
        small leaves ....*Ptilota* (p. 330)
    38. Short branches not markedly flattened......................39
39. Long and short branches regularly alternate.*Bonnemaisonia* (p. 191)
39. Long and short branches not regularly alternate...*Baylesia* (p. 201)
    40. Branchlets bent upward and with a knee-like
        bending at base.........................*Gelidium* (p. 193)
    40. Branchlets without a knee-like bending at base..............41
41. Tips of branchlets straight.....................*Gigartina* (p. 277)
41. Tips of branchlets curved toward apex of branch
      bearing them ....*Microcladia* (p. 329)
    42. Surface of branches covered with minute
        spines ....*Endocladia* (p. 210)
    42. Surface of branches smooth..............................43
43. Apices of branches acutely pointed............................44
43. Apices of branches rounded...................................46
    44. Ultimate branchlets more than 5 cm. long..*Agardhiella* (p. 259)
    44. Ultimate branchlets less than 1 cm. long....................45
45. Texture of thallus hard and firm..........*Cryptosiphonia* (p. 199)
45. Texture of thallus soft and gelatinous.......*Gloiosiphonia* (p. 208)
    46. Branches hollow and transversely septate.*Gastroclonium* (p. 302)
    46. Branches not hollow and transversely septate...............47
47. Center of branches with parallel filaments....*Helminthora* (p. 187)
47. Center of branches parenchymatous............................48
    48. Apices of branchlets with a small pit........*Laurencia* (p. 376)
    48. Apices of branchlets without pits, frequently
        with a tuft of hairs....................*Chondria* (p. 372)

89. Blades linear ....*Anisocladella* (p. 343)
89. Blades ovate ....*Phycodrys* (p. 342)
90. Flattened segments of thallus with a midrib in lower portion
     and a network of veins in upper portion.................91
90. Flattened portion of thallus without a
     midrib but with a network of veins......*Polyneura* (p. 340)
91. Margins of segments with numerous pro-
     liferous outgrowths ....*Botryoglossum* (p. 353)
91. Margins of segments usually without proliferous outgrowths.....92
92. Tetrasporangial sori restricted to
     margins of segments.................*Cryptopleura* (p. 351)
92. Tetrasporangial sori over entire surface
     of thallus segments....................*Hymenena* (p. 348)
93. Flattened surfaces of thallus covered with outgrowths............94
93. Flattened surfaces of thallus without outgrowths................95
94. Outgrowths spiny, wart-like, or flattened.....*Gigartina* (p. 277)
94. Outgrowths cylindrical, simple or branched..*Cumagloia* (p. 188)
95. Thallus margin fringed with branched
     filaments ....*Dasyopsis* (p. 356)
95. Thallus margin without branched filaments.....................96
96. Margins of segments with many proliferous outgrowths.....97
96. Margins of segments lacking proliferous outgrowths........98
97. All segments approximately the same breadth....*Prionitis* (p. 243)
97. Successive segments progressively narrower...*Leptocladia* (p. 205)
98. Thallus divided in a more or less fan-like manner............99
98. Thallus not divided in a fan-like manner...................101
99. Medulla composed of interwoven filaments.......*Farlowia* (p. 203)
99. Medulla not filamentous...................................100
100. Medulla with intermingled large and
     small cells ....*Callophyllis* (p. 249)
100. Medulla with large cells only..............*Fauchea* (p. 295)
101. Thallus pinnately divided..................................102
101. Thallus not pinnately divided.............................107
102. Cells in regular transverse series..........*Taenioma* (p. 370)
102. Cells not in regular transverse series.....................103
103. The two branches of an opposite pair alike...................104
103. The two branches of an opposite pair unlike..................105
104. Tips of branchlets acute......................*Pikea* (p. 201)
104. Tips of branchlets broadly rounded........*Laurencia* (p. 376)
105. The shorter of a pair of branches flattened
     and resembling a small leaf................*Ptilota* (p. 330)
105. The shorter of a pair of branches spine-like...................106
106. Long and short branches regularly
     alternate ....*Bonnemaisonia* (p. 191)
106. Long and short branches not regularly
     alternate ....*Baylesia* (p. 201)
107. Leaf-like lobes of thallus somewhat pointed....*Iridophycus* (p. 287)
107. Leaf-like lobes of thallus broadly rounded...................108

125. Surface of thallus smooth....................................126
125. Surface of thallus tuberculate or with minute leaflets..........128
126. Thallus nearly as dark on host, parasitic
    on *Prionitis* ....*Lobocolax* (p. 247)
126. Thallus whitish, not parasitic on *Prionitis*..................127
127. Parasitic on *Gracilaria Sjoestedtii*.........*Gracilariophila* (p. 268)
127. Parasitic on *Polysiphonia*...................*Choreocolax* (p. 255)
128. Surface of thallus with minute leaflèts,
    parasitic on *Nienburgia Andersonii*.....*Polycoryne* (p. 347)
128. Surface of thallus tuberculate...........................129
129. Parasitic on *Fauchea media*...............*Faucheocolax* (p. 296)
129. Parasitic on *Callophyllis*......................*Callocolax* (p. 252)
129. Parasitic on *Laurencia spectabilis*...........*Janczewskia* (p. 381)
129. Parasitic on *Agardhiella Coulteri*...........*Gardneriella* (p. 261)
130. Filaments unbranched 131
130. Filaments branched 132
131. Spores formed singly and separated from
    parent cell by a diagonal wall.......*Erythrotrichia* (p. 162)
131. Spores not formed singly and not separated from
    other cells by diagonal walls..............*Bangia* (p. 167)
132. Filaments with a gelatinous sheath and ends of cells not
    touching one another...............................133
132. Filaments lacking a gelatinous sheath and ends of cells
    touching one another...............................134
133. Each cell with a single stellate chromatophore. *Goniotrichum* (p. 161)
133. Each cell with several disc-shaped
    chromatophores ....*Goniotrichopsis* (p. 161)
134. Cells of major branches with opposite branches............135
134. Lateral branches not opposite.........................137
135. With two opposite branches on each cell....*Antithamnion* (p. 306)
135. With a verticil of three or four branchlets on each cell of a
    major branch 136
136. Each verticil with all branchlets
    the same length...................*Antithamnion* (p. 306)
136. Each verticil with two long and two
    short branchlets ....*Platythamnion* (p. 314)
137. Branching regularly alternate..............................138
137. Branching either predominately unilateral, predominately
    subdichotomous, or irregular.........................139
138. Sporangia with four spores...........*Callithamnion* (p. 317)
138. Sporangia with more than four spores
    (usually sixteen) ....*Pleonosporium* (p. 320)
139. Cells up to 0.5 mm. broad, upper end broader
    than lower, branching subdichotomous....*Griffithsia* (p. 323)
139. Cells cylindrical, less than 0.2 mm. broad.....................140
140. Branching predominately unilateral......................141
140. Branching irregular 143
141. Sporangia with one spore.................*Acrochaetium* (p. 178)
141. Sporangia with more than one spore........................142

PLATES 1—98

EXPLANATION OF PLATE 1

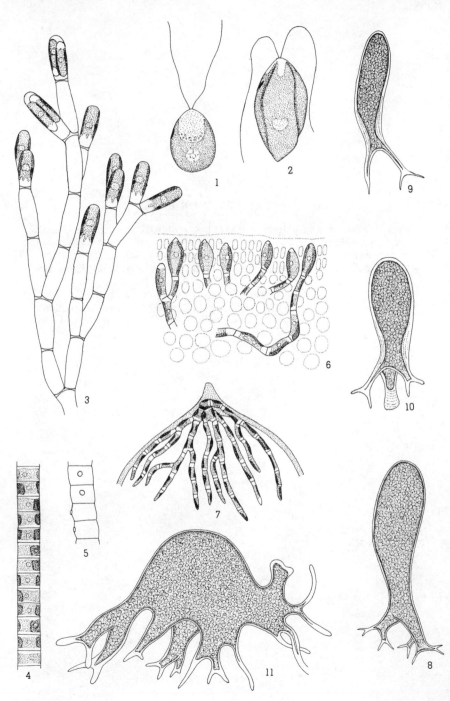

EXPLANATION OF PLATE 2

PAGE

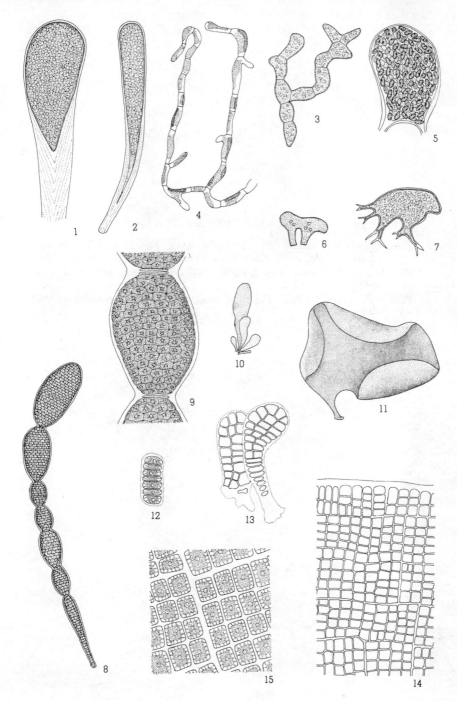

EXPLANATION OF PLATE 3

PLATE 3

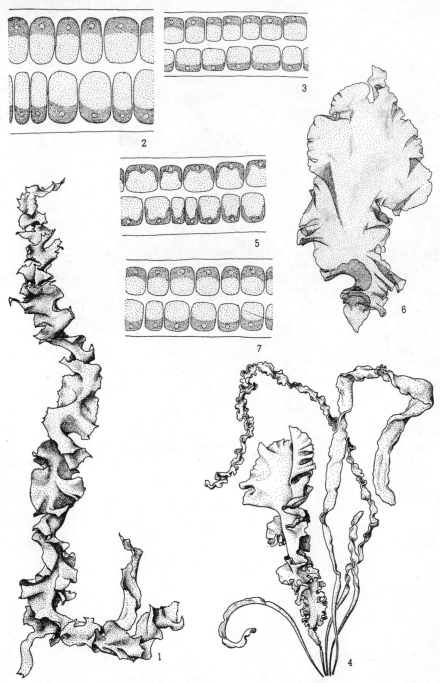

EXPLANATION OF PLATE 4

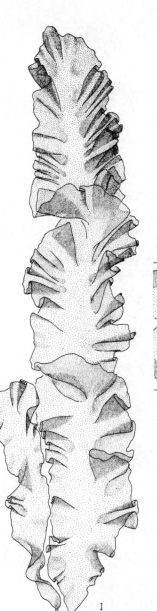

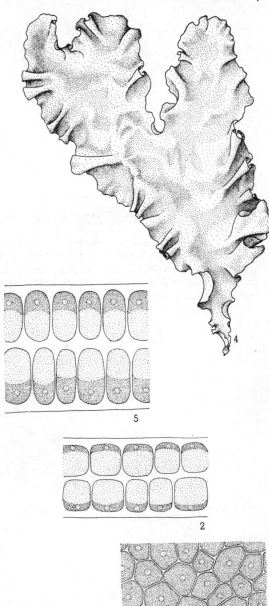

EXPLANATION OF PLATE 5

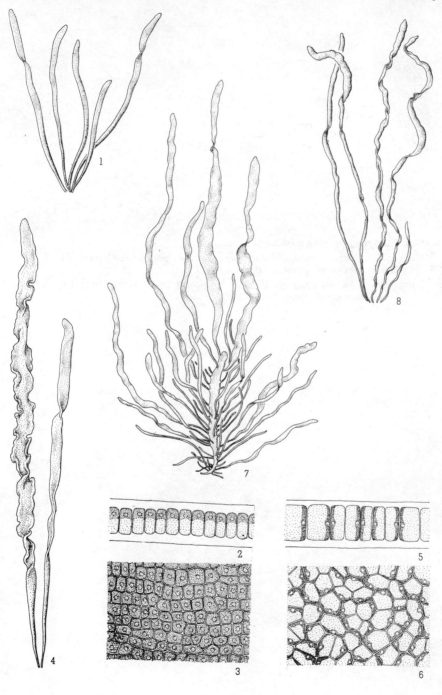

EXPLANATION OF PLATE 6

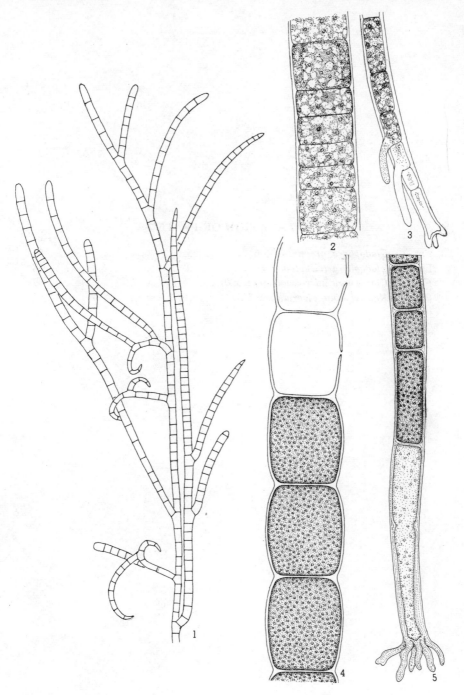

EXPLANATION OF PLATE 7

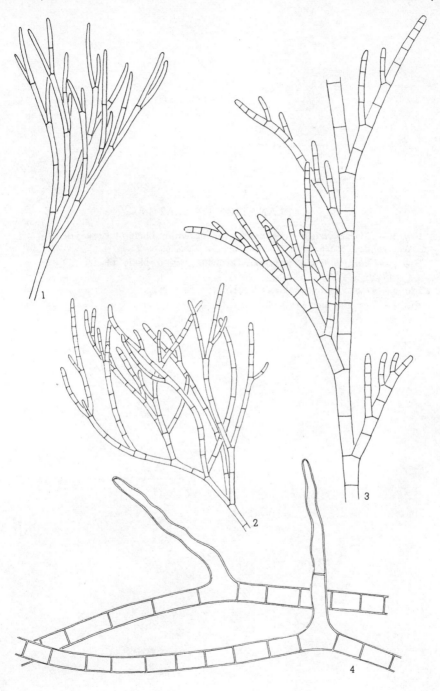

EXPLANATION OF PLATE 8

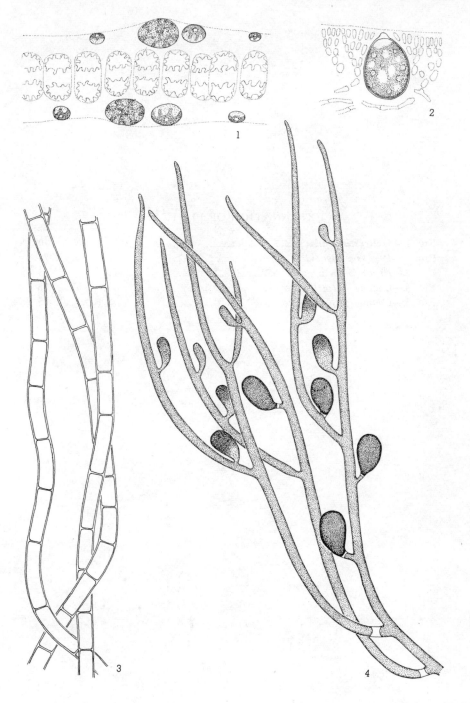

EXPLANATION OF PLATE 9

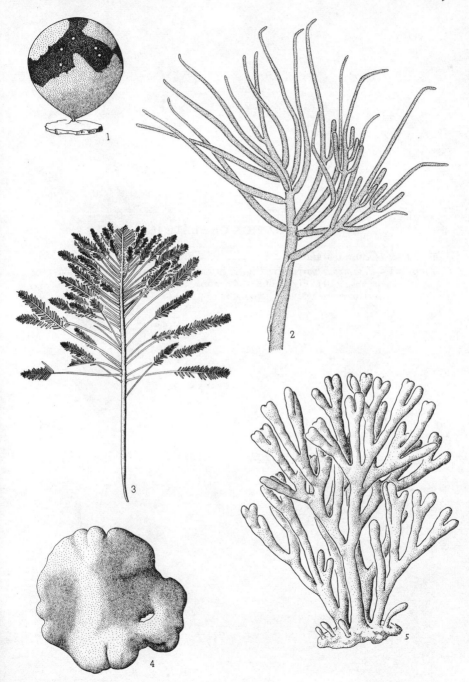

EXPLANATION OF PLATE 10

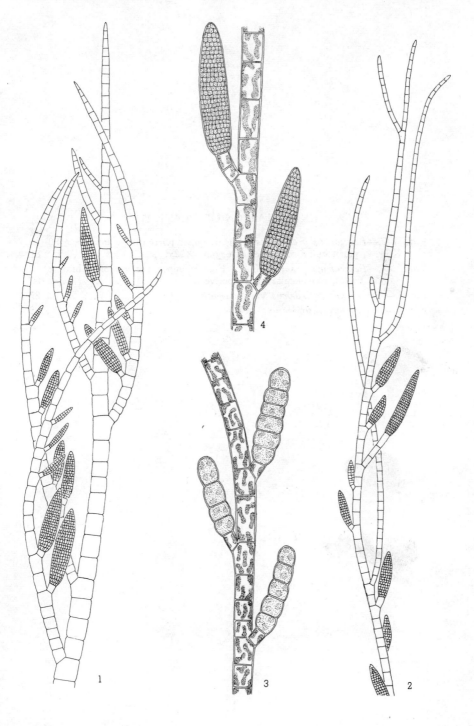

EXPLANATION OF PLATE 11

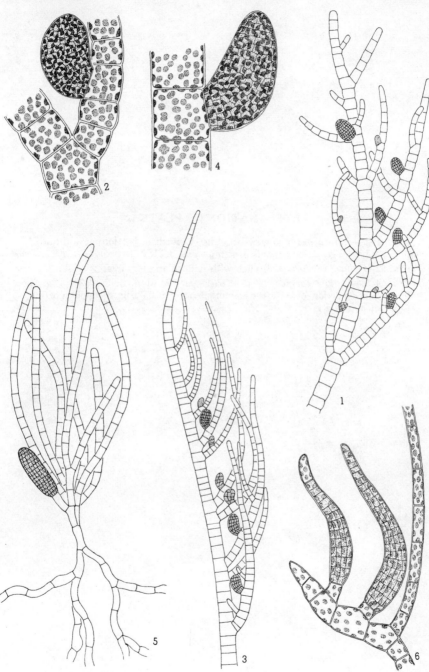

EXPLANATION OF PLATE 12

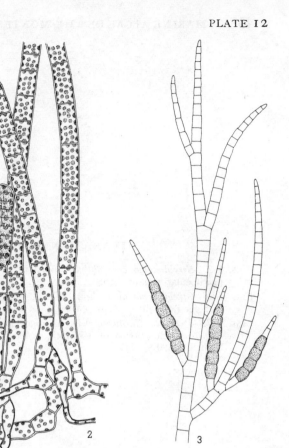

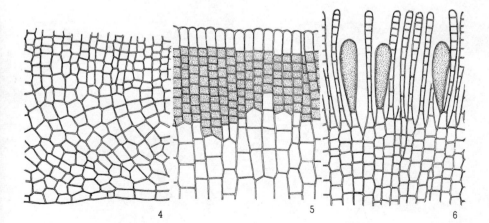

EXPLANATION OF PLATE 13

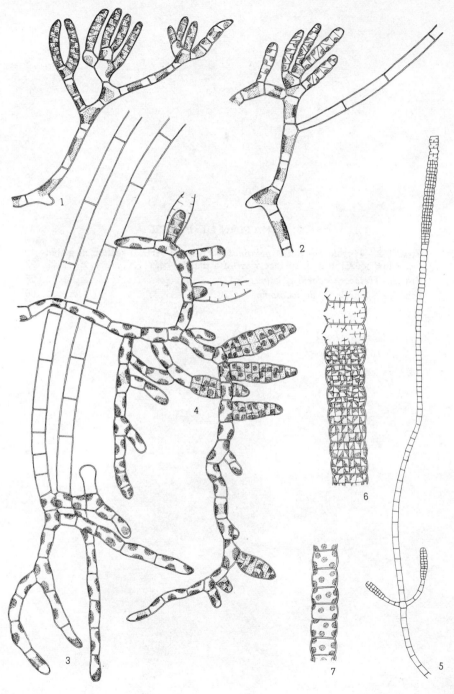

EXPLANATION OF PLATE 14

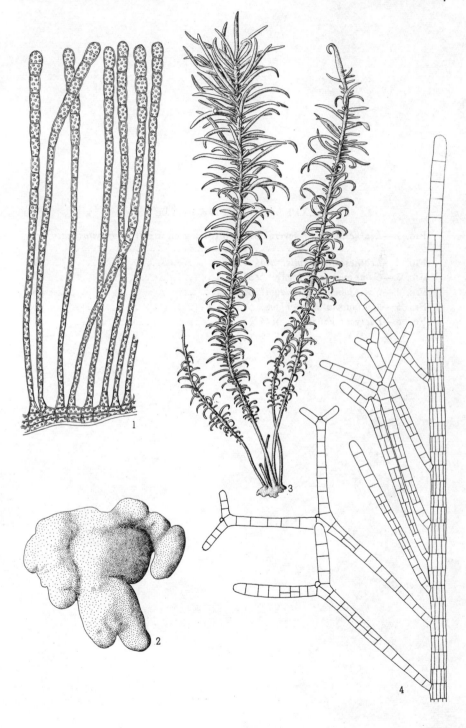

EXPLANATION OF PLATE 15

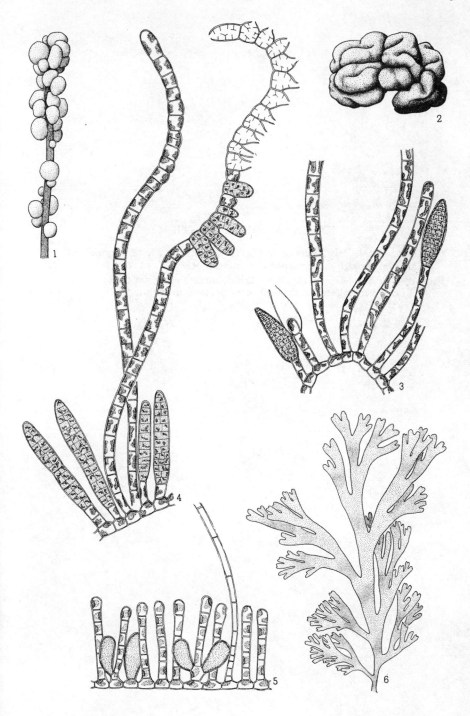

EXPLANATION OF PLATE 16

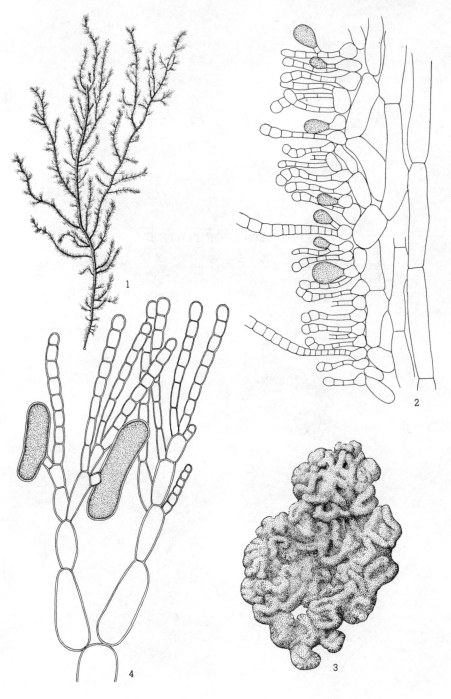

EXPLANATION OF PLATE 17

EXPLANATION OF PLATE 18

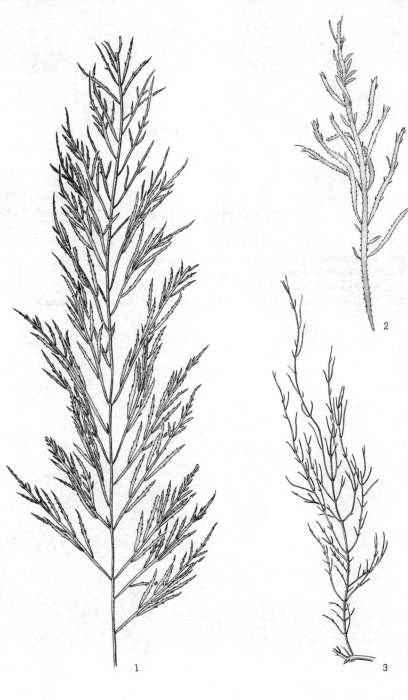

1

2

3

EXPLANATION OF PLATE 19

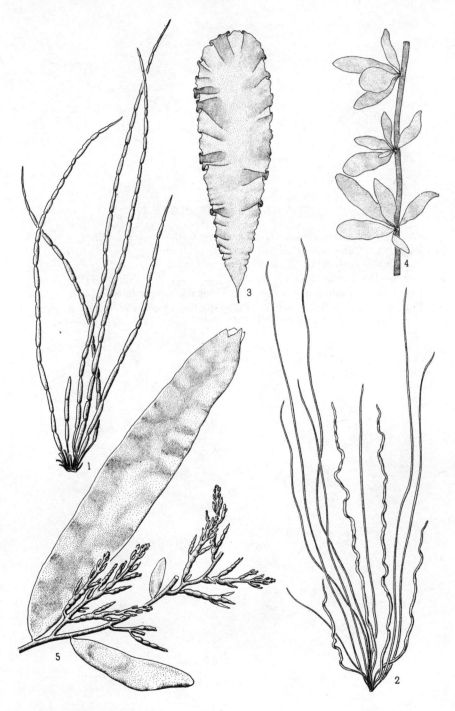

EXPLANATION OF PLATE 20

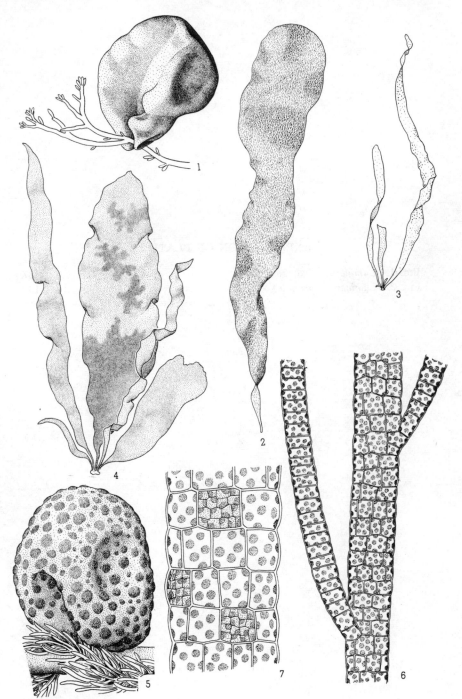

EXPLANATION OF PLATE 21

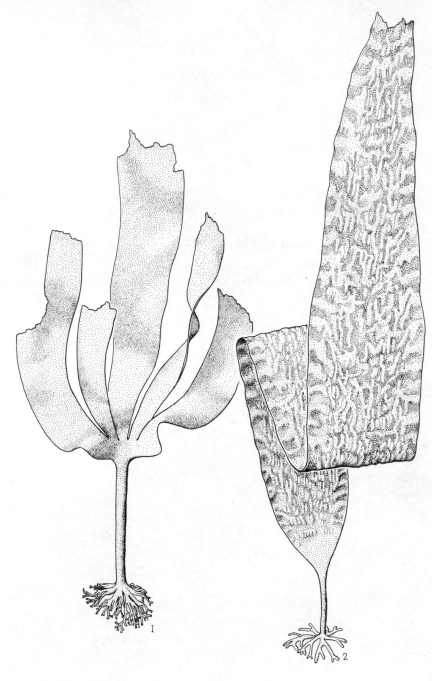

EXPLANATION OF PLATE 22

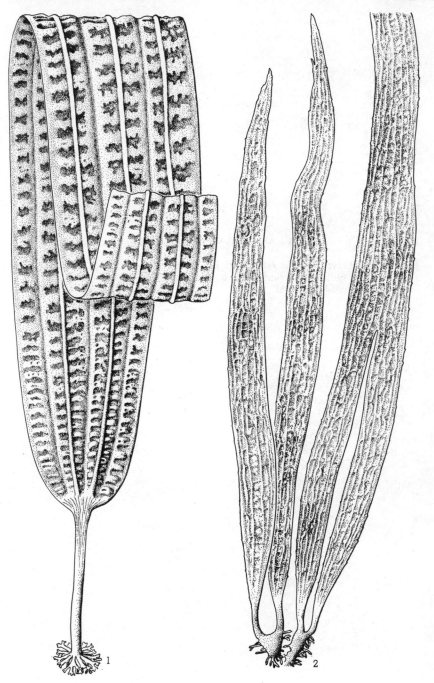

EXPLANATION OF PLATE 23

PAGE

FIGS. 1–4.—*Dictyoneuropsis reticulata:* Fig. 1, mature plant. Fig. 2, beginning of splitting of midrib of a blade. Figs. 3–4, stages in formation of new half-blades. All ×¼..................................... 140

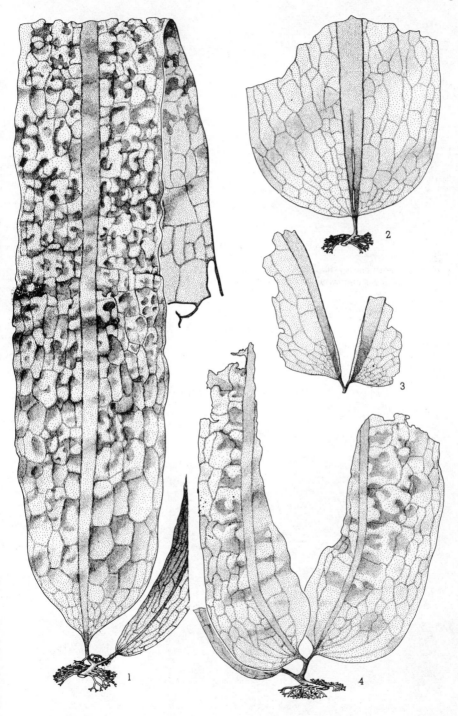

EXPLANATION OF PLATE 24

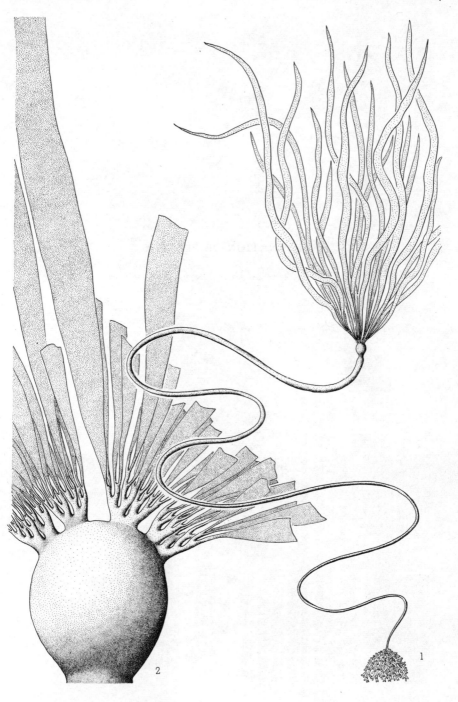

EXPLANATION OF PLATE 25

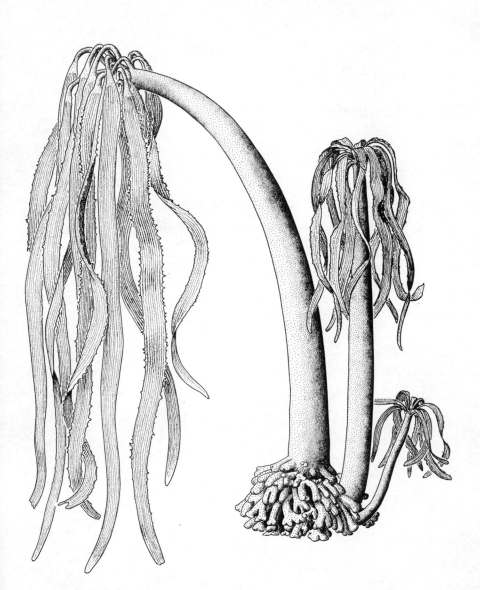

EXPLANATION OF PLATE 26

PAGE

FIGS. 1-3.—*Macrocystis integrifolia:* Fig. 1, entire plant, ×⅛. Fig. 2, upper portion of a branch, ×½. Fig. 3, holdfast, ×½.................. 143

EXPLANATION OF PLATE 27

PAGE

Figs. 1–2.—*Lessoniopsis littoralis:* Fig. 1, entire plant, $\times\frac{1}{12}$. Fig. 2, plant
with most of the blades removed, $\times\frac{1}{4}$.............................. 145

EXPLANATION OF PLATE 28

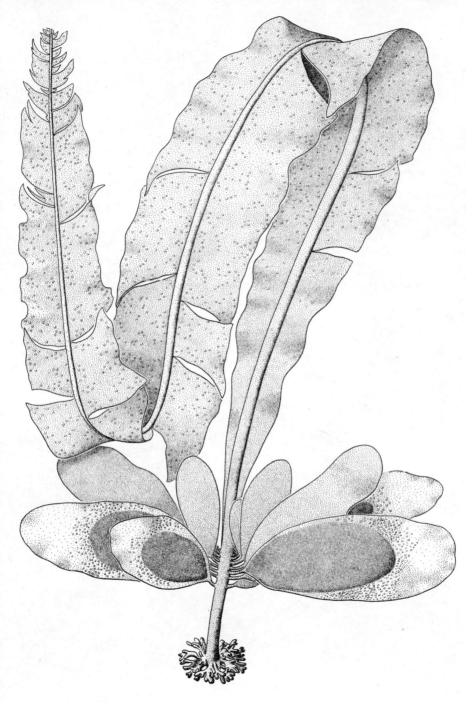

EXPLANATION OF PLATE 29

PAGE

Pterygophora californica: a small plant with unusually long blades, ×⅙.... 148

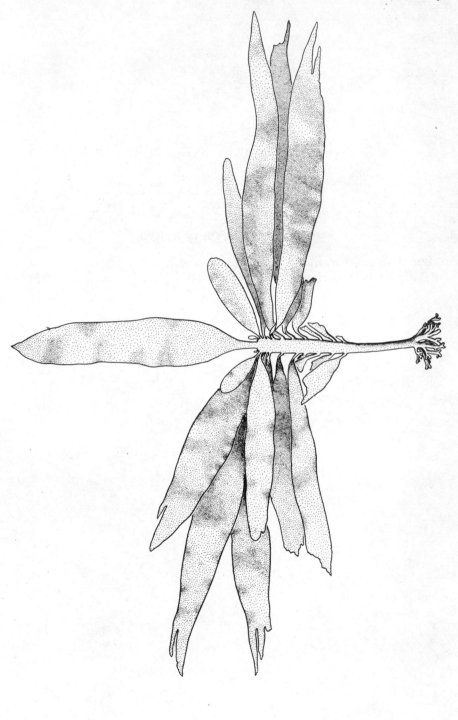

EXPLANATION OF PLATE 30

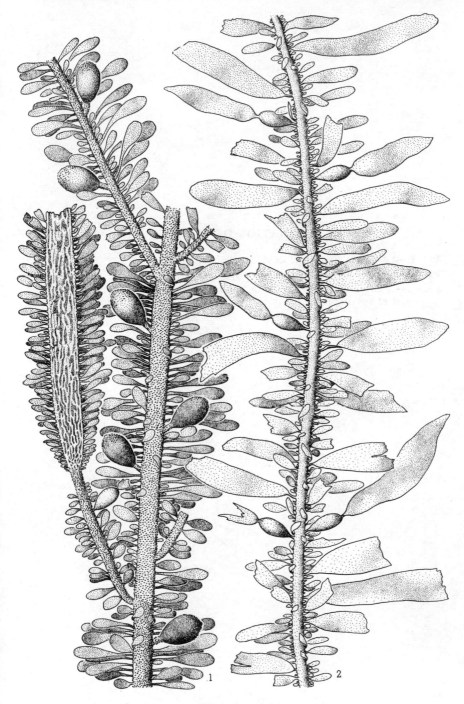

EXPLANATION OF PLATE 31

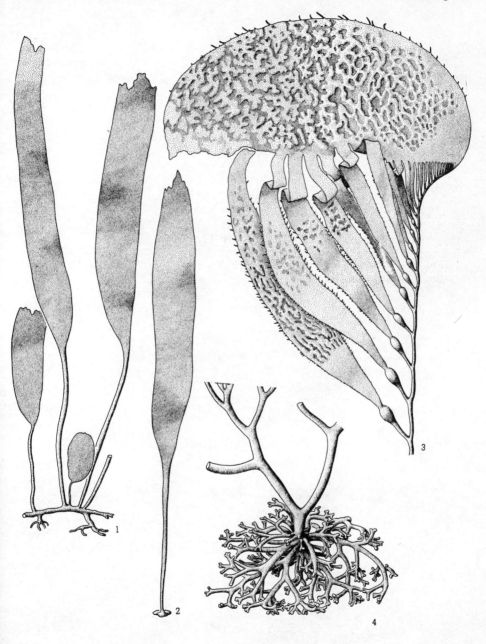

1

2

3

4

EXPLANATION OF PLATE 32

EXPLANATION OF PLATE 33

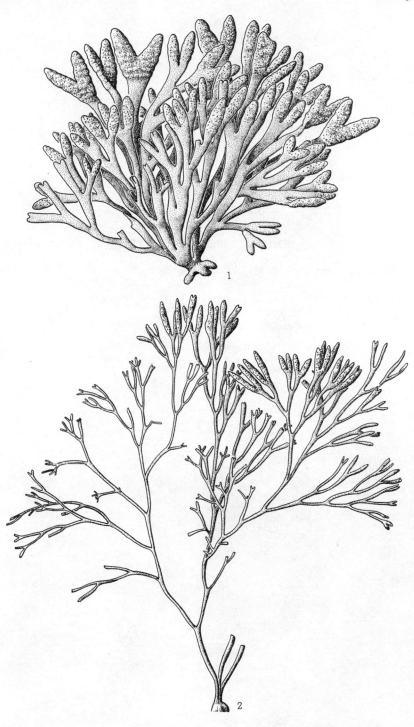

EXPLANATION OF PLATE 34

EXPLANATION OF PLATE 35

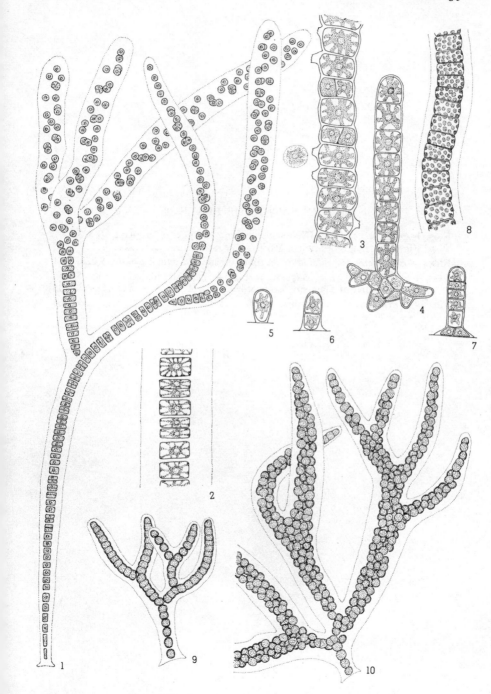

EXPLANATION OF PLATE 36

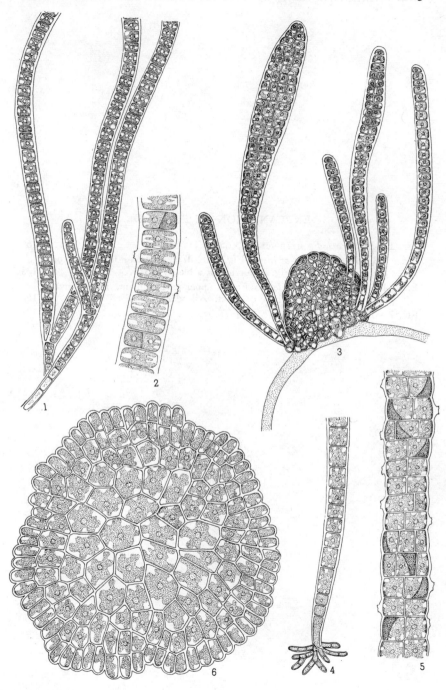

EXPLANATION OF PLATE 37

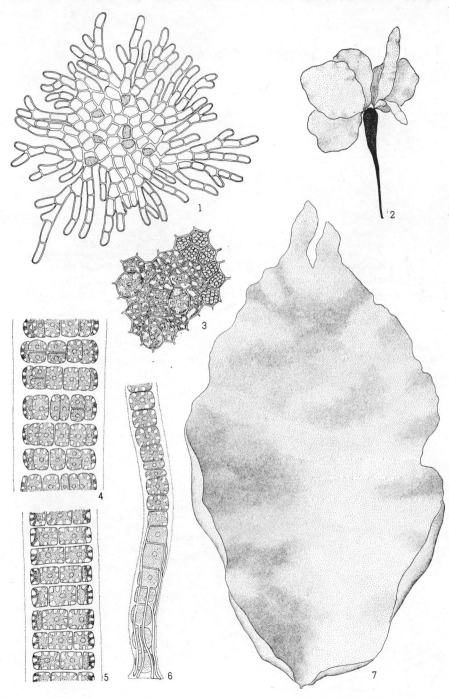

EXPLANATION OF PLATE 38

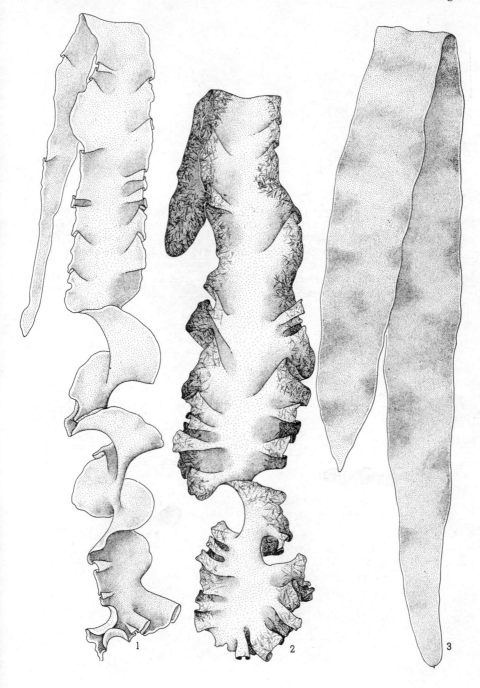

EXPLANATION OF PLATE 39

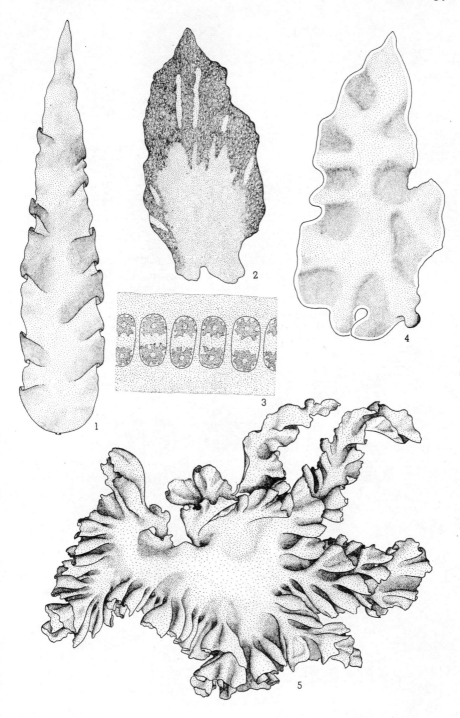

EXPLANATION OF PLATE 40

PLATE 40

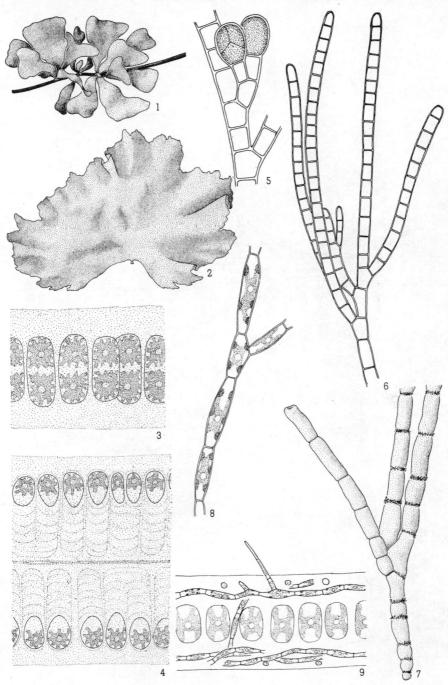

EXPLANATION OF PLATE 41

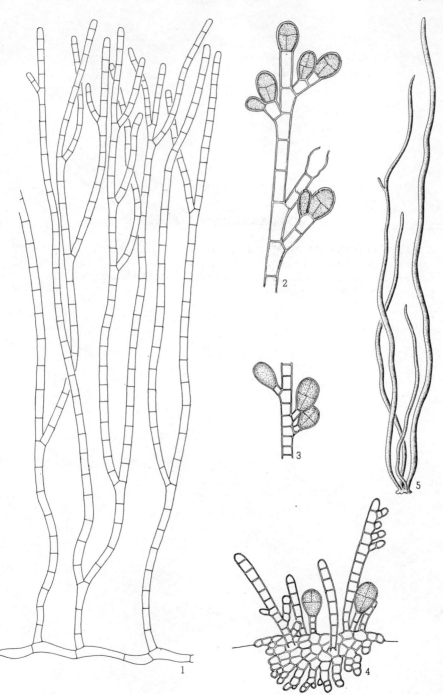

EXPLANATION OF PLATE 42

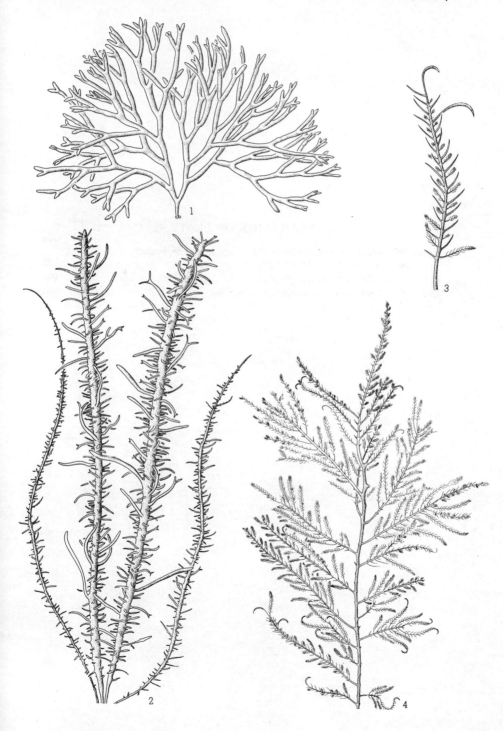

EXPLANATION OF PLATE 43

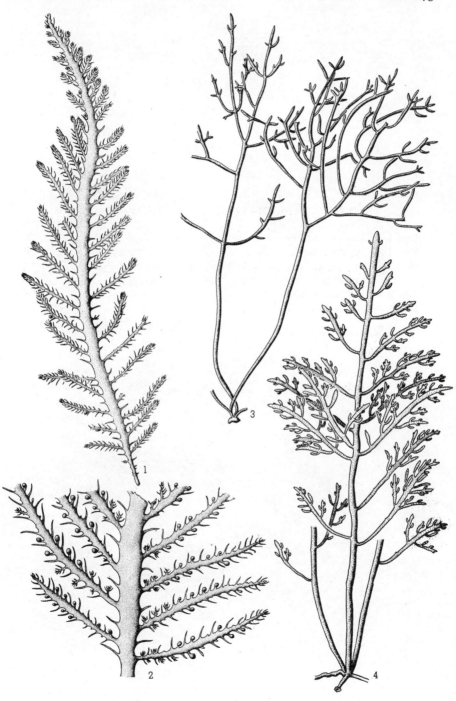

EXPLANATION OF PLATE 44

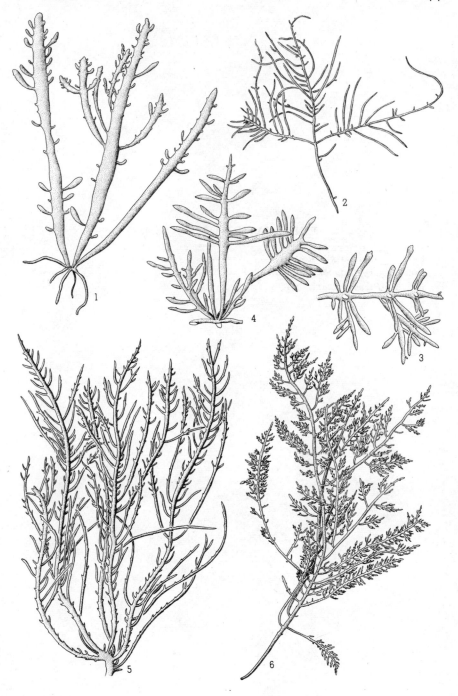

EXPLANATION OF PLATE 45

EXPLANATION OF PLATE 46

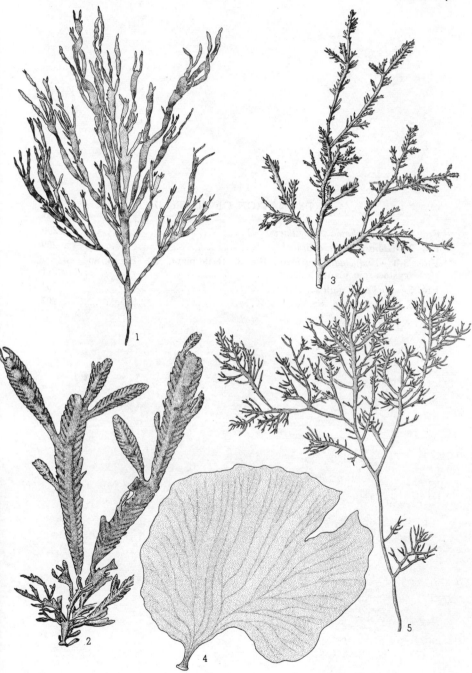

EXPLANATION OF PLATE 47

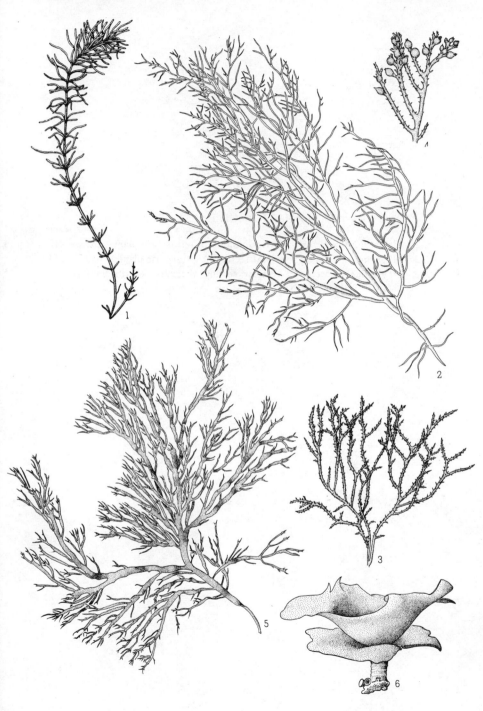

EXPLANATION OF PLATE 48

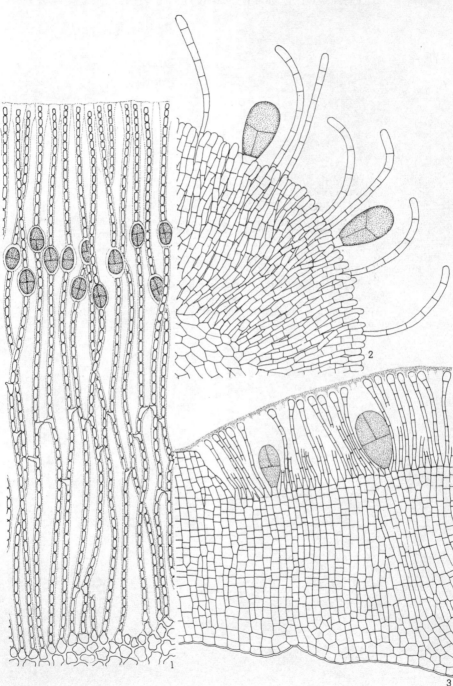

EXPLANATION OF PLATE 49

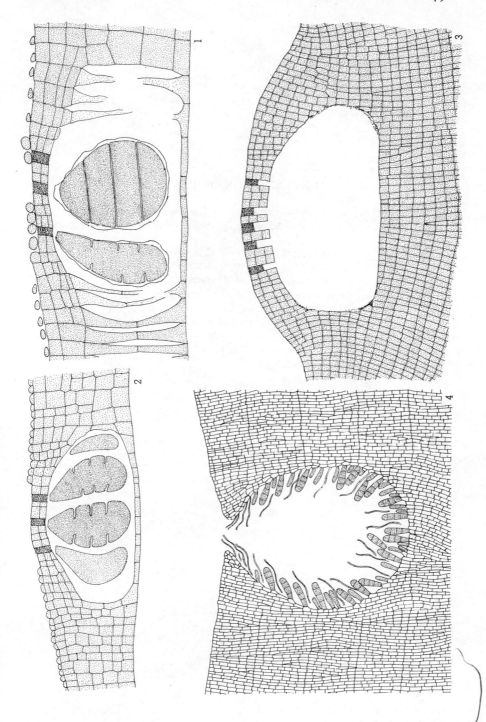

EXPLANATION OF PLATE 50

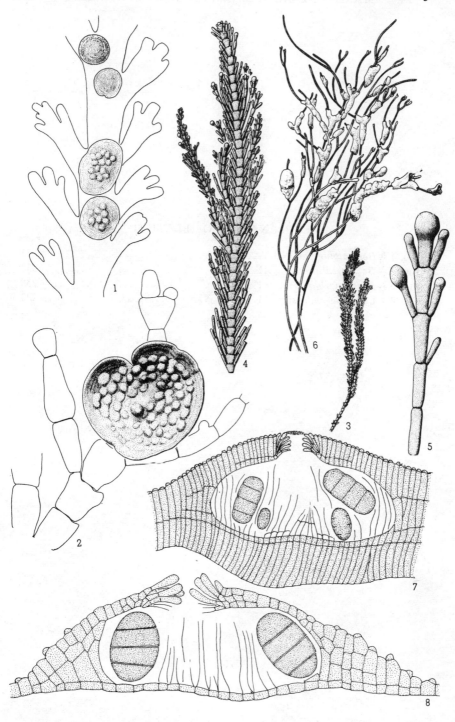

EXPLANATION OF PLATE 51

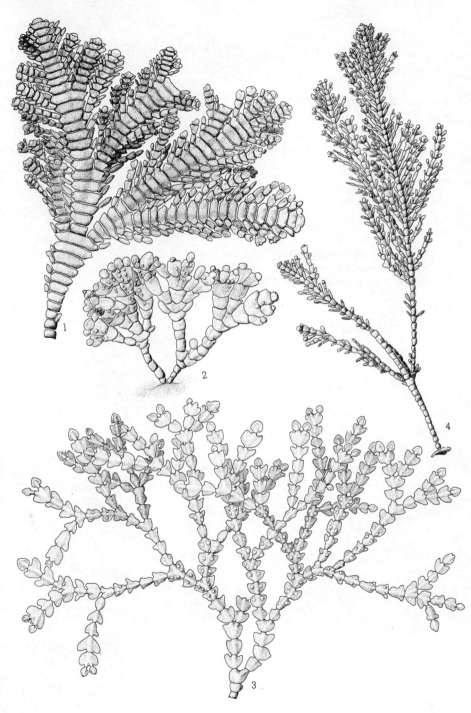

EXPLANATION OF PLATE 52

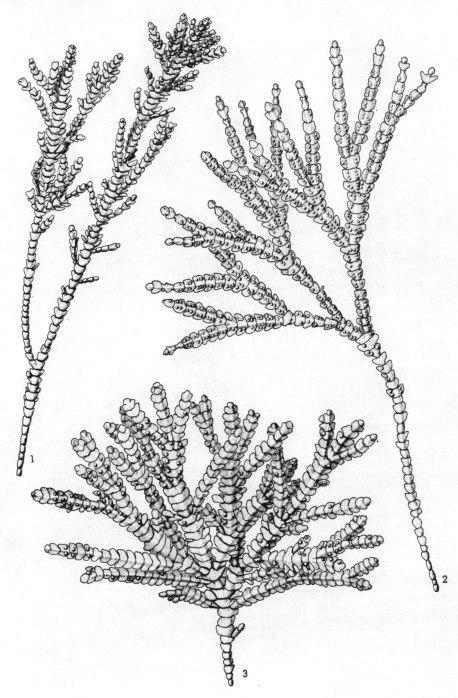

EXPLANATION OF PLATE 53

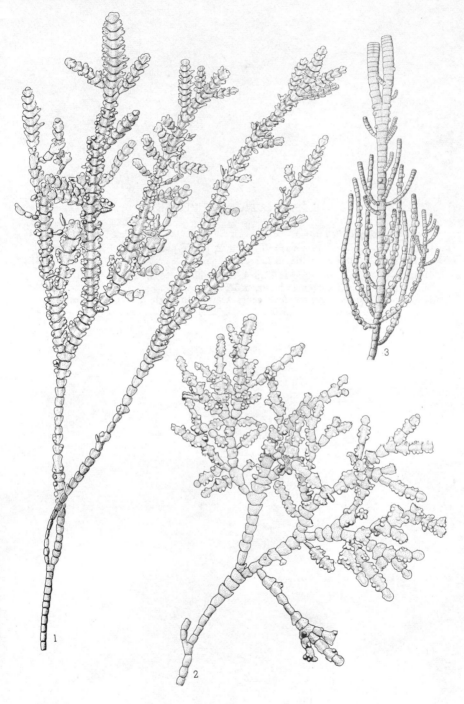

EXPLANATION OF PLATE 54

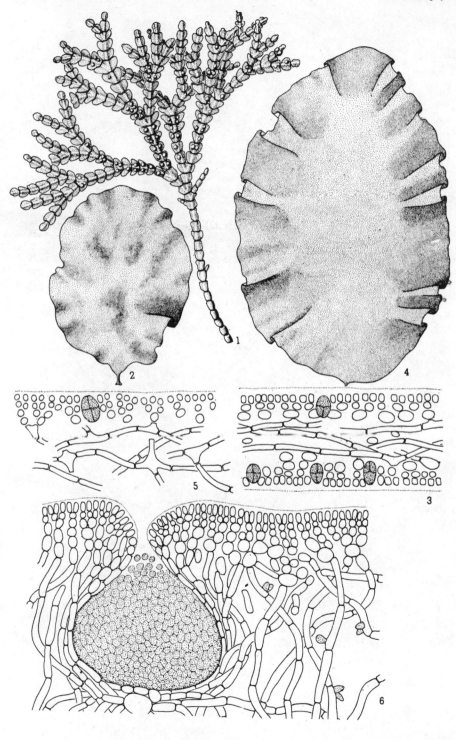

EXPLANATION OF PLATE 55

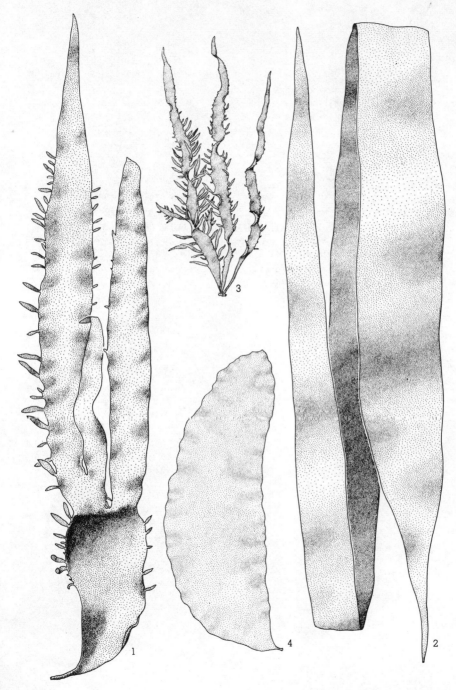

EXPLANATION OF PLATE 56

EXPLANATION OF PLATE 57

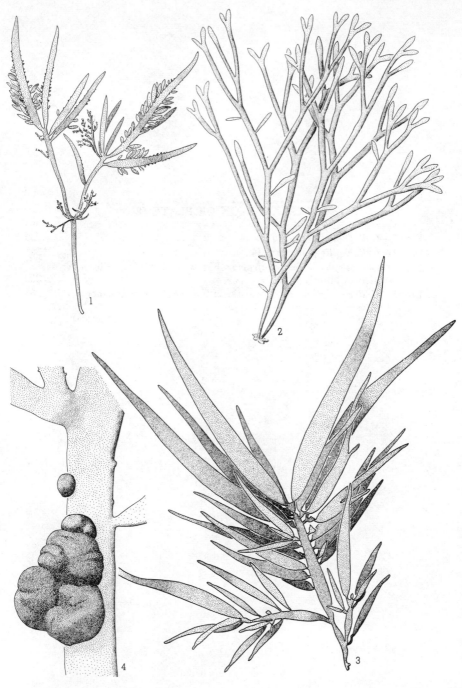

EXPLANATION OF PLATE 58

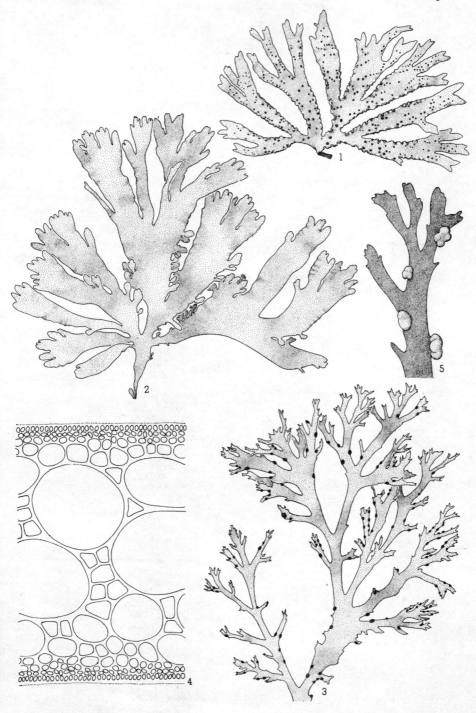

EXPLANATION OF PLATE 59

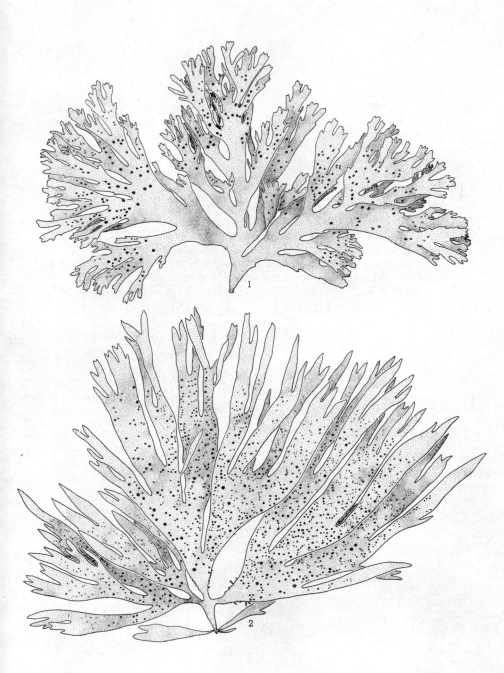

EXPLANATION OF PLATE 60

PAGE

FIG. 1.—*Pugetia firma:* viewed from under side, ×¾ 254

FIGS. 2–3.—*Schizymenia epiphytica:* Fig. 2, sterile plant, ×1. Fig. 2, cross section through fertile blade with nemathecia, ×375 258

FIG. 4.—*Schizymenia pacifica:* cross section through a sterile blade with gland cells, ×325 258

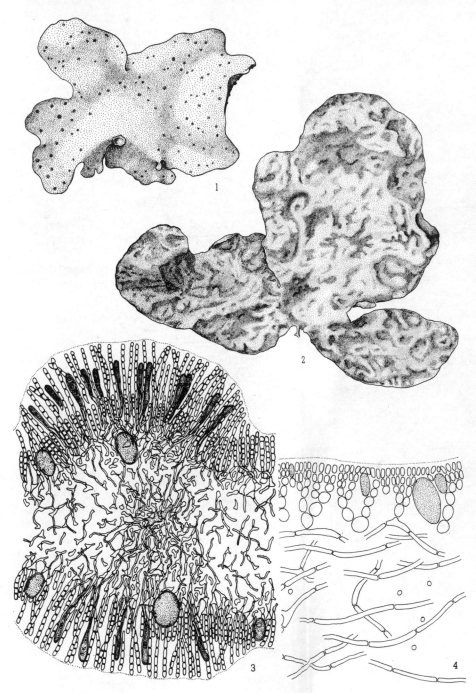

EXPLANATION OF PLATE 61

EXPLANATION OF PLATE 62

EXPLANATION OF PLATE 63

EXPLANATION OF PLATE 64

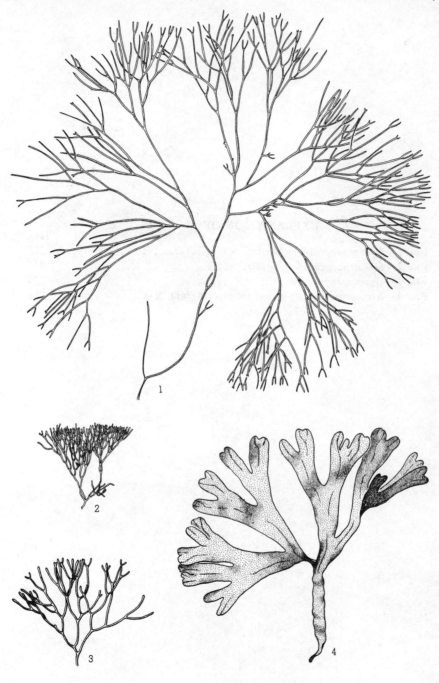

EXPLANATION OF PLATE 65

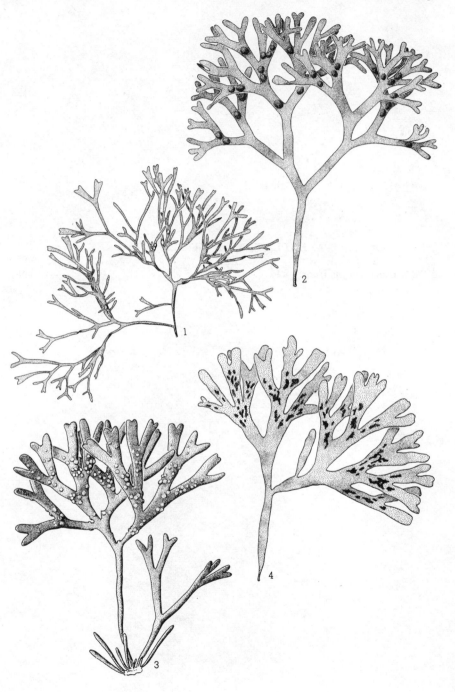

EXPLANATION OF PLATE 66

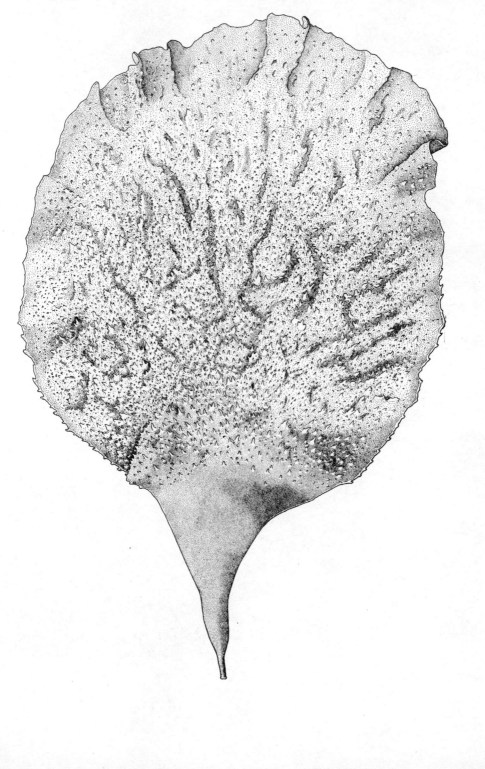

EXPLANATION OF PLATE 67

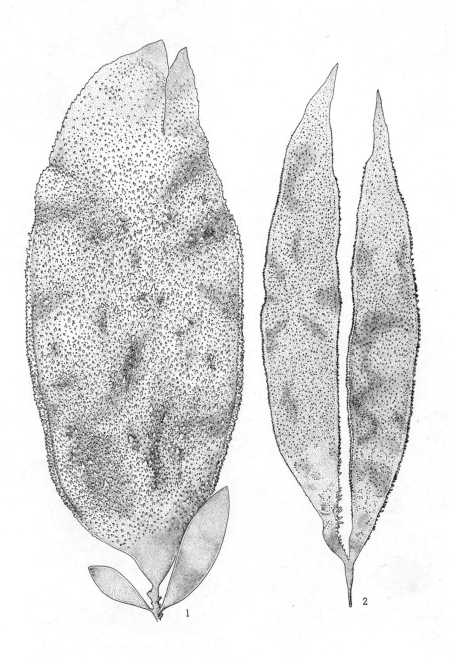

EXPLANATION OF PLATE 68

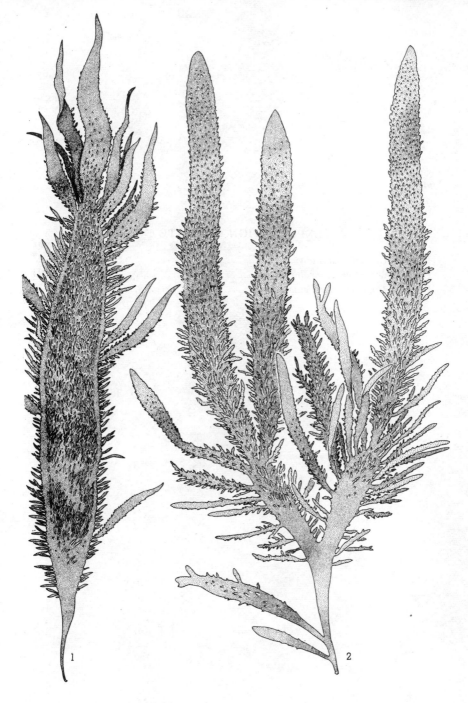

EXPLANATION OF PLATE 69

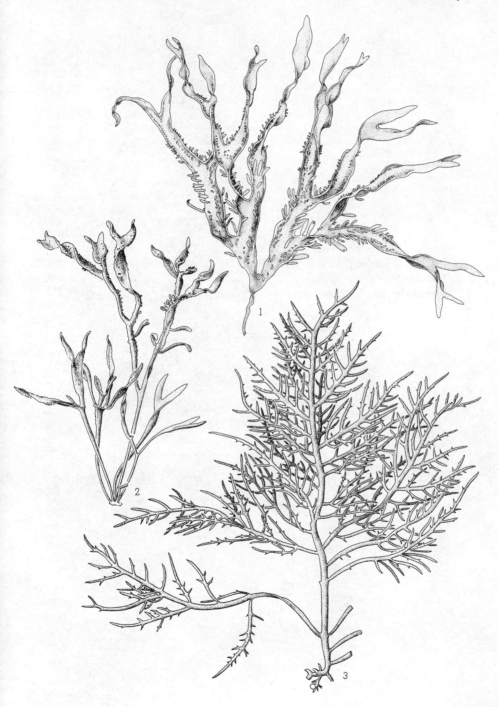

EXPLANATION OF PLATE 70

1

2

3

4   5

EXPLANATION OF PLATE 71

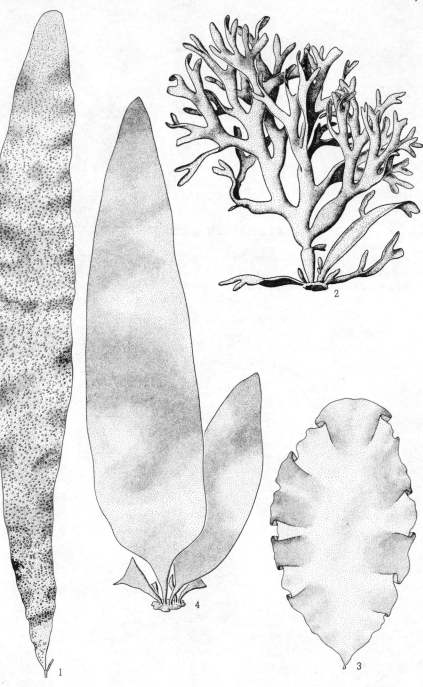

EXPLANATION OF PLATE 72

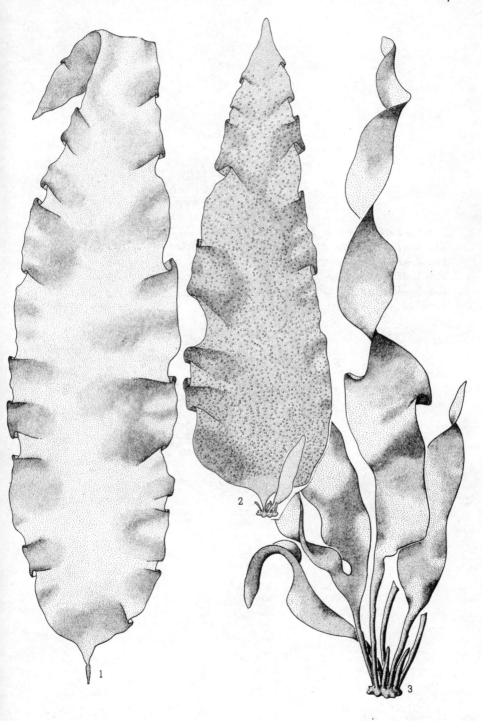

EXPLANATION OF PLATE 73

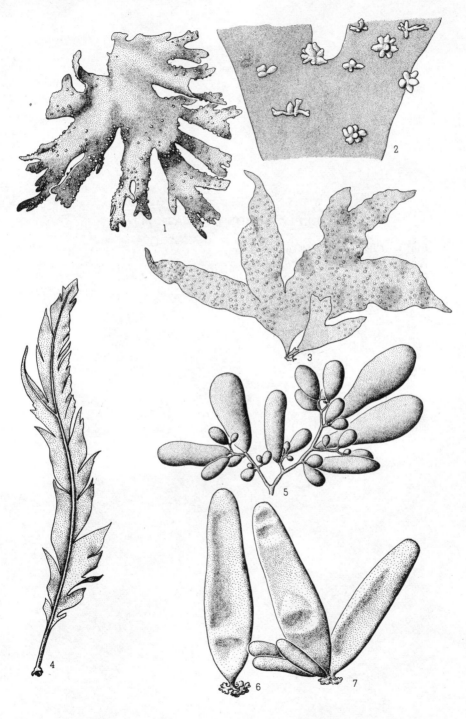

EXPLANATION OF PLATE 74

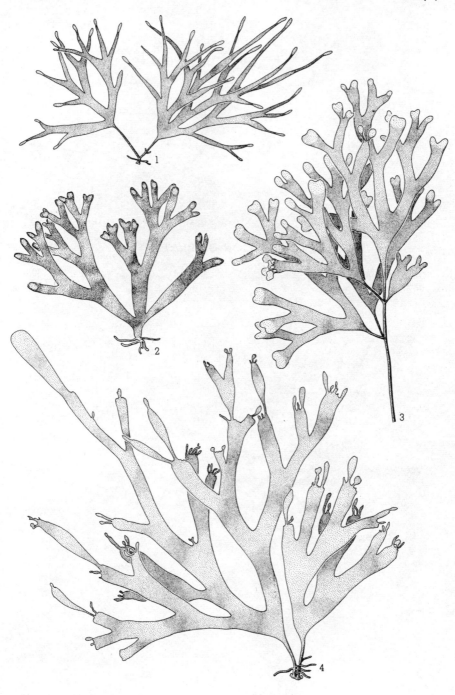

EXPLANATION OF PLATE 75

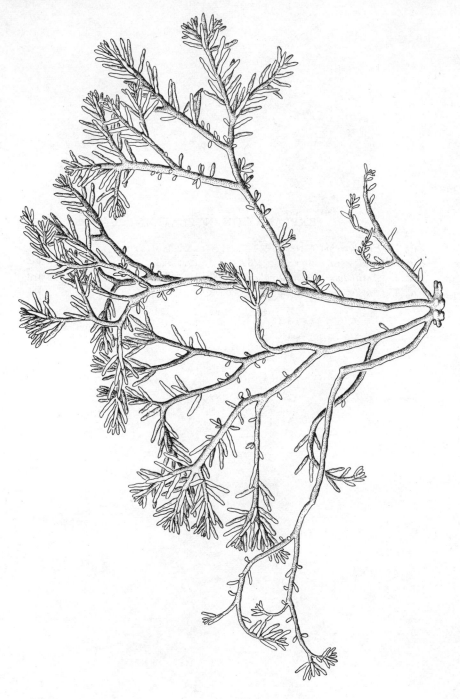

EXPLANATION OF PLATE 76

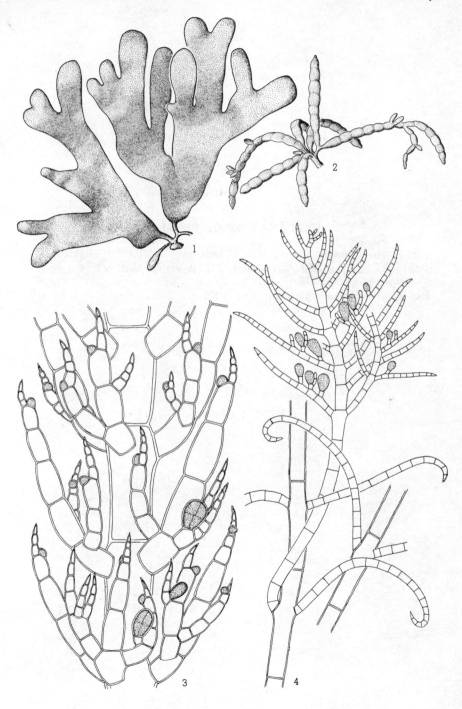

EXPLANATION OF PLATE 77

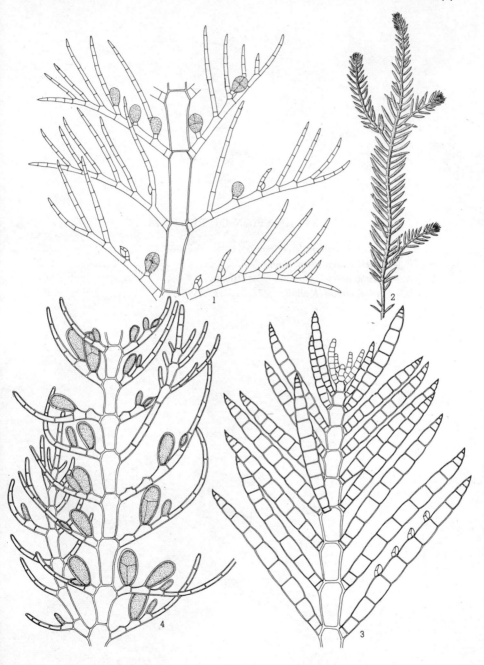

1
2
3
4

EXPLANATION OF PLATE 78

PLATE 78

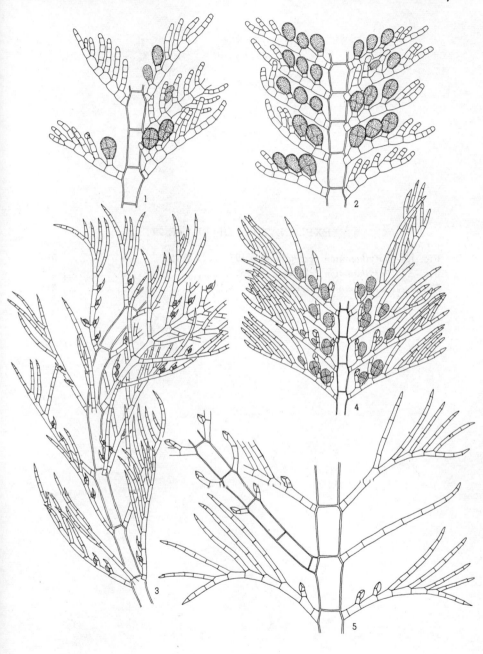

EXPLANATION OF PLATE 79

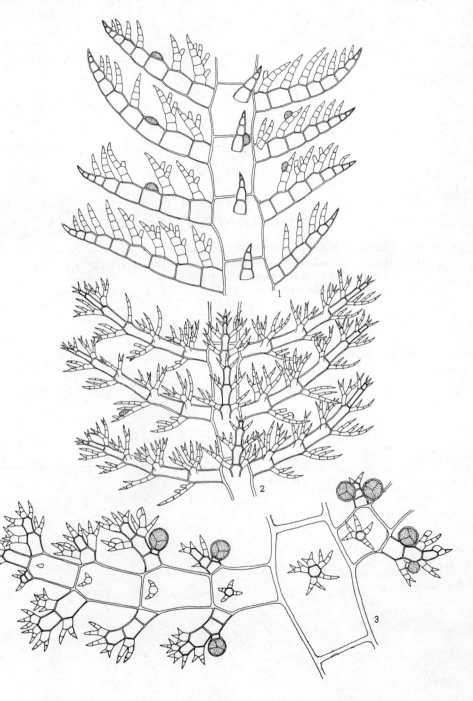

EXPLANATION OF PLATE 80

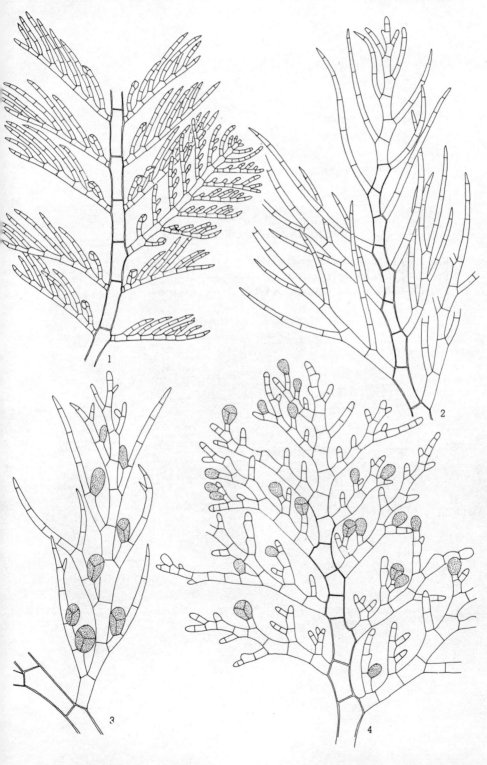

EXPLANATION OF PLATE 81

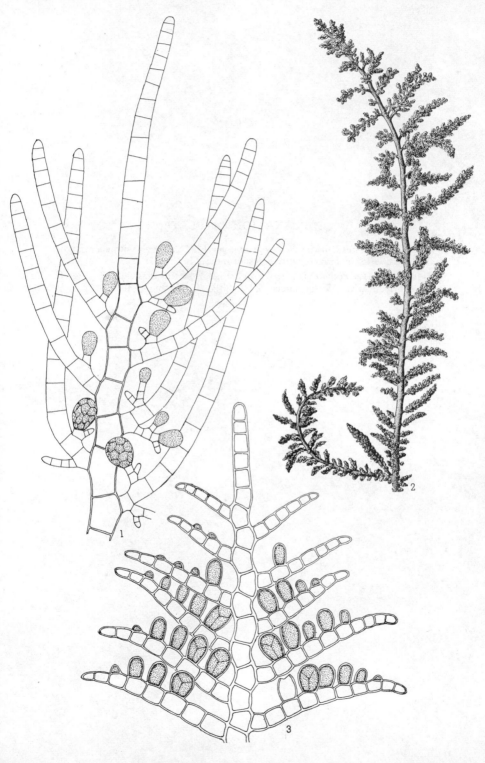

EXPLANATION OF PLATE 82

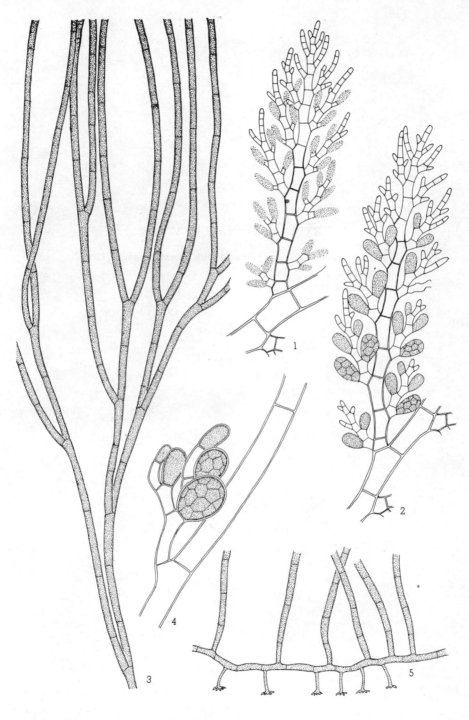

•

EXPLANATION OF PLATE 83

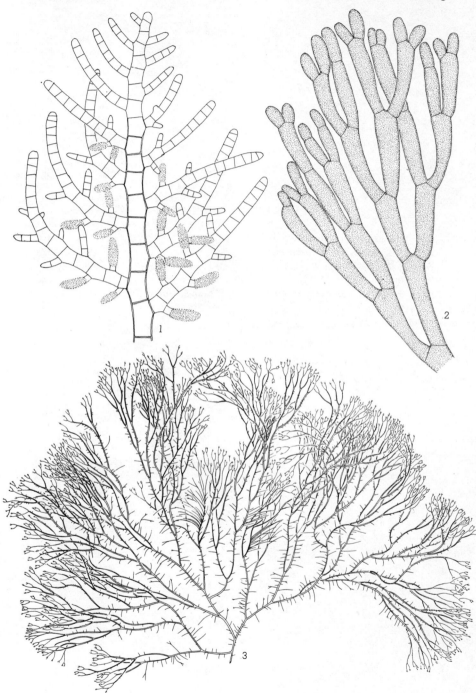

EXPLANATION OF PLATE 84

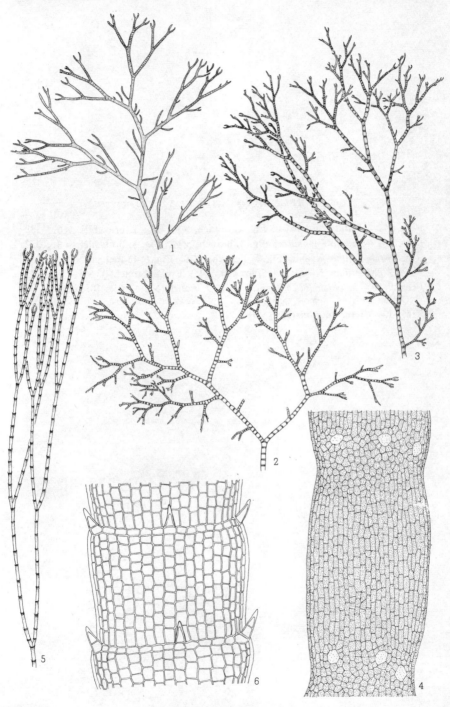

EXPLANATION OF PLATE 85

EXPLANATION OF PLATE 86

PLATE 86

EXPLANATION OF PLATE 87

EXPLANATION OF PLATE 88

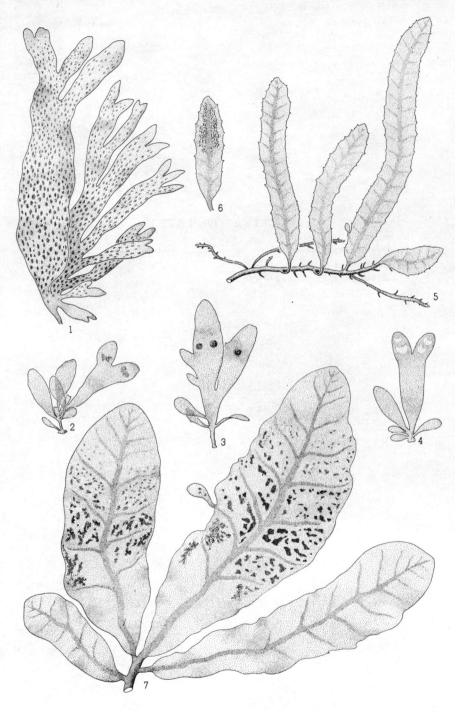

EXPLANATION OF PLATE 89

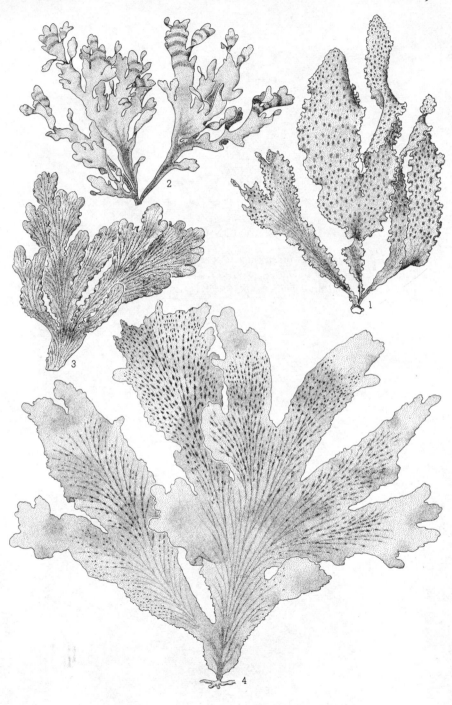

EXPLANATION OF PLATE 90

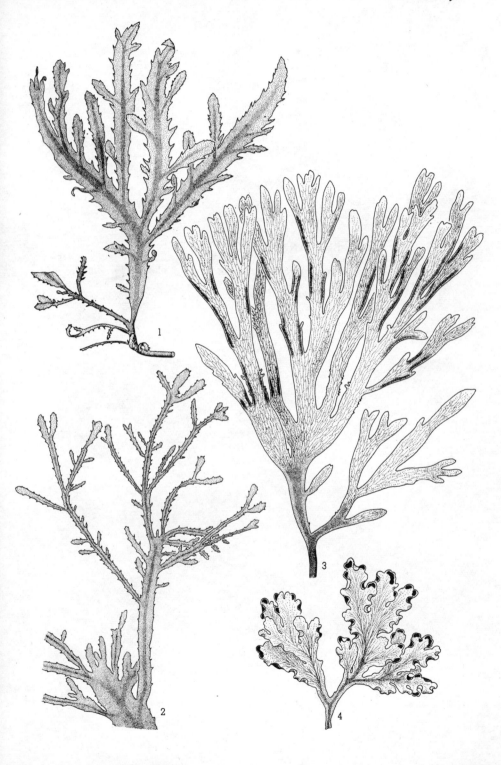

EXPLANATION OF PLATE 91

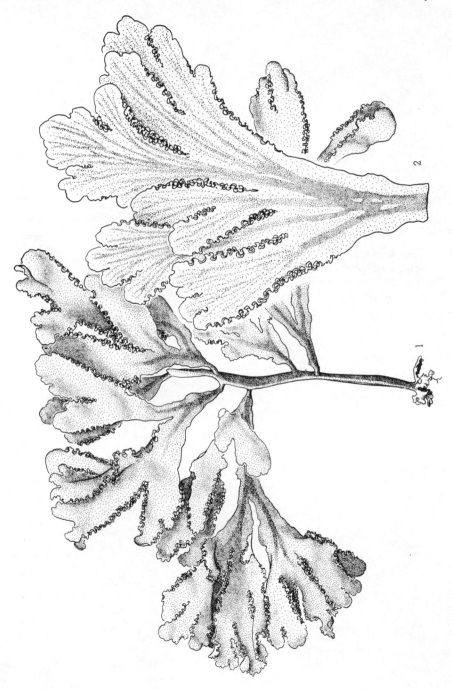

EXPLANATION OF PLATE 92

EXPLANATION OF PLATE 93

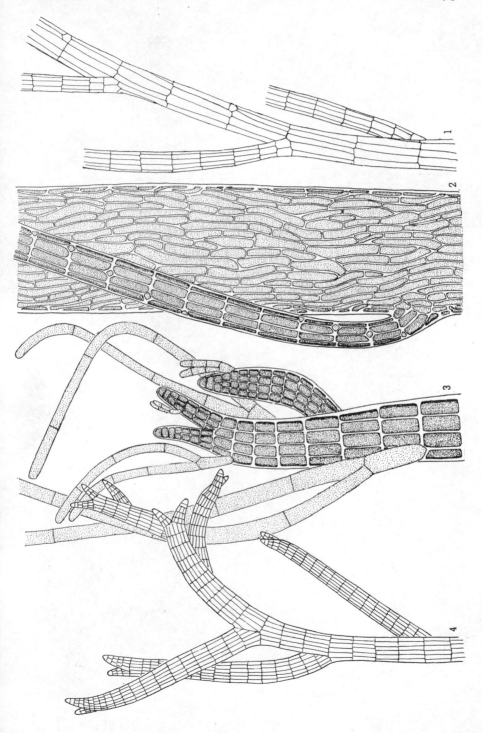

EXPLANATION OF PLATE 94

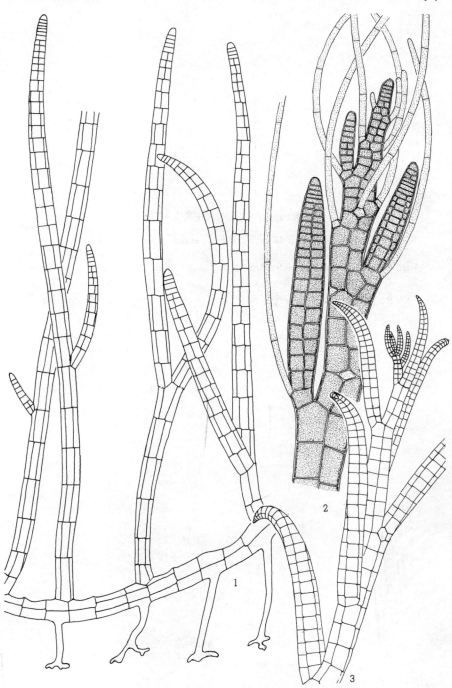

EXPLANATION OF PLATE 95

EXPLANATION OF PLATE 96

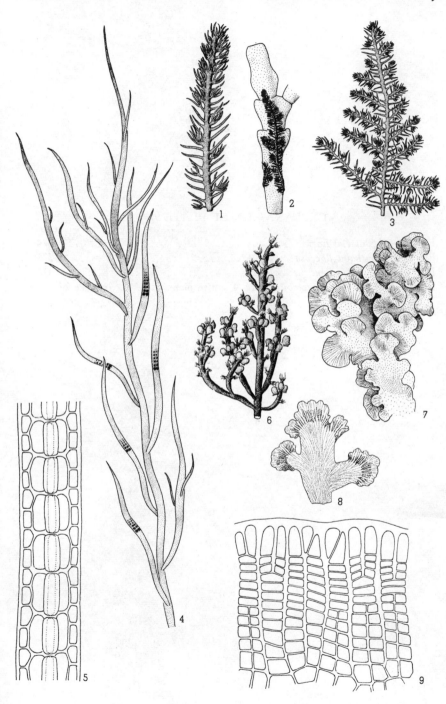

EXPLANATION OF PLATE 97

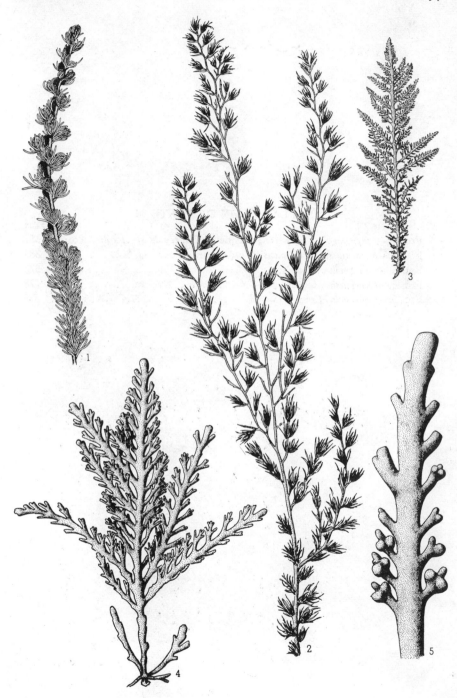

EXPLANATION OF PLATE 98

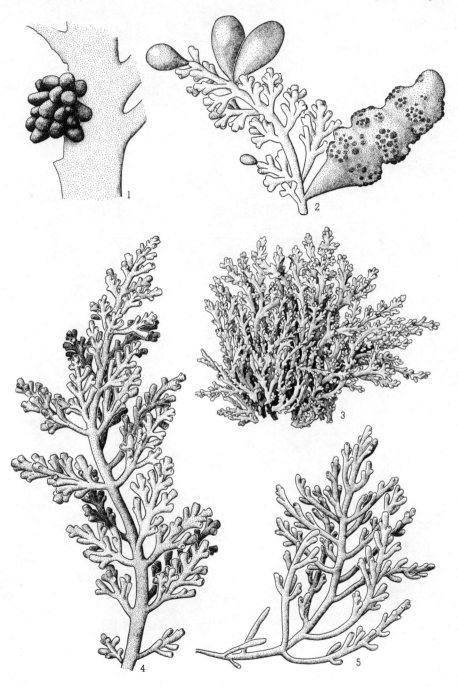

INDEX

611